Amateur Radio Operating Manual

FOURTH EDITION

Editor: Ray Eckersley, G4FTJ

Contributors:
Peter Aitchison, G3LSQ
John Allaway, G3FKM
Martin Atherton, G3ZAY
John Bazley, G3HCT
Ron Broadbent, MBE, G3AAJ
T C Bryant, GW3SB
Hilary Claytonsmith, G4JKS
Andy Cook, G4PIQ
Dave Coomber, G8UYZ
L W Craven, G4EQI
Mike Dixon, G3PFR
George Dobbs, G3RJV
Geoff Dover, G4AFJ
David Evans, G3OUF
Michael Fadil, G4CCA
Harold Fenton, G8GG
Don Field, G3XTT
Norman Fitch, G3FPK
Richard Gardner, G4WKN
Ron Glaisher, G6LX
Bill Hall, G4FRN
David Johnson, G4DHF
Mike Kerry, G4BMK
Dave Lawley, G4BUO
Robin Page-Jones, G3JWI
Phillip Smith, GW1XBG
Steve Thompson, GW8GSQ
Robert Vickers, G3ORI
Mike Wooding, G6IQM

Radio Society of Great Britain

Published by the Radio Society of Great Britain, Cranborne Road, Potters Bar, Herts EN6 3JE.

First published 1979
Fourth edition 1995

ISBN 1 872309 34 8

Cover design: Jennifer Crocker.

Cover photo: G3OAY operating the contest station GW8GT/P in 1992.

Illustrations: Derek Cole and Bob Ryan (Radio Society of Great Britain), and Ray Eckersley.

Production and typography: Ray Eckersley, Seven Stars Publishing.

Printed in Great Britain by Bell & Bain Ltd, Glasgow.

Contents

Preface

Welcome to the fourth edition of the *Amateur Radio Operating Manual*. The aim of this edition, as with the previous ones, is to present a detailed guide to good operating practice on the amateur bands, combined with a comprehensive set of operating aids. It is not intended to be a technical book and where necessary it refers the reader to appropriate sources of information.

The favourable reception accorded to previous editions has led to the retention of the basic structure of the book, but the last edition was published some 10 years ago and amateur radio has moved on quite considerably in the meantime. This edition reflects these advances and also includes for the first time coverage of microwave DXing, moonbounce, 2m foxhunting, digital communications and fast-scan TV.

The editor is greatly indebted to the many amateurs who have enthusiastically contributed in some way, large or small. Some of the chapters contain revised versions of material supplied by various contributors to previous editions, and due acknowledgement is made to this fact.

Chapter 5 includes material taken from the *VHF Contesting Guide* written by the VHF Contests Committee and published by the RSGB.

Appendix 8 is based on the memory sheets devised by L Craven, G4EQI, for which the following provided translations and assistance: W Baker, G3HDQ, J Gaudron, F9OJ, G G Goodfield, GW4CNL, and H Hahn, DJ7TF.

Grateful thanks are due to several amateurs for helpful comments on the previous edition, in particular Keijo 'Max' Koskela, OH2OT/OH0BT, and Denzil Roden, G3KXF.

Ray Eckersley, G4FTJ

1 The Amateur Service

AMATEUR radio is an officially recognised radio service, the *Amateur Service*, bound and protected by both national and international legislation. It also has its own codes of operating practice and procedures which set it apart from other radio services. Although many of these are unofficial (though nevertheless established as good practice), many others are recommended and standardised by national and international societies of radio amateurs.

In this first chapter a brief look is taken at this formal background to amateur radio as it affects operating matters, in order to give some perspective to the more detailed practical discussions in later chapters.

INTERNATIONAL TELECOMMUNICATION UNION

The ITU is the intergovernmental agency responsible for the co-ordination, standardisation and planning of world telecommunications. This United Nations organisation, founded in 1865, unites the telecommunication administrations of over 150 member countries. Its headquarters are located in Switzerland [1].

ITU regulations cover the activities of all telecommunication services, including amateur radio, and are published by the general secretariat of the ITU [2]. These regulations define international telecommunication law, and therefore are the cornerstone of amateur licence conditions in all countries.

From time to time, the ITU organises conferences attended by delegates from national administrations where aspects of the current regulations are reviewed to take into account developments in communications techniques. Major conferences used to be held every 20 years or so, and the last of this series took place in 1992 (the 1992 World Administrative Radio Conference).

At this conference it was realised that such conferences in future were going to have to take place more frequently because technology was changing so rapidly and more countries were requiring access to sections of the spectrum. It was also realised that they would have to be more specialised, either in subject or range of frequencies under consideration. It was therefore decided to hold conferences every two years in future, and the next one will be in 1997.

It is important that amateurs understand the basis of the service that they use.

Definitions

Within the ITU Radio Regulations the Amateur Service is defined as:

A radiocommunication service for the purpose of self-training, intercommunication and technical investigations carried out by amateurs, that is, by duly authorised persons interested in radio technique solely with a personal aim and without pecuniary interest.

It should be noted that the ITU considers amateur-satellite activities as a separate *Amateur-Satellite Service* defined as:

A radiocommunication service using space stations on earth satellites for the same purposes as those of the Amateur Service.

The section of the regulations dealing specifically with amateur radio is Article 32, and this is shown in the panel overleaf.

Callsigns

It is a requirement of the regulations that all radio amateurs identify themselves by transmitting an identification code, known as the *callsign,* at short intervals during their transmissions.

The initial characters of the callsign denote the country to which the amateur station belongs and is operating from. The ITU allocates the telecommunication administration of each country blocks of letters and numbers in order to form callsigns, not just for amateur stations but for all radio stations in that country. The ITU allocation blocks are of three types:

(a) letter-letter-letter, eg LAA–LNZ;
(b) digit-letter-letter, eg 2AA–2ZZ; and
(c) letter-digit-letter, eg H4A–H4Z.

Amateur callsigns are normally made up of the first *two* characters from the allocation, followed by a *single digit* and then a *group of not more than three letters.* However, if a country has the whole of a letter-letter-letter block, eg WAA–WZZ, then it is also entitled to form callsigns consisting of the first letter in front of the digit (in this case W).

For example, the UK has been allocated GAA–GZZ, MAA–MZZ and 2AA–2ZZ, of which the series GAA–GZZ and 2AA–2ZZ are currently used to form amateur callsigns. This means that UK amateur callsigns can have GA, GB, GC etc as the first two characters. (As the UK has the whole GAA–GZZ block, it is also entitled to use the single letter G.) Similarly, it can form callsigns starting with 2A, 2B, 2C etc.

The first two characters of the allocation are usually unique to a country but the ITU occasionally allocates 'half-series': eg 3DA–3DM to Swaziland and 3DN–3DZ to Fiji. In practice, Swaziland callsigns commence with 3DA and Fiji amateur radio callsigns with 3D2.

Certain limitations are imposed by the ITU to ensure that callsigns issued cannot be confused with internationally agreed distress signals such as SOS (eg G4SOS was not issued) or the international Q-code (QAA–QZZ was not allocated by the ITU and also, for example, G4QAA was not issued).

Further information on the allocation of callsigns is given in the section later on dealing with the work of the national telecommunications administration.

Designation of emissions

There are very many ways in which a radio signal can be modulated so as to convey information. In order to define the types

ARTICLE 32

I. Amateur Service

1. Radio communications between amateur stations of different countries shall be forbidden if the administration of one of the countries concerned has notified that it objects to such radio communications.

2. (1) When transmissions between amateur stations of different countries are permitted, they shall be made in plain language and shall be limited to messages of a technical nature relating to tests and to remarks of a personal character for which, by reason of their unimportance, recourse to the public telecommunications service is not justified.

    (1A) It is absolutely forbidden for amateur stations to be used for transmitting international communications on behalf of third parties.

    (2) The preceding provisions may be modified by special arrangements between the administrations of the countries concerned.

3. (1) Any person seeking a licence to operate the apparatus of an amateur station shall have proved that he is able to send correctly by hand and to receive correctly by ear, texts in morse code signals. The administrations concerned may, however, waive this requirement in the case of stations making use exclusively of frequencies above 30MHz.

    (2) Administrations shall take such measures as they judge necessary to verify the operational and technical qualifications of any person operating the apparatus of an amateur station.

4. The maximum power of amateur stations shall be fixed by the administrations concerned, having regard to the technical qualifications of the operators and to the conditions under which these stations are to operate.

5. (1) All the general rules of the Convention and of these Regulations shall apply to amateur stations. In particular, the emitted frequency shall be as stable and as free from spurious emissions as the state of technical development for such stations permits.

    (2) During the course of their transmissions, amateur stations shall transmit their callsign at short intervals.

II. Amateur-Satellite Service

6. The provisions of Section I of this Article shall apply equally, as appropriate, to the Amateur-Satellite Service.

7. Space stations in the Amateur-Satellite Service operating in bands shared with other services shall be fitted with appropriate devices for controlling emissions in the event that harmful interference is reported in accordance with the procedure laid down in Article 22. Administrations authorising such space stations shall inform the IFRB and shall ensure that sufficient earth command stations are established before launch to guarantee that any harmful interference which might be reported can be terminated by the authorising administration.

of emission a special code has been internationally agreed and implemented by the ITU.

The code is in two parts, the first specifying the *necessary bandwidth* and the second the *classification of emission*.

The necessary bandwidth is specified as follows: between 0.001 and 999Hz in hertz (H); between 10 and 999kHz in kilohertz (K); between 1.00 and 999MHz in megahertz (M); between 100 and 999GHz in gigahertz (G). For example, 400Hz would be '400H', 2.4kHz as '2K40' and 12.5kHz as '12K5'.

The classification is specified by three symbols. The first denotes the type of modulation of the main carrier, the second the nature of the modulating signal(s) and the third the type of information to be transmitted. Table 1 gives the symbols and

Table 1. Classification of emissions

FIRST SYMBOL – Type of modulation of main carrier

1. Emission of unmodulated carrier: N.
2. Emission in which the main carrier is amplitude modulated including cases where sub-carriers are angle modulated. Double sideband: A. Single sideband, full carrier: H. Single sideband, reduced or variable carrier: R. Single sideband, suppressed carrier: J. Independent sideband: B. Vestigial sideband: C.
3. Emission in which the main carrier is angle modulated. Frequency modulation: F. Phase modulation: G.
4. Emission in which the main carrier is amplitude or angle modulated either simultaneously or in a pre-arranged sequence: D.
5. Emission of pulses. Unmodulated sequence of pulses: P. A sequence of pulses (a) modulated in amplitude: K, (b) modulated in width/duration: L, (c) modulated in position/phase: M, (d) in which the carrier is angle modulated during the period of the pulse: Q, (e) which is a combination of the foregoing or is produced by other means: V.
6. Cases not covered above, in which an emission consists of the main carrier modulated, either simultaneously or in a pre-established sequence, in a combination of two or more of the following modes – amplitude, angle, pulse: W.
7. Cases not otherwise covered: X.

Note: Emissions where the main carrier is directly modulated by a signal which has been coded into quantised form (eg pulse code modulation) should be designated by A, H, R, J, B, C, F, or G as appropriate.

SECOND SYMBOL – Nature of signal(s) modulating main carrier

1. No modulating signal: 0.
2. A single channel containing quantised or digital information without the use of a modulating subcarrier (excluding time-division multiplex): 1.
3. A single channel containing quantised or digital information with the use of a modulating subcarrier (excluding time-division multiplex): 2.
4. A single channel containing analogue information: 3.
5. Two or more channels containing quantised or digital information: 7.
6. Two or more channels containing analogue information: 8.
7. Composite system with one or more channels containing quantised or digital information, together with one or more channels containing analogue information: 9.
8. Cases not otherwise covered: X.

THIRD SYMBOL – Type of information to be transmitted

1. No information transmitted: N.
2. Telegraphy – for aural reception: A
3. Telegraphy – for automatic reception: B.
4. Facsimile: C.
5. Data transmission, telemetry, telecommand: D.
6. Telephony (including sound broadcasting): E.
7. Television (video): F.
8. Combination of the above: W.
9. Cases not otherwise covered: X.

Note: In this context the word 'information' does not include information of a constant, unvarying nature such as provided by standard frequency emissions, continuous wave and pulse radars etc.

EXAMPLES OF THE USE OF EMISSION CODES

Telephony (speech)

Single sideband, suppressed carrier (SSB)	J3E
Frequency modulation (FM)	F3E
Phase modulation (PM)	G3E
Amplitude modulation	A3E

Morse code

Hand sent, on/off keying of carrier	A1A
Hand-sent, on/off keying of the audio tone (FM transmitter)	F2A

RTTY/AMTOR

Direct frequency shift keying of carrier	F1B
Frequency shift keyed audio tone (FM transmitter)	F2B
Frequency shift keyed audio tone (SSB transmitter)	J2B

Packet/Data

Direct frequency shift keying of carrier	F1D
Frequency shift keyed audio tone (FM transmitter)	F2D
Frequency shift keyed audio tone (SSB transmitter)	J2D

Television

Vestigial sideband (AM transmitter)	C3F
Slow-scan TV (SSB transmitter)	J2F

Facsimile

Frequency shift keyed audio tone (SSB transmitter)	J2C

Fig 1. The three ITU regions. Region 1 includes the area limited on the east by line A (lines A, B and C are defined below) and on the west by line B, excluding any of the territory of Iran which lies between these limits. It also includes that part of the territory of Turkey and the former USSR lying outside of these limits, the territory of the Mongolian People's Republic, and the area to the north of the former USSR which lies between lines A and C.

Region 2 includes the area limited on the east by line B and on the west by line C.

Region 3 includes the area limited on the east by line C and on the west by line A, except the territories of the Mongolian People's Republic, Turkey, the former USSR, and the area to the north of the former USSR. It also includes that part of the territory of Iran lying outside of those limits. Lines A, B and C are defined as follows:

Line A extends from the North Pole along meridian 40°E to parallel 40°N, thence by great-circle arc to the intersection of meridian 60°E and the Tropic of Cancer; thence along the meridian 60°E to the South Pole.

Line B extends from the North Pole along meridian 10°W to its intersection with parallel 72°N, thence by great-circle arc to the intersection of meridian 20°W and parallel 10°S; thence along meridian 20°W to the South Pole.

Line C extends from the North Pole by great-circle arc to the intersection of parallel 65° 30'N with the international boundary in Behring Strait, thence by great-circle arc to the intersection of meridian 165°E and parallel 50°N; thence by great-circle arc to the intersection of meridian 170°W and parallel 10°N, thence along parallel 10°N to its intersection with meridian 120°W; thence along meridian 120°W to the South Pole

their meanings. Some examples relevant to amateur radio are also shown.

Note that for the purposes of the UK licence, modulation used only for short periods and for incidental purposes, such as identification or calling, may be ignored when calculating the emission designator. Double sideband emissions with reduced or suppressed carrier are included in the first character A.

Frequency allocations

One of the most important tasks of the ITU is to allocate parts of the radio spectrum to various radio services in such a way that the spectrum is utilised as efficiently as possible without mutual interference. The claims on the available frequency space are many and are continually changing.

The range of frequencies covered by the present ITU regulations is 9kHz–400GHz. For the allocation of these frequencies, and for various administrative reasons, the world has been divided into three regions (see Fig 1).

Region 1 comprises Europe and Africa, and including Mongolia, Turkey and the whole of the CIS. Region 2 comprises North and South America, while Region 3 comprises Asia, Australasia and Oceania. The more formal ITU definitions of these areas are given in Fig 1. Note that these three ITU regions should not be confused with the ITU broadcasting zones, which are used for scoring purposes in some amateur radio contests (see Appendices 1 and 3).

Sometimes the ITU finds it necessary to allocate part of the radio spectrum to two or more radio services. Where this is done it is always specified which if any of the services has priority over the others, by placing the service in one of three categories: *primary, permitted* or *secondary*.

Permitted and primary services have equal status except that in the preparation of ITU frequency plans the primary service has prior choice of frequencies.

Services allocated a band on a secondary basis must not cause harmful interference to stations within that allocation having primary or permitted status, and cannot claim protection from harmful interference caused by the latter. They can, however, claim protection from interference generated by stations in the same service or other secondary services.

What this means is that primary and permitted services have the 'right of way' over secondary services. When operating in a shared allocation in which the Amateur Service is a secondary service, the amateur operator must take care not to cause interference to primary users. If these start transmitting on the same frequency, even while an amateur contact is already in progress, the amateurs must change frequency and leave the channel clear.

Appendix 6 shows all amateur allocations between 9kHz and 275GHz in the three ITU regions, the status of these allocations and the nature of services (if any) sharing the allocations. The information is shown in generalised form, and may not apply to particular countries within each ITU region. Most variations from these allocations are however given in Chapter 4 on a band-by-band basis.

NATIONAL TELECOMMUNICATION ADMINISTRATION

This is the government department in each country which has the responsibility of controlling all its telecommunication services and the issue of licences. This same body usually represents that government at the ITU conferences.

In the UK this function is undertaken by the Radiocommunications Agency (RA) of the Department of Trade and Industry (DTI).

Although based on the ITU regulations, the amateur licence conditions for each country can be quite different: some countries do not allow amateur radio at all, while in others its operation is restricted.

The national telecommunication administration assigns callsigns to individual amateur stations using its ITU-allocated character blocks as previously noted. It may choose to use these to denote the geographical area or licence category of the station. Similarly the single digit following the ITU characters is sometimes used to denote licence category or geographical area, while in other cases it has no particular significance and may be regarded as part of the serial letter group.

The serial letters following the single digit are the part of the callsign which identifies individual stations. In a few countries the first or last letter of this group indicates geographical area or licence category. The serial letters are usually assigned in strict alphabetical order, but in some smaller countries it is possible to request letters to correspond with the licensee's initials.

The part of the callsign which precedes the serial letters is known as the *prefix*. If the single digit is simply part of the serial allocation it is not included in the prefix, though it is customary in amateur usage not to split two consecutive figures, eg C31 (not C3, which is more correct) is often given as the Andorran prefix.

Notes on systems are given for each country where known in Appendix 2.

Sometimes the administration will temporarily allocate special callsign prefixes outside its normal series to stations commemorating some national event or celebration, and this results in some strange callsigns being heard on the air from time to time which may be difficult to identify. The important thing to note is that *any* prefix so used must conform with the ITU block allocation(s) for the country concerned, and the list of these in Appendix 3 should be consulted in cases of doubt.

It is also possible for a callsign to have a *suffix*, which is always separated from the rest of the callsign by a solidus (/). A suffix usually indicates temporary operation away from the registered address of the station. In the UK, for example, '/M' denotes a mobile station and '/P' a temporary location. Another use for a suffix is to denote a licence issued to a foreign amateur (see below).

Operation abroad

Many countries now allow foreign amateurs to operate within their boundaries, but the conditions are set by the national administration and vary widely. In some cases, the administration acts unilaterally and permits amateurs from certain countries to apply for licences while in others there must exist a formal reciprocal agreement with the amateur's country. A recent and welcome development in Europe is the agreement

IARU meetings take place regularly all over the world, and liaison with the telecommunication administrations is an important part of its work. Here IARU Region 1 chairman Lou Van de Nadort, PA0LOU (left) is shown with the Minister of Telecommunications of Oman, H E Ahmed Bin Suwaidan Al-Balushi, at a Region 1 Executive Committee meeting in Oman

of common standards for an amateur radio licence (known as Recommendation T/R-61-01) by the European Conference of Postal and Telecommunication Administrations (CEPT) which is a group of national telecommunication administrations from over 40 European countries. Once an administration has confirmed that its amateur radio licence conforms to the CEPT minimum standard, its amateurs may operate portable or mobile within the other participating countries with the minimum of formality. The text of the Recommendation is shown in the panel. It should be noted that not all member administrations have implemented this Recommendation but over 20 have done so and the list is growing all the time. In addition, some non-CEPT countries such as Israel, New Zealand and Peru are prepared to authorise operation on similar lines.

Note: the CEPT Radio Amateur Licence has been incorporated into the UK licence, and is not a separate document.

The temporary callsigns issued to foreign amateurs vary. Sometimes the foreign country prefix is added to the amateur's own call, either before the call or after it and separated by a solidus (/). For example, G4FTJ may become OE/G4FTJ in Austria but G4FTJ/ZL in New Zealand. In some smaller countries, or in other cases for extended operating periods, a separate callsign may be issued. Since CEPT operation is mobile or portable, the host country will normally require a /M or /P suffix to be added.

Further information on operating abroad is given in Chapter 6 and Appendix 2.

INTERNATIONAL AMATEUR RADIO UNION

The Amateur Service and Amateur-Satellite Service have their own international organisation which has the specific objective of promoting, protecting and advancing these services within the framework of regulations established by the International Telecommunication Union. It also provides support to member societies in the pursuit of these objectives at the national level, with special reference to the following:

(a) representation of the interests of amateur radio at and between conferences and meetings of international telecommunications organisations;

(b) encouragement of agreements between national amateur radio societies on matters of common interest;

RECOMMENDATION T/R 61-01 (NICE 1985)

Concerning the CEPT Radio Amateur Licence

The European Conference of Posts and Telecommunications Administrations,

Whereas:

(a) the Amateur Service is a telecommunications service governed by the Radio Regulations and by the national regulations of the countries of the CEPT;

(b) administration are responsible, in accordance with Article 32 Para 3 of the Radio Regulations, for taking such measures as they judge necessary to verify the operational and technical qualifications of radio amateurs, and for ensuring that they undergo a morse telegraphy test, permitting them to operate on frequencies below 30MHz;

(c) the issue and administration of temporary authorisations based on existing bilateral agreements involves a considerable increase in work for CEPT member administrations;

(d) technical developments and the growing standardisation of amateur radio equipment in the CEPT member countries mean a reduction of the risks of harmful interference;

(e) certain CEPT member administration have concluded or are drawing up agreements to simplify the current procedure for the issue of temporary licences;

Noting, however:

(f) that this Recommendation bears no relation to the import and export of amateur radio equipment, which is subject only to the relevant customs regulations,

Recommends:

that the CEPT member administration recognise the principle of a 'CEPT radio amateur licence' under the conditions specified in Appendix 1, on which the member administration will levy neither duties nor taxes, only the Administration issuing the licence being entitled to do so.

Appendix I – General conditions for allocation of a CEPT licence

1. General provisions relating to the 'CEPT amateur radio licence'

The 'CEPT amateur radio licence' will take a form similar to a national licence or a special document issued by the same authority, and will be drafted in the national language, and in German, English and French; it will be valid for non-residents only, for the duration of their temporary stay in CEPT member countries having adopted the Recommendation, and within the limit of validity of the national licence. Radio amateurs holding a temporary licence may not benefit from the provisions of the Recommendation.

The minimum requirements for a CEPT licence will be:

- a declaration according to which the holder is authorised to utilise his amateur radio station in accordance with this Recommendation in countries where the latter applies;
- the name and address of the holder;
- the callsign;
- the CEPT licence class;
- the validity;
- the issuing authority.

It is recommended that a list be added of the administrations applying the Recommendation.

2. Licence classes

Each of the CEPT classes described below will only be considered as equivalent to a national class in cases where conditions of utilisation in another country are not considerably broader than those in the country where the licence was issued. Equivalents are given in columns 3 and 4 of the Table in Appendix II [*not shown in this book*].

Class 1 – This class permits utilisation of all frequencies allocated to the Amateur Service and authorised in the country where the station is to be operated. It will be open only to those amateurs who have proved their competence with morse code to their own administration.

Class 2 – This class limits utilisation of stations to frequency allocations above 144MHz, authorised for the Amateur Service in the country where the station is to be installed.

3. Conditions of utilisation

3.1. The holder shall present his CEPT radio amateur licence on request to the supervisory authorities in the country visited.

3.2. Authorisation is granted for utilisation of a portable or mobile station only. A portable station shall, for the purposes of this Recommendation, include any station using mains electricity at a temporary location, eg a hotel.

3.3. Authorisation is also granted for utilisation of the station of a radio amateur holding a licence in the host country.

3.4. The holder shall observe the provisions of the Radio Regulations, this Recommendation and the regulations in force in the country visited; he shall, furthermore, respect any restriction placed on him concerning local conditions of a technical nature regarding the public authorities.

(c) enhancement of amateur radio as a means of technical self-training for young people;

(d) promotion of technical and scientific investigations in the field of radio communication;

(e) promotion of amateur radio as a means of providing relief in the event of natural disasters;

(f) encouragement of international goodwill and friendship;

(g) support of member societies in developing amateur radio as a valuable national resource, particularly in developing countries; and

(h) development of amateur radio in those countries not represented by member societies.

The International Amateur Radio Union was founded in 1925 and its headquarters in located at ARRL HQ in Newington, Connecticut, USA; it has separate organisations in each of the ITU regions. Membership is restricted to national societies just as the members of the ITU are national administrations, not radio services or individuals. There are nearly 150 national societies which are members of the IARU. The largest region is Region 1 which contains more than 80 societies located in Europe, Africa, the Middle East and the Commonwealth of Independent States.

In a similar way to that in which the ITU regulates and co-ordinates frequency allocations as a whole, the IARU regulates and co-ordinates amateur activities within individual amateur bands. This is on a voluntary basis within the UK but mandatory in some other countries. Whether mandatory or voluntary, they should always be obeyed because they have resulted from long debate and discussion within the world's national amateur radio societies. Band plans are discussed in Chapter 3, and the UK plans are detailed in Appendix 9.

The IARU also agrees and makes recommendations concerning specialised activities such as meteor scatter and direction finding.

Another valuable service, the IARU Monitoring System (IARUMS), monitors unauthorised transmissions by other services within amateur allocations. Volunteers located throughout the world record the characteristics of the signal and if possible identify the country of origin. These reports are collected and collated, and the administrations notified that they are causing problems. This can be very effective.

NATIONAL SOCIETY

The fourth arbiter of operating standards and practice is the national society of the country concerned. Recommendations may come from the specialist committees within each society whose recommendations are considered and debated at regional conferences. Within the UK these areas are represented by the RSGB Licensing Advisory Committee, Microwave Committee, VHF Committee and the HF Committee.

In the UK the RSGB has in the past co-ordinated a team of observers through whom licensed amateurs are notified of breaches in licence conditions which, if heard by official channels, would result in suspension of their licences. This Amateur Radio Observation Service (AROS) is no longer active but it is hoped to re-establish it in the near future.

FURTHER INFORMATION

[1] International Telecommunication Union, Place des Nations, CH-1211 Geneva 20, Switzerland.

[2] *Radio Regulations,* ITU, Geneva, 1982.

[3] International Amateur Radio Union, Box 31905, Newington, Connecticut 06111-0905, USA. Region 1 Secretary: Dr E J Allaway, G3FKM, 10 Knightlow Road, Birmingham B17 8QB, UK. Region 2 Secretary: Pedro Seidemann, YV5BPG, PO Box 2253, Caracas 101A, Venezuela. Region 3 Secretary: Keigo Komuro, JA1KAB, PO Box 73, Toshima, Tokyo, Tokyo 170-91, Japan.

2 Setting up a station

MOST radio amateurs begin as listeners, perhaps using a simple home-constructed receiver or a factory-made general-coverage receiver. As interest in the hobby grows, various items of equipment are then added to the basic set-up – perhaps a pair of headphones to assist concentration on weak signals, an audio filter for CW reception or an antenna tuning unit. Fairly soon it becomes inconvenient to set this system up on the kitchen table for each listening session, and a permanent place in the home for it (known as the *shack) is* required, often to the consternation of the rest of the family!

Later on, when the coveted licence arrives, a fresh flurry of building, buying and borrowing takes place, and another amateur transmitting station is born, usually to be completely transformed just a few months later.

This chapter is intended to assist with some of the decisions involved in this process, possibly at risk of making them sound too complex and important. This is of course not so – a little common sense as an antidote to an overdose of enthusiasm works wonders!

CHOOSING EQUIPMENT

Ideally, the station should be planned as a system, and each piece of equipment under consideration should be evaluated in terms of its enhancement of the whole rather than its individual advantages. High performance in one unit may be of little real use if it is never matched in the rest of the system.

Unfortunately this approach presupposes the exact station function is known and is rarely useful for the newcomer who does not know upon entering the hobby which aspect of it is likely to prove of lasting interest.

A fairly flexible low-cost approach is probably the safest course in these circumstances. There is much excellent equipment available on the second-hand market which is suitable for the newcomer, and which should enable him or her to experience the thrills and interest of amateur radio without investing too much time and money, for there is of course plenty of time to specialise later on. Some amateurs deliberately put off even thinking about acquiring any equipment until they have passed the examination and obtained a licence. This is not necessarily as sensible as it sounds. Owning equipment and understanding its operation is of value in studying for the examination. Furthermore a full appreciation of what is available on the amateur radio equipment market takes much more time than the couple of weeks or so between getting an examination pass slip and an amateur licence, and should be started early. Otherwise the newly licensed amateur may be tempted to rush out and buy the first rig in sight just to get on the air!

In fact, one of the pitfalls of amateur radio is the choice of equipment for the station, be it a £1000 transceiver or a £20 SWR bridge. It is not that there is any shortage of equipment available, nor are the prices unreasonable for such a specialised market. It is rather that the newcomer in particular can get confused by refinements and technicalities, and the claims and counter-claims of the various manufacturers. Unlike the professional, he or she cannot very well take away a selection of sets and test them in an electronics laboratory prior to deciding which one to order.

It follows that most of the manufacturers' specifications have to be taken on trust rather than be measured beforehand. Fortunately both manufacturers and reliable dealers are unlikely to put their reputation at risk by claiming their equipment performs better than it actually does. Even so, with a large amount of money possibly at stake it does pay to take some basic precautions.

First make sure the equipment is really necessary at all! If this seems too obvious, read the second-hand advertisements and note the amount of equipment used 'once only'. It is not advisable to buy equipment for a particular band or mode until you are sure this will interest you. Try to find other amateurs interested in those bands or modes and find out more first, if you cannot listen to them with existing equipment. Make sure any accessories acquired will give a useful increase in the *overall* performance of your station.

Understand the basic technical principles of the equipment you are buying or building. Not only will this enable you to read manufacturers' specifications and catalogues more critically but also to choose the most suitable type of equipment for your station. The standard handbooks should be consulted; references [1–3] are particularly useful.

Consider whether building the equipment might be cheaper, more fun and more instructional. This obviously depends on the ability of the amateur as a constructor and the test equipment available. The newcomer is advised to buy any complex equipment such as multi-band receivers or transmitters readymade. Any 'home-brewing' at this stage is best confined to simple accessory projects where *complete* constructional details are available and little or no test equipment is required. Complete kits are available which sometimes save money on the ready-made article and allow the constructor to gain experience and the extra satisfaction of building.

Make sure the performance will be adequate. The last thing a newcomer needs is a 'deaf' receiver and an under-powered transmitter. A good superhet receiver is highly desirable because, as emphasised in Chapter 4, "if you can't hear 'em, you can't work 'em". Although the world can be worked on a couple of watts on HF, the beginner will definitely find it a lot easier if the transmitter is capable of the standard 100W RF output.

Don't narrow the choice down until all possibilities have been considered. Accumulate plenty of brochures and catalogues, and study all the equipment reviews. These are frequently published in *Radio Communication* and other leading amateur radio journals. Ask other amateurs their opinion of the equipment they are using. Of course, opinions vary, but if a number of people have similar criticisms this point may be worth considering further.

Examine a sample of the equipment carefully. Check that the controls and displays are designed for your operating convenience, not the designer's convenience. This is particularly important with mobile transceivers. Check such fine points as backlash on the tuning dial, whether a digital display can be read outdoors if necessary, how long it takes to set up a particular frequency, and so on. Be choosy. Ask awkward questions. After all, it is you who has eventually to operate the rig, not the dealer!

Consider reliability. If the equipment is not one of the major brands, have the seller or dealer open up the cabinet for inspection. Note the quality of construction and components used, and (if second-hand) check if any modifications appear to have been made. Have a good look and not just a superficial glance. Plug-in boards and a tidy layout may make servicing easier. If the equipment is imported, check the availability of spare parts, whether the dealer can handle repairs or whether he might have to send it away, and so on. A reputable dealer will have a ready answer to all these questions and might even be prepared to show you over the workshop to prove it exists! If a fault does develop after equipment is purchased, take it back to the dealer, even if the guarantee has run out. Give him a chance to have a look at it, and to express an opinion. It may be found that he will repair it free of charge even if he is under no legal obligation to do so. Alternatively his repair charge may be very reasonable. Don't tamper with faulty equipment under guarantee before the dealer has had a chance to inspect it – not only may it invalidate the guarantee but if further damage is caused it will make the eventual repair that much more difficult.

So what *should* the newcomer buy? A transceiver is recommended rather than a separate transmitter and receiver simply because it is easier to use and is more compact. A popular model from a major manufacturer is also a better bet because spares, such as valves, are more likely to be available and there is a extensive fund of knowledge on servicing and modification techniques. With most HF transceivers, for example, now costing well over £1000, the second-hand market is the place to start for most beginners.

On HF, the classic transceivers were the Trio (Kenwood) TS-520 and Yaesu FT101; later versions were the TS-530 and FT101Z. These are still available on the second-hand market for £200–£500, depending on the model, and represent good choices. Other possibilities in this price range include the Drake TR4 and Kenwood TS130S. If possible, buy a spare pair of PA valves at the same time.

On VHF, 2m FM hand-held transceivers have always been inexpensive, and it should be possible to pick them up for less than £100 second-hand. These will let you experience all the fun of portable operation and repeaters. For multimode operation, you could consider the Yaesu FT290 portable, giving 2.5W output on 2m FM, SSB and CW, or a base station like the Trio (Kenwood) TR9130, both available for under £300 second-hand.

Some years ago, the RSGB published a book giving reviews of many items of amateur radio equipment [1]. Although now out of print, it would be worth trying to get hold of a copy. Reviews also appear regularly in *Radio Communication* and it may be possible to borrow back issues from your radio club. Club members will also be able to advise you on good buys.

Most radio magazines carry second-hand equipment advertisements, while many dealers also sell traded-in equipment, often with a short-term guarantee.

Some further notes on selecting equipment for optimum DX performance are given in Chapter 4.

CHOOSING ANTENNAS

Much of the foregoing also applies to antennas. The beginner is unlikely to be able to make the correct choice if the elementary theory of antennas is not understood, while it also pays to be conversant with the basic details of all the popular antennas before making a choice. Information on both these aspects is given in references [2–4]. The beginner is advised to start by building simple wire antennas such as dipoles which should work first time.

If a beam antenna is required, then it is probably best to buy a commercial three-band beam which should work right away. Construction of beam antennas is definitely not for the newcomer. Although such antennas have the useful property of increasing both effective radiated power and received signals in the desired direction, it should not be thought that it is impossible to work DX without them, particularly on HF. A gain of 5dB, typical of many HF beam antennas, corresponds to only 1–2 S-points and under favourable conditions may only mean the difference between a strong signal and an extremely strong signal at the other end. In general a lower-performance antenna may have the effect of decreasing the amount of time that DX can be worked rather than prohibiting it altogether, and this may be perfectly acceptable, particularly near the peak of the sunspot cycle on HF, or in summer when sporadic-E gives frequent lifts' on VHF.

Many other factors have to be taken in account in choosing an antenna for installation near the home, such as space, whether a mast or tower can be erected, the attitude of neighbours, whether planning permission may be required etc. Some further notes on siting antennas are given later on.

The newcomer should be careful not to underestimate the importance of the correct choice of feeder, particularly on VHF and UHF. Losses in poor-quality coaxial cable can be unacceptably high at these frequencies, and many VHF/UHF enthusiasts find it worthwhile to spend quite large sums of money on their feeder system. The characteristics of typical coaxial cables are given in references [2–4], and should be consulted before purchase. Be sure to also check with the dealer that the cable is suitable for the purpose for which it is intended, and is of the correct impedance for the system.

The antenna and its feeder system is often undervalued by amateurs, almost as if it were an optional extra, but attention to detail in this area is however one of the most cost-effective ways of improving station performance.

Some further notes on selecting HF antennas for optimum DX performance are given in Chapter 4.

CHOOSING A SITE FOR THE SHACK

In any household, there is often only one reasonable possibility open to the amateur in respect of siting the shack. In many cases this will be a spare room or the garden shed, already overflowing with domestic bric-à-brac. In others it will be the only empty corner of the living room or even the cupboard underneath the stairs.

In other cases a choice may be made between several possibilities, and this section will discuss briefly the various factors involved, as follows:

- Accessibility and privacy
- Acoustics and acoustic noise
- Comfort
- Distance from antenna
- Power
- Space

Accessibility and privacy

Accessibility is used here in its negative sense. It is the duty of the operator to ensure that the station is inaccessible to any other person who might inadvertently injure themself or deliberately operate the station. If young children are present in the household a separate room or shed is desirable, with a door which can be locked when the station is not in use. If this is not possible some way of discreetly disabling the power to the station will be necessary.

Privacy is often another requirement. The garden shed may have windows through which the neighbours and their children can peer, and the noises coming from such a shack might attract the attention of the curious. For some amateurs this may not matter, for others it could almost amount to harassment.

Acoustics and acoustic noise

If phone operation is contemplated, the site should be reasonably free from room echo and external noise. Such extraneous noises will be made much worse if some form of speech processing is used. If such effects are present, it should be ascertained whether it will be possible to remove them. Heavy curtains, acoustic tiles on walls or ceilings, carpets and soft furniture may be required to deaden room echo, while it may be necessary to fit double glazing to lessen external noise if a busy road, railway or airport is nearby. Phone operation also means that the station will generate considerable acoustic noise itself, particularly when the operator is 'shouting for DX'! It is possible that this may be audible to neighbours, or disturb other members of the household.

Comfort

Comfort in the shack allows an operator to concentrate and enjoy the hobby. It is foolish to spend hundreds or maybe thousands of pounds on equipment and then to sit shivering in the cold with hands too numb to operate a key properly.

A site should be chosen which can be kept between about 19–24°C (65–75°F) summer or winter, at least during use. Many lofts heat up on a summer's day to well over 40°C (104°F) even in the UK, yet can be unbearably cold in the winter. Apart from operator discomfort, temperature extremes are not good for equipment. Oscillators can malfunction in the cold, and high-power operation in very hot conditions might lead to damage to transmitters unless cooling is very efficient.

Unheated sites are also likely to be damp, and again this is bad for both the operator and equipment. Damp chairs are not only uncomfortable but liable to be damaged by mildew. Condensation can form inside equipment and cause malfunctions which may be difficult to trace.

Other environmental factors such as ventilation and lighting may also be important in some cases and should also be considered.

Distance from antenna

This is not normally a problem on bands below 432MHz as good-quality low-loss feeders are readily available. However, if VHF and UHF operation is the main interest, the site-to-antenna distance may become important, especially if the chosen site is on the opposite side of the house to the antenna. It should be checked that there will be no problems running feeders from the station to the antenna. Some large-diameter feeders are quite stiff and cannot in any case be bent round sharp corners due to risk of bruising. A hole to take the feeder may be needed in a window pane or window frame. Feeders should not be run through an open window, except on a temporary basis, to avoid any security risk.

Power

A correctly wired mains power supply with an effective earth should be available. Lighting circuits should not be used. As a temporary measure, low-power mobile equipment can be run off an old car battery, but the cost of a new battery is likely to be just as high as that of a proper mains-operated supply, which is far more convenient.

When arranging the power supply, consideration should be given to future expansion of the station and the additional demands this will make on the supply.

Space

Adequate space should also be available not only for the present equipment but future expansion. It is highly undesirable to set up a station site with considerable trouble only to have to move when an interest develops which requires additional equipment. In general, completely home-constructed stations can require up to three times the space of 'off-the shelf' shacks. Not only is home-constructed equipment often somewhat larger than factory made items, but a separate workbench is desirable. A test facility area may also be required to accommodate the oscilloscope, signal generators and other equipment.

SITING THE ANTENNA

For maximum efficiency, the antenna should be sited as high as possible, away from the ground, buildings and other obstructions. The advantages of even a hill-top site will not be realised unless this is done. For this purpose distances and heights should be thought of in terms of wavelengths rather than metres or feet, and the various publications describing particular antennas often give useful information on their performance at varying heights. A rule-of-thumb employed by many amateurs is a gain of 6dB for each doubling of the antenna height, but this can be somewhat optimistic, particularly in urban conditions.

Transmitting antennas should be kept away from metalwork, such as iron drainpipes. This can influence the directional properties of the antenna, and can also lead to radiation of harmonics of the transmitted signal if the metalwork contains joints capable of acting as metal-oxide diodes (the 'rusty bolt effect').

TV sets radiate timebase interference on harmonics of 15kHz in the HF bands, and antennas intended for HF reception should be kept as far as possible from such equipment. Transmitting antennas should also be located as far as possible from TV antennas and their feeders to avoid electromagnetic compatibility problems (see later). TV feeders usually run vertically, and are therefore particularly prone to RF pick-up from vertical transmitting antennas.

Unfortunately TV equipment is not the only category of equipment susceptible to high RF field strengths. Hi-fi equipment, radios, electronic organs and solid-state switching circuits can all be adversely affected. Similarly other domestic equipment can also radiate interference. Electric motors, thermostats, and fluorescent or neon lighting are frequent culprits.

If the antenna is fixed in position and thereby unable to rotate, it may be of advantage to position it so that equipment susceptible to RF (or generating interference) is in a position of minimum antenna gain. This is particularly important where high transmitter powers or high-gain antennas are in use. The safety and social aspects of the antenna site should not be forgotten. Antennas such as dipoles have dangerous RF voltages at their ends when high-power transmissions are being made, and it should not be possible for children or animals to reach up and touch them.

The aesthetic aspect is more a function of the type of antenna used than its location, but it may sometimes be better to have an antenna located lower than optimum to avoid antagonising neighbours or drawing attention to the presence of a radio station.

For more information on the practical aspects of siting antennas, see references [3] and [5].

PLANNING PERMISSION FOR AMATEUR RADIO MASTS AND ANTENNAS

Town and Country Planning legislation is aimed at securing 'the proper use of land' and, as part of this, to safeguard amenities, natural and otherwise, enjoyed by local inhabitants. In the UK, permission is been required before undertaking 'development' which is defined as "carrying out of building, engineering, mining or other operations in, on, over or under land, or the making of any material change in the use of any buildings or other land".

Such applications are considered by Local Planning Authorities (usually the District Council in the case of amateur radio masts or antennas) and will entail an assessment of the pros and cons, balancing the issues involved and making a final judgement upon the merits of the proposal. The Secretary of State for the Environment and his opposite numbers for Wales, Scotland and Northern Ireland have appellate roles over these decisions and can also issue guidance on procedures. Councils also may publish guidance policies, either in the form of 'Local Plans' relating to all or part of their areas or on specific topics. Look out for them.

The overall definition of 'development' set out in the first paragraph is subject to some exclusions set out in the legislation (currently in Section 55 of the Town and Country Planning Act 1990 as amended) and *two* are of relevance to radio amateurs. The first is that the carrying out for the maintenance, improvement or other alteration of any building of works which affect only the interior of the building or do not materially affect the external appearance of the building (the word 'materially' being very relevant here). The second is the use of any buildings or other land within the curtilage (the area attached to the dwelling) of a dwelling house for any purpose incidental to the enjoyment of the dwelling house as such. Amateur radio, as a hobby, falls within this and thus the 'transmitting' component of the hobby cannot be challenged in the way that, say, a PMR base station might be.

In addition to the exclusions set out above, the Act provides for General Development Orders (GDOs), to be prepared which in effect represent automatic permission for things which may not warrant developers or local authorities having to go to the trouble and cost of preparing and processing applications of little moment to the community or where the 'benefits', in a national context, will override any possible costs. Such GDO permissions can be qualified in a variety of ways not practicable in general legislation. This Secondary Statutory Regulation

system has a more simple Parliamentary procedure and thus can be revised more easily. The provisions which allow the extensions to a dwelling by 10 or 15% of its cubic capacity, subject to not coming in front of the forward-most part, nor exceeding the maximum height of the roof of the original dwelling, for many years allowed substantial dormer windows to be built on the front and/or back faces of dwelling roofs and so providing a very cheap way of enlarging dwellings. However, in 1988 this provision was changed to preclude such dormers on roofs facing a public highway and thus reducing some unsightly alterations to street scenes.

Satellite antennas on houses have also caused much criticism, more so on blocks of flats (where in fact the GDO permissions do not apply), but also because the 90cm size constraint produced difficulties in those northern parts of the British Isles where the satellite footprints were less strong. Adverse amenity impacts from the numerous dishes in street schemes and the adverse picture effects were dealt with in July 1991 by changes which varied the size according to the location in the country, allowing smaller (45cm) dishes on the chimney and 70cm elsewhere on the building but retained the 90cm below the roof top in the South West and the area North of the Humber.

There are also two other parts of the GDO which relate specifically to telecommunications; one is the Telecom Code Systems (BT and Mercury) and the other to other commercial microwave systems. Neither is relevant to radio amateurs, apart from these limitations to commercial systems, they specifically exclude siting on dwelling houses.

The 'exclusions', set out in the third paragraph above, together with the automatic permissions referred to in the fourth paragraph may well meet the needs of many amateurs. Remember that neighbours and others may not regard a mast and antenna as a thing of beauty!

In other cases it will be necessary to make an application for permission. *A study of the brochure 'Planning Permission – Advice to Members', which is available free to members from RSGB Headquarters, is strongly recommended.* Think carefully what you really *need* – not what you would like because a local amateur has received permission for a pair of 17m telescopic masts with a variety of HF, VHF and UHF antennas. Don't forget that his house is set in a pocket of woodland and that your corner bungalow on an estate will pose a very different set of 'costs' when your application is being considered. Do make sure that your application sets out fully why you *need* whatever it is that you show on the application forms and plans. Think about the siting and design of your proposal. Slimline (box-section or tubular) masts are more acceptable than square or triangular lattice masts although they won't carry so high wind loads at such heights. Some antennas are of better *visual* design than others – they don't have so many excrescences or breaks in their general lines which draw attention to them in an irritating way. Look at your proposal as if through a neighbour's eyes and show them where and why you want it. If you want a high mast to get antennas up to reduce EMC problems already existing, can you get help to have a report prepared to illustrate how the new set-up will reduce close-in field strengths? Don't try to mislead with antenna details. The Planning Authority is fully entitled to require details and a failure to supply them may result in permission subject to a condition which requires approval of detail drawings of the antenna before the mast is erected! At least one inspector endorsed this course of action; others have dismissed appeals because of the absence of clear information about antennas.

Make sure the mast, any guys and the antenna elements are *entirely* within your own land and do not trespass onto next door's airspace; if you do encroach, you must get his permission in writing and refer to this in supporting material, saying why the space is needed. Remember that an antenna which cannot be accommodated on your own land invites the comment "It's too big for this site".

Make good plans and fair copies of any explanatory material and show them to your neighbours; the Council has to consult your neighbours and it is better if you get to them first and explain things. Ask the Case Officer in the Planning Department if he or his chief has any query. If so, offer to come into the office and explain things.

Some amateurs believe in erecting things first and hoping that nobody will notice them! If you are lucky, you may get away with this for four years after which the Council cannot serve an enforcement notice. It often happens, however, that a new neighbour arrives after three years and can cause problems. In any event, if you have altered the antenna at all within the four years, you may well have put the mast and all at risk. This is currently a grey area and the enforcement law is being steadily tightened. The four-year rule now only applies to building or engineering works and changes of use can now be challenged for longer periods from the change taking place.

One final point. You will know, if you have got the planning permission brochure mentioned above, that the RSGB has a panel of advisers who may be able to help you, perhaps to avoid problems or to overcome them by negotiation with the authority or to appeal to the Secretary of State if you have been refused permission.

STATION LAYOUT

Assuming a suitable site for the shack has been found the next question is how the equipment shall be arranged in the most convenient manner. Obviously this depends upon the type of operation envisaged, and the quantity of equipment to be accommodated, but there are some basic rules common to most situations.

In general, the equipment should be arranged so that all controls in frequent use are within reach of the comfortably seated operator, without any need to bend very far forward. Similarly, it should be possible to read meters and dials accurately without straining to one side or peering.

Units which generate appreciable heat should not be stacked on top of one another, and care should be taken that any ventilation holes in the cabinets are unobstructed. Solid-state transceivers may have cooling fins on the rear of the cabinet, which should have unobstructed air flow. No heating radiator should be located in the vicinity.

Sufficient clearance behind the equipment should be allowed for the connecting leads, especially if large-diameter coaxial cable is in use. Adequate lengths of cable should be used to connect equipment together, so as to permit the sliding forward of any unit for inspection or adjustment while it remains

At GW4YKL a large piece of wood over a cabinet makes a good 'table top' – the wooden shelf has several vertical supporting pieces to take the weight of the equipment which can be considerable. Note the convenient power sockets

connected to the rest of the station. Any strain in connecting leads *will* lead to failure sooner or later (Murphy's law).

The transceiver is the most important item of electronic equipment in an amateur radio station, and it is recommended that the rest of the operating area be built around it. It should be placed on a large firm table which allows plenty of space in front for a logbook, scrap pad and any other material, and so positioned that its tuning knob can be turned easily with the elbow resting lightly on the table.

Opinion varies as to whether the transceiver should be placed to the left or right of the operator or dead centre. Possibly one could get used to it placed in any of these positions. If, however, the set is placed to the left, the right-handed operator can tune the set with the left hand, leaving the right free to write

Fig 1. A 'customised' radio desk design. Dimensions are approximate, and assume the station equipment is fairly bulky. For example, the 450mm separation of the shelf and desk could be reduced if compact modern equipment was in use. Note the 35mm clearance between the rear of the desk shelf and wall to allow for connecting cables. If required, multiple power sockets may be installed under the table on one of the side pieces

Siting a well-equipped station in a corner is a natural way to achieve an L-shaped layout so that controls on all the gear are to hand. This fine example belongs to G3HTA

the log and operate the key or microphone. It may be found convenient to tilt the transceiver slightly so that its tuning dial is more easily visible, or so that its controls are more easily operated. Some transceiver manufacturers have extensions already fitted to the front pair of rubber feet for this purpose. If there is still insufficient tilt, packing can be inserted under the front rubber feet of the set. Such packing should not obstruct ventilation holes, and should provide a firm mounting. A scrap length of wood about 150mm wide should be suitable, with a strip of foam rubber on top to deaden vibration.

Other equipment such as an antenna tuning unit, linear amplifier and computer may be positioned either side of the receiver as convenient, preferably in a U-shaped layout as this ensures all displays are facing the operator. The power/SWR meter, monitor oscilloscope and clock are best arranged on a shelf above the operating position, but low enough to be easily viewed. All equipment which does not need to be adjusted or monitored while routinely operating, such as a low-pass filter or frequency meter, does not really belong to the operating area, and can be positioned elsewhere in the shack to save space.

A suggested line-up on the table in front of the electronics is (from left to right) microphone, logbook, scrap pad and morse key, but the operator will no doubt have individual preferences. The main thing to ensure is that these items can be used with the minimum of effort.

The best place for maps and lists constantly in use is the wall immediately above the operating position, but if this is not possible then the material can be laid out on the table and a thin sheet of glass placed on top to keep it clean and in position.

Last, but not least, a comfortable chair with adequate back support should be chosen, for this will allow the operator to concentrate properly on the job without any fears of aches and pains when a long listening session is over.

SAFETY PRECAUTIONS

Safety is of paramount importance and every precaution should be taken to ensure that the equipment is perfectly safe, not only for the operator himself but also for the other members of the household or visitors. Double-pole switches should be used for all AC supply circuits, and interconnected switches should

be fitted to home-constructed equipment so that no part of it can have high voltage applied to it until the valve heaters and low-power stages have been switched on. This precaution may not only save the life of the operator, but also protects the transmitter against damage.

Linear amplifiers using valves should have a microswitch fitted so that the EHT is switched off when the cabinet is opened. Where interconnecting plugs and sockets are used for high voltages, ensure that the female connector is connected to the supply unit, and the male to the unit to be supplied.

It should be possible to turn off power to the entire station by operating one master switch, located in a very prominent position, and all members of the household should know that in the event of an emergency this must be switched off before anything is touched.

The antenna may require the provision of a lightning conductor in the immediate vicinity, or the use of lightning arresters. The most satisfactory type of arrester is the gas-filled type fitted in an adequately insulated mounting which includes a parallel air spark gap. Arresters for coaxial cable are also available. Lightning protection should always be located outside the building, providing as direct a path to earth as possible – "lightning doesn't go round corners!" Great care should be exercised before touching feeders which have been disconnected before a thunderstorm as they may hold a dangerous charge for a considerable time after the storm. Further information on lightning protection is given in references [3] and [5].

An often-overlooked precaution concerns the current-carrying capability of the mains supply to the station. An amateur station fully equipped with ancillary apparatus can draw quite a heavy current from the supply, and when assembling the equipment it is important to calculate the current that will be drawn when everything is in use and to check that the house wiring will carry this amount. If there is any doubt new wiring should be installed.

It is most important that every amateur should develop a strict code of safety discipline for use when handling his radio equipment. It should be the rule never to work on equipment which is plugged into the AC supply if this can possibly be avoided. However, there are occasions when this is unavoidable and under these circumstances the following precautions should be followed:

1. Keep one hand in a pocket.
2. Remove metal bracelets or watch straps.
3. Never wear headphones.
4. Be certain that no part of the body is touching an object which is earthed and use a rubber or similar non-conductive covering over concrete floors.
5. Use insulated tools.

Before working on equipment of any kind, plugged into the mains or not, it is vital to make sure that all filter capacitors are fully discharged – these are capable of retaining what could be a lethal charge for a considerable time. Use an insulated screwdriver to short each capacitor in turn.

SAFETY RECOMMENDATIONS FOR THE AMATEUR RADIO STATION

1. All equipment should be controlled by one master switch, the position of which should be well known to others in the house or club.

2. All equipment should be properly connected to a good and permanent earth. *Note*: Protective multiple earthing (PME) is now used in the majority of dwellings in Great Britain. With this the neutral is bonded to the earth at the electricity sub-station and all the metalwork (such as gas and water pipes, the latter including central heating pipes and radiators) in the house is also bonded to earth and therefore to neutral. Although it is unlikely, there is a small chance that a fault occurs in the neutral at the sub-station. If this happens, all the metalwork becomes LIVE. If an outside (RF) earth is in place, the full mains voltage will be present between the metalwork and the outside earth – DANGER! One solution is to disconnect the mains earth from all amateur equipment and rely on the outside earth. Alternatively, all the amateur equipment should be placed far enough from any metal connected to the mains earth so that the two cannot be touched at the same time. Another idea is to fit a heavy cable to the outside (RF) earth, feed it through some ferrite rings (toroids) and bond it to the mains earth. The equipment is connected to the earth rod side of the toroids. The purpose of the toroids is to prevent RF interference from the mains earth from getting to the equipment. Four turns on five toroids using 10mm² insulated wire is recommended. (Note A and reference [6])

3. Wiring should be adequately insulated, especially where voltages greater than 500V are used. Terminals should be suitably protected.

4. Transformers operating at more than 100V RMS should be fitted with an earthed screen between the primary and secondary windings or have them in separate slots in the bobbin.

5. Capacitors of more than 0.01µF capacitance operating in power packs, modulators, etc (other than for RF bypass or coupling) should have a bleeder resistor connected directly across their terminals. The value of the bleeder resistor should be low enough to ensure rapid discharge. A value of 1/C megohms (where C is in microfarads) is recommended. The use of earthed probe leads for discharging capacitors in case the bleeder resistor is defective is also recommended. (Note B). Low-leakage capacitors, such as paper and oil-filled types, should be stored with their terminals short-circuited to prevent static charging.

6. Indicator lamps should be installed showing that the equipment is live. These should be clearly visible at the operating and test position. Faulty indicator lamps should be replaced immediately. Gas-filled (neon) lamps and LEDs are more reliable than filament types.

7. Double-pole switches should be used for breaking mains circuits on equipment. Fuses of correct rating should be connected to the equipment side of each switch in the live lead only. (Note C.) Always switch off before changing a fuse. The use of AC/DC equipment should be avoided.

8. In metal-enclosed equipment install primary circuit breakers, such as micro-switches, which operate when the door or lid is opened. Check their operation frequently.

9. Test prods and test lamps should be of the insulated pattern.

10. A rubber mat should be used when the equipment is installed on a floor that is likely to become damp.

11. Switch off before making any adjustments. If adjustments must be made while the equipment is live, use one hand only and keep the other in your pocket. Never attempt two-handed work without switching off first. Use good-quality insulated tools for adjustments.

12. Do not wear headphones while making internal adjustments on live equipment.

13. Ensure that the metal cases of microphones, morse keys etc are properly connected to the chassis.

14. Do not use meters with metal zero-adjusting screws in high-voltage circuits. Beware of live shafts projecting through panels, particularly when metal grub screws are used in control knobs.

15. Antennas should not, under any circumstances, be connected to the mains or other HT source. Where feeders are connected through a capacitor, which may have HT on the other side, a low resistance DC path to earth should be provided (RF choke).

16. Antennas must be designed with due allowance for wind loading. For this, guidance from the antenna manufacturer is necessary and British Standard (BS) CP3 Chapter 5 for guyed masts and BS 8100 for self-supporting masts should be consulted [7].

17. Certain chemicals occur in electronic devices which are harmful. Notable amongst these are the *polychlorinated biphenyls* (PCBs) which have been used in the past to fill transformers and high-voltage capacitors and *beryllium oxide* (BeO) which is used as an insulator *inside* the case of some high-power semiconductors. In the case of PCBs, the names to look out for on capacitors are: ARACLOR, PYROCHLOR, PYRANOL, ASBESTOL, NO-FLAMOL, SAF-T-KUL and others [8]. If one of these is present in a device, it must be disposed of carefully. The local Health and Safety Authority will advise. In the case of beryllium oxide, the simple rule is DON'T OPEN ANY DEVICE THAT *MAY* CONTAIN IT.

Note A. – Owing to the common use of plastic water main and sections of plastic pipe in effecting repairs, it is no longer safe to assume that a mains water pipe is effectively connected to earth. Steps must be taken, therefore, to ensure that the earth connection is of sufficiently low resistance to provide safety in the event of a fault. Checks should be made whenever repairs are made to the mains water system in the building.

Note B. – A 'wandering earth lead' or an 'insulated earthed probe lead' is an insulated lead permanently connected via a high-power 1kW resistor or a 15W 250V lamp at one end to the chassis of the equipment; at the other end a suitable length of bare wire with an insulated handle is provided for touch contacting the high-potential terminals to be discharged.

Note C. – Where necessary, surge-proof fuses can be used.

The vast majority of shocks sustained from electrical apparatus are derived from the 240V mains line lead. Every year there are 100 or more deaths in the UK due to electrocution, mostly as a result of accidental contact with mains voltage. There is evidence to suggest that because of the different physiological effects, those who receive shocks from voltages of more than 1000V have a better chance of survival than those subjected to severe medium-voltage shocks. Voltages as low as 32V have been known to cause death – as the jingle says: "It's volts that jolts but mils that kills".

The danger of electrocution is increased where the victim's skin resistance is lowered by dampness or perspiration, or where he grips an extensive area of 'live' metal while in good contact with earth. It is against this second possibility that particular care is needed in amateur stations.

A particular hazard is equipment which has a chassis

Fig 2. The correct wiring for three-pin plugs in the UK. To test that a socket is correctly wired, a lamp should light when connected between 'L' and 'N' or 'L' and 'E', but not when connected between 'N' and 'E'. A neon bulb will glow when touched against 'L'

connected to the mains which is being used under conditions for which it was not intended. Some old British TV sets and domestic broadcast receivers fall into this category; not only the 'AC/DC' sets but also – and this is not always appreciated – a large proportion of 'AC only' models. If there is any such equipment in your station, the exposed parts should be checked with a neon screwdriver to make certain that they are not 'live' with the on/off switch in either position. Remember that a single-pole switch in the neutral lead will leave the chassis 'live' even with the set apparently turned off. After such checks have been carried out non-reversible plugs should be fitted to AC supply leads.

It is wise to check all three-pin supply sockets in the house to see whether they have been correctly wired; all too often this is not the case. A three-pin plug with the 'earth' contact at the top should have the 'neutral' contact on the bottom left, and the live 'line' contact on the bottom right – these directions apply when looking at the back of the plug for wiring purposes (see Fig 2). Correct colour coding of leads in the UK has been for many years: 'live', brown ; 'neutral', blue ; 'earth', yellow and green. It is very important to note that this coding may not apply to the wiring on some imported equipment, and the manufacturer's instructions should be very carefully studied before plugging into the supply. The use of modern fused plugs is recommended.

An even greater hazard, because it is seldom anticipated, can arise under fault conditions on equipment fitted with a double wound (ie 'isolating') transformer of the type so often used in amateur equipment. It is by no means unusual or unknown for the primary winding to short circuit to the screen between the primary and secondary, the core, or to one of the secondary windings, so that the chassis of the equipment becomes 'live'. Such equipment will often continue to operate quite normally and can thus represent a very real danger over a considerable period. The best safeguard against this danger is to ensure that the screen between the primary and the other windings, the

core and the chassis are all effectively earthed. The earth connection must be of very low resistance otherwise the supply fuses may not blow. These fuses should be of the minimum practicable rating – it is no use having a 50Ω resistance to earth and a 10A fuse – if this should be the case the size of the electricity bills may be surprising, but the hazard is likely to remain undetected! Another source of danger is the electric tool which has developed a fault and which has a 'live' casing. This can happen, for example, with soldering irons and electric drills. A very careful check should be kept on the leads to all such tools, and any 'tingles' felt when they are in use must be investigated immediately.

Many amateurs fit extra power sockets in their stations and the control arrangements may call for quite a lot of semi-permanent AC wiring and switching. In the UK these should always conform with the high standards laid down in the IEE Wiring Regulations. These are rather formidable reading for the non-professional but a number of books giving sound advice on modern wiring practice, based on the IEE recommendations, have been published and can often be obtained from local libraries. Advice can also be obtained from the offices of local electricity boards. In most countries overseas, similar regulations exist and operators in these areas are recommended to obtain copies or seek the advice of the supply authorities.

Another problem is the use of protective multiple earthing (PME) in some UK houses (see 'Safety Recommendations').

Finally, taking the worst possible event into consideration the operator and members of his household are advised to familiarise themselves with the procedures for the treatment of electric shock.

It is often not realised that low-voltage, high-current equipment can also have dangerous aspects. Some recent solid-state transceivers have power supply requirements of some 20–30A at 12V. It is vital that suitable cable is used to connect any external power supply and that all electrical connections are of low resistance, otherwise there could be a fire risk. There is also a considerable personal danger through hot or molten metal if the user inadvertently short-circuits such a power supply – the resultant current through, say, a wedding ring could cause severe burns.

It is a wise precaution to have a fire extinguisher of the type suitable for use on electrical equipment in the shack. The best type is that which directs a stream of carbon dioxide gas on to the burning area; the powder and Halon types may be used but are liable to cause further damage to electrical equipment with which they come into contact.

SECURITY

Many amateur stations now contain easily portable equipment worth well over £2000 in total. Sometimes this is located in a shack remote from the house, possibly on view to the passer-by. It is not surprising that an amateur station can attract attention of the wrong sort, and some elementary precautions should always be taken.

Make a note of the *model number, serial number* and *distinguishing features* of each item of equipment and keep this somewhere in the house (*not* in the shack) where it is unlikely to be seen by an intruder. Make sure the shack is *secure* by checking (and using) the locks on windows and doors. Consider fitting a *burglar alarm*, especially if a separate shack in the garden is in use. If in doubt on these matters, seek the advice of the crime prevention officer at the local police station. When going on holiday, let the police know.

Equipment left in cars is at particular risk. Never leave hand-portable transceivers (or any other valuables, for that matter) lying around on the seats of cars. Keep them with you or, if this is not convenient, locked up in the boot. Remove mobile transceivers when the car is left parked outside the house. Make sure the car is fitted with an alarm.

If the worst comes to the worst, make it difficult for the thief. Give the details of the theft and the equipment to the local radio club(s) and the RSGB (or appropriate national society) as well as the police and insurers. The local radio shops should also be warned, particularly any dealing in second-hand equipment.

INSURANCE

While every amateur will try to construct and maintain his station so that it is completely safe for himself and any others who may visit it, there is always the possibility that an accident may occur. Owing to a component failure a visitor may receive an electric shock, or an antenna or mast may fall and injure someone or damage property. Such an occurrence can result in a legal action, and these days it can result in the award of very substantial damages against the person held to be responsible for the accident. This risk can, and should, be insured against, either by an extension to the existing Householder's Comprehensive policy or by taking out a separate public liability policy if only fire insurance is held. The annual premium for this will only be quite a small amount and readers cannot be too strongly urged to consult their insurance advisers over this matter.

The other insurance risk is of course theft. Again, the existing household insurance should be checked to ensure that the equipment is covered and the cover should be increased if necessary. Some years ago the RSGB introduced a special insurance scheme for its members which fully covers the above liabilities and risks.

TRANSMITTER CHECKS AND ADJUSTMENTS

The UK licence stipulates that transmitters should be tested from time to time to ensure that the licence requirements concerning non-interference to other telecommunications can be met; details of such tests must be recorded in the station logbook.

Adverse comments made on the air concerning modulation quality (including that of CW signals) should be treated with concern, and the fault or incorrect adjustment traced before further transmissions are made. Most amateurs tend to be uncritical of other stations' signals out of politeness, and therefore when comments are made it is often the case that something is quite seriously wrong.

Most transceivers have built-in calibrators or digital frequency readouts. As with any other frequency measuring equipment, these should be checked periodically against one of the standard frequency stations in Appendix 7 either directly or via a calibrated general-coverage receiver.

If available, the manufacturer's handbook should be carefully consulted for details of adjustments and tuning up procedure, and the operator should be fully conversant with these *before* putting the transmitter on the air.

The standard handbooks (in particular [9]) should be consulted for test methods and circuits. Most test gear required is either inexpensively obtainable on the second-hand market or easy to construct at home. Its regular use is not only the mark of a responsible operator, but also one who is sure that his or her transmitter is really giving peak performance in those DX pile-ups !

EMC – DEALING WITH INTERFERENCE

The most common problem in amateur radio is interference caused by the fundamental transmission getting into all types of electronic equipment. The term 'breakthrough' is normally used to describe this phenomenon; emphasising the fact that it is really a shortcoming on the part of the equipment being interfered with, and not a transmitter fault.

Good radio housekeeping

The main object of good radio housekeeping is to minimise breakthrough, by making sure that as little as possible of the precious RF energy finds its way into neighbouring TV, videos, telephones, and the multitude of electronic gadgets which are part and parcel of the modern home.

In many cases it can be rightly argued that the immunity of the domestic equipment is inadequate, but this does not absolve the amateur from the responsibility of keeping his RF under reasonable control. Many of the features which contribute to minimising breakthrough also help in reducing received interference, so that the virtue of good neighbourliness has the bonus of better all-round station performance.

Antennas

By far the most important factor in preventing both breakthrough and received interference problems is the antenna and its siting. The aim is to site the antenna as high as you can, and as far as possible from your own house and from neighbouring houses (see Fig 3). If there is any choice to be made in this regard give your neighbours the benefit of the increased distance – it is usually much easier to deal with any problems in your own home. It is a sad fact that many amateurs are persuaded by social pressures into using low, poorly sited, antennas only to find that breakthrough problems sour the local relations far more than fears of obtrusive antennas would have done.

HF antennas

The question of which antenna to use is a perennial topic and the last thing that anyone would want to do is to discourage experimentation, but there is no doubt that certain types of antenna are more likely to cause breakthrough than others. It is simply a question of horses for courses; what you can get away with in a large garden, or on HF field day, may well be unsuitable for a confined city location. Where EMC is of prime importance, the antenna system should be:

(a) *Horizontally polarised*. TV down leads and other household wiring tend to look like an earthed vertical antenna so far as HF is concerned, and are more susceptible to vertically polarised radiation.

(b) *Balanced*. This avoids out-of-balance currents in feeders giving rise to radiation which has a large vertically polarised component. Generally, end-fed antennas are unsatisfactory from the EMC point of view and are best kept for portable and low-power operation. Where a balanced antenna is fed with coaxial feeder, then a balun must be used.

(c) *Compact*. So that neither end comes close to the house and consequently to TV down leads and mains wiring. Antennas to be careful with are the extended types such as the W3DZZ trap dipole or the G5RV, because almost inevitably, in restricted situations, one end is close to the house.

On frequencies of 14MHz upwards it is not too difficult to arrange an antenna fulfilling these requirements, even in quite a small garden. A half wave dipole or small beam up as high as possible, and 15m or more from the house is the sort of thing to aim for.

At lower frequencies compromise becomes inevitable, and at 3.5MHz most of us have no choice but to have one end of the antenna near the house, or to go for a loaded vertical antenna which can be mounted further away. A small loop antenna is another possibility, but in general any antenna which is very small compared to a wavelength will have a narrow bandwidth, and a relatively low efficiency. Many stations use a G5RV or W3DZZ trap dipole for the lower frequencies, but have separate dipoles (or a beam) for the higher frequencies, sited as far down the garden as possible.

Fig 3. Good radio housekeeping – site your antenna and feeder system well away from the house

VHF antennas

The main problem with VHF is that large beams can cause very high field strengths. For instance 100W fed to an isotropic transmitting antenna in free space would give a field strength of about 3.6V/m at a distance of 15m.

The same transmitter into a beam with a gain of 20dB would give a field strength, in the direction of the beam, of 36V/m the same distance away. Again, it comes down to the fact that if you want to run high power to a high-gain beam, the antenna must be kept as far from neighbouring houses as possible, and of course, as high as practical.

Operation in adverse situations

The obvious question arises as to what to do if your garden is small or non-existent, or domestic conditions make a simple wire tuned against ground the only possibility.

First of all, and most important, don't get discouraged – many amateurs operate very well from amazingly unpromising locations. It is really a question of cutting your coat according to your cloth. If there is no choice but to have antennas very close to the house, or even in the loft, then it will almost certainly be necessary to restrict the transmitted power. It is worth remembering that it is good radio operating practice not to use more power than is required for satisfactory communication. In many cases relations with neighbours could be significantly improved by observance of this simple rule.

Not all modes are equally 'EMC friendly', and it is worth looking at some of the more frequently used modes from this point of view.

SSB   This is one of the least EMC friendly modes, particularly where audio breakthrough is concerned.

FM   This is a very EMC friendly mode, mainly because in most cases the susceptible equipment sees only a constant carrier turned on and off every minute of so.

CW   This is the old faithful for those with EMC problems, because it has two very big advantages. First, providing the keying waveform is well shaped with rise and fall times of about 10ms or so, the rectified carrier is not such a problem to audio equipment as SSB. The second is that it is possible to use lower power for a given contact. Of course, low-power CW is not everybody's favourite mode, but it does provide a way of staying on the air, even in the most difficult circumstances.

Data   Generally the data modes used by amateurs are based on frequency shift keying (FSK), and should be EMC friendly. All data systems involve the carrier being keyed on and off – when going from receive to transmit, and vice versa – and consideration should be given the carrier rise and fall times; just as in CW.

Earths

From the EMC point of view, the purpose of an earth is to provide a low impedance path for RF currents which would otherwise find their way into household wiring, and hence into susceptible electronic equipment in the vicinity. In effect the RF earth is in parallel with the mains earth path. Good EMC practice dictates that any earth currents should be reduced to a minimum by making sure that antennas are balanced as well as possible. An inductively coupled ATU can be used to improve the isolation between the antenna/RF earth system and the mains earth. The impedance of the mains earth path can be increased by winding the mains lead supplying the transceiver and its ancillaries onto ferrite cores to from a common-mode choke.

Antennas which use the earth as part of the radiating system – that is antennas tuned against earth – should be avoided since these inevitably involve large RF currents flowing in the earth system. If this type of antenna must be used, arrange for it to be fed through coaxial cable so that the earth, or better some form of counterpoise, can be arranged at some distance from the house.

The minimum requirement for an RF earth is several copper pipes 1.5m long or more, driven into the ground at least 1 metre apart and connected together by thick cable. The connection to the station should be as short as possible using thick cable or flat copper strip/braid.

Where the shack is installed in an upstairs room, the provision of a satisfactory RF earth is a difficult problem, and sometimes it may found that connecting an RF earth makes interference problems worse. In such cases it is probably best to avoid the need for an RF earth, by using a well-balanced antenna system – but don't forget to provide lightning protection.

Harmonics

Harmonics and other spurious emissions in general are much less of a problem than formerly, partly due to the closing down of VHF TV in the UK and partly to the much greater awareness by home-brewers and commercial manufacturers alike of the importance of good design and construction. Not withstanding this, if there is any doubt about the harmonic performance of a transceiver, then a low-pass filter should be used. Particular care should be taken where harmonics can fall into broadcast radio or TV bands, in particular:

1. The harmonics of some HF bands fall into the VHF broadcast band, 88–108MHz, as does the second harmonic of 50MHz.
2. The fourth harmonic from the 144MHz band could cause problems on TV channels 34 and 35 and the fifth on channels 52 and 53.
3. The second harmonic of 18MHz falls into the IF band of TV receivers.

For further information on EMC problems, see reference [10], from which the above notes have been taken.

FURTHER INFORMATION

[1] *The Buyer's Guide to Amateur Radio*, Angus MacKenzie, G3OSS, RSGB, 1986.

[2] *A Guide to Amateur Radio,* Pat Hawker, G3VA, RSGB.

[3] *Radio Communication Handbook,* 6th edn, ed Dick Biddulph, G8DPS, RSGB, 1994.

[4] *VHF/UHF Manual*, 4th edn, ed G R Jessop, G6JP, RSGB, 1984.

[5] *HF Antenna Collection*, ed Erwin David, G4LQI, RSGB, 1991.

[6] 'The killing ground', Peter Chadwick, G3RZP, *Radio Communication* 1987, p404. Also appears in reference [5], page xii.

[7] 'Wind loading', D J Reynolds, G3ZPF, *Radio Communication* 1988, pp252–255, 340–344 and 629. Also appears in reference [5], p155.

[8] 'Technical Topics', Pat Hawker, G3VA, *Radio Communication* 1984, p295.

[9] *Test Equipment for the Radio Amateur,* 3rd edn, C V Smith, G4FZH, RSGB, 1995.

[10] *The Radio Amateur's Guide to EMC,* Robin Page-Jones, G3JWI, RSGB, 1992.

3 Operating practices and procedures

HOWEVER much time and effort is spent on setting up a station, its success or otherwise depends on the skill and behaviour of the operator. Unfortunately there is no mandatory period for acquiring listening experience or a practical test of operating technique prior to gaining an amateur transmitting licence, and it is possible to tune around the bands at almost any time and hear dreadful examples of incompetent operating. These are usually more the result of lack of experience and knowledge than a deliberate attempt to be a nuisance.

Operating techniques and procedures vary from band to band and many regular HF band users might find themselves in difficulty when using a VHF repeater for the first time. Each set of techniques is appropriate for the particular circumstances, and the only way to become familiar with them is to spend time listening to the good operators, noting how and why their methods succeed where those of the poor operators do not.

It is quite important that the newcomer should be discriminating in this respect, and not simply mimic whatever he or she has heard previously when going on the air for the first time. To put it more bluntly – copy the good operators, not the bad ones!

Whatever band, mode or type of operating one is undertaking, there are three fundamental things to remember. The first is that *courtesy costs very little* and is very often amply rewarded by bringing out the best in others. The second is that the aim of each radio contact should be *100% effective communication.* The good operator is never satisfied with anything less, and adjusts his or her technique accordingly. The third is that the 'private' conversation with the other station is *actually in public*. Never discuss emotive subjects such as politics, race or religion over the air to avoid any possibility of giving offence to others. Never give any information over the air which might be of assistance to the criminally inclined, such as the time the house is unoccupied, dates of holidays and valuables in the house.

Preparing to transmit

Older transmitters and receivers with a free-running VFO can exhibit appreciable drift within the first 15 minutes or so of operation and should therefore be switched on and allowed a reasonable period to warm up before they are actually used, particularly if a narrow-band mode such as CW is going to be employed. There is nothing more irritating than 'following' a CW station down the band, and of course it may drift onto another station's frequency and be lost altogether. Part of this warm-up period can usefully be employed by searching the band for interesting stations. Each time one is heard, its callsign and frequency can be noted on the scrap pad. In this way a short list of frequencies to be monitored is built up, which will be useful during the operating session. This process can be automated if a modern transceiver with memories is used.

Only those tuning adjustments which directly involve the

antenna system should be carried out with the latter connected to the transmitter. All others should be made with the transmitter connected to a suitable screened dummy load.

In a typical system the transmitter should first be tuned up into the dummy load. The transmitter may then be connected to the ATU. Power should be decreased if possible at this stage (not by detuning!) to avoid possible damage to the transmitter's output devices. The ATU should be adjusted for minimum SWR and maximum forward power in the normal way. Power can then be increased to the desired level and the adjustments repeated. Only very minor adjustment of the transmitter output stage should be necessary to ensure optimum working conditions at this point.

If the transmitter has grid or preselector circuits which require peaking every 50kHz or so, a most useful accessory is a screened coaxial switch which will allow the dummy load to be quickly switched in for tune-up purposes.

It is most important that any tune-up signal radiated by the antenna should *not* cause interference to stations already using the band, and a careful check of the chosen frequency should first be made. In particular, any temptation to tune up on the frequency of a DX station before calling should be very firmly resisted for obvious reasons.

When near a band-edge, great care must be taken to ensure that the transmission does not accidentally occur outside the amateur band. Allowance should be made for drift, calibration accuracy and sidebands, particularly those of FM signals (NBFM carriers should be at least 10kHz within the limits of the band in use).

By common agreement in IARU Region 1, each amateur band has been divided into sections which cater for SSB or CW operation, and also more specialised modes such as RTTY and SSTV. These *band plans* are given in Appendix 9. Transmissions in a particular mode should only be made in the appropriate section of the band.

Establishing contact

There are two accepted ways of establishing contact with another amateur station. The first method is to put out a general call or broadcast to all stations, known as *a CQ call,* and to hope that another station responds. The second is to call another specific station by prior arrangement (known as *keeping a sked)* or after the other station has just finished a contact or made a CQ call.

Calling a specific station which has just finished a contact or made a CQ call has the advantage that one knows who is likely to reply, and the signal strength of that reply. This is important on the HF bands because likely fading can be taken into account to determine whether a contact can be sustained. Another factor is that any rare or distant (DX) station on the band is probably already having a contact and would not reply to a CQ call.

When calling a specific station it is good practice to keep calls short and to use the callsign of the station called once or twice only, followed by one's own repeated several times and pronounced or keyed carefully and clearly (particularly when signal strengths are not good or in the presence of interference). The calling procedure should be repeated as required until a reply is obtained or it is clear that someone else is in contact. VOX operation (or break-in on CW) is very useful, because if it is properly adjusted it will be possible to listen between words and know what is happening at all times.

This basic procedure may be summarised as follows:

1. Listen – to find out just what is happening on the frequency.
2. Be patient – wait until any other station already in contact has finished.
3. Make calls short – give the other station's callsign once or at the most twice, but your own two or three times.
4. Listen carefully – between words if possible.
5. Be ready to stop transmitting if the station being called replies to someone else.
6. If unlucky, be patient! Wait for another chance and call again.

If activity on the band is low and a reasonable amount of power is available, a CQ call may be useful. When this is transmitted just as 'CQ' it can be answered by any other station. If the call is 'CQ DX' this limits replies to calls from distant (DX) stations. The definition of DX varies from band to band, and also on conditions (see Chapter 4). Make sure this is understood before making (or answering) a CQ DX call. If stations which are not DX call they should be politely ignored, and it should be a practice never to call anyone else who has made a CQ DX call unless one is DX to that station.

If it is desired to make contact with a particular country a directional CQ call can be made, such as 'CQ VK', which means that only replies from Australia will be answered.

Before making a CQ call it is important to find a frequency which appears unoccupied by any other station. This may not be easy, particularly in crowded band conditions. Listen carefully – perhaps a DX station is on the frequency which is difficult to hear. If a beam antenna is in use, rotate it to make sure. If after a reasonable time the frequency still seems clear, ask if the frequency is in use before transmitting the CQ call (On CW this can be done by transmitting 'QRL?' or just '?'). If two or three CQ calls produce no answer it may be that interference is present on that frequency for distant stations and a new frequency should be sought.

Each CQ call should be short with a break to listen for replies. It may then be repeated as often as required. Long calls without breaks denote poor operating technique – interference may be unwittingly caused to stations which were already on the frequency but which the caller did not hear in the initial check, and moreover stations intending to reply to the call may become impatient and move on to another frequency.

CQ calls on VHF should include details of the location so that those stations using a beam antenna can work out the rough bearing and swing their antenna round before answering the call.

Summarising, the important points in making a CQ call are:

1. Find a clear frequency – check that this is so.
2. Keep calls short as possible and listen frequently.
3. Do not answer directional calls unless in the category of station being called.

Conducting the contact

If contact has been established on a special calling channel, the frequency should be vacated as soon as possible, and the contact completed elsewhere.

After the usual greetings it is customary to exchange details of signal strength, name, location and information on the equipment being used, the latter often consisting only of the model number of the transceiver, the antenna and, if not immediately obvious, the power in use. Often on the VHF bands the height above sea level (ASL) of the location is also given, while HF operators usually mention the local weather and radio conditions.

A contact limited to such information exchanged (quite common on the HF bands) is often known, somewhat disparagingly, as a 'rubber stamp' contact. Yet many overseas amateurs deserve great credit for learning enough of a foreign language (such as English) to enable them to do this. They may not be familiar with other words and expressions, certainly not colloquialisms, and if a contact goes beyond the basic details with a foreign-language amateur it is always wise to use the simplest words possible (including international Q-codes on telephony). A further point is that in poor conditions it may be necessary to keep the whole contact short in case fading or interference occur. The good operator takes both these factors into account when expanding on a basic contact.

On VHF contacts tend to be much less formal due to the usual absence of language difficulty, and 'rubber stamp' contacts are rare except under good conditions when DX contacts are possible.

On both HF and VHF it is good operating practice to use the minimum amount of RF power output consistent with 100% copy at the other station. Any reports of better than S9 received, eg "S9 + 20dB", indicate too much power is in use and this should be reduced if possible to avoid interference to other band users.

Concluding the contact

It is customary in a final transmission for an operator to express some gratitude for the contact, and to convey best wishes to the other person, with often a hope that another contact may be made at a later date.

After concluding the contact, both stations will listen carefully for callers, and what happens next depends on which station was using the frequency or channel prior to the contact. This station has some claim to the frequency, and it is usual and polite for the other station to move off elsewhere after the contact. However, this convention may be modified to suit the circumstances. Good operators move off a frequency where they have been fortunate enough to be called by a rare or DX station, to enable others to contact it. No band is so crowded that it is not possible to find another frequency.

CW OPERATING

The amateur who never learns or uses the morse code (Table 2) is missing a very large part of the enjoyment available from holding a transmitting licence. These days there are many aids to learning morse, including tapes, computer programs and even a multimedia CD-ROM. Though some effort is involved, it is not as difficult to do this as many seem to fear.

To say that it is easier to copy morse signals than telephony under adverse conditions can be something of an understatement. Actually for many amateurs CW provides the *only* possible method of working DX stations. So superior is CW to even RF-clipped SSB as a DX mode on the HF bands, that it has been estimated that the difference is roughly equivalent to at least a 20dB power gain.

Another advantage of CW is that it is possible to communicate and exchange information with another person who does not know one word of one's own language by using standard abbreviations and codes.

A further advantage is that CW takes up much less frequency space in bands which are severely overcrowded, and it usually seems to be easier to find another station to contact without interference, especially if a good CW filter is in use.

Why with all these advantages is not CW even more popular? It must be admitted that it takes much longer to really feel at home on CW than on phone, and many operators do not feel the effort is worth it once they have passed the elementary morse test to qualify for a licence. The high powers and beam antennas many use on the HF bands mean that is possible to work worldwide using phone, and thus the DX advantage of CW is to some degree eroded. Last but not least, many operators are able to exchange signal reports, name and location at quite high speed using CW, but their ability falls off quickly when the conversation becomes less stereotyped and the available codes and abbreviations no longer apply. This does not apply to phone operation, provided of course that both stations are fully readable and the operators speak the same language fluently.

Sending CW

The best CW operator is the one who is easy to read, and who does not impress by sending faster than he or she is competent to. The correct sending speed depends on individual circumstances, and it is sensible to reduce it when conditions are poor, signals are weak or the other operator is a novice. It is good practice to adjust one's speed to match that of the person with whom one is in contact, and not to be reluctant to slow down if it is clear that he or she is not copying fully.

The maximum sending speed should never be faster than the maximum receiving speed. In particular, newcomers to CW operating are advised not to answer a high-speed CQ call at the same speed if they cannot receive at that speed! The correct procedure is to answer at normal speed and request that the other operator slows down. This may be done by use of the QRS signal (see later).

There is nothing like practice for those who wish to become CW operators, and the aim of those using a straight key should be to produce morse which sounds exactly like that being sent by an automatic morse generator. There is one, and only one, proper way to form morse code with character length and spacing correctly timed according to international recommendations (Table 1).

However, operators are not machines, and the natural rhythm of sending (known as the 'fist') does vary slightly from person to person – the experienced operator can sometimes recognise the person sending the code! Some operators deliberately send the first dah of each character longer than the others, giving rise to a syncopation of the normal morse rhythm. This 'swing' may make for a distinctive 'fist' but can make copying more difficult for the beginner.

A steady rhythm is important and failure to achieve this may be due to use of an inferior key or not holding the key properly. Some operators use fast character speeds with relatively slow overall speeds. It is difficult to keep the inter-character spacing uniform in such circumstances and the result may be an unsteady rhythm.

It is most important to monitor all CW transmissions as this

Table 1. The morse code and sound equivalents

Alphabet and numerals

A	di-dah	S	di-di-dit
B	dah-di-di-dit	T	dah
C	dah-di-dah-dit	U	di-di-dah
D	dah-di-dit	V	di-di-di-dah
E	dit	W	di-dah-dah
F	di-di-dah-dit	X	dah-di-di-dah
G	dah-dah-dit	Y	dah-di-dah-dah
H	di-di-di-dit	Z	dah-dah-di-dit
I	di-dit	1	di-dah-dah-dah-dah
J	di-dah-dah-dah	2	di-di-dah-dah-dah
K	dah-di-dah	3	di-di-di-dah-dah
L	di-dah-di-dit	4	di-di-di-di-dah
M	dah-dah	5	di-di-di-di-di
N	dah-dit	6	dah-di-di-di-dit
O	dah-dah-dah	7	dah-dah-di-di-dit
P	di-dah-dah-dit	8	dah-dah-dah-di-dit
Q	dah-dah-di-dah	9	dah-dah-dah-dah-dit
R	di-dah-dit	0	dah-dah-dah-dah-dah

Accented letters

à, á, â	di-dah-dah-di-dah	ê	dah-di-di-dah-dit
ä	di-dah-di-dah	ñ	dah-dah-di-dah-dah
ç	dah-di-dah-di-dit	ö, ó, ô	dah-dah-dah-dit
ch	dah-dah-dah-dah	ü, û	di-di-dah-dah
è, é	di-di-dah-di-dit		

Abbreviated numerals

1	di-dah	6	dah-di-di-di-dit
2	di-di-dah	7	dah-di-di-dit
3	di-di-di-dah	8	dah-di-dit
4	di-di-di-di-dah	9	dah-dit
5	di-di-di-di-dit	0	daaah (long dash)

Punctuation

Full stop (.)	di-dah-di-dah-di-dah
Comma (,)	dah-dah-di-di-dah-dah
Colon (:)	dah-dah-dah-di-di-dit
Question mark (?)	di-di-dah-dah-di-dit
Apostrophe (')	di-dah-dah-dah-dah-dit
Hyphen or dash (-)	dah-di-di-di-di-dah
Fraction bar or solidus (/)	dah-di-di-dah-dit
Brackets – open [(]	dah-di-dah-dah-dit
– close [)]	dah-di-dah-dah-di-dah
Double hyphen (=)	dah-di-di-di-dah
Quotation marks (")	di-dah-di-dah-dit
Error	di-di-di-di-di-di-di-dit

Spacing and length of signals
1. A dash is equal to three dots.
2. The space between the signals which form the same letter is equal to one dot.
3. The space between two letters is equal to three dots.
4. The space between two words is equal to seven dots.

is the only way to tell whether they are being sent properly, and a tape recording of these should show up any defects in the sender's 'fist'.

Complete and properly adjusted full break-in facilities are a great asset because they enable received signals to be heard between transmitted characters. This means that any interference appearing on the frequency can be detected instantly, and it also becomes possible to conduct a two-way dialogue similar to that possible on phone using VOX. However, don't get the impression that full break-in is essential – slick operators do manage snappy break-in QSOs without it.

CW abbreviations, codes and procedure signals

Amateur CW operating procedures are in the most part derived from commercial telegraphy procedures and, while not so strict, retain two valuable features which assist fast and efficient communication.

The first is the extensive use of codes and abbreviations to cut down transmission time, for if brevity is the soul of wit it is also the soul of good CW operating! The two commonest codes

Table 2. International Q-code (extract)

Code	Meaning
QRA	What is the name of your station? The name of my station is . . .
QRB	How far approximately are you from my station? The approximate distance between our stations is . . . kilometres.
QRG	Will you tell me my exact frequency (or that of . . .)? Your exact frequency (or that of . . .) is . . . kHz (or MHz).
QRH	Does my frequency vary? Your frequency varies.
QRI	How is the tone of my transmission? The tone of your transmission is . . . (amateur T1-T9).
QRK	What is the intelligibility of my signals (or those of . . .)? The intelligibility of your signals (or those of . . .) is . . . (amateur R1-R5).
QRL	Are you busy? I am busy (or I am busy with . . .). Please do not interfere.
QRM	Are you being interfered with? I am being interfered with.
QRN	Are you troubled by static? I am troubled by static.
QRO	Shall I increase transmitter power? Increase transmitter power.
QRP	Shall I decrease transmitter power? Decrease transmitter power.
QRQ	Shall I send faster? Send faster (. . . words per minute).
QRR	Are you ready for automatic operation? I am ready for automatic operation. Send at . . . words per minute.
QRS	Shall I send more slowly? Send more slowly (. . . words per minute).
QRT	Shall I stop sending? Stop sending.
QRU	Have you anything for me? I have nothing for you.
QRV	Are you ready? I am ready.
QRW	Shall I inform . . . that you are calling him on . . . kHz (or MHz)? Please inform . . . that I am calling him on . . . kHz (or MHz).
QRX	When will you call me again? I will call you again at . . . hours (on . . . kHz (or MHz)).
QRY	What is my turn? (Relates to communication). Your turn is Number . . . (or according to any other indication). (Relates to communication.)
QRZ	Who is calling me? You are being called by . . . (on . . . kHz (or MHz)).
QSA	What is the strength of my signals (or those of . . .)? The strength of your signals (or those of . . .) is . . . (amateur S1-S9).
QSB	Are my signals fading? Your signals are fading.
QSD	Is my keying defective? Your keying is defective.
QSI	I have been unable to break in on your transmission or Will you inform . . . (callsign) that I have been unable to break in on his transmission (on . . . kHz (or MHz)).
QSK	Can you hear me between your signals and if so can I break in on your transmission? I can hear you between my signals, break in on my transmission.
QSL	Can you acknowledge receipt? I am acknowledging receipt.
QSN	Did you hear me (or . . . (callsign)) on . . . kHz (or MHz)? I did hear you (or . . . (callsign)) on . . . kHz (or MHz).
QSO	Can you communicate with . . . direct (or by relay)? I can communicate with . . . direct (or by relay through . . .)
QSP	Will you relay to . . .? I will relay to . . .
QSR	Shall I repeat the call on the calling frequency? Repeat your call on the calling frequency; did not hear you (or have interference).
QSS	What working frequency will you use? I will use the working frequency . . . kHz (Normally only the last three figures of the frequency need be given).
QSU	Shall I send or reply on this frequency (or on . . . kHz (or MHz)) (with emissions of class . . .)? Send or reply on this frequency (or on . . . kHz (or MHz)) (with emissions of class . . .).
QSV	Shall I send a series of V's on this frequency (or . . . kHz (or MHz))? Send a series of V's on this frequency (or . . . kHz (or MHz)).
QSW	Will you send on this frequency (or on . . . kHz (or MHz)) (with emissions of class . . .)? I am going to send on this frequency (or on . . . kHz (or MHz)) (with emissions of class . . .).
QSX	Will you listen to . . . (callsign(s)) on . . . kHz (or MHz)? I am listening to . . . (callsign(s)) on . . . kHz (or MHz).
QSY	Shall I change to transmission on another frequency? Change to transmission on another frequency (or on . . . kHz (or MHz)).
QSZ	Shall I send each word or group more than once? Send each word or group twice (or . . . times).
QTC	How many messages have you to send? I have . . . messages for you (or for . . .).
QTH	What is your position in latitude and longitude (or according to any other indication)? My position is . . . latitude . . . longitude (or according to any other indication).
QTQ	Can you communicate with my station by means of the International Code of Signals? I am going to communicate with your station by means of the International Code of Signals.
QTR	What is the correct time? The correct time is . . . hours.
QTS	Will you send your callsign for tuning purposes or so that your frequency can by measured now (or at . . . hours) on . . . kHz (or MHz)? I will send my callsign for tuning purposes or so that my frequency may be measured now (or at . . . hours) on . . . kHz (or MHz).
QTV	Shall I stand guard for you on the frequency of . . . kHz (or MHz) (from . . . to . . . hours)? Stand guard for me on the frequency of . . . kHz (or MHz) (from . . . to . . . hours).
QTX	Will you keep your station open for further communication with me until further notice (or until . . . hours)? I will keep my station open for further communication with you until further notice (or until . . . hours)
QUA	Have you news of . . . (callsign)? Here is news of . . . (callsign).
QUM	May I resume normal working? Normal working may be resumed.

are the Q-code for information and procedure signals, and the RST code for signal reports. The second feature is the use of a special procedure signal at the end of each transmission to indicate to the other station (and any other listeners) that the transmission is over, the status of that transmission, and other procedural information. Table 2 gives the official meanings of Q-codes of possible value in the amateur service. When a 'Q' group is followed by a question mark an answer is required, and where appropriate this should be followed by the addition of a number according to the following classification: 1 – very slight; 2 – slight; 3 – moderate; 4 – severe; 5 – extreme. For example 'QRM?' means "is there any interference?" and 'QRM5' means "there is extreme interference".

It should be noted that the very value of the Q-code is that it is an internationally agreed code, and care should be taken to use it correctly if misunderstandings are not to arise. For example, 'QRZ?' is not an alternative to 'CQ'!

Some Q-codes have also come to be used as abbreviated nouns or verbs in amateur parlance, eg 'QSO' means 'contact' in the sentence "Thank you for the QSO". See Table 3.

The RST code (Table 4), due originally to W2BSR, gives readability (R1–R5), signal strength (S1–S9) and tone (T1–T9). The report is usually given as one three-digit combination, eg

Table 3. Informal use of the most common Q-codes

Code	Meaning
QRG	Frequency.
QRM	Interference from other stations.
QRN	Interference from atmospheric noise or from nearby electrical apparatus.
QRO	High-power.
QRP	Low-power.
QRT	Close(d) down.
QRV	Ready.
QRX	Stand by.
QSB	Fading.
QSL	Verification card; confirm contact.
QSO	Radio contact.
QSY	Change frequency.
QTC	Message.
QTH	Location.
QTR	Time.

Note also: QSLL (card sent in receipt of yours) and QTHR (address is correct in the current *RSGB Amateur Radio Call Book*)

Table 4. RST code

Readability

R1	Unreadable.
R2	Barely readable, occasional words distinguishable.
R3	Readable with considerable difficulty.
R4	Readable with practically no difficulty.
R5	Perfectly readable.

Signal strength

S1	Faint, signals barely perceptible.
S2	Very weak signals.
S3	Weak signals.
S4	Fair signals.
S5	Fairly good signals.
S6	Good signals.
S7	Moderately strong signals.
S8	Strong signals.
S9	Extremely strong signals.

Tone

T1	Extremely rough hissing note.
T2	Very rough AC note, no trace of musicality.
T3	Rough, low-pitched AC note, slightly musical.
T4	Rather rough AC note, moderately musical.
T5	Musically modulated note.
T6	Modulated note, slight trace of whistle.
T7	Near DC note, smooth ripple.
T8	Good DC note, just a trace of ripple.
T9	Purest DC note.

'579' denotes "Fully readable signals, moderately strong with pure DC note."

The report can be qualified further by adding letters: 'X' denotes tone as steady as if crystal control was in use and 'C' denotes 'chirp'. However, the use of such qualifiers these days

is rare, probably due to the widespread use of modern factory-made transmitters.

One important point about giving signal reports using this code is that they should be as honest as possible if they are to have any value at all. "A fully readable signal" means just that, and 'R5' should not be given if the signal is being drowned in noise and interference – it is not an insult to the other station to send 'R3' or as appropriate. Such action also warns the other station to slow down or take other steps to improve readability. Nowadays nearly every receiver has an S-meter which gives some relative indication of signal strength.

This meter is more often than not *useless* for giving signal reports. On many receivers it is possible for a CW signal (and often even a phone signal) to be fully readable and yet not lift the S-meter needle off the zero position. This does *not* mean the report should be 'S0'! In this case the meter should be ignored and an aural estimate made of the signal strength using the RST definitions. The appropriate S-number may then be chosen.

In addition to the Q-code and the RST code, a great many abbreviations are in use, such as 'tnx' or 'tks' for "thanks" (Table 5). There is, however, no need for the newcomer to try to start using all these at once. It is perhaps better to use the most common ones and leave the rest until code proficiency increases.

Last but certainly not least are the procedure signals sent at the end of each message (Table 5). A bar over letters in what follows denotes these are sent as one character.

Table 5. CW abbreviations and procedure signals

AA	All after . . . (used after a question mark or RPT to request a repetition)	BD	bad	NR	number
		BLV	believe	OM	old man
		B4	before	OP	operator
AB	All before . . . (see AA)	CK	check	OT	old-timer
$\overline{AR}$	End of transmission	CLD	called	PA	power amplifier
$\overline{AS}$	Wait a moment	CNT	cannot	PP	push-pull
BK	Signal used to interrupt a transmission in progress	CNDX	conditions	PSE	please
		CPSE	counterpoise	PWR	power
		CRD	card	RCVR	receiver
BN	All between . . . and . . . (see AA)	CUD	could	RPRT	report
$\overline{BT}$	Signal to mark the separation between different parts of the same transmission	CUAGN	see you again	RX	receiver
		CUL	see you later	SA	say
		DR	dear	SED	said
		DX	long distance	SIGS	signals
CFM	Confirm (or I confirm)	ELBUG	electronic key	SKED	schedule (prearranged transmis-
CL	I am closing my station	ENUF	enough		sion)
CQ	General call to all stations	ES	and	SN	soon
DE	"from . . ." (precedes the callsign of the station transmitting)	FB	fine business	SRI	sorry
		FER	for	STN	station
K	Invitation to transmit	FONE	telephony	SUM	some
$\overline{KA}$	Starting signal	FQ	frequency	SWL	short-wave listener
$\overline{KN}$	Invitation to transmit (named station only)	FREQ	frequency	TDA	today
		GA	good afternoon (or go ahead)	TKS	thanks
NW	Now	GB	goodbye	TMW	tomorrow
OK	We agree (or It is correct)	GD	good day	TNX	thanks
PSE	Please	GE	good evening	TRX	transceiver
R	Received	GLD	glad	TT	that
RPT	Repeat (or I repeat or Repeat . . .)	GM	good morning	TX	transmitter
$\overline{SK}$	End of work	GN	good night	U	you
TFC	Traffic	GND	ground (earth)	UR	your
TU	Thank you	GUD	good	VY	very
WA	Word after . . . (see AA)	HI	laughter	WID	with
WB	Word before . . . (see AA)	HPE	hope	WKD	worked
WX	Weather report (or Weather report follows)	HR	here	WKG	working
		HV	have	WL	will
HRD	heard	HVY	heavy	WUD	would
HV	have	HW	how	XYL	wife
		INPT	input	YDA	yesterday
Informal amateur CW abbreviations		LID	poor operator	YF	wife
ABT	about	LOC	locator	YL	young lady
ADR	address	LSN	listen	55	best success
AGN	again	MNI	many	73	best regards
ANI	any	MSG	message	88	love and kisses
ANT	antenna	ND	nothing doing		
BCNU	be seeing you				

'K' means "invitation to transmit". It is sent right at the end of a transmission in all cases where a reply or call is desired. '$\overline{KN}$' is more specific. It means "invitation to transmit, named station only". It is therefore sent when replies are desired from the specific station given only. It may be sent after each transmission when other stations joining the contact ('breakers') are not welcome. It is also of use to DX or rare stations to send it at the end of each transmission to make it quite clear they were not making a CQ call, in case someone just hears their callsign and a 'K'.

'$\overline{AR}$' means "end of message". It is usually sent after the callsigns when replying to a CQ call or before them when contact has been established.

'$\overline{SK}$' (often written '$\overline{VA}$') means "end of work". It is sent immediately after the callsigns in each operator's final transmission. It signals to listening stations that they are now free to call.

'CL' means "closing down" and is sent right at the end of a transmission if that station is closing down and is not listening for any other calls. These signals are usually sent in association with callsigns but there are two procedure signals which are not.

'BK' means "break" and is used where a quick response to a question is desired without the inconvenience of repeating callsigns. 'BK' is sent after the question, before and after the answer, and before normal transmission resumes.

As noted earlier, if full break-in facilities are available the whole contact can be conducted as a two-way dialogue and in this case 'BK' is superfluous. It may however be used after a CQ call to denote full break-in facilities are available, for example "CQ CQ CQ DE G4ZZZ BK". The Q-code combination 'QSK' may alternatively be used in this case instead of 'BK'. The other such procedure signal is '$\overline{AS}$' which means "stand by for a moment".

There is some slight worldwide variance in the order of CW procedure signals. The ARRL recommends that '$\overline{SK}$' be sent *before* the callsigns in the final transmission, and also that the 'K' is not necessary after '$\overline{AR}$' at the end of a call to a specific station before contact has been established (some East European stations do not use '$\overline{AR}$' at all in this case, sending 'PSE K' instead). In practice these points are unlikely to lead to any difficulty and are only mentioned here so that the reader is aware of the variations.

There is occasionally a couple of spaced dots sent after the final transmission which are usually echoed by the other station. This is just a final goodbye and has no special significance.

A typical CW contact

All these codes and abbreviations may seem rather daunting to the newcomer – it is difficult enough to learn the morse code without having a whole new set of codes superimposed. Yet after a few CW contacts have been heard and understood the usage begins to become clear and the value of the codes and abbreviations can be appreciated. To assist this learning process, an imaginary CW contact and its literal equivalent is reproduced below as an example.

CQ CQ CQ CQ DE G4ZZZ G4ZZZ K

"General call to all stations from G4ZZZ. Over"

This is known as a 'four by two' CQ call, meaning that 'CQ' is sent four times and the callsign twice. A much longer call is not recommended, as noted earlier.

G4ZZZ G4ZZZ DE WD9ZZZ WD9ZZZ $\overline{AR}$

"G4ZZZ from WD9ZZZ. Over"

Note that the call is short, only 'two by two'. Quite often it is possible to hear a station still calling when the station called has replied to another station. Note also that the USA station did not send 'K'.

WD9ZZZ DE G4ZZZ GA OM ES MNI TNX FER CALL = UR RST 57 = NAME JOHN ES QTH LONDON = SO HW CPY? $\overline{AR}$ WD9ZZZ DE G4ZZZ K

"WD9ZZZ from G4ZZZ. Good afternoon old man and many thanks for the call. Your signals are fully readable and moderately strong, with pure DC note. My name is John and my location is London. So how do you copy me? WD9ZZZ from G4ZZZ. Over"

Each station has the other's callsign correct, so there is now no need to give callsigns more than once.

G4ZZZ DE WD9ZZZ R FB JOHN ES GM OM = UR RST 559 = QTH SR [error] SPRINGFIELD, ILL = NAME IS ED = SO HW? $\overline{AR}$ G4ZZZ DE WD9ZZZ K

"G4ZZZ from WD9ZZZ. Roger. Fine business John and good morning old man. Your signals are fully readable, fairly good strength, and pure DC note. My location is Springfield, Illinois. My name is Ed. So how do you copy me? G4ZZZ from WD9ZZZ. Over."

'R' denotes *all* received correct and should not be sent if there was any part of the message which was not copied or understood. Some operators send it before the callsigns. Note the error made in giving the location and correction; '[error]' means the eight-dot error signal was sent.

WD9ZZZ DE G4ZZZ SRI OM QRM5 = PSE RPT UR NAME?? BK

"WD9ZZZ from G4ZZZ. Sorry old man, extreme interference here. Please repeat your name. Break."

BK NAME IS ED ED ED BK

"My name is Ed. Break."

BK R R TNX ED = QRM GONE = RIG IS HOMEBREW WID 75W INPT = ANT IS DIPOLE = MNI TNX FER QSO ES CUAGN = 73 ES GB $\overline{AR}$ WD9ZZZ DE G4ZZZ $\overline{SK}$

"Roger. Thanks (for the repeat) Ed. The interference has gone now. My rig is homebrew with an input power of 75W. My antenna is a dipole. Many thanks for the contact and I hope to see you again some time. Best wishes to you and goodbye now. WD9ZZZ from G4ZZZ. Over and out."

G4ZZZ DE WD9ZZZ R UR RIG T9X ES FB = RIG HR IS TS520 = ANT IS 2EL QUAD = WL QSL VIA BURO = SO 73 ES GUD DX = GB $\overline{SK}$ G4ZZZ DE WD9ZZZ

"G4ZZZ from WD9ZZZ. Roger. Your rig sounds crystal controlled, and very nice. The rig here is a TS520. The antenna is a two-element quad. I will send my QSL card via the bureau (and I hope to receive one in return). So best wishes and good DX. Goodbye. G4ZZZ from WD9ZZZ. Over and out."

Both stations having sent '$\overline{SK}$' the contact is at an end, and either station may be called by a third station for another contact. The reader will appreciate that this is a basic contact with only the essential details exchanged between the stations.

Nevertheless this type of contact can still give much pleasure. There is of course nothing to prevent much more information being transmitted in such favourable circumstances, although the individual transmissions should be kept reasonably short. Strictly speaking, such details as name, location and signal report should be sent only once as shown here, and if the other operator does not copy the details he or she should ask for a repeat. However most amateurs find it easier to repeat these basic details once, rather than risking time-wasting queries, especially if conditions are poor. The established CW operator may also like to bear this point in mind when contacting stations obviously new to CW operating.

CW operation in a foreign language

It is sometimes claimed that CW operation consists entirely of code groups and thus amateurs who do not possess a common language can communicate with each other. This is only partly true. A typical reply by a Russian amateur to a call would be "GM OM TNX FR QSO UR RST 589 QTH MOSCOW OP VLAD HW?". Apart from the two Q-code groups, every word is an English abbreviation.

The Russian amateur does not necessarily see it like this – unless he is a linguist, he will probably have a list of phrases with the Russian equivalents and he will treat these phrases as code groups and not as abbreviations of English words.

Given a similar list of phrases in other languages, there is nothing to prevent a monoglot English speaker from having contacts in those languages. No knowledge of the language concerned is necessary, and on CW there is no problem of pronunciation or understanding the accent of the foreign amateur.

For generations, English speakers have expected everyone else to learn English in order to communicate with them but this attitude is not universally popular! Amateurs, with a minimum of effort, can make a real contribution to international goodwill by greeting fellow amateurs in their mother tongues. A list of 24 phrases (see next page), which may be combined in various ways, will cover the requirements of most simple contacts and enable a QSL card to be made out in the appropriate language.

Although this author can only speak two, he regularly enjoys CW contacts in 14 different languages. By noting phrases used by other amateurs and written on incoming QSL cards, a stock of idiomatic phrases, in addition to the basic ones, will soon be acquired. It is even possible to adapt phrases which have been collected when travelling abroad or half-remembered from one's schooldays!

There is always the danger that the other amateur may assume that one's knowledge of his language is greater than it really is. A combination of phrases 17 and 18 will meet this situation without giving offence.

The words in roman type are for general use in almost all contacts. Those in *italic* type are for occasional use or for use on QSL cards. It is desirable to write the month in words on QSL cards to avoid the confusion which may arise from different conventions when figures only are used. After each list will be found information regarding accented letters for easy reference. It should, however, be noted that in French and Spanish working, the accents are often omitted and in German 'Ä' is sometimes sent as 'AE', 'Ö' as 'OE' and 'Ü' as 'UE'.

In English, the use of endearments between persons of the same sex would be regarded as unusual, but these are quite common in some languages – *lieber* Hans, *cher* Marcel, *amigo* Juan etc. To avoid complications, feminine forms have not been given and so care should be taken when working YLs!

Table 6. 'Goodbye' in 15 languages

Danish:	FARVEL
Dutch:	TOT WERKENS
English:	GB (CHEERS)
Esperanto:	ĜIS
Finnish:	HEI
French:	AU REVOIR
German:	AWDH
Italian:	CIAO
Norwegian:	HEI
Polish:	CZESC
Portuguese:	ATÉ BREVE
Russian:	DSW
Spanish:	ADIOS (HLV)
Swedish:	HEJ
Welsh:	POB HWYL

$\bar{G}$ = dah-dah-di-dah-dit $\acute{E}$ = di-di-dah-di-dit

Phrase 8 can be easily adapted; if the rig is an internationally known one, the type number can be inserted in place of '100 WATTS'. As to antennas, those known by the inventor's callsign present no difficulty and the expressions '3 EL', 'YAGI' and 'QUAD' are used in all languages.

It is suggested that German should be the first language to be attempted because it is already used extensively in CW operation and the procedure and abbreviations are well known. In addition to Austria and Germany, the language is used in a large part of Switzerland. All these countries are easy to contact on a number of bands and it is much better for one's first contacts in a foreign language to be with nearby countries when readability is usually good.

French is not so easily abbreviated but it is used over the air quite extensively. The language is still spoken in parts of Africa and it is the first language in Quebec Province (VE2). French-speaking Canadians particularly value contacts in their own language.

Spanish is used throughout South America (except in Brazil) and it is for that reason that it has been selected as one of the languages for inclusion here.

The original versions of the German, French and Spanish text were prepared by DL1RK, F3AT/G5BRV and G3HVG/EA6 (now G8VG) respectively. The author has, however, made some modifications to these texts as a result of his experience over the air, eg 'MCI POUR' instead of 'MCI DE'. It will be noticed that in some cases, the English abbreviations are retained (or given as alternatives) when the equivalent wording in the foreign language is rather long. In contacts between (say) two Italian amateurs, one will often hear a number of English expressions.

In recent years, it has become popular to say 'Goodbye' in the appropriate language, and a list is given in Table 6.

The effort involved in using a foreign language is well repaid by the thanks which will be expressed in almost every contact, and the final courtesy should be to include a few remarks in the language on the outgoing QSL card.

It is necessary to remember that, in some countries, language is an explosive political matter. This usually occurs in a country where only a very small minority of the people speak a particular language. In these circumstances, it is wise to make sure that use of the language concerned will be welcome before using it over the air.

TELEPHONY TECHNIQUES AND PROCEDURES

The major portion of amateur radio traffic is now carried out using telephony, especially on VHF and above. Though this

CW PHRASES IN ENGLISH, FRENCH, GERMAN AND SPANISH

ENGLISH

1. GM/GA/GE/GN OM
2. TNX FR CALL (ES FIRST QSO)
3. *Nice to meet u agn*
4. *We have met B4*
5. UR RST . . . QTH . . . NAME . . .
6. HW?
7. TNX . . . FR (FB) REPORT
8. HR RIG [100 WATTS] ANT [DIPOLE]
9. WX (1) FINE (2) CLEAR (3) CLOUDY (4) RAINY (5) WINDY (6) FOGGY (7) WARM (8) COLD (9) SNOW TEMP . . . C
10. TNX . . . FR INFO ON UR RIG (ES WX)
11. *Only partly OK*
12. *All OK except ur QTH*
13. *Some/much/too much QSB, QRM (etc)*
14. *Pse rpt my report/ur name/ur QTH*
15. *Pse QSY up/down . . . kHz*
16. *Band vy noisy*
17. *Sri but I do not understand completely*
18. *I speak only a little English*
19. QSL OK VIA BURO
20. *I have recd ur crd*
21. *Have u recd my crd?*
22. *I am QRU nw*
23. *Best 73 es DX*
24. TNX . . . FR QSO NW QRU 73 DX ES GB

January	*April*	*July*	*October*
February	*May*	*August*	*November*
March	*June*	*September*	*December*

FRENCH

1. BJR/—/BSR/BN MON VIEUX
2. MCI BCP POUR VOTRE APPEL (ET POUR PREMIER QSO)
3. *Je suis enchanté de vous rencontrer de nouveau*
4. *Nous avons déja fait QSO*
5. VOTRE RST . . . QTH . . . NOM . . .
6. HW? (*Quel est mon contrôle?*) (*Bien aimable*)
7. MCI BCP . . . POUR RPRT (*contrôle*)
8. ICI RIG (*appareil*) [100 WATTS] ANT [DIPOLE]
9. WX (1) MERVEILLEUX (2) CLAIR (3) NUAGEUX (4) PLUVIEUX (5) IL Y A DU VENT (6) IL Y A BROUILLARD (7) CHAUD (8) FROID (9) IL NEIGE TEMP . . . C
10. MCI BCP . . . POUR L'INFO SUR VOTRE RIG (*appareil*) (ET WX)
11. *OK seulement en partie*
12. *Complètement OK excepté votre QTH*
13. *Peu/bcp/trop de QSB, de QRM (etc)*
14. *Repetez mon rprt (contrôle)/votre nom/votre QTH svp*
15. *QSY plus haut/plus bas . . . kHz svp*
16. *Il y a bcp be bruit sur la bande*
17. *Je regrette bcp mais je ne vous ai pas complètement compris*
18. *Je parle un peu le français*
19. QSL OK PAR BUREAU
20. *J'ai reçu votre carte mci bcp*
21. *Avez vous reçu ma carte?*
22. *Je suis maintenant QRU*
23. *Mes meilleurs amitiés et bonne chance pour le DX*
24. MCI BCP . . . POUR QSO ICI QRU 73 DX ET AU REVOIR

janvier	*avril*	*juillet*	*octobre*
février	*mai*	*août*	*novembre*
mars	*juin*	*septembre*	*décembre*

À = di-dah-dah-di-dah È and É = di-di-dah-di-dit
Ô = dah-dah-dah-dit Ç = dah-di-dah-di-dit
Ê = dah-di-di-dah-dit Ù = di-di-dah-dah

GERMAN

1. GM/GT/GA/GN LBR FRD
2. VLN DK . . . FR DEN ANRUF (UND ERSTES QSO)
3. *Es freut mich sehr Sie wiederzutreffen*
4. *Wir haben uns schon mal getroffen*
5. IHR RST . . . QTH . . . NAME . . .
6. WIE?
7. VLN DK FR DEN (NETTEN) RPRT
8. RIG (*Gerät*) HR IST [100 WATT] UND ANT IST [EIN DIPOL]
9. DAS WX IST (1) SCHÖN (2) KLAR (3) BEWÖLKT (4) REGNERISCH (5) WINDIG (6) DIESIG (7) WARM (8) KALT (9) ES SCHNEIT TEMP . . . C
10. DKE . . . FR BRT ÜBER IHR RIG (*Gerät*) (UND WX)
11. *Nur teilweise OK*
12. *Alles OK ausser Ihrem QTH*
13. *Etwas/vl/zu vl QSB, QRM (etc)*
14. *Bte wiederholen Sie meinen Rprt/Ihren Namen/Ihr QTH*
15. *Bte QSY/höher/tiefer . . . kHz*
16. *Auf dem Bande ist vl Lärm*
17. *Leider habe ich nicht alles verstanden*
18. *Ich spreche nur wenig Deutsch*
19. QSL OK VIA BÜRO
20. *Ich habe Ihre Karte bekommen*
21. *Haben Sie meine Karte bekommen?*
22. *Ich bin nun QRU*
23. *Die besten Grüsse und DX*
24. DKE SEHR . . . FR QSO NUN QRU 73 GUTES DX UND AWDH (*auf wiederhören*)

Januar	*April*	*Juli*	*Oktober*
Februar	*Mai*	*August*	*November*
März	*Juni*	*September*	*Dezember*

Ä = di-dah-di-dah Ö = dah-dah-dah-dit
Ü = di-di-dah-dah

SPANISH

1. GM/GA/GE/GN OM
2. MUCHAS GRACIAS POR TU LLAMADA (Y POR ESTE PRIMER QSO)
3. *Tengo un gran placer en encontrarle*
4. *Nos hemos encontrado ya antes*
5. TU RST . . . QTH . . . NOMBRE . . .
6. HW?
7. MUY TNX (*muchas gracias*) . . . POR RPRT
8. MI TX TIENE [100 VATIOS] MI ANT ES [UN DIPOLO]
9. EL WX AQUÍ ES (1) MUY BUENO (2) CLARO (3) NUBLADO (4) LLUVOSO (5) VENTOSO (6) NEBULOSO (7) ACALORADO (8) FRIO (9) ESTA NEVANDO TEMP . . . C
10. TNX FR INFO
11. *OK sólo en parte*
12. *Completamente OK con excepción de tu QTH*
13. *Poco/mucho/demasiado QSB, QRM (etc)*
14. *Pse repetirme mi RST/tu nombre/tu QTH*
15. *Pse QSY más alto/más bajo cerca . . . kHz*
16. *La banda esta muy turbulenta*
17. *Sri pero no he comprendido completamente*
18. *Hablo solamente un poco español*
19. QSL OK VIA BURO
20. *He recibido tu QSL tnx*
21. *Has recibido mi QSL?*
22. *Tengo ahora QRU*
23. *73 y buenos DX*
24. MUCHAS GRACIAS . . . POR QSO QRU 73 DX Y ADIOS

Enero	*Abril*	*Julio*	*Octobre*
Febrero	*Mayo*	*Agosto*	*Novembre*
Marzo	*Junio*	*Septembre*	*Dicembre*

Á = di-dah-dah-di-dah Ñ = dah-dah-di-dah-dah
Ó = dah-dah-dah-dit

mode does not require the knowledge of codes and abbreviations, correct operation is more difficult than it may appear at first sight, as is only too apparent after a listen to any amateur band.

Part of the problem is that many operators will have acquired some bad habits in their pronunciation, intonation and phraseology even before entering amateur radio. To these are then added a whole new set of clichés and mannerisms derived from listening to bad operators. Some of these can be extremely difficult to remove once learnt, even if a conscious effort is made.

Microphone technique

Unless there is very little external noise and room echo, it is best to hold the microphone fairly near the mouth, between 70 and 140mm away. Some microphones are unduly sensitive to letters like 'S' and 'P', and better audio quality may then be obtained by speaking *across* the microphone.

The audio quality should be tested by running the transmitter into a dummy load and monitoring the output on a receiver with headphones. In this way the characteristics of the microphone and the optimum speaking distance will be apparent. If a separate receiver is not available, the opinion of a local amateur should be sought on the air. Speech processing is often a mixed blessing. If too much is used, the modulation quality suffers greatly and the PA transistors or valves could overheat due to the increased duty cycle if SSB is used. Tests should be made to determine the maximum level which can effectively be used, and this noted or marked on the control. Be ready to turn it down if it is not really required during a contact.

Conversation

It is important to speak clearly and not too quickly, not just when talking to someone who does not fully understand the language, but at all times as this is excellent practice.

The use of CW abbreviations (including 'HI') should normally be avoided and the Q-code should really only be used when there is a language difficulty or where it has become accepted practice, eg "QRZ?" or "Please QSL via the bureau." Plain language should be used where possible, and clichés and jargon should be kept to a minimum. In particular, avoid the use of 'we' when 'I' is meant and 'handle' when 'name' is meant. Other rather silly habits include saying "that's a roger" instead of "that's correct", and "affirmative" instead of "yes". You'll no doubt have heard many more – just don't feel you have to copy them.

Phonetic alphabets should only be employed when they are necessary to clarify the spelling of a word or callsign. If they are to be effective the listener should know them, and it follows that only the internationally recommended phonetic alphabet should be used (see Table 7). It is confusing to the listener to use other phonetic alphabets and especially to generate new letter words. An exception is when it is found that a letter is being consistently miscopied. Although the recommended alphabet was selected to avoid ambiguity, it can happen in very poor reception conditions that, for example, 'Oscar' sounds like 'Alpha'. In this case, the use of an alternative like 'Ontario' might be the solution.

Unlike CW operation, it is very easy to forget that the conversation is not taking place down a telephone line. The listening station cannot interject a query if something is not understood and cannot give an answer until the transmitting station has finished. The result, especially on VHF, is often a long monologue in which the listening station has to take notes of all the points raised and questions asked if a useful reply is to

Table 7. International phonetic alphabet

Letter	Word	Pronounced
A	Alfa	*AL* FAH
B	Bravo	*BRAH* VOH
C	Charlie	*CHAR* LEE or *SHAR* LEE
D	Delta	*DELL* TAH
E	Echo	*ECK* OH
F	Foxtrot	*FOKS* TROT
G	Golf	GOLF
H	Hotel	HOH *TELL*
I	India	*IN* DEE AH
J	Juliett	*JEW* LEE *ETT*
K	Kilo	*KEY* LOH
L	Lima	*LEE* MAH
M	Mike	MIKE
N	November	NO *VEM* BER
O	Oscar	*OSS* CAH
P	Papa	PAH *PAH*
Q	Quebec	KEH *BECK*
R	Romeo	*ROW* ME OH
S	Sierra	SEE *AIR* RA
T	Tango	*TANG* GO
U	Uniform	*YOU* NEE FORM or *OO* NEE FORM
V	Victor	*VIK* TAH
W	Whiskey	*WISS* KEY
X	X-Ray	*ECKS* RAY
Y	Yankee	*YANG* KEY
Z	Zulu	*ZOO* LOO

be given. This should not be necessary if these points are dealt with one at a time.

Voice-operated changeover (VOX) operation should be used where possible as it enables a more normal two-way conversation to be carried on, which tends to avoid long monologues. However, it must be remembered that relays are supposed to be changing over frequently and prolonged "aaahs" spoken to prevent this happening are bad practice. Remember to give callsigns as often as required by the licensing authority in this type of contact. If VOX is not available, nimble use of the push-to-talk (PTT) switch is an acceptable substitute, but of course this requires more effort.

Both PTT and VOX operation are *simplex* systems, ie communication can take place in only one direction at any given time. The capability of instant and spontaneous response typical of an ordinary telephone conversation is only possible if *duplex* operation is used, ie simultaneous communication in both directions. This requires two communication channels which must be well spaced to avoid the transmitter desensitising the receiver, they may be located in the same band (*in-band* duplex) or in two separate bands (*cross-band* duplex).

Generally in-band duplex is not practical on the narrow HF phone bands due to receiver desensitisation and not too popular even at VHF and UHF because separate transmitters and receivers for those frequencies are unusual items these days, and many amateurs cannot afford two transceivers for the same band! Most duplex work therefore takes place cross-band (usually 144–432MHz).

If harmonically related bands are chosen, the receiver frequency needs to be well clear of any transmitter harmonics. Care should also be taken to comply with the relevant band plan(s) which may be difficult with in-band duplex. It is best to avoid the usual simplex channels for what will appear to others as a one-sided conversation. In any case, it is wise to check that the transmit channel is clear at, say, five-minute intervals. As with VOX operation, remember to give callsigns as frequently as required by the licence authority, in this case also stating the other station's transmit frequency. Generally headphones should be used at least at one end of a duplex contact to avoid 'howl-round' but a carefully adjusted loudspeaker output does allow the other operator to hear how his transmissions sound and may even give a more natural quality to the contact; after all, this is what duplex operation 'is all about'!

Procedure

As noted earlier, when calling a specific station it is good practice to keep calls short and to use the callsign of the station called once or twice only, followed by one's own callsign pronounced carefully and clearly at least twice using a phonetic alphabet, for example:

"WD9ZZZ. This is Golf Four Zulu Zulu Zulu calling, and Golf Four Zulu Zulu Zulu standing by."

Emphasis should be placed on the caller's own callsign and not on that of the station called. If there is no response, the caller's callsign may be repeated once more after a brief listen. Some stations send very long calls because operators think that when everybody else has finished calling they will still be heard. The reader is advised to forget this 'trick of the trade', partly because it rarely seems to work(!), and partly because it causes severe interference to the station called when it goes back to another station. As in CW operation CQ calls should also be kept short and repeated as often as desired. An example would be:

"CQ, CQ, CQ, CQ. This is Golf Four Zulu Zulu Zulu calling, Golf Four Zulu Zulu Zulu calling CQ and standing by."

There is no need to say what band is being used, and certainly no need to add "for any possible calls, dah-di-dah!" or "K someone please" etc!

When replying to a call both callsigns should be given clearly, usually in the phonetic alphabet, so that the calling station can check its callsign has been received correctly. From then on it is not necessary to use the phonetic alphabet for callsigns until the final transmissions. An example would be:

"Whiskey Delta Nine Zulu Zulu Zulu. This is Golf Four Zulu Zulu Zulu."

Once contact is established it is only necessary to give one's callsign at the intervals required by the licensing authority. A normal two-way conversation can thus be enjoyed, without the need for continual identification. If necessary the words 'break' or 'over' may be added at the end of a transmission to signal a reply from the other station. In good conditions this will not normally be found necessary. When FM is in use it is self-evident when the other station has stopped transmitting and is listening, because the carrier drops.

The situation is more complex where three or more stations are involved, and it is a good idea to give one's own callsign briefly before each transmission, for example:

"From G4ZZZ . . ."

At the end of the transmission the callsign should again be given together with an indication of whose turn to speak it is next, for example:

". . . WD9ZZZ to transmit. G4ZZZ in the group."

It is not necessary to run through a list of who is in the group, who has just signed off (and who may possibly be listening) after each transmission, although it may be useful for one person in the group to do this occasionally.

Signal reports on telephony are usually given using the RST code although of course in this case an indication of tone is not required. The report is given as a single two-digit number, in a similar fashion to the three-digit CW RST code.

When the time comes to end the contact, *end it.* Thank the other operator (once) for the pleasure of the contact and say goodbye. This is all that is required. Unless the operator is a good friend there is no need to start sending best wishes to everyone in the household including the family dog! Nor is this the time to start digging up extra comments on the contact which will require a 'final final' from the other station to answer – there may be other stations patiently waiting to call. It is recommended that both callsigns be given in the final transmission using the phonetic alphabet so that listening stations can check that they have them correct before calling, for example:

". . . This is Golf Four Zulu Zulu Zulu signing clear with Whiskey Delta Nine Zulu Zulu Zulu and Golf Four Zulu Zulu Zulu is now standing by for a call."

Note that some indication to listening stations is useful to indicate what is planned next. Such an indication is also appropriate if an immediate change to another frequency is intended, for example:

". . . This is Golf Four Zulu Zulu Zulu signing clear with Golf Two X-Ray Yankee Zulu Mobile. Golf Four Zulu Zulu Zulu now monitoring S20 for a call."

Further notes on operating procedures for more specialised modes and activities will be found in the relevant chapters.

Phone operation in a foreign language

The ability to conduct a straightforward contact in, say, French or Spanish is most useful for the DXer. Unlike the method of CW operation described earlier this does require an elementary knowledge of the language, but it can still be broadly based on a few stock phrases committed to memory such as those given in Appendix 8. The best way of learning them is to listen to contacts in the target language, recording them on tape if possible.

If the two speakers are fluent a good deal of the conversation will not be understood but this is not important. The main thing is to discover how contacts are initiated, how details like name, QTH and signal report are exchanged, and how contacts are completed. If a few other useful phrases can be acquired at the same time, so much the better but be sure to learn the appropriate responses.

The process should be completed before any attempt is made to use this new-found knowledge, otherwise the results could be a little embarrassing. However, most foreign amateurs do appreciate the effort being made and assist where possible, so perfection is certainly not required. Many of the comments made in the foreign CW section are just as relevant to phone operation and should be noted.

THAT FIRST CONTACT

No matter how much has been read about amateur radio operating nor how many hours have been spent listening to other amateurs on the air, the thrill of the first contact one makes is usually an unforgettable experience. It can, however, also be an unnerving one if too much is attempted too soon!

It is recommended that the first few contacts should be with local stations, for three reasons, First, the high signal strength will allow any defects in the transmitter to show up at the other station and it will be able to give a useful report on audio quality, splatter, key clicks, drift etc, as a final check that nothing is wrong. Second, the high received signal strength should allow concentration on the contact itself, without any need to worry about fading, noise or interference. Third, it is much better to make any mistakes when going on the air for the first time in a non-competitive situation, preferably with a friend operating the other station.

Working through a repeater (Chapter 6) is not recommended until the operator has made a few simplex contacts and feels 'in control' of the standard procedures. Similarly someone who has previously held a VHF telephony-only licence is advised to have a few SSB contacts on HF before attempting to use the key.

One common problem is 'microphone shyness', which often results in new operators suddenly feeling lost for words in the middle of a transmission. This can be particularly noticeable if the other operator has made a long transmission and a long reply is felt to be necessary. Of course this is not the case, and each contact should be regarded as a *conversation* rather than an exchange of 'speeches'. Fortunately microphone shyness tends to disappear as soon as the operator has made a few successful contacts and it is often a case of needing to limit each transmission!

NET OPERATION

As experience is gained an operator will undoubtedly wish to participate in one of the many nets which operate regularly throughout the British Isles. These nets can involve three or four (or 30 or 40 stations) in a multiway link-up. A tidy size for a net is, however, no more than 10 or a dozen operators; even with this number a time limit needs to be set on the length of overs. In a net of 10, it will take 10 minutes before the first operator's turn comes round again even if overs are set at only one minute each.

Such 'round tables' are preferably confined to local bands such as 3.5MHz for inter-UK working and 1.8MHz and 144/433MHz for local working. It is positively anti-social to occupy intercontinental bands for such activity. Some regular nets favour the use of a net control station (popularly, a *master of ceremonies*). In fact this procedure can become insufferably long-winded and a better substitute for it is 'Callbook order'. This system utilises the very simple alphanumerical sequence used in the *RSGB Amateur Radio Call Book*. In other words, every station with a G0 + 3 callsign transmits first, then come the G1 + 3, and so on. Any two-letter callsign may be slotted in at the relevant position when his or her turn to transmit comes around. In practice the 'batting order' of such a net could look like this: G3OUF, G4FTJ, G5UM, G6BBC, G8LM, G8IBA. Every operator thus knows his or her place.

Note the special provisions for callsign identification for net operating in the UK licence conditions.

EMERGENCY OPERATION IN THE UK

UK radio amateurs are advised against getting involved in requests for assistance from foreign countries. Requests for assistance or distress calls from ships or aircraft must *immediately* be passed to HM Coastguards or the police. Under no circumstances should the radio amateur 'go it alone'.

In the UK radio amateurs are permitted to pass third-party traffic on behalf of four user services (the British Red Cross Society, the St John Ambulance Brigade, the County Emergency Planning Officers or any police force in the UK) during an emergency or properly constituted exercise. Amateurs interested in such emergency working are urged to join Raynet,

the radio amateurs' emergency network. There are at present over 150 groups and over 3000 members of Raynet, all trained and prepared to react against a known plan to provide communications under emergency conditions. Clearly it is desirable that emergency communicators be trained in message handling and procedure since this type of working is very different from that described elsewhere in this chapter [3]. Further details of Raynet, membership of which is open to both listeners and licensed amateurs, may be obtained from the RSGB's emergency communications officer at the address given in the *RSGB Amateur Radio Call Book*.

Logkeeping

Radio amateurs in most countries are obliged by their licensing administration to keep a log of their transmissions so that if interference to other services is experienced it can be ascertained whether or not the amateur was transmitting at the time. For some amateurs the keeping of a log appears to be an inescapable chore and an official intrusion into their privacy, but in fact the log is a most useful part of the station.

Because it is a history of the amateur operator's activity over the years it is deserving of more attention than simply the minimum called for by the licensing authority. The log may act as a permanent record of band conditions and propagation, station performance, and the other stations details. In addition, in conjunction with a simple indexing system, it may be used to assist the operator in gaining various operating awards.

Fig 1 shows a sample of a standard logbook correctly filled in according to current UK licence regulations. No log entry need be made if the station is only used for a period of reception. Only the frequency *band* (not the exact frequency) is required, although the keen operator may find it useful to record the exact frequency (especially of DX or rare stations). The 'Mode' column should be filled in with the international emission code (see Chapter 1), and not 'CW' or 'FM'. Calls to specific stations which went unanswered should be logged, as should both successful and unsuccessful CQ calls. 'No contact' may be written in the 'Remarks' column to differentiate any unsuccessful attempts.

Any further information added to the log naturally depends on the operator's interests. The casual operator may perhaps record only the names and locations of stations worked for the first time. Those interested in propagation may find it useful to record details of the equipment and antennas at the other stations so that their ERP can be roughly ascertained. Award-chasers may note when a new station, country, prefix, locator square etc is worked for the first time. QSL information can likewise be recorded, and a 'D' or 'B' written in the 'QSL' columns to indicate direct' or 'via bureau'.

There is, however, a limit to how much information can be entered in a standard printed log. No matter how carefully this is designed it has to cater for all interests and is bound to be a compromise. If found inadequate there is nothing to prevent the operator from designing one more suited to his or her needs, provided of course that it complies with the licence regulations.

Another possibility is to use a standard log in conjunction with a scrap pad/notebook. A small reporter's notebook is ideal for this purpose because it can be folded back on itself to take minimal space on the shack table. The date may be entered at the top of each page for future reference, and then rough notes made from each contact. This will be found useful for slow CW contacts or the long monologues often heard on VHF FM.

AMATEUR RADIO STATION LOG

DATE	TIME (UTC) start	finish	FREQUENCY (MHz)	MODE	POWER (dBW)	STATION called/worked	REPORT sent	received	QSL sent	rcvd	REMARKS
2 Nov '88	0800	0810	3	J3E	20	GM5ABC	59+10	59+5			Bert
"	0811	0820	145	F3E	16	G7XYZ	57	56			Terry first G7
"	0825	0830	14	J3E	20	CQ					No reply
"	1725	1735	145	F2D	16	GB7XYZ					Local packet mailbox
"	1740		Station closed down								
4 Nov '88	1030	/P	from 73 Antenna Lane, Squelch-on-Sea								
"	1031	1036	50	J3E	10	G1ØXYZ	55	56			Jim, Bridgetown
"	1036	1045	50	J3E	10	G7XYL	58	58			Anne, Nr Squelch-on-Sea. QRM
"	1205	1215	433	F3E	13	G2XYZ	46	47			
"	1220		Station closed down								
5 Nov '88	0945	/P	from 73 Antenna Lane, Squelch-on-Sea								
"	0950	1005	144	J3E	16	GB2GUY	56	56	✓		Catherine Fawkesville
"	1010	1015	144	A1A	16	GD5ZZZ	542	541	✓		QSB! QSL via WF9XYZ
"	1526	1530	144	A1A	16	G7CW	579	589			Good keying!
"	1535		Station closed down and dismantled								
7 Nov '88	1810	1902	435	C3F	10	G7ZZZ	P3	P3			Ted, first ATV contact!
"	1930	1945	21	J2B	16	VK2ABC	559	569	✓		RTTY, Sid at Bandedge
"	1946	2005	21	J2B	16	ZL3ZZZ	569	559	✓		1st ZL on RTTY
"	2010		Test for TVI/Harmonic Radiation – Nothing noted								
"	2020		Station closed down								
8 Nov '88	1735	1737	7	J3E	20	CQ					
	1738	1805	7	J3E	20	G1Ø2ZZZ	58	58			Nobby – chatted about G5RV ant
	1930	1945	51	F3E	10	GØ5IX	55	55			Allen, wanted W19B ref.
	1950		Station closed down								
NOTES											

Fig 1. Typical logbook entries

Simple indexing

Any log can be made even more useful if it is provided with some sort of index. The simplest and least efficient method of retrieval is to use no index system at all, but simply to rely on memory and thumb through the log or logs until past details are recovered an irritating procedure if someone else is being kept waiting on the air.

At the other extreme is a card index which lists every contact made with every station on every band in use. All too often the sheer labour of maintaining such an index deters its compiler from keeping it up to date for very long, not to mention the inconvenience of boxes full of index cards to be sorted in the middle of a contact.

Many amateurs use personal computers for this purpose (see below), but if you do not have a computer something much simpler will suffice. It need be nothing more than an exercise book in which several pages are allocated to each band in use. These pages are then headed by domestic callsign blocks, starting with, for example, one page for the G2 + 2 series, another for the G2 + 3 block (as there are not many of these callsigns extant) and so on, and devoting at least one page to the newer G1 + 3 blocks, as very many of these are likely to be worked if the operator uses the UK VHF bands. One page per foreign country should also be allocated for VHF use, while on the other hand the HF operator may choose to allocate, say, one page per USA call area.

When a station is worked for the first time the callsign is entered on the appropriate page together with the date of this initial contact. Fig 2 shows a typical page in such an index. It allows plenty of space between entries to admit subsequent contact information. Extra information such as the name of the station could easily be added to the entries.

2m. : G8N—			
G8NAD	7·3·77		
		G8NNV	19·8·77
		G8NNV/M	20·9·77
G8NBT	20·5·77		
G8NCR/A	27·6·77 (R)		
G8NCR/A	21·4·77		
		G8NQS	27·9·77
G8NDT	4·9·77 (R)	G8NQU	26·9·77
G8NDT	16·3·77		
G8NDT/P	9·4·77		
		G8NSB/M	5·10·77 (R)
G8NEC	30·9·77		
G8NEL	20·3·77	G8NTD	22·9·77
G8NEL/M	24·4·77		
G8NET/M	15·7·77 (R)	G8NWQ	6·10·77
		G8NWZ	23·9·77 (R)
G8NJD/M	12·11·77 (R)	G8NXN/A	12·10·77
		G8NYH	6·10·77
G8NLA	20·7·77		
		G8NYS	3·10·77

Fig 2. Typical entries in suggested log index. Each first contact is recorded on a page-per-callsign block per band, together with the date. Here '(R)' denotes the station has been worked via a repeater

```
   LOG    2  QSL    3 TYPE    4 MODE    5  CQ     6  QSY    7  DEL    8 CANCEL 9 MAIN
 17:10:57   144MHz 25w          C:14      New QSO       Called       Q:8072        22FEB94
 CALL          F5TR                                          G3PMR LOG
 COUNTRY       FRANCE
 MODE          A1A                          K1AR     20FEB94 2125  7   A1A
 RST IN        599                          K5NA     20FEB94 1820 14   A1A
 RST OUT       599     Beam:180             K2TB     20FEB94 1819 14   A1A
 MHz                                        W3USS    20FEB94 1818 14   A1A
 NAME                                       K1TR     20FEB94 1817 14   A1A
 QTH                                        AA1K     20FEB94 1816 14   A1A
 REMARKS                                    W3LPL    20FEB94 1815 14   A1A
 QSL OUT                                    AA3B     20FEB94 1814 14   A1A
 QSL IN               IN97XL                K8MFO    20FEB94 1814 14   A1A
 IOTA            47.45N 0.8W                W3FV     20FEB94 1813 14   A1A
 ZONE            Distance:1228.73 km        VE9ST    20FEB94 1812 14   A1A
 REGION          Bearing: 180.0 deg         WA0QOA   20FEB94 1811 14   A1A
 LOCATOR     -> IN97XL                      W3BGN    20FEB94 1811 14   A1A
 DATE           22FEB94                     VE3EJ    20FEB94 1810 14   A1A
 TIME ON        1706                        K2LE     20FEB94 1809 14   A1A
 TIME OFF       1710
 New country this band!
```

Computer logging programs do much more than just record contacts. Here Shacklog is keeping track of countries worked, giving beam headings, distances and more

Logkeeping using a computer

The UK licence allows you to maintain a log on your personal computer, and this has many benefits, particularly for contests. Typical non-contest features include: major awards progress indication, distance and bearing indication, instant indexing, printing of records, and access to databases (such as call book directories). Some sophisticated software is available commercially but there are also some simpler programs available as shareware.

QSL CARDS

In the early days of amateur radio, contacts were infrequent and long-distance (DX) contacts were often records. Operators were keen to obtain written confirmation but writing and exchanging letters became rather too repetitive and onerous. Someone had the bright idea of printing the callsign and all the station details on a postcard, leaving spaces for details of the contact, weather report, interference etc to be filled in. Thus many contacts could be confirmed with the minimum amount of effort. These cards became known as *QSL cards* from the international Q-code meaning "I acknowledge receipt" (see p22).

The pioneering days on many amateur bands are long past, but the exchanging of QSL cards is still one of the most popular activities within amateur radio. The cards serve as a reminder of interesting contacts or a rare country worked or heard and are often required as confirmation for one of the many operating awards available (see Chapter 4).

To lessen the heavy cost of posting each card individually to other stations, most national societies operate what is called a *QSL bureau*. This is a 'clearing house' which accepts cards in from members, sorts them into countries, and mails them in batches to bureaux in those countries which in turn sort them into batches for individual stations. The great advantage is that all posting is done in bulk, a considerable saving to everyone concerned. Furthermore it is only necessary to send cards to one well-known address in one's own country, which is considerably more convenient than taking foreign addresses down over the air, with the possibility of errors.

Nevertheless many amateurs still occasionally send cards direct, even if they are members of national societies. Sometimes the urge to receive confirmation of contact with a rare or DX station is too great to wait the few months cards take to work their way through the QSL bureaux system. In fact, some DX stations only reply to direct QSLs. Furthermore, a few countries do not have a QSL bureau and all cards must be sent direct in these cases.

Designing cards

There are various ways in which QSL cards can be produced. Some cards are designed by the operator and then home-made or printed professionally, while others are selected from a range of standard designs produced by a firm specialising in the printing of QSL cards. Some large firms provide QSL cards to members of their staff who are radio amateurs, and such cards may also be provided to special-event stations.

The card should not exceed the standard postcard size (140 by 90mm), especially if a QSL bureau is to be used. The RSGB QSL Bureau sends cards abroad in 2kg packets which, in order to conform with the postal regulations concerning Printed Paper Rate Post, have to be open-ended and tied round with string. Consequently larger cards have to be folded to keep the packet tight and this spoils their appearance. Sometimes cards provided by employers exceed postcard dimensions, usually for advertising reasons. As they are often provided free of charge, it is not easy to criticise but, where possible, a little liaison with the provider can save a lot of difficulty.

Cards should be printed on ordinary postcard board, not on thick heavy cardboard which makes them difficult to handle and more expensive in the post. The use of unorthodox materials is *not* advised. Over the years, the RSGB QSL Bureau has handled cards printed on cork, wafer-thin sheets of wood, plastic and silk. The worst were those printed on thin aluminium or copper sheet which could cause painful cuts to the unsuspecting sorter. It is not difficult to produce original and attractive cards without resorting to these means.

The object of sending a QSL card is primarily to confirm a contact but it is also a means of conveying brief information about the contact, the sender's station and its location. The essential printed data should therefore include the sender's name and address with space for details of the contact (date, time, frequency, method of communication and report) and the equipment used. It is important that the wording does confirm two-way communication; the phrase 'Confirming contact' is often used. A popular layout is shown in Fig 3. Some operators add extra information such as the station's locator (see p64). The space for the addressee's callsign should be in the left-hand portion of the card, and the sender's callsign should feature prominently on the front of the card either as part of the design or as an overprint in a contrasting colour.

The artistic design of the card can be the subject of much

ENGLAND

G9ZZZ

S. Brown, Fourways, Steeple Hill, Notown, Blankshire BX1 2AS

Confirming contact

To radio	Date	GMT	Freq	RST	Mode

RX . . . .   TX . . . .   Ant . . . .

PSE/TNX QSL   73 . . . .

Fig 3. Transmitting-station basic QSL card layout

ingenuity. Undoubtedly the more original and attractive it is, the more interest it will create for the recipient. This is perhaps a subject best left to the reader's own imagination but a few suggestions for the fronts of printed QSL cards are as follows:

1. A colour picture postcard of the locality overprinted with the callsign.
2. A black-and-white photograph of the station which shows the callsign prominently, either as part of the photo or over-printed in a contrasting colour.
3. A humorous cartoon or message of radio interest.
4. A sketch map of the country, with some indication of the whereabouts of the station.

It is not generally necessary to use more than two colours (or a colour-tinted card and one other colour) when printing cards. Each additional colour will significantly increase the cost of the card and may add little to the overall impact. When deciding how many cards to print, think ahead and estimate how many are going to be required over a reasonable period, say, two years. It is much more economical to have one large printing than several smaller ones, particularly if any original design is being used. The design of listener cards should follow the same basic principles as those for transmitting stations in respect of size, material and information, except that it should be clear that they are reception reports. The registered listener 'ARS' or 'BRS' number should be prominent in the case of RSGB members. The card should also have spaces for details of radio conditions and other countries audible at the time, and also the callsign of the station which the recipient was heard working or calling, a typical layout being shown in Fig 4.

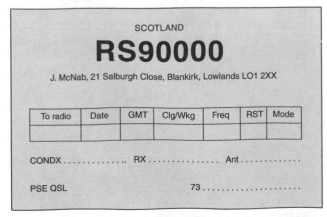

SCOTLAND

RS90000

J. McNab, 21 Salburgh Close, Blankirk, Lowlands LO1 2XX

To radio	Date	GMT	Clg/Wkg	Freq	RST	Mode

CONDX . . . .   RX . . . .   Ant . . . .

PSE QSL   73 . . . .

Fig 4. Receiving-station basic QSL card layout

A selection of QSL cards showing different styles – perhaps one will inspire you!

If you don't require many cards and have access to a computer with a good-quality printer that can cope with thin card, you may be able to produce all the cards you need that way, especially if you can use a drawing software package to design an interesting layout or include a photo image. If the printer is capable of colour, so much the better, but don't overdo it.

Sending cards

It is usual to send cards for three good reasons: because a return card is wanted; to acknowledge the receipt of a card; or because a card has been requested during the contact.

The sending of a card for every contact is both costly and wasteful, resulting in large numbers of unclaimed cards having to be destroyed. Many amateurs, particularly in the rarer countries, do not send QSL cards unless they receive one first from the other station.

If a card is sent direct to an amateur with the object of receiving one direct in return, sufficient International Reply Coupons should be enclosed to cover the cost of the return postage. These coupons are available at main post offices, although IRCs have assumed the status of a 'currency' among DXers and can be purchased more economically from amateurs with a surplus who advertise from time to time in the DX news-sheets. It is also common practice, particularly among American amateurs, to enclose dollar bills rather than IRCs. This carries a risk of theft and, worse, citizens of some countries can be imprisoned for being in possession of foreign currency. This method of payment is therefore not recommended.

THE RSGB QSL BUREAU

The purpose of the Bureau is to facilitate the exchange of QSL cards between RSGB members and other radio amateurs. Most national radio societies operate such a bureau, some making an extra charge for this service. The RSGB provides it as a free service, though only members may make use of the outgoing service.

Use of the bureau is the cheapest way of sending cards in these days of high postal charges.

Sending cards through the Bureau

All cards for distribution should be sent to the RSGB QSL Bureau at Headquarters. There is no limit to the number of cards which may be sent at any one time.

When the cards arrive at the bureau, those destined for abroad are sorted into countries and despatched in bulk to the appropriate overseas QSL bureaux, most of which are operated by members societies of the International Amateur Radio Union.

Cards for stations within the UK are sorted into callsign groups, each of which is in the charge of a volunteer sub-manager. It is this person's task to associate the cards sent to the sub-bureau from the main QSL Bureau with the envelopes which are on file.

Collecting cards from the bureau

Supply your sub-manager with stamped self-addressed envelopes of a suitable size and strong material – 8in × 5in is ideal.

Print your callsign or RS number in the top left hand corner of each envelope.

Envelopes should be numbered and 'Last envelope' marked on one so that it is known when a fresh batch is needed.

Envelopes are not normally returned until full weight has been reached for the postage paid; those wishing to receive cards at more frequent intervals should mark their envelopes 'Wait 6' etc.

An up-to-date list of names and addresses of sub-managers is available from RSGB HQ on request. Changes to the list are broadcast on GB2RS and in the QSL column in *Radio Communication*.

General notes

1. Licensed UK amateurs who are non-members of the RSGB may send stamped addressed envelopes to their sub-manager for collection of their cards, but they *may not* send cards for distribution.
2. Cards for amateurs who have neglected to send envelopes are retained for three months, after which the cards are destroyed. Amateurs who do not wish to collect cards should notify the QSL Bureau accordingly.

3. Amateurs who operate from a part of the United Kingdom which has a different prefix should deposit envelopes with the appropriate sub-manager for the different prefix. For example a G7 station who operates temporarily from Wales and who wishes to receive cards should leave envelopes with the GW7 submanager.
4. Overseas members of RSGB in countries where there is no QSL service operated by the IARU member society for that country may send their cards to the RSGB QSL Bureau for distribution.
5. Overseas members who are not members of the RSGB may send cards addressed to UK stations only, direct to the RSGB QSL Bureau.
6. The facilities of the RSGB QSL Bureau are available both to transmitting and receiving members of the Society. Listeners are reminded, however, that their reports should contain sufficient information to be of genuine value to the transmitting amateurs concerned. Reception reports relating to short-wave broadcasting stations unfortunately cannot be accepted.

All QSL cards and correspondence relating to the RSGB QSL Bureau should be sent to the QSL Bureau at RSGB Headquarters.

Adhesive address labels are available free of charge on receipt of an SAE.

Envelopes for the collection of cards and correspondence concerning incoming cards should be sent to the appropriate sub-manager.

Sending cards through the bureau

Choose QSL cards which do not exceed normal postcard size, viz 5.5in × 3.5in (140 × 80 mm). Large cards invariably have to be folded, while small ones and those of a thin nature are difficult to handle.

Print the addressee's callsign on both sides of the cards.

Separate cards destined for within the UK from foreign-going ones. Sort all cards alphabetically by prefix. Sort USA cards into call areas regardless of prefix. When a QSL Manager is involved, sort under *his* callsign. Please pack the cards so that they are all the same way up, and do not space cards with markers or similar. Pack cards adequately, so that they do not get damaged in transit, and with the correct postage to reach RSGB, and send them to:

RSGB QSL Bureau
PO Box 1773
POTTERS BAR
Herts.
EN6 3EP

If unused stamps from the country concerned can be obtained, these can be used as payment for return postage, as an alternative to IRCs.

The addresses of United Kingdom amateurs can be found in [4] and the addresses of amateurs worldwide in [5]. There are now also CD-ROMs available with call book information.

Quite often rare stations will give their QSL mailing address over the air, but not necessarily in every contact if they are working a string of stations rapidly. It must be appreciated that such a station has to spend a quite considerable amount of time and money in preparing and sending QSL cards because practically every station worked will want a card. With this in mind, some DX stations appoint their own QSL manager to cope with the workload. Cards should then be sent *direct* to the manager, and marked 'via . . .'. Much useful QSL information is given in *Radio Communication* and other amateur radio magazines, especially the DX news-sheets (see Chapter 4).

A self-addressed envelope should always be enclosed when QSLing rare DX stations or their managers direct. This not only saves them stationery costs but also a great deal of time and effort copying out your name and address from your card. The rare station's name and address should be added to the reverse of the envelope prefixed by 'From . . .' for the same reason. Some DXers even send out their own special QSL card which merely has to be endorsed and returned by the DX station, saving further expense.

It is difficult to give hard and fast rules on how many IRCs to enclose. Most rare DX stations or their managers make sure they are not out-of-pocket on QSL costs, and may subtract the price of the card from the total value of any enclosed coupons before deciding what balance is available for return postage. Normally, however, three IRCs should be sufficient for first-class airmail return from all but the most distant parts of the world. Two IRCs may be enough for some areas. A single coupon will only pay the postage for surface-mail return and leave nothing for other expenses.

Avoid sending cards through QSL bureaux with IRCs attached, as these have a habit of disappearing on route. For the same reason, use normal stamps on direct QSLs, rather than special commemorative issues.

When making out the card, be careful not to make any amendment, or to cross out anything written, or alter the callsign. Some societies which issue awards automatically reject 'altered cards', even if the alteration was made by the sender.

Many amateur transmitting stations will send their QSL cards in exchange for listeners' cards, and these can be used to gain the various listener operating awards (see Chapter 4). However, this is likely only if the listener report is of interest or of value. For example, a station in the USA working long strings of UK stations on 14MHz is unlikely to find a UK listener report helpful. He *knows* he can work the UK! It is therefore advisable to send reports to some of the weaker signals or to the people who do not seem to be making many contacts.

To be useful to the recipient, a report should preferably contain observations made at several different times, a comparison with other signals heard at the same time, together with useful comments on quality, depth of modulation etc, although there may not be very much room on a card for all this. Some listeners go to the extreme of sending separate QSL cards each time they hear the same station – this is a waste of time and money as one card is quite sufficient.

One last tip: if you need confirmation badly for an operating award, why not say so on the card? It might just make the difference!

FURTHER INFORMATION

[1] *Radio Communication Handbook,* 6th edn, RSGB, 1994.
[2] *A Guide to Amateur Radio,* Pat Hawker, G3VA, RSGB.
[3] *Raynet Manual,* RSGB, 1984.
[4] *RSGB Amateur Radio Call Book* (published annually). Also available on disc as the Skycall call book program.
[5] *Radio Amateur Callbook,* Radio Amateur Callbook Inc (published annually in two volumes: *USA listings* and *DX listings* with supplements).

4 DX

ALTHOUGH one of the oldest aspects of amateur radio, 'working DX' remains as popular a pastime today as ever. Basically 'DX' means 'long distance' but of course this is relative and depends on the band, mode and even the equipment in use. In fact DX has more to do with 'difficulty' than with distance in absolute terms, and herein lies its fascination, for of course the more effort is put into making a contact, the greater the satisfaction that will be the reward. Perhaps this point is worth emphasising in these days of so-called 'push-button DX' and kilowatt linears.

This chapter deals first with the HF bands, then with the VHF/UHF region and microwaves. These arbitrary divisions nevertheless reflect the fact that many, perhaps most, operators choose to use one set of these bands in preference to the other, although the object of DXing remains much the same whatever frequency is in use.

DX ON THE HF BANDS

Generally speaking, on the bands below 30MHz, signals emanating from one's own continent would not qualify as 'DX'. However, those using very low power and simple equipment might consider that this is not so. There are different degrees of 'DX'ness' and quite obviously the distance between transmitter and listener is the most important factor here. Another is the band being used – it is no great achievement to hear Japanese signals on 14, 21 and 28MHz under the right circumstances, it is more difficult on 7 and 3.5MHz, but very difficult on 1.8MHz. There is also a rarity factor – it is much more probable that, given suitable propagation conditions, signals from the southern USA will be heard than from northern Mexico. The reason is of course that there are very few XE2 amateurs, but many thousands north of the border.

LISTENING FOR DX AS AN SWL

This is one of the most interesting aspects of amateur radio, and attracts a very large number of those who never aspire to a transmitting licence but prefer to listen to what is happening on our bands. The number of enthusiastic shortwave listeners probably exceeds that of licensed amateurs, and it is these very same individuals who often make the best operators when they do obtain a licence.

Keen short-wave listeners are especially cared for by the International Short Wave League [1] and the International Listeners Association [2]. The former organisation produces an excellent monthly magazine which contains a great deal of information on both amateur and broadcast DX listening. The League also has many transmitting members.

Most of the tips given below are just as applicable for listeners as transmitting amateurs.

'RARE' COUNTRIES

What is a 'rare' country? An idea may be gained by reference to the following lists which were applicable in 1995.

1. **Countries where legitimate amateur radio activity is infrequent:**

Afghanistan (YA)	Myanmar (Burma) (XZ)
Bangladesh (S2)	North Korea
Bhutan (A5)	Yemen (7O).
Libya (5A)	

2. **Countries where activity is usually by an operator at a weather station, military base or scientific research base:**

Crozet Is (FT)	S Georgia (VP8)
Kerguelen Is (FT)	S Orkney (VP8)
Amsterdam & St Paul Is (FT)	S Shetland (VP8)
Glorioso Is (FR/G)	Auckland I & Campbell Is (ZL9)
Tromelin Is (FR/T)	Kermadec Is (ZL8)
Kure Is (KH7)	Marion Is (ZS8)
Wake Is (KH9)	Jan Mayen (JX)
Midway Is (KH4)	N Cooks Is (ZK)
Willis Is (VK9)	Guantanamo Bay (KG4).
Macquarie Is (VK0)	

3. **Countries only activated by special expeditions:**

San Felix Is (CE0X)	Heard Is (HK0)
Clipperton Is (FO)	S Sandwich Is (VP8)
Juan de Nova Is (FR/J)	Andaman Is (VU)
Malpelo Is (HK0)	Laccadive Is (VU)
Navassa Is (KP1)	Revilla Gigedo Is (XF4)
Desecheo Is (KP5)	Aves Is (YV0)
Kingman Reef (KH5K)	Spratly Is
Palmyra Is (KH5)	Annobon Is (3C0)
Market Reef (OJ0)	Bouvet Is (3Y)
Malyj Vysotskii Is (R1M)	Peter 1st Is (3Y)
Sovereign Military Order of Malta (1A0)	Conway Reef (3D2)
Sable Is (CY0)	Rotuma (3D2)
St Paul Is (CY9)	Banaba (T33)
Mellish Reef (VK9)	Wallis and Futuna Is (FW)

GETTING IN SHAPE FOR DXING

Most rare DX stations will have many stations calling them so DXing is very competitive. How can you can ensure that there's a good chance of the DX station coming back to *your* call? Three key elements of your station need to work together to achieve this goal – the antenna, the radio and *you*.

The antenna

Some years ago the RSGB conducted a survey of leading UK DXers, covering antennas, equipment and operating practice, and this, together with other information, was published in *Radio Communication* [3]. Some of the information in this series of articles is summarised here but they are well worth consulting if you are serious about working DX. The survey found that most of the respondents use triband Yagi beams on towers of about 60ft for 14, 21 and 28MHz and a variety of wire antennas or verticals for the LF bands. Of course, other antennas also put out good signals, and the quad and delta loop antennas have their devotees. But the important point is that 'off-the-shelf' commercial triband beams will do the job until you find something better.

For working DX it is clear that a good front-to-back ratio is more important than forward gain – often the limiting factor in copying a weak signal is interference coming from the opposite direction, and if this can be lessened there is a much better chance of making contact.

Height is also very important. An increase in antenna height will improve the low-angle radiation, and it is generally reckoned that a doubling of antenna height from, say, 30ft to 60ft will result in something like a 6dB better signal at a DX location! A word of warning: do make sure your tower and rotator are up to it – get professional advice from your suppliers, don't guess. If even a small tower blows down, the results could be catastrophic.

Don't despair if you don't have room for a tower and a big beam. Working DX on the LF bands using a vertical can be a good bet. These antennas need very little space, and will be a lot more competitive on 7MHz than 14MHz. Another possibility is to build a wire antenna for working in certain directions. There is a lot of fun to be had in experimenting to find an antenna to suit your situation. Many designs for antennas are available in the standard handbooks covering all likely situations at your station [4–12].

Remember, if you have a poor antenna you can still work DX but you'll maybe have to wait a bit longer and be more cunning!

The transceiver

Modern radios will provide some or all of the following features, which are highly desirable for working DX. Older ones, particularly those of the valve era, may lack them in spite of having generally good performance.

- Twin VFOs or a VFO with memories. They are almost essential for working DXpeditions as these usually work split frequency (see later).
- Total control over the shape and width of the IF passband for SSB reception. This can be achieved by variable bandwidth tuning (VBT), slope tuning, and IF shift.
- A 500Hz filter (or, ideally, a 500Hz and a 200Hz filter) for CW reception. A good audio filter can improve the performance of a 500Hz filter.
- A notch filter for removing particular sources of interference to either CW or SSB within the IF passband. This should preferably operate at the IF rather than at AF.
- An RF attenuator for use on the LF bands such as 7MHz where cross-modulation is often a problem.
- A receiver noise blanker, ideally with variable time constants.
- The ability to work properly with a linear amplifier.
- A facility to connect a separate receiver antenna.

Of course, these features will count for little if the performance of the receiver is poor. Generally modern radios offer a high level of performance but, if you are in the market for another one, you should understand the factors which affect receiver performance so you can make the best use of reviews in magazines. These are outside the scope of this book and you should refer to references [12–14] for further information.

If you have an older radio, there is often a great deal that can be done to improve its performance, perhaps by fitting an optional internal CW filter and adding external units: an RF attenuator for LF band operation; an RF amplifier for, say, 28MHz; a speech processor; an AF filter etc. These are often simple to build; see reference [4] for details.

Linear amplifier

This is a definite asset for working competitive DX, especially if you are limited to a modest antenna or operation at evenings and weekends. The bad news is that it will make any EMC problems you have a lot worse. So you must make absolutely sure you have a clean signal into it and also do your EMC 'housekeeping'. See Chapter 3 for more information.

The cost of a decibel

In *HF Antennas for All Locations* [4] Les Moxon, G6XN, asks "How much is a decibel worth?" and this is an important question for all DXers. Every improvement in performance, even 1dB, is worth having in a pile-up, but some decibels cost a lot more than others. Make sure you have got all the cheap ones before spending money on the expensive ones!

THE DX OPERATOR

So much for the equipment – what about you? The most important requirement for a budding DXer is spare time. The RSGB survey respondents were firm on that point. If you aren't in the shack you aren't going to work anything, however wonderful your station might be. Roger Balister, G3KMA, took the theme further with the rather awkward advice: "Don't go away on holiday – ever!" And Bill Ricalton, G4ADD, likewise advised cancelling any holiday that clashes with a new DX-pedition.

To make the most of the odd spare minute an anonymous respondent recommends locating the equipment as close as possible to the living areas of the house, and the survey heard from several others who have a rig next to the bed for those early morning skeds – CW of course, so as not to wake the XYL . . .

The mention of CW is important because top DXers use all modes. If you ignore all CW activity your progress up the DX tables will be slowed. But don't be put off by any thought that vast competence is required. To be honest, all you need in many cases is the ability to read the DX callsign, recognise your own and send 599! For large split-frequency pile-ups you will have to develop the ability to recognise other calls in the QRM (as discussed later) but this will come with practice.

Background knowledge

A good knowledge of subjects such as geography, current affairs and foreign languages can also be of great help to the serious DX chaser. Information on time-zone differences (see Appendix 5), public holidays and normal working hours in different countries can also be very helpful. For example, French public holidays are observed in all overseas French provinces so that any of the overseas F prefixes are more likely to be heard on such a day. Remember also that in Islamic countries Friday is the day of prayer and equates with our Sunday. Fridays are thus good days for looking out for some of the rarer countries in North Africa, the Middle East and certain parts of Asia.

Amateur radio often gives the keen listener an interest in other countries. One essential is naturally a good atlas – not the schoolbook kind but instead one of those large (and expensive)

volumes. Unfortunately the publishers of these often see fit to
include much extraneous material on such subjects as the gal-
axy, aerial navigation or trade
routes etc. Choose one in which
the money has been spent instead
on the maps and gazetteer, for this
is what an atlas is all about!

Complementing the atlas may
be one or more wall maps. These
are available in great-circle or
Mercator projections. Great-circle maps are centred on one particular location, usually London
in the case of UK maps. They give
the true bearing and distance of
any other place in the world relative to that location, and are thus
more useful to the operator using
a beam antenna. See Fig 1.

The more familiar Mercator
projection map is more generally
available at lower cost than the
great-circle type, and is often more
detailed and colourful. Both types
are available from RSGB HQ.

As time goes on, you will need
to know not just where countries
and towns are, but something of
the internal administrative divisions in many countries. This is
because a large proportion of
countries vary their amateur radio

Fig 1. Example of a great-circle map, available from the RSGB in a large size suitable for wall mounting

prefixes according to the region of the country (see Chapter 1).
A knowledge of these divisions and their corresponding amateur radio prefixes is most useful for the DXer, and DXpeditions
often choose uninhabited areas of a country so that they can use
a rare prefix.

The reader will already no doubt be familiar with the UK
countries, the Australian and USA states, and the Canadian
territories. Many other countries, however, have divisions which
affect the prefix, two examples being the Australian states and
the 25 Swedish läns (provinces). Full details of such callsign
systems are given in Appendix 2.

A callsign list by ITU allocation is given in Appendix 3. A
more detailed list, which is updated regularly, is available in
the *RSGB Prefix Guide* compiled by John Forward, G3HTA,
and published by the RSGB. This contains a lot of other useful
information and is a 'must' for any serious DXer.

LISTENING TIPS

You need to tune the bands to find out what is happening but
what are you listening for? How do you separate the unusual
from the commonplace?

- Check around the standard DX frequencies: 5 and 25kHz up
  from the band edge on CW; 3795, 14,195, 21,295, 28,495
  and 28,595kHz on SSB. Don't forget the IOTA frequencies
  (14,260, 21,260 and 28,460kHz) as many islands are also
  DXCC countries. Fred, G3NSY, has all of these frequencies
  programmed into the memories of his transceiver to simplify the search.

- DX stations often sound 'different': weak, fluttery, or with
  some wobble on the transmission as a result of local power
  supply problems. They are often heard working pile-up-style,
  giving quick reports to get as many QSOs in the log as they
  can.

- Get to know the names of active DX operators. For example
  Cav is probably V63JC in Micronesia, and Tom, VR6TC,
  on Pitcairn Island, Antoine might have been 3D2AG on
  Rotuma; and Martti is probably OH2BH who could be almost anywhere rare – or soon will be.

- Watch out for an unusual accent. An American voice when
  the band is not open to the States indicates something different, perhaps Hawaii or Guam.

- An operator talking about his QSL manager is normally
  somewhere interesting.

- Listen to the snippets of conversation as you tune across the
  band. You should be able to tell in seconds if it is a normal
  ragchew or an exotic DX station stopping for a chat. Obvious giveaways include remarks about postal delays, supply
  ships, missionaries, coral atolls, etc. In the run-up to a major
  expedition you will also hear all sorts of rumours, some of
  which may have a useful basis in fact!

- Check out the pile-ups. You will generally find the DX station on the same frequency but underneath all the callers, or
  about 5kHz lower, or on a standard DX frequency.

THE INFORMATION TRADE-OFF

Those of us with families, jobs, and other commitments can
fortunately make use of other sources of information besides

hours spent listening on the bands. If you know exactly when the stations you need will be active, you only have to fire up your rig at the right moment, work them, and get back to watching TV. In the survey Peter Wallis, G3YJI, and many others listed "good information" as the principal requirement for DXing success.

So how do you find out what's happening?

- Get on the DX PacketCluster network, a wonderful development which enables all active DXers to share each other's ears. If a DX station is heard on the band, an alert (called a 'spot') will be fed into the system and will be seen by all users. PacketCluster also offers other facilities, such as being able list the last 10 spots on 14MHz, or the last five spots related to stations with a particular prefix. Also available are WWV propagation data, QSL information, together with the facility to calculate beam headings, propagation predictions and other data of value to HF DXers.
- Take out a subscription to the RSGB's weekly *DX News Sheet*. This has the latest news on expeditions, DX stations, frequencies to listen, and a survey of recent DX.
- Use the RSGB DXNS Voicebank system, a computerised voice messaging system operated by British Telecom. Access is at local call rates from all over the UK, and there are two separate numbers: 01426 925240 plays back tips recorded by DXers over the last three days and 01426 910240 is available for inputting DX tips (up to one minute).
- Get on the Internet. There is an e-mail 'reflector' system which covers HF DX and HF contests. Via World Wide Web (or the Telnet/Finger protocols), you can also log on to or read remote PacketCluster systems, download DX bulletins, receive ARRL and RSGB news bulletins, access news and other discussion groups, and acquire masses of solar/propagation information.
- Make sure your friends know which countries, islands, zones, or oblasts you still need and get them to call you on the phone if they hear one of them. This can generally be set up as a group activity, perhaps based around the most enthusiastic members of your local club.
- Ask a local. In the survey Bob Whelan, G3PJT, commented that "If you need KH7 then ask the KH6s, who will probably know of any planned activity".

WORKING DX STATIONS

Vital to those who wish to make a success of DX working is patience and politeness. The rarest stations are often running simple equipment and using low power. Their antennas may be poor and they may be a very long way away. They may not speak the caller's language very well, and they may not have any particular desire to talk to yet another European! This means that it is helpful to listen to a few contacts before trying to call, and thereby get to know the way in which calls are accepted. Causing interference by calling at the wrong time or on the wrong frequency very rapidly loses friends – on the other hand there is a great deal of satisfaction to be gained from getting a reply from one's first call made at the right time and in the right place. DXing is indeed remarkably like fishing!

When and where are the correct times and places to call? Techniques are decided by two possibilities:

1. Is the station working callers on his own frequency?
2. Is he listening elsewhere?

In condition 1 (which often arises if the DX station was just looking for a contact and things got out of hand!), careful

A one-man DXpedition: Nao, NX1L, operating FO0AKI on Rurutu Island in June 1994

listening is more than ever important because ill-timed calls will cause interference. If it is found that 'tail-ender' calls are being accepted it is then permissible to drop one's callsign in just as the station currently in contact is signing off. However, this should never be done unless it is absolutely clear that that is the end of the contact, and that the DX station has the callsign of the person he is talking to logged correctly. Tail-ending is more likely to be successful if only a few are waiting on frequency and it often becomes a sign for a 'free-for-all' to develop. Note that when using SSB, calls must be made on a frequency exactly zero-beat with that of the station being called. In the case of CW calls there may be some advantage to be gained from making calls a few hundred hertz away from zero-beat. When operating on CW some stations seem to follow a pattern, perhaps taking callers from either side of their frequency alternately, or gradually tuning outwards on one side or other. Listening will establish that this is happening and may save a lot of wasted calls.

If condition 2 applies things are totally different and calling so as to cause interference on the DX station's frequency is to be avoided at all costs. The more experienced resident DX stations, and nearly all expeditionary type stations, follow this course as it is impossible to cope with many hundreds of callers within a few hertz of each other. Such stations make a practice of announcing where they will listen and often specify a section of the band over which they will tune, eg they may be transmitting on 14,195kHz and listening over the range 14,200–14,210kHz. Under these circumstances the user of a transceiver without a second VFO is at a severe disadvantage, and the serious DX operator should bear this in mind when setting up his or her station.

Once again listening is all important, first of all to establish where to transmit, and also to check that the frequencies mentioned are in fact those being tuned. It is not unusual to discover that stations calling outside these are being worked! Once again there may be a recognisable tuning pattern and it may be possible to hear stations in contact and to work out the best place to place a call.

Perhaps the DX station is tuning slowly from the bottom of the range to the top, perhaps sticking to a single frequency inside the announced range, or even listening somewhere completely different. A few DXpeditioners make a habit of listening below their transmit frequencies when they've announced "Listening up" and vice versa. It is also worth checking whether the listening frequency changes after each QSO or whether the DX operator pauses in one place until everybody discovers that frequency and the rising QRM forces him to tune elsewhere.

Another reason to listen before calling is that DXpeditions frequently limit the pile-up by asking only for stations with a particular number or letter in their callsign. To take advantage of propagation they may even ask for particular regions or countries only. For example "European 1s only" or "North American 5s call now". Failure to observe these restrictions may result in your call being added to a blacklist of people who find it difficult to get a QSO or a QSL card from that expedition.

Once the DX tuning pattern has been established, opinions differ on the best technique. In the RSGB survey, G4ADD recommended finding the quietest in-range frequency and sticking to it, while others like Pat Gowen, G3IOR, suggested anticipating the tuning direction and always trying to be next in line. Chris Eyles, G3SJH, reminded us that an instruction to the pile-up to "Spread out" is often a cue to call at the extreme ends of the announced listening range. The famous DXpeditioner SM0AGD likes to program up to 10 discrete listening frequencies into his transceiver and, randomly or predictably, to hop between them.

Frequencies are usually publicised in advance or announced on the air. If you're trying to be next in line for the DX, you first have to find the frequency of the station he's currently working. Then make your call either on that frequency or a bit further in the direction that the DX station seems to be tuning. You may have only two or three seconds to find the other station in the QRM of the whole pile-up, and you probably won't have propagation to all callers, so even highly experienced DXers may only track down 25% of the stations being worked in a big pile-up. There is no time to stop on each signal; you have to identify calls as the dial is turning and develop a mental 'map' of those present. With time and experience you develop a sixth sense about your competitors' habits and can go immediately to their frequency if you hear the DX pick up one of their calls. When you get everything right and the DX station comes straight back to your call the thrill is indescribable!

Yet another reason for listening first is that it is always advisable to find out what kind of contacts the DX station is making before calling. Is he making short snappy ones? If so it is not sensible to try to tell him all about the weather and full details of the equipment being used. The best idea is to give information similar to that which is being sent, and if the contact is a CW one this should be sent at the same speed (or slower if conditions are poor) as that at which the distant station is operating. It is quicker and more effective to send a report once at 13wpm than twice at 25wpm! When using phone, ITU phonetics should be used and pronounced clearly and slowly.

Calls themselves should be short. The DX station knows his own callsign and does not want to hear this being repeated many times but it is best to give one's own callsign more than once. The full use of VOX or break-in enables close watch to be kept on the time that the station being called is transmitting, and further calling can be avoided until he is listening again.

It is all too often possible to hear blind calls being made by those who quite clearly cannot hear the DX station, and also to hear a group of those waiting to work him talking on the frequency where he is expected to transmit (or is or has been transmitting). Both practices are to be deplored. Either is capable of causing severe interference to those located in other parts of the world.

Having made contact it is important to make sure that one's callsign has been logged correctly – if there is any doubt it is quite acceptable to continue to call and to make a second contact. However, during the usual DXpeditionary activity one contact only should be the rule. This may be extended to one per mode or one per band if the opportunity arises. It is important to log the time of the contact accurately, and quite a good idea to note the callsigns of others who make contact just before and just after – this may be helpful to the DX station in locating a log entry at a later date.

In conclusion, it is possible to list a few general rules which help when trying to make interesting DX contacts. They are as follows:

1. Listen carefully.
2. Be aware of what is happening.
3. If in any doubt – do not call.

By following these rules a few contacts will be missed because ruder and less well-behaved callers will sometimes succeed in crushing opposition. However, in the world of DXing these individuals are well known and receive no credit for their behaviour from good operators.

More pile-up tips

What more is there to do? Well, in the survey G4ADD advised paying lots of attention to your audio quality so that your voice stands out from the pack and others suggest you make sure your voice and your call are well known to DXpeditioners. Faced with a mass of signals the familiar voice or call is much more likely to be recognised by a tired DXpeditioner. Language skills can help on the occasions when listening frequencies are announced in a foreign language – but some techniques defeat even the best prepared. For example, BT's Directory Enquiry service had a sudden surge of calls when a DXpeditioner announced he was listening on the frequency given by the last three digits of his phone number! In addition to their publicised frequencies, most DXpeditions have unannounced frequencies for contact with members of their home clubs; identifying these by careful tuning can be an easy way to avoid the main pile-up. You can usually tell when they are in use because the DXpedition will suddenly, and quickly, work a run of calls from the same country or town.

A controversial pile-up point is whether you should spell out your whole callsign (in this author's case "Golf Three Zulu Alpha Yankee") or just repeat the last two letters "Alpha Yankee, Alpha Yankee". This author's view is that the full call is better. If the DX station hears you clearly he won't want to waste time establishing your full callsign (especially as you may not be in the clear on the second go round). If he is only going to catch a fragment then "Golf Three Zulu" is probably as useful to him as "Alpha Yankee", and when the last two letters are repeated he may come back to "Yankee Alpha Yankee" and get hopelessly confused.

Before leaving the subject of pile-ups a point must be stressed again: never, ever transmit on the DX station's frequency in a split-frequency pile-up. Don't ask "Where's he listening?". And don't ask "Who's his QSL manager?" while other people are still trying to work him. In most cases it's the failure to listen that leads to unnecessary interference. However, it's also possible to call on the DX station's frequency by cancelling or inverting the split settings on the transceiver – so please take care!

Perhaps total immersion in a wild 20m weekend pile-up is not the best way to start your DXing career. So it's worth remembering that weekdays are more relaxed on all bands, and the 10, 18 and 24MHz bands are still oases of tranquillity where a barefoot transceiver and a simple dipole can crack most of the embryo pile-ups that occur.

LISTS AND NETS

An increasingly common practice among users of SSB transceivers is the formation of lists of those who wish to contact a particular station. The 'master of ceremonies' then passes the list of callsigns to the DX station who proceeds to call in each station in turn. This almost inevitably degenerates into bad behaviour and chaos caused by those who arrive on the scene after the list has been made and who cannot therefore get a chance to call, and lack the manners to play the game the way the DX station is asking.

There are some circumstances when a station can only be contacted by this method – for instance he may only have a transceiver without dual VFOs, or he may speak a language not widely understood and may need help with translation.

How does one get on a list? Yet again the first and most important thing to do is to listen carefully. If the operation is being well conducted the operator in charge will keep those listening informed and will frequently say when a further list will be taken and on what frequency. Calling on the DX station's frequency to get onto a list should not be attempted – it could result in your call being added to another type of list altogether – a blacklist! Having registered your call it is important to return to the original frequency and to remain silent but listen carefully until called in to transmit. When this happens a bare minimum of information should be given – this may even be limited to a signal report if that is the normal routine of the particular operation. Many others will be waiting and to try to prolong such a contact will not impress them.

In the RSGB survey the respondents' attitudes to lists and nets varied from grudging acceptance to outright hostility – nobody had anything positive to say about them! G3PJT: "Time wasted in a list cannot be regained". Tom Austin, G3RCA: "They are a waste of time where you spend hours listening to 'No call thanks' all night".

This author's personal view is that they have a place for the less rare DX and can sometimes help the novice DXer who would not be strong enough to crack a pile-up. The notion that net QSOs are 'always less valid' than freestyle QSOs is strongly rejected; quite often a lot more information is passed between stations in a net than in a pile-up. Only too often one hears the comment after a pile-up battle "I think he came back to me but I couldn't really tell through the QRM so I'll send off a QSL and see if I get a card back" – so much for the sanctity of pile-up QSOs! In the end, it's always between yourself and your own conscience.

Of course, DX stations are entitled to operate as they wish and some really do prefer the more relaxed atmosphere of a DX net to a full-scale pile-up. In rare cases there may even be good reasons for the list technique. For example, if the DX station's only source of power is a small battery it makes sense to minimise the amount of transmitting by allowing the net controller to organise the callers and put them through one at a time.

If you use DX nets and lists then you may be interested in a regular publication by Dieter Konrad, OE2DYL, which gives the meeting times and frequencies of all such operations worldwide. Write to him at Rosengasse 1, A-5020, Salzburg, Austria, for the latest price. And one final tip: if you do use lists, never miss a chance to get on one! You can always duck out if it doesn't seem worth the wait. You never know what other

LISTS AND NETS – A CODE OF PRACTICE

1. The 'master of ceremonies' (MC), when taking the list, should endeavour to ensure a fair and even representation from all those countries calling to participate.
2. It is not desirable to take a list for use at some future date. In the case of poor propagation, however, a running list may be held over and continued when possible.
3. It is desirable to establish with the DX station beforehand how much time he or she has available, or how many stations can be worked in the time available.
4. A valid QSO requires some minimum two-way exchange of information. As stations are usually addressed by callsign this information has already been imparted to the DX station; nevertheless the MC should seek to avoid passing the whole callsign if possible. Convention has established that the exchange need only be a correctly received RS report by both parties. It is therefore the responsibility of the MC at all times to ensure that this is accomplished fairly, accurately and without assistance. While repeats are in order, if necessary, verification of partly received reports is not. Should a relay or a guess be suspected by the MC, the transmitting station should be instructed to make a second attempt with a changed report. The MC should not flinch from giving "negative QSO" when not satisfied with the exchange.
5. It is acceptable practice for the MC to nominate another station to monitor and assist with the procedure in difficult circumstances due to interference or linking for example.
6. If conditions fail the MC should terminate the operation rather than allow a 'free for all' under the guise of the list.
7. It is very important that the MC gives information out at regular intervals, relating to new lists, QSL managers, length of current list etc. This will be of great assistance to waiting stations not on the list, and minimise breaking and interference.

DX may join the net, even while a list is running for something you already have confirmed.

HF BAND CHARACTERISTICS

A major part of the fascination of amateur radio as a hobby lies in the tremendous variety of communication paths provided by the HF amateur bands. This enables them to cater for a wide range of interests, from regular schedules across town or across the world to the search for contact with rare and exotic DX stations and a variety of competitive activities and contests. In all these aspects, satisfaction and competitive success benefit from a thorough knowledge of the possibilities presented by the individual bands at different times of day and year.

Amateurs can and do learn from their own experience and from others, either through contact or by listening, and a comprehensive account would need to draw on the experience of all users – so someone's favourite 'wrinkle' will certainly be missing from what follows. There are, however, some general rules underlying the whole process of HF communication and its variability. These are outlined and the characteristics of the individual bands are described.

The whole business of HF band conditions is moderately complex and it is not the purpose of this book to deal in detail with the theoretical aspects, which are well covered in the *Radio Communication Handbook* [20] and in much professional literature. One cannot, however, discuss the subject without touching on the main technical considerations and a general understanding of these can be both interesting and helpful to the amateur communicator.

The technical background

The ionosphere, on which we depend for all HF contacts beyond the ground-wave zone, is itself dependent on the intensity of a variety of wave and particle emissions from the Sun and it is the variation of these, both as a whole and in their individual intensities, that causes the considerable variations in propagation on the HF bands. The principal variations, affecting all those bands in their different ways, are:

Diurnal: variations within the day due to the varying altitude of the Sun in relation to a particular path as the Earth rotates.

Seasonal: variations from month to month, again due to alterations in mean solar altitude and the duration of daylight.

Solar: changes from day to day in the intensity and mix of the solar radiations responsible for ionisation in the upper atmosphere. These changes can be considerable over quite short periods of time as well as showing longer-term trends, of which the 11-year cycle is the best known.

Geomagnetic: variations in ionospheric behaviour caused by alterations in the intensity and shape of the Earth's magnetic field. The magnetic variations are themselves caused by certain solar emissions.

To complete the picture it must be said that variation as used above refers to two distinct features of the ionosphere:

(a) its ability to reflect HF waves of a particular frequency at a given time and angle of incidence;
(b) the absorption (attenuation) suffered by the waves passing through the lower regions of the atmosphere on the way to and from the reflecting regions.

Both these vary but not by any means always in step. Both reduce as frequency is increased, the absorption decreasing roughly with the square of frequency. In general, communication is possible over a given path at a given time if the frequency is low enough to be reflected and high enough not to be attenuated below the noise level at the receiver.

The practical implications of the above for the amateur user of the bands from 1.8 to 28MHz are the purpose of the rest of this section but even this requires an understanding of a few basic concepts and terms.

For any path at any time there is a maximum frequency above which the signal is not reflected to the receiving station, however powerful the transmitter and however effective the transmitting and receiving antennas ('scatter' communication is dealt with later). Since, for reasons already mentioned, that frequency will vary from day to day, most statements on ionospheric behaviour must be of a statistical nature. A common measure for both recording and predicting is the monthly median maximum usable frequency (the median is the value likely to be exceeded on 15 days in the month and not reached on 15, the maximum variation above or below the median being from 30% to as much as 50%.) This value relates to a given path at a given time and takes account of all reflection points. If, however, the monthly median MUF is determined for a single-hop path, that MUF can be regarded as a measure of the statistical behaviour of the ionosphere at the point of reflection for any path of the same length reflected at that point, irrespective of direction.

It is therefore possible to produce worldwide maps of monthly median MUF distribution at various times in the day. Figs 1–5 show such distributions on a great circle map for five times of day in October at a time of fairly high solar activity (smoothed sunspot number about 100). Such a plot is not a forecast but the consolidation of a very large number of observations. The contours shown are for the F2 layer and for a single-hop path length of 4000km which is the practical limit for most single-hop F2 communications. Hops of about 5000km can sometimes be achieved where antenna and site favour very low angle paths on the higher frequencies*.

October was chosen because it is representative of peak winter DX conditions and is the month of several major contests. To keep the plots simple only the contours for the 14, 21 and 28MHz amateur bands are shown, the frequency being printed on the side of the contour where the 4000km MUF is above the contour value. On the 0600 GMT map only, the 40MHz contour is lightly sketched in and the 'high' of over 50MHz is over the South China Sea at this time. There are no 3.5 or 7MHz contours for the simple reason that nowhere is the 4000km median MUF below 7MHz. For those to whom this form of presentation is new, the contours for hops of less than 4000km lie to the 'up-hill' side of those shown.

A smoothed sunspot number of 100 was chosen as the value likely to be relevant when the maps were originally drawn and enables the potentialities of the highest HF bands to be fully illustrated. The solar cycle is now in its declining phase and MUFs as high as those shown are becoming less and less likely.

To complete the picture each map shows the position of the Sun and the sunrise/sunset line. The solid circle round London marks the 2000km normal limit for a single-hop reflection and the dotted circle the normal limit for single-hop communication. Maps of this type conveniently illustrate all the main characteristics of HF amateur-band communication. In fact the main factors at work can be seen by studying the map for 0600 GMT (Fig 2).

In order to understand what is happening there is a crucial question to be answered. If the 4000km MUF is well above 7MHz in all directions why cannot contacts be made on that band and on 3.5MHz with the whole world at this time? The same question applies to 14MHz except for the sector where the 2000km line crosses a 'pool' in which the MUF is below 14MHz. The answer is that such communication is theoretically possible, given sufficient radiated power. The obstacle to be overcome is ionospheric absorption. This is relatively low on the night side of the day/night line, the lowest values being about an hour inside the area of darkness since the Sun rises earlier and sets later in the relevant parts of the ionosphere than it does at ground level. The area of daylight in Fig 2 is best seen as a 'mountain' of absorption, roughly sinusoidal in section, with absorption rising steeply after dawn and falling steeply towards dark with a relatively flat peak under the Sun.

In short, for any frequency below the MUF, long-distance communication is always best (and with amateur EIRPs often only possible) when the path lies across the lower slopes of the absorption 'mountain' and/or through areas of darkness. The higher the frequency, the smaller is the absorption so that 28MHz signals can cross the 'mountain' when those on 21MHz are at best weak and those on 14MHz and below are attenuated below the noise level. On average, higher solar activity means higher absorption but the latter can vary considerably from day to day without a corresponding change in MUFs, and this variation is often responsible for the difference between 'good' and 'bad' conditions as seen by the amateur, the effect being particularly noticeable on the lower frequencies. The dramatic

---

* Plots of this type but on Mercator charts and with E-layer contours included are contained in OT/TRER 13, Vols 1–4 published by US Dept of Commerce, Office of Telecommunications, Boulder, Colorado 80302, USA. Contours are provided at 2h intervals for each month and for smoothed sunspot numbers of 10, 110 and 160.

Fig 2. Global distribution of 4000km median MUF contours for 14, 21 and 28MHz, and day/night zones at 0600 GMT in October (sunspot number = 100)

assuming its daytime role as essentially a local band.

7MHz. As regards DX much the same considerations apply as for 3.5MHz except that the lower ionospheric absorption means stronger signals and makes possible contacts that would at best be marginal on the lower band. The long path opening to New Zealand starts at about local dawn and can last an hour or more with stations from East Australia appearing somewhat later and overlapping the New Zealanders. Conditions with the Americas are at a peak but will remain good longer than on 3.5MHz. The skip zone is shrinking to the east so European interference is rising.

14MHz. The significant feature is the 'pool' in which the 4000km median MUF is below 14MHz. On below-average days this grows larger and on a very low day will join with that over North America and fill much of the area bounded by the median 21MHz contour. Conversely, on above-average days it shrinks. It must also be remembered that the 'pool' is larger for hops of less than 4000km.

On an average day, therefore, there is a take-off for 14MHz from north through east and south to about 240°. In the sector from about 030° to 150° absorption is too high for more than single-hop contacts and the single-hop skip is rapidly shortening, particularly to the south-east.

Thus the path to Cape Town, which may have been open most of the night, is about to close. West Africa, the South Atlantic and South America are all good. The MUF is above 14MHz on the long path to New Zealand and East Australia and the dip in absorption which causes the LF openings will result in excellent signals on 14MHz during the next hour to those areas the islands of the West Pacific and NE Asia (Japan and the Far Eastern Russia.)

At the same time a low-absorption path is just opening to the north, giving access to Alaska and the Central Pacific, and this path will improve as the contours rotate clockwise (compare Fig 3 for 0800), peaking at around 0700.

Finally, on better days the 14MHz 'pool' will be small enough for there to be paths to at least parts of North America.

21MHz. At this time a 'wave' of rising MUF is sweeping in from the east. The 21MHz contour intersects the 2000km take-off circle at about 035° and 180° and contacts are possible within this sector with the shortest skip to the east, in which direction stations well within the 4000km circle will be workable. At the same time absorption is high in the direction of the Sun and on most days long-distance contacts (more than two hops) will only be good along the lower slopes of the 'mountain', ie to NE Asia and East Africa.

On a day with exceptionally high MUF and low absorption, long-path contacts with the Central Pacific should be possible at about this time – even the west coast of the USA is a

effect of this absorption can be seen from the following example. For a daytime path on 21MHz for which the absorption per hop is 6dB the corresponding figure for 7MHz is around 40dB and for 3.5MHz is around 100dB.

Band characteristics in a typical month

Against this background it is possible to see what to expect on an undisturbed day in October with fairly high solar activity. Referring to Fig 2 and looking at the bands in turn:

3.5MHz. A station in the UK is 'firing into darkness' over a sector from approximately north through 270° to 180°, and the zone of minimum absorption lies somewhat to the west of this line. This is near the peak time for contact with North America including the west coast, Central and South America, the western 'bulge' of Africa and the South Atlantic Is. If absorption is exceptionally low, contacts may be possible with the Pacific islands from Fiji to the west (seen from the UK).

The shadow line is slowly rotating clockwise and by 0625 (in the middle of the month) will pass through London and, being a great circle, will lie along the line 015°/295°, intersecting northern New Zealand. During the next 30min or so the absorption on the southerly 'long path' to New Zealand passes through a short minimum during which UK-New Zealand contact is possible. The peak time gets later as the month progresses and also depends on the location of both UK and New Zealand stations, since the times of sunrise and sunset vary and so does the direction of the great circle path.

There is no skip zone on 3.5MHz at this time and in easterly directions the absorption rises steeply so that the band is rapidly possibility. On above-average days, long-path contact with ZL1/2 should open soon after 0600.

28MHz. On average or above-average days the band is open to the east (about 060°–150°), the first stations to appear being about 4000km away. High absorption towards the Sun may keep signals from long distances weak or inaudible but contact with East Africa and the Indian Ocean should be good and the short path to Australia and intermediate areas is opening, though at this time it tends to be better for stations in East and South Europe.

Finally it will be seen that on exceptional days there is a possibility of long-path contact with the Central Pacific and the California area, particularly if helped by sporadic-E (see below) reflection south of Australia.

The above analysis shows that there is a great deal to be said about just one time period in one month. It is outside the scope of this book to extend this detailed analysis to every hour of every month in each of the 11 years of a typical solar cycle! Having established a basis, however, it becomes easier to follow the general trends. Dealing

Fig 3. Fig 2 data at 0800 GMT

first with the diurnal variations, let us move forward to 0800 GMT (Fig 3). Note that the whole contour pattern has rotated clockwise by about 30°. In fact some changes in shape do occur due to the influence of the geomagnetic field on the position of the contours at different geomagnetic longitudes, but these are incorporated in the charts.

The position at 0800 GMT is:

3.5MHz. Most of the path to North America is still in darkness but attenuation is rising at the UK end of the path. Contact with the east coast and with Central America will soon fade but at this time UK stations have the advantage that interference from more easterly stations in Europe has faded at the DX end. For the next eight hours the band will be essentially local in character.

7MHz. The path to North and Central America may well last another hour or more and, on good days, South America and Australia may still be workable after 0800. The skip zone will reduce to zero at about 0800 and from then on the band will become a daytime local band. Absorption will increase until noon, with the effective range of communication with European stations steadily decreasing as signals from the more distant fall below the noise level.

14MHz. This is the peak time for the long-path opening to Australia, eastern areas peaking before western ones, and the path can extend 'round the back' as far as India. Note that the path to ZL3/4 is similar to that to Australia. For ZL1/2, however, the attenuation on the long path increases from 0800 onwards, while that on the short path decreases, the 'turn round' usually occurring between 0900 and 1000 and sometimes including a

'both ways' period. There is still a path to the north to parts of the Central Pacific and good contact with West Africa, South Atlantic and Central and South America but these will in turn succumb to rising attenuation during the next two hours or so. On a day with average MUFs or above there will be contact with at least parts of North America though reliable conditions may not develop until after 0900.

21MHz. There is now a take-off from the north clockwise to the south-west and the skip is short enough to the south-east to bring in the more distant Europeans.

On many days there is a low-absorption 'round the world' path at this time on the approximate line 030°/210°. This gives good communication with, for example, ZL1/2, UA0 and Japan over either short or long path, with the latter normally providing the stronger signals. Over the next two hours the long path extends to ZL3/4 and Australia, and sometimes to East Asia, eg Hong Kong, while the short path continues to ZL1/2.

On exceptional days contact is possible over the North Pole with the Central Pacific (eg Fiji) somewhere between 0800 and 1000, but this path is more likely to be good in March and September than in other months.

The band is now good to West Africa and the South Atlantic, and is opening to South America, the first to appear usually being Brazil. It is sunset in Tokyo and from now on the signal strengths of East Asian stations will improve as attenuation falls, the most northerly peaking first.

In East Africa noon is approaching and signals from this area may become weak or unreadable for a while, to appear again later.

Fig 4. Fig 2 data at 1200 GMT

28MHz. From the run of the contours it can be seen that the band is about to open to Japan and beyond in the north-east direction, is fully open to most of Asia and all of Africa and is about to open to Brazil.

This is also the peak time for contacts with East Australia, though the path may have opened soon after 0600 and may remain until after 1200, the closure being mainly determined by falling MUF at the far end and with stations in the north and west of the continent lasting longest. MUFs well above average are needed for 28MHz contacts with ZL1/2 which is most likely between 0700 and 0900. ZL3/4 is less critical, the path being similar to that to East Australia.

The position at 1200 GMT (Fig 4) is:

14MHz. On average and above days there is still a path to the north to Alaska, the Central Pacific and ZL1/2, and the band is opening to Japan and the West Pacific islands (which bear north-east from the UK). With most of the path now in darkness short-path signals from ZL3/4 and Australia will begin to show but will be better later in the afternoon. The same applies to East and SE Asia. Note that on days of low attenuation the long path may still be open to West Australia and SE Asia at this time, but not for long after 1200.

At this time the skip is short enough for contact with much of Europe and interference is a limiting factor on DX operation – but a good time for multipliers or bonuses in a contest. To the west, Central American stations have passed their morning peak and will soon fade but the band is well open to North America with the west coast just opening on an average day.

21MHz. Except on the best days the path to ZL1/2 will have closed and Japan is about to follow. Conditions to Australia and ZL3/4 are approaching their peak and, during the afternoon, stations in East Asia south of 040° will peak before the paths close due to falling MUFs, the northernmost peaking first.

Skip is now short enough for contact with the more distant Europeans. DX signals from the south will be weak or unreadable due to high attenuation and this is beginning to affect the path to South America. The band is now well open to Central America and the east coast of the USA and Canada.

28MHz. On the short path to Australia the MUF is falling at the DX end. On an average day the multi-hop take-off from the UK is limited to paths south of 040°. The Australia path will close in the next hour or so, VK6 lasting longest. At the same time the paths to Hong Kong, SE Asia, India and the Indian Ocean are good.

Skip is short enough for contacts of 1500km or less, a good time for European multipliers in a contest. On days of high absorption African stations may be weak but will soon improve. Communication with South America is well established and is open to Central America and the east coast of the USA and Canada. (If active, VO and some VE1 stations may show soon after 1000 on good days.)

With regard to the position at 1600 GMT (Fig 5), sunset is just after 1700 in the middle of the month and the approach of the twilight zone is a significant feature, while inside the area of daylight attenuation is low along the line 150°/330°. From 1600 the two LF bands must again be considered from a DX point of view.

3.5 and 7MHz. As attenuation falls, ranges in the sector 000° to 090° will increase. At sunset the day/night line lies along the great circle 170°/350° and on days of low absorption there is a chance to contact the Central Pacific at that time. The paths to New Zealand, the West Pacific islands and East Asia are all in darkness but are at their best as the Sun rises at the DX end – 1800 to 1900 for New Zealand and progressively later for more westerly areas. There is a dip in the absorption on the path to East Africa during the period 1700–1800.

14MHz. In the area of darkness the only obstacle is the small pool to the north, particularly on below-average days. Communication is good to all of Asia and beyond, and to Australia and ZL3/4. On above-average days the band is open to the Central Pacific and ZL1/2, if not at 1600, certainly by 1800.

Falling attenuation means that communication is now again good with the Indian Ocean and East Africa. Note also that the long path to the western USA is mostly in darkness and there is often a good opening between about 1500 and 1600 with signals much stronger than on the short path. This path crosses the Pacific and some islands en route may also be worked in this manner at this time. (Note that in mid-December the twilight zone at sunset lies along the great circle between London and San Francisco, and LF band contacts are sometimes possible.)

High attenuation still keeps 14MHz signals weak or unreadable to West Africa and South and Central America, and may even affect contact with southern areas of the USA at this time. On more northerly paths absorption is relatively low and the band is opening to Hawaii and other Pacific islands bearing north to north-west from the UK.

21MHz. On an average day the sector from 340° through north to about 070° is only suitable for single-hop contacts up to about 4000km. This means that the band is still open to parts of Australia and to SE Asia, the Indian Ocean, Africa, the South Atlantic and the Americas, the opening having reached the West Coast around 1400. The 21MHz contour will be optimum for the Hawaii area at or soon after 1800, and may reach due north and the Central Pacific on exceptional days.

28MHz. On a few days the path

Fig 5. Fig 2 data at 1600 GMT

to SE Asia and parts of Australia may still be open but will soon close. Good contacts are possible over the whole arc from east through south to north-west where on all but the worst days the west coast of the USA will have opened up. On below-average days this opening may be rather brief but under exceptional conditions (28MHz contour near median contour for 21MHz) the opening to the West Coast may last several hours and extend to the Hawaii area.

The position at 2000 GMT (Fig 6) is:

3.5MHz. This is the time of the short opening to East Australia, the more westerly stations peaking later as dawn moves across the continent, reaching VK6 by 2200. Depending on absorption levels (and interference) contact is possible with all of Asia and Africa during the next two hours and with west of 90°E until midnight. The band will soon open to Brazil and Canada.

7MHz. Since it is absorption, not MUF, which controls the openings, the same pattern applies as for 3.5MHz except that openings will start earlier and last longer, and signals will be generally stronger. On average or above-average days there is still no skip zone at this time and interference is a major obstacle to DX working.

14MHz. At this time it is possible to contact all continents with ease. On average or above-average days the band is still open to at least southern New Zealand, Australia, the Far East, the rest of Asia and to Africa. Falling attenuation opens the path to South America, and North American signals will reach peak levels during the next few hours. Long hauls into the

Pacific in the sector 330° to 010° are still possible but attenuation is rising rapidly as most of the path is now in daylight.

21MHz. The sector from north to south-east is now useless except on a few days. Communication is good to Africa, the South Atlantic and the Americas and on a good day the Hawaii area may still be accessible.

On days of high MUF and low absorption the long path to New Zealand and East Australia can produce good contacts at about this time.

28MHz. On an average day the band will be just about closing in all directions (28MHz contour passing out of 2000km circle) except for stations with very good low-angle take-off. On exceptional days it can still be open to most of the Americas and to the south, and under these conditions 28MHz contact on the long path to ZL3/4 and East Australia is possible.

The preceding sections show the main diurnal features of the amateur bands from 3.5 to 28MHz in October. The remarks made about the 3.5MHz band apply also in general to the 1.8MHz band, except that D layer absorption is higher and therefore the conditions for making DX contacts are even more difficult to fulfil. They can only be made when the path lies in darkness – propagation during daylight hours is mainly by ground wave only, and with the low powers permitted to UK amateurs, the range typically covered will be only up to about 400km. As with the other bands, DX propagation is by ionospheric reflection from the E and F layers and, as the critical frequency for the E layer is almost always higher than 2MHz, there is rarely a silent zone on this band.

Fig 6. Fig 2 data at 2000 GMT

which the dawn/dusk line lies at those times. Applying this data to a great-circle map will show which areas are in darkness and which lie along the zone of lowest absorption which is just inside the area of darkness. Remember that the dawn/dusk line is only a straight line on a great-circle map at sunrise and sunset. Its position at other times may be roughly extrapolated by reference to Figs 1–5.

Sunrise and sunset times are different elsewhere in the UK – typically 10min later in Birmingham and as much as 40min later in Glasgow and Belfast in summer – and the differences are not the same for sunrise and sunset. To make a table for your own location, borrow a copy of Whitaker's Almanac from the local library. The bearing of the dawn/dusk line in Fig 7(b) is accurate within a few degrees for any location in the UK at local sunrise and sunset.

Fig 8 shows this information incorporated into a great-circle map by Ray Flavell, G3LTP [20].

In this connection it should be remembered that the standard great-circle map centred on London, while applying with sufficient accuracy to the whole of the UK

Dealing with one month in detail seemed to be the best way of bringing out the underlying factors but naturally the amateur is interested in the whole year.

Seasonal variations and grey-line propagation

Even with unchanging solar activity F2 layer MUFs are much higher in local winter than in the summer, being highest in the Northern Hemisphere in January/February and October/November with something of a dip in December. The situation is not all that different in March and September when the distribution of MUFs in the two hemispheres is similar. To this extent the pattern of band behaviour described for October is broadly representative of the winter months as a whole.

Account must of course be taken of the distribution of daylight and darkness which varies continuously throughout the period. In general shorter days mean shorter openings on 14, 21 and 28MHz and longer periods during which 7 and 3.5MHz are potentially available for DX.

In the case of 3.5 and 7MHz the position of the twilight zone is also important as well as the distribution of light and dark.

Computer software is available to calculate the times and bearings when this occurs. An example is DX Edge by Xantec (available from RSGB HQ). However, there is also a method of determining this involving a great circle map, an aid which no keen DX operator should be without. Figs 6(a) and 6(b) show the variation in the time of sunrise and sunset at London throughout the year together with the great circle bearing along

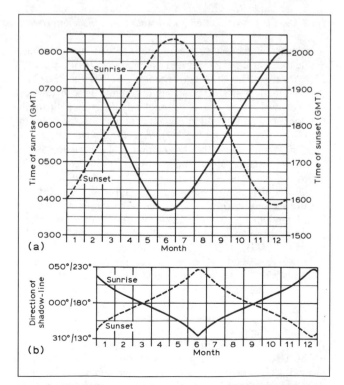

Fig 7. (a) Time of sunrise and sunset at London. (b) Approximate great-circle direction of shadow-line at local sunrise and sunset in UK

Fig 8. Grey-line propagation map *(Radio Communication Handbook)*

in most cases, can be misleading with paths to the antipodes. While the bearing of ZL4 from London is 060°/240°, it is 030°/ 210° from Belfast. The corresponding values for ZL1/2 are 010°/190° and 350°/170° respectively. While these differences may seem small they mean a completely different path for the two locations and should imply, for example, that the best time for GI/ZL1 contacts on 3.5 MHz is at local dawn in April to August, though this author has no practical experience of this.

The importance of the twilight zone can be seen from the following example. At sunset in mid-April and mid-August the sunset line lies along the great circle path from the UK to Ascension Is and absorption goes through a minimum about an hour later. During this period contact between these two places has been made successfully on 21, 14, 7 and 3.5MHz, with a return to 21MHz to complete the contact.

However, as G3LTP points out in reference [20], it must be remembered that it is not the ground-based shadow that determines the state of the ionosphere because the Earth's shadow is shaped like a cone; the area of darkness at F2 heights is appreciably less than that at ground level. Sunrise comes earlier than on the ground, sunset later. In fact, in mid-summer the F2 layer is in sunlight for all 24 hours of the day over the whole of the UK. So the ionospheric grey line (as opposed to the ground-based grey line) cannot be considered as a great circle and, therefore, cannot be represented by the straight line on the map. This should not stop you from trying your luck, however! But there is no point in trying to calculate the true outline of

the Earth's shadow, because your signals are going to take the great-circle route no matter what you come up with on your computer. You may as well make all your plans using ground-based data, because it is easy to come by, and make up for its likely deficiencies by being generous with your timing. At the sort of frequency you are using, the beamwidth of the antenna will be wide enough to take care of direction.

To summarise, DX can be worked throughout the year on the LF bands although interference and noise level may make life difficult in the summer months. Basically the rules are simple. Most or all of the path must be in darkness and the best times, particularly for long hauls, are when much or all of the path lies just inside the area of darkness, a situation which occurs if it is near sunrise or sunset at both ends of the path. The latter condition cannot of course always be met, in which case there are two optimum times – around sunset at the western end of the path and near sunrise at the eastern end. With the shorter paths, eg to North America, the path is open between these times but with long hauls, eg to the Far East and Australasia, the openings can only be expected at these times.

The characteristics of the higher bands during summer are mainly determined by four factors:

1. Daytime MUFs are considerably lower than in winter but the difference between day and night is much less marked apart from a drop before dawn.
2. Higher solar altitude means higher average attenuation than in winter and the longer days mean that paths in the Northern Hemisphere are in daylight for much longer periods.
3. The lower E layer (with a maximum single-hop range of 2000km) is more likely to play a part in DX communications than in winter ('sporadic-E' is dealt with later).
4. Stations in the Southern Hemisphere are experiencing winter conditions so that in communications with them the MUFs at the remote ends are more often a critical factor than in our winter.

The effects of this on the three higher bands are roughly as follows:

14MHz. DX communications are mainly conditioned by absorption. Between about 0800 and 1400 only shorter-range signals are strong enough for contact – on days of exceptionally low absorption this may include contacts with the eastern USA. The band is best at night. Particular features of summer are a good long path to the west coast of North America in the early mornings (at dawn in mid-June the twilight zone lies along the UK-California path) and this path also covers parts of the Pacific. There is also a possibility of long-path contact with Australasia in the hours before and sometimes after midnight but this is more reliable when solar activity is relatively low.

21MHz. The band is open to the south of the east-west line on most days except perhaps for a brief interruption before local dawn. Particularly on paths crossing the Equator, attenuation may make signals weak or unreadable during the period when the path passes near to the sub-solar point.

The 21MHz contour is usually not far enough to the north to provide short-path contact on more northerly paths, eg to Japan and the west coast of the USA, but the summer months provide conditions for long-path communications to these areas to the USA west coast in the early mornings and to Australasia, Japan and New Zealand both in the early morning and in the period from 2000 to midnight.

28MHz. In midsummer the median 4000km 28MHz contour lies about 2000km south of London. This means that stations in the southern UK are best placed for making DX contacts. Only on days well above average will reliable contacts be possible except to stations in the sector from roughly 120° to 240°. Contacts with North America and NE Asia are most unlikely except for a remote possibility of long-path contacts with California soon after dawn. On good days there can, however, be a good long path to ZL3/4 and eastern Australia around 2100–2200.

Sporadic-E conditions (see below) are most frequent in summer and as well as bringing in signals in the range 500–2000km may help with DX communication by providing a first hop of up to 2000km into an area of higher F2 MUF both on 28 and 21MHz.

The above discussion is concentrated on midsummer. In practice, band characteristics change gradually so that conditions in April and August show characteristics midway between extreme summer and winter.

The whole discussion has also assumed higher mean solar activity than is likely during the next few years, though there could be some days when MUFs approach those described. The best available guide to when the various bands are likely to be open to various parts of the world is to be found in the HF propagation predictions which appear monthly in *Radio Communication*. It should be noted, however, that brief openings due to short-lived minima in ionospheric absorption, such as the regular early morning openings to New Zealand on 3.5MHz, do not show up in this presentation.

It must be remembered that even amateurs must sleep and most must work so that their times of activity may not always correspond with the times of best communication. The charts show when the bands should be open but necessarily include times when, except perhaps during major contests, the DX stations are not likely to be very active.

The 10, 18 and 24MHz bands

Each of these bands is located in terms of frequency approximately midway between two of the amateur bands already discussed and, as might be expected, their propagation characteristics are intermediate between those of their neighbours. One way of looking at this is to sketch in the 10, 18 and 24MHz contours in Figs 1–5. Those for 10MHz lie inside those given for 14MHz. The contours for 18 and 24MHz lie approximately midway between those for 14, 21 and 28 MHz and illustrate the main propagation features of the two bands.

The 10MHz band

During sunspot maxima this band is not usually 'MUF-limited' except for a short period around dawn in midwinter, but as solar activity declines there will be an increasing tendency for the MUF on more northerly paths to fall below 10MHz during darkness. Apart from this, absorption will be the main factor affecting DX working which will generally be best when much of the path is in darkness or, if not, is reasonably close to the twilight zone. DX openings will therefore follow the same pattern as those on 7MHz but, because absorption is lower, they will start earlier and end later than on the lower band, and peak signals will be stronger. During daylight short-range communication within Europe will be possible by both E and F layers with zero-skip conditions around noon on better days in winter.

The 18 and 24MHz bands

While there will be detailed differences with different levels of solar and geomagnetic activity the propagation characteristics of these two bands show marked similarities to those of their immediate neighbours, sometimes behaving more like the next lower band and sometimes resembling the next higher. As the solar cycle declines it will be found that 24MHz will remain open for DX on days when 28MHz is no longer useful, while the 1.8MHz band should prove good for daytime DX working even during solar minimum when the 18MHz median MUF contour will occupy the approximate position shown for the 28MHz contour in Figs 1–5.

Anomalous propagation, disturbances and blackouts

There are various ways in which band characteristics depart from the general pattern and the effect of those of most concern to the amateur are briefly described below.

Sporadic-E (Es)

Patches of high ionisation can appear without warning and disappear as suddenly. In the UK area they are most likely in the daytime and from March to September, and can result in communication over ranges of 500–2000km at frequencies very much above the F2 MUF. For the HF operator their effect is most noticeable on 21 and 28MHz where, as already mentioned, they not only give good contact with Europe but may 'help' a DX signal into a region of higher F2 MUF. Es elsewhere in the world can also help the DX operator. It is common throughout the year in daytime in equatorial regions and mainly at night in the auroral zones. The so-called 'M' reflection, involving a signal on its way down from the F2 region being 'bounced' back off the *top* of an Es cloud, can help your signal cross an area of low F2 MUF and has low attenuation because the signal still only passes twice through the absorbing regions. Es is also discussed in the VHF DX section (see p68).

Extended ('chordal') hops

When transmitting in a direction in which there is a 'valley' in the MUF contours (eg to the south-west in Fig 3) the F2 ionisation gradient, though not steep enough to return your signal to earth, may bend it sufficiently for it to follow the curvature of the Earth until it encounters rising MUF on the far side of the 'valley' when it will be deflected downwards. Such hops have low attenuation and can be very much longer than 4000km.

Ground scatter

At certain times of the day and in certain directions the path attenuation may be low enough for quite strong signals to be scattered from the point of ground reflection both sideways and back along the transmitting path. This is useful to the amateur in three ways:

1. If a beam antenna is used to determine the direction from which the back scatter from other UK or Continental stations

is arriving, this is evidence of a good DX path in that direction.

2. It can be used to contact stations who are in the skip zone if both beam towards the scatter source.

3. When there is no normal path to, say, the USA it may still be possible to communicate if both stations beam towards West Africa or South America.

An interesting example of this can be seen in the evenings on 14 and sometimes 21MHz when there is no direct path to Australasia but a good path to South Africa. Good communication is then possible with the Australasian and UK stations both beaming on Cape Town. Whether the scatter occurs in Africa or in the South Polar Region is an open question. In fact both the long and short paths to stations near the antipode sometimes show significant deviations from the great circle route from 'over the pole' before the opening is fully developed to north of (LP) or south of (SP) the true direction as the path closes. Side scatter, ionospheric tilts and polar Es may all contribute to these effects.

Skip focussing

When operating well below the MUF the various vertical rays from and to your antenna follow different vertical paths with different hop lengths When, however, the operating frequency is close to the MUF for the path, these rays tend to converge and this *skip focussing* can provide significant signal enhancement, equivalent to the difference between a typical dipole and a good beam antenna (6–9dB). Thi accounts for the signal peak which often occurs soon after an MUF-limited path has opened and shortly before it closes, and is the best time for the operator with low power (see p56).

Disturbances and blackouts

Events taking place in the Sun can cause major and minor upsets to HF communication in basically two ways. As already mentioned, a rise in certain emissions can cause daytime absorption to rise to high levels. On such occasions paths in a generally westerly direction which are normally open at a given time may show signals for a short time after opening, but signals will then fade to return after dark if the path MUF is still high enough.

In extreme cases, usually associated with solar flares, the absorption rises suddenly to a high value and all daylight paths are 'blacked out'. Such a *sudden ionospheric disturbance* (SID) may last minutes or hours. Sometimes solar noise is high on 21 and 28MHz before the blackout and MUFs may be abnormally high both before and after the disturbance.

Particle radiation from flares or through *coronal holes* affects the intensity and shape of the Earth's magnetic field and therefore the shape of the MUF contours. These magnetic disturbances or 'storms' generally result in lower MUFs and higher absorption in high latitudes, particularly in the auroral zones. Under such conditions paths in northerly directions, notably to North America, may be badly affected while conditions to the south may even be improved. Disturbances resulting from persistent solar anomalies are predictable since they recur at 27-day intervals (see below and also p69).

Solar variations

The various ionising radiations from the Sun are not constant in their effect. Since the sources of radiation are not evenly distributed over the Sun's surface there is usually a 27-day cycle of variation due to the Sun's rotation relative to the Earth.

The daily count of sunspots has been the traditional measure of solar activity, a more modern and somewhat more objective one being the power received on the Earth at 2800MHz (solar flux). On average the two vary together and are nearly linearly related. For practical purposes the relation:

$$R = 1.1 \,(\text{S.F.} - 60) \quad (R = \text{sunspot number})$$

gives an answer sufficiently accurate for amateur purposes, enabling the WWV 18 minutes-after-the-hour broadcast of the daily solar flux value (SFU) to be converted to an approximate sunspot number if so desired (see below).

The most well-known aspect of solar variation is the approximately 11-year cycle of rise and fall in the 12-month mean of the daily sunspot numbers and solar flux – 'approximately' since Cycles 15–19 were all nearer 10 years while a recent one lasted nearly 12 years. The average rise time is about four years.

Since the cause of this cyclic behaviour is not yet fully understood (there is even evidence that it is not always present, the last absence being in the 75 years from 1650AD), prediction of future trends is based on extrapolation from the past. For the amateur communicator it is important to remember that professional propagation predictions are based on forecasts of solar activity and that these are based on heavily smoothed data. While the ionosphere does not respond instantly to solar variations its smoothing effect spreads over days rather than months, and generally the higher the mean solar activity, the greater the short-term fluctuations. For example, during the peak months from November 1957 to March 1958 the highest daily sunspot number was 342 and the lowest 90. Since forecasts have to be prepared well ahead of events one should always be on the look out for conditions which are outside the limits predicted.

There are also from time to time shorter periodicities within the 11-year cycle. On its down slope one recent cycle had distinct subsidiary peaks at intervals of rather more than two years [21], and over the years 1975–77 there was a fairly regular rise and fall with a period of approximately 120 days.

Professional forecasts smooth out these variations and, since they perforce are based on data which is many months old by the time the prediction appears in print, they can even get 180° out of phase with them. The amateur, on the other hand, would like to know what band conditions will be like the next day, or for the following weekend's contest. As with weather forecasting there can be no certainty but a surprising amount can be done with relatively little effort.

Do-it-yourself prediction

The 27-day (28 in the early stages of a cycle) solar rotation is a key factor in short-term prediction. Some amateurs keep a record of their own assessment of band conditions on this basis and know that similar conditions, both good and bad, can often be predicted 27 days ahead. The criteria to be used depend on individual interests. A useful one is the duration and penetration of the North American opening because there is plenty of activity and the path is a good indicator of general conditions.

Not everyone has the time to make the necessary observations and an alternative or supplementary approach is to make use of the WWV broadcasts at 18 minutes past each hour. These give the most recent value of 2800MHz flux which is recorded at 1700 GMT each day, ie WWV broadcasts from 1818 GMT usually contain the current day's value. The broadcast also gives a daily geomagnetic index (A-index) and mentions events such as solar flares and gives a 24-hour projection of solar and geomagnetic trends. Reliable copy of WWV needs a good

Fig 9. Daily 2800MHz solar flux from November 1977 to March 1978

antenna, preferably with a good null to the east to reduce interference from other standard transmissions and intruders, but if the flux and 'A' values can be copied on most days and the gaps filled by a friendly North American contact, a really up-to-date picture of solar activity and trends is available [22, 23]. If you have difficulty in receiving WWV, remember that propagation data is available on the packet network, Internet (World Wide Web) and the GB2RS news bulletins.

Fig 9 plots the solar flux as published by NOAA Boulder, over the period from November 1977 to March 1978. It will be seen that the excellent high-band conditions in early February and March were easily predictable. A plot of daily sunspot numbers is very similar in shape so that if WWV cannot be received with sufficient reliability the numbers can be obtained from the Sunspot Index Data Centre, Brussels for a small fee. They arrive in monthly batches in the first week of the following month, providing a somewhat less timely but still valuable base for short-term prediction. The A-index is a measure of worldwide geomagnetic activity. In itself, a low value (15 or less) means a stable magnetic field and stable radio conditions, usually with low absorption. A low A-index with a high flux value means excellent conditions, particularly on the high bands (it was around 10 during the early February and March flux peaks in Fig 9). For good LF band conditions look out for low flux values together with very low 'A'.

A 27-day plot of the A-index shows recurrent peaks due to persistent sources of particle emission from the Sun and coronal holes. High peaks mean disturbed conditions, magnetic storms and possibly auroral effects, and if recurrent these can be predicted from the 'A' plots. However, an SID caused by a flare cannot be so predicted since it is a 'new' event and the rise in the A-index follows a day or two later when the effects of the flare disturb the magnetic field. All that can be said is that such events are more likely to appear near a peak in the solar flux plot. 27-day calendars are also of importance in VHF auroral communication (see p71).

The above should serve to show that with not too much effort an amateur can form quite a reliable view of the likely trend of radio conditions a month or more ahead, and with the help of the WWV reports be aware of what is happening more or less currently.

At this stage of the solar cycle (1995) solar flux values above 80–85 SFU should generally point to above-average conditions on the higher bands.

For those interested in the trend of the solar cycle a three-month running mean plot of the provisional sunspot number

(published in *Radio Communication* about two months later) gives a good idea how things are going.

Since the geomagnetic field is affected by emissions from the Sun it also shows cyclic behaviour although this is not so clearly defined. Geomagnetic activity, ie the incidence and intensity of disturbances, ionospheric storms and auroral activity, certainly increases as the sunspot peak approaches but may continue to rise for a further two to five years before reaching its own peak.

The next geomagnetic peak will not occur for several years and activity will remain low until the late 'nineties. Many books are available on this topic [24–26].

Computer programs such as MINIMUF, MINIPROP and IONSOUND are available; these give propagation predictions based on solar data.

Perhaps the easiest method of all is just to read the propagation predictions printed each month in *Radio Communication*!

The beacon network

Propagation predictions are all very well but if you have just switched on your radio and want to work DX, it's obviously better to know what is happening right now, rather than what has been forecast. This is where beacons can help.

On 14, 21 and 28MHz there are several beacons situated in strategic locations all over the world which can provide an excellent clue to band conditions, and these are proving valuable in both amateur and professional propagation research. A list of these beacons is given in Appendix 10.

The beacons on the 14MHz band, organised and financed by the Northern California DX Foundation (NCDXF) are all on one shared frequency, 14.100MHz, and currently follow a 10-minute cycle (although as the network expands, this will change to 15 minutes). Each beacon transmits for one minute on the minute, first sending a sign-on message "QST DE [callsign]" at 100W, then four continuous tones for about nine seconds each at 100, 10, 1 and 0.1W, then signing off at 100W. The varying power levels are a good clue to propagation, especially for those using QRP. It is planned to cover other bands, and already there is at least one triband (14/21/28MHz) beacon.

The beacons on 28MHz all have their own frequencies in the 28.190–28.225MHz sub-band, and run continuously.

Never transmit on, or very close to, a beacon frequency or in a beacon sub-band, even if you can't hear anything – your signals will cause severe interference to others straining to catch the faint signals.

DX ON THE BANDS BELOW 30MHz

Many factors, both technical and social, combine to give each amateur band a distinct 'character' and the bands below 30MHz are no exception. Each has characteristics which appeal to its own enthusiastic users. Those with limited facilities often find it worthwhile to specialise in DX working on one particular band.

This section takes a look around the various bands with this in mind, and gives some indication of the type of DX activity going on so that the newcomer knows what to look out for. Some hints on equipment and antennas are also given in the case of 1.8 and 3.5MHz as these bands pose particular technical problems for the DXer.

IARU Region 1 has recommended band plans for the 3.5–28MHz bands which set aside segments of each band for use by various modes, and these are shown in Appendix 9. Although voluntary in the UK they are mandatory in some Region 1 countries and should be observed at all times. It is recommended that the portions dealing with the bands in use be memorised.

It should also be noted that, following a CCIR (International Radio Consultative Committee) recommendation, it is an accepted convention to transmit *lower* sideband *below* 10MHz and *upper* sideband *above* 10MHz.

1.8MHz (160m) band

It is difficult to define 1.8MHz DX in terms of distance, but 3000 to 5000km would generally be considered to qualify. 160m propagation is not dissimilar to that experienced on the medium wave broadcast band, with little sky-wave propagation during daylight hours, but with long-distance working possible throughout the hours of darkness. In years gone by, achieving DXCC (100 countries worked) on 160m would have been considered an almost unattainable goal. However, recent years have seen a substantial increase in activity on the band which, combined with improvements in antennas and receiver technology (and in some instances, such as in the UK, increased power limits) have led to scores of 200 countries or more becoming relatively commonplace. A well-equipped UK amateur prepared to lose sleep in the cause of 160m DXing could nowadays expect to work 100 countries or more in a season, and the day cannot be far off when a large contest station will achieve DXCC in a contest weekend. Even with 10W, many stations have worked all continents.

DX propagation on 160m requires that the whole path lies in darkness, though there can be significant signal enhancement at dawn and dusk due to ionospheric tilting. For example, the path between Europe and Australia often opens for about 10–15 minutes before and after Australian sunrise. Such openings will not occur every day, and openings can be very short (just two to three minutes) with signals peaking at good strength and then falling away very rapidly indeed. To some extent, propagation will depend on ionospheric activity. In particular, signal paths through the auroral zone will be subject to strong attenuation when auroral activity is high. In the northern hemisphere, signals from the north also arrive at much lower wave angles than those from the south. To achieve these wave angles with a horizontal antenna would require antenna heights of 250ft or more, so vertical antennas are generally favoured by 160m DXers.

On shorter paths (eg Europe to North America), the path can be open for several hours, although signals may still peak around sunset in North America and around sunrise in Europe. Having said this, peak time for paths between Europe and Central America is often around local midnight at the mid-point of the path, and therefore around 0200 or so European time. North-south paths, such as that between Europe and South Africa, frequently peak around midnight European time. In broad terms, DX working during the winter period tends to be more productive for stations in the northern hemisphere due to the longer hours of darkness and lower static levels. However, the converse is that this is the worst period for activity from the southern hemisphere and European DXers are increasingly recognising the need to be alert during the summer for activity from southern Africa, South America and even Australia.

Because of the uncertainty surrounding 1.8MHz propagation, and the way in which signal strengths can vary significantly over a short period, successful 1.8MHz DXing demands regular monitoring of the band, often at unsociable hours. For this reason it is not uncommon for 160m DXers to work together, each taking turns in monitoring, and agreeing to alert one another if a rare station becomes workable.

As mentioned above, 1.8MHz DXers typically use some sort of vertical antenna, which may be an inverted-L, a loaded vertical, or perhaps a shunt-fed tower. All such systems require an excellent earth system if reasonable efficiency is to be achieved. Details of suitable antenna systems can be found in references [4–9]. As ground-wave communication is more effective with vertically polarised antennas, the use of a vertical antenna will also enable good daylight distances to be achieved on 160m in addition to the DX capability.

The main limitation with vertical antennas is that they are more prone to noise pick-up than horizontal antennas. Serious 160m DXers therefore use separate receiving antennas. This may be a small tuned loop or, if space is available, a Beverage antenna. Neither is suitable for transmitting purposes, but both can give significant signal to noise enhancement on received signals.

Receiver performance is important on 160m, not so much in terms of absolute sensitivity but more in respect of being able to receive weak DX signals in the presence of very strong local signals on adjacent frequencies. Good intermodulation performance is therefore crucial. Although less common than it used to be, many DX stations and DXpeditions will operate 'split frequency', and in some cases split-frequency operation is essential due to differing frequency allocations (for example, Japanese stations operate only between 1907.5 and 1912.5kHz, but will usually listen around 1830kHz for European stations). The ability to operate 'split' is therefore essential. Most DX operation takes place on CW, and good-quality narrow CW filters make reception of weak signals that much easier. SSB DX working is, however, becoming more common as station improvements compensate for the inherent disadvantages of the mode (wider bandwidth and lower average power, resulting in significantly poorer signal-to-noise ratio than with CW, all other factors being equal).

160m has long been regarded as the 'gentleman's band', with users helping each other out and extending courtesy to one another. To an extent this is still true, though increasing levels of activity and competition have taken away some of the exclusiveness previously felt by 160m enthusiasts. Activity in the major contests can be especially frenetic and, although these are an opportunity for the newcomer to increase his tally of DX, they can be somewhat intimidating. Better, perhaps, to cut your teeth on working relatively common DX, for example European stations working the US, from where there is plenty of activity.

The IARU Region 1 Band Plan restricts SSB operation to frequencies above 1840kHz (which, given that LSB is used, means that the carrier frequency should be no lower than about 1842.5kHz), and the majority of CW activity takes place below 1840kHz. Because of the narrowness of the band, this split tends to be treated with flexibility in the major contests, but most Region 1 stations adhere to it at other times to the benefit of all users.

It should also be noted that, although 160m frequency allocations have been brought much more into harmony than was previously the case, there are still differences from country to country. The one band segment which is common to most users is 1810 to 1850kHz, which is why most DX activity takes place in this part of the band.

On CW, operating speed is very much dependent on conditions. If signals are strong each way, there is no reason why normal speeds of operation should not be used. Some stations advocate slower speeds when signals are weak, though often it is better to operate at normal speeds but with several repeats in the hope that at least one transmission will be heard through the noise or fading. Remember that band openings can be of short duration so, in fairness to other operators, contacts should be completed in the shortest possible time. Equally, it is unreasonable to work a rare station several times, on consecutive nights for example, when others are trying to make a first contact.

Most rare stations and DXpeditions nowadays will make at least some effort on 160m, although some are more prepared than others to cope with the more demanding operating and lower QSO rates than on the other HF bands. In some cases it can be productive to work a rare station on one of the higher bands and make a schedule for a 160m contact, but not all DX operators will be prepared to do this. In any case, do not waste their time unless you feel there is a good chance of making a contact at the time and on the frequency agreed.

Unfortunately there are few reliable propagation indicators for European stations on 1.8MHz, but activity is high enough nowadays for the presence and strength of DX stations to be used instead. The signal strengths of local and semi-local stations provide no guide at all to DX conditions. Careful listening can provide clues, and the occasional directional CQ at what ought to be an optimum propagation peak (for example a grey-line propagation path) can sometimes yield a call from a rare DX station.

Although significant parts of 160m are now primary amateur allocations, UK amateurs are still restricted to lower power levels above 1850kHz and must avoid interference to other non-amateur band users. In the segment 1810–1830kHz there continue to be non-UK commercial users and, again, amateurs should exercise restraint and avoid interference to these other services.

1.8MHz has always been regarded as a specialist DX challenge. The late W1BB, the first station to gain DXCC on the band, took many years to achieve his goal. Even though DX working on the band is now much more commonplace, 1.8MHz remains the most challenging of the HF bands, requiring persistence and perseverance to achieve competitive results.

3.5MHz (80m) band

This is a most useful band for local and near-European working during daylight hours and for longer-distance contacts after dark. In winter, particularly during the years when solar activity is low in the sunspot cycle, it is an excellent DX band, capable of providing worldwide communication on CW and SSB. In summer, transequatorial contacts with Oceania, the Pacific and Africa are possible and there are openings to other parts of the world. Timing is all-important and static can be a limiting factor during the summer months. Particular attention should be paid to the use of 'grey-line' or 'shadow-line' paths (see p45).

In Europe and some other parts of the world the band is allocated to amateurs on a shared basis, with military and commercial stations and specialised point-to-point services taking many of the available frequencies. This sharing results in high levels of interference from on-frequency blanketing, and also from receiver-generated spurious signals and cross-modulation caused by high-powered non-amateur stations working off-frequency. While many countries allow their amateurs to operate between 3.5 and 4.0MHz, Europe, including the UK, uses 3.5–3.8MHz.

For CW DX working, the bottom 30kHz are used, with the lower 10kHz being most favoured in accordance with the IARU Region 1 Band Plan. As the USA restricts the use of the 3500

to 3525kHz segment to Extra Class licensees, it is necessary to monitor above this segment for contacts with American amateurs who do not hold the higher licence. US Novices and Technicians may use CW between 3.7 and 3.75MHz. As with other bands, DXpeditions and 'rare' stations often use split-frequency working, listening for calls in a specified band of frequencies away from their transmit frequency.

The majority of DX working on phone is in the upper 20kHz of the European band (3780–3800kHz) although the band plan actually allows the upper 25kHz for this. When the band is open, DX contacts should always be given priority in this segment and ideally no local QSOs should take place at all to allow faint DX signals to be heard. Local contacts in this DX 'window' should also be avoided whenever the band is capable of supporting DX traffic to/from anywhere in Europe. In practice this means around the clock in December and January and from two hours before sunset to two hours after sunrise for the rest of the year.

For contacts with countries which are not permitted to use this segment, it is the custom to operate in the upper 10kHz of the band that is allocated to the DX country. Just as for CW working, the USA phone-band allocations are based on the class of licence held, and many of their amateurs are not allowed to work below 3775 or 3850kHz. For contacts with these stations it is necessary to work cross-band, viz non-USA stations below 3775kHz and USA stations above this frequency. At peak times when this band is open there is always substantial interference from a large number of stations working in a relatively small segment and it is often good practice for European stations to operate below 3750kHz and nominate the frequencies where they are listening for calls.

The introduction of the five-band DXCC awards and Worked All Zones has encouraged many more DX-minded operators to use the band and this has resulted in very substantial pile-ups of stations whenever a new or rare country appears. Some of these operators work split-frequency (particularly on CW), but on telephony the trend has been to use the list system (see p39). Many 3.5MHz operators dislike the list system, but it has become an established part of the scene and there is little that can be done, other than to persuade the DX station to adopt split-frequency working.

With simple antennas at moderate heights it is possible to take advantage of midwinter conditions and work into North America and other parts of the world during the hours of darkness. For more consistent DX working, some form of low-angle antenna is required and this is often the base-fed vertical radiator operated against ground. While a $\lambda/4$ vertical is capable of excellent performance, it can be quite inefficient unless the ground system is extensive, and being omni-directional and vertically polarised means it picks up more man-made noise and atmospheric static than a horizontal antenna. A further disadvantage is of course that it provides no directional discrimination against interference from amateur and non-amateur signals. Many amateurs who have plenty of ground area available use a vertical antenna for transmission in conjunction with highly directional low-angle receiving antennas such as the Beverage type. This is an ideal combination but not at all practical when space is at a premium.

In addition to the conventional vertical, another type of semi-vertical antenna is now finding favour with many users. This is the sloping dipole (usually called a *sloper*), and this is basically a vertical dipole mounted from a single support and sloped at an angle of approximately 45°. To reduce the height of the support mast, the lower half of the dipole is often bent so as to run parallel with the ground in the direction of the support mast. Slopers exhibit some directivity towards the slope and radiate at the low vertical angles suitable for long-distance working. It is possible to use more than one sloper mounted from the same support mast, and to phase the feed-lines to enhance the directivity characteristics and to provide electrical rotation of the polar pattern. Vertical antennas including slopers radiate little or no high-angle signals; they do not therefore perform well under daylight conditions when high-angle radiation is required.

Horizontally mounted dipoles and simple wire antennas radiate at too high a vertical angle unless the support height is at least λ/2 above ground. As few amateurs have the facilities to erect antennas in excess of 40m high, recourse is made to other configurations that work satisfactorily at lower support heights. The pulled-out single quad and delta-loop, particularly when corner-fed for vertical polarisation, have found favour with many operators and support heights of 13–15m have been proved to be effective for DX working. Although smaller non-resonant loops have been suggested by G6XN and others in *Radio Communication*, it is probably easier to use the 1λ loop and extend the horizontal sides to make up for the shorter vertical sections of the loop. If the support height and mast structure is not a problem and there is plenty of ground area available, then almost any type of horizontally polarised low-angle antenna will give good results. Some amateurs take the provision of specialised antennas to the extreme and erect complex phased arrays and rotary beams. In the USA it is even possible to purchase complete four-element rotary Yagi antennas for the band.

Earlier in this summary, mention was made of receiver-generated spurious signals and cross-modulation problems. Unfortunately, many of the older solid-state transceivers and receivers suffer from these defects as a result of non-linearity and insufficient dynamic range in the RF and mixer stages. Often the user may be unaware of the problem, as strong off-frequency and out-of-band commercial signals appear in-band, perhaps on a completely different frequency, due to the non-linear mixing process in the receiver. As most receivers have more gain than is required at 3.5MHz, passive preselectors comprising several loosely coupled ganged tuned circuits will usually provide some improvement. Front-end attenuators [11] are also helpful in reducing cross-modulation, but they are not usually as effective as the passive preselector in clearing up the spurious signals. Some valve receivers also suffer from the same problems and benefit from the addition of the passive extra tuned circuits and or a front-end attenuator.

The number of countries that could be contacted on the band was once relatively small in comparison with those available on the higher frequency bands. The Five-Band DXCC Award and Worked All Zones dramatically changed the situation and it is now much easier to achieve quite high country scores. A substantial number of operators have been able to contact in excess of 100 countries and there are some who have more than 200 countries confirmed for 3.5MHz CW and telephony working. A low-angle antenna system, a good receiver and an amount of single-minded persistence are needed, but for the newcomer to amateur radio and the operator who wishes to try a new band, DXing on the 3.5MHz band can be most rewarding.

7MHz (40m) band

The widely differing propagation conditions that exist on 7MHz during a 24-hour period, and the differences between winter and summer conditions, make this a very useful band for both local

and DX working. In many ways there is a marked similarity to 3.5MHz, with signal attenuation through ionospheric absorption being the main limiting factor for DX working. Other common factors are the 'grey line', dusk-dawn openings (see p45) and the band's shared nature, resulting in high levels of interference from non-amateur stations, although this situation has improved due to IARU/ITU action to remove 'intruders'.

During daylight hours, ionospheric absorption is high and the skip zone is very short or is non-existent, thus limiting communication to local contacts and distances of a few hundred kilometres. Around sunset, there are long-haul grey-line openings and, because attenuation is less than on 3.5MHz, these are longer in duration and signals are usually stronger than on the lower frequency. After dark, the skip zone lengthens and good medium-distance contacts are possible with North and South America, Asia and Africa. Because of the varied conditions that are found on the band, many operators regard 7MHz as the key to making a winning score in the RSGB Commonwealth Contest and other multi-band CW events.

The full band of 7.0–7.3MHz is not available to amateurs in Region 1 who are generally restricted to the 7.0–7.1MHz segment. The band is shared with broadcasting and at night, particularly during the winter months, the level of direct interference is high. This, together with cross-modulation problems and the likelihood of receiver-generated spurious signals from off-frequency broadcast stations, limits the frequencies available for amateur use. Under these crowded conditions, receiver performance is critical and the parameters outlined for 3.5MHz equally apply to this band. The use of front-end attenuators and or passive preselectors will help to alleviate the problem. The use of rotary directional antennas is becoming commonplace as, apart from providing extra gain, the semi-unidirectional pattern helps to reduce interference. While low-angle radiation is desirable, dipoles, loops and other horizontal antennas are very popular and are capable of providing good DX performance. Ground planes, base-fed verticals and 'slopers' are also widely used.

The IARU Region 1 Band Plan recommends that 7.0–7.04MHz is used for CW and that 7.04–7.1MHz is shared between phone and CW with a small segment for data. As a result of the high interference levels, most CW DX operators use the bottom 10kHz during the peak broadcasting hours up to midnight GMT. Later in the night and in the early morning hours, the interference is less and more of the band can be used for CW DX operation. For phone working the situation is worse and it is often a case of finding a gap between the broadcast stations. The segment between 7.07 and 7.09MHz is popular, and often intercontinental telephony contacts are possible on these frequencies during the peak broadcasting periods.

US phone operation commences on 7.15MHz for Advanced and Extra Class licensees and 7.225MHz for General Class. US Novices and Technicians may use 7.1–7.15MHz for CW.

10MHz (30m) band

Allocated for amateur use at the 1979 World Administrative Conference, over 200 countries, including the UK, permit their amateurs to use 10.100–10.150MHz on a shared basis. Most operation is on CW and IARU Region 1 has recommended that phone operation and contests be excluded. Contacts on the band do count for a number of awards such as IOTA, DXCC, Commonwealth CC, WAB and IARU Region 1.

Propagation reflects the characteristics of the adjacent 7 and 14MHz bands. In daytime the skip shortens as MUF rises but a skip zone generally persists all day except under exceptional sunspot maximum conditions. Absorption is lower than 7MHz. Under night-time conditions propagation can become world-wide as absorption falls, being best towards the dark sector and being enhanced at the onset of sunset or sunrise. Grey-line effects are very noticeable, offering worldwide propagation between, for example, the UK and the Far East or South Africa. During periods of sunspot minima long-range propagation can persist all day, such an effect being noticeable in the last sunspot minimum – this allowed propagation between the Far East and the UK in the mid-afternoon (UK time). Under such conditions the MUF may not rise much above 10MHz at any time of day.

Long-path propagation, especially to VK/ZL, occurs most mornings under undisturbed conditions. This path starts at around sunrise and can extend for up to two hours afterwards. The closure of this long path is often signalled by a short enhancement of Central American signals, followed by rapid closure of both paths. In order to exploit 10MHz propagation some form of grey-line calculator is useful (see p45).

A major problem on 10MHz is commercial interference. This confines most amateur activity to a series of narrow 'slots' centred on 10.102, 10.104 and 10.110MHz, for example. These 'slots' tend to move under the pressure of commercial stations. Interference tends to limit the development of amateur activity since stations operate on the band for a limited period and little regular usage occurs. This is especially true of DX stations. With 10MHz now counting for many awards, it is to be hoped that DXpeditions will make an appearance on the band and stimulate more regular activity.

The characteristics of the 10MHz band mean that it is suited to antenna and propagation experimentation, Compact directional antennas for reception and a better understanding of the many propagation modes will allow good DX results to be achieved by the average CW amateur.

14MHz (20m) band

This is the band which carries the main load of intercontinental communication throughout the whole of the sunspot cycle. There are very few days even at the time of sunspot minima and in the middle of winter when propagation is not available for at least some time into each continent. A result of this is that for much of the time the band is very congested, and this situation is made worse by the ITU regulation which permits stations of the fixed service in the CIS and other countries to use the 14,250–14,350kHz segment on a shared basis with amateurs.

The IARU Region 1 Band Plan recommends that 14,000–14,099kHz be reserved for CW use – with the area 14,070–14,099kHz being used for data communications. In the USA only stations with Extra Class licences are allowed to use 14,000–14,025kHz.

Particular care should be taken to avoid causing interference to the beacon chain on 14,100kHz. Packet operation should take place in the data sub-band, preferably in the upper half.

DXpedition stations often tend to use CW frequencies which are multiples of 5kHz above the lower band limit but rarely go above 14,050kHz, and 14,025kHz is perhaps the most widely used. They listen for replies a few kilohertz either side of their transmitting frequency and usually announce their tuning procedure.

The part of the band below 14,150kHz is not available to phone stations in the USA and is therefore often used by non-USA stations working each other or by non-USA stations working 'split-frequency' and listening in the American band for callers (this is often helpful when interference is heavy). At the lower end of the segment there are very often nets of French speaking stations – including those from all over the world as well as France itself. DXpeditions operating from areas other than those controlled by the USA usually transmit in this part of the band, and listen for callers from the USA above 14,200kHz and from elsewhere below that frequency in areas as announced from time to time. The most used DXpedition frequency is 14,195kHz, with 14,145kHz as second choice. The USA phone segment starts at 14,150kHz and the first 25kHz is reserved for those who have Extra Class licences. The Advanced Class phone section commences at 14,175kHz and the General Class at 14,225kHz. SSTV signals from all over the world will be found around 14,230kHz (see Chapter 9). The area above 14,300kHz is very often used by USA stations running 'phone patches' with servicemen overseas in those countries with which FCC regulations permit third-party communication. This area is also favoured by a number of special interest group nets.

18MHz (17m) band

Allocated for amateur use at the 1979 World Administrative Radio Conference but only released for service some years later, this band is now very popular with some excellent DX around; most DXpeditions provide some operation on it. However, although commercial multiband beams are available for the band, many stations still use dipoles, especially if they have already put up, say, a triband Yagi for 14/21/28MHz, and this does limit the number of strong signals around.

As already mentioned earlier, propagation is similar to the 14 and 21MHz bands, and the band is a useful 'half-way' house – some stations have been known to move up from the crowded 14MHz band on days when the MUF makes this possible.

The IARU Region 1 Band Plan recommends that the segment 18.068–18.100 is reserved for CW use only, with the area 18.101–18.108 for data modes and CW. Phone operation is allowed from 18.111–18.168MHz.

21MHz (15m) band

This is a favourite band with many HF operators, with more space than the crowded 14MHz band, but significantly more reliable than 28MHz except perhaps near sunspot maxima.

The IARU Region 1 Band Plan recommends that the segment 21,000–21,149kHz be reserved for CW use with the area 21,080–21,120kHz for data operation. DX on CW, although fairly evenly distributed in the first 75kHz or so, tends to be heaviest around 21,025kHz, this being a popular frequency for DXpeditions. It is the calling frequency of the FOC (First Class Operators' Club) and is the upper limit of the CW frequency allocation exclusive to the Extra Class licensees of the USA. Contest stations usually operate in the first 50kHz of this segment although in the bigger contests they may spread up to the proximity of 21,100kHz. The rest of the Region 1 CW sub-band falls within the USA Novice allocation (21,100–21,200kHz) and is mainly used for working the USA. When conditions are good this part of the band is very crowded and is therefore one of the simplest indicators of propagation into North America.

Moving up the band, SSB signals commence around 21,151kHz with German and French language stations showing a preference for DX work around the lower end. When conditions are good SSB signals may be heard from the low-power Australian Novice stations in the segment 21,151–21,200kHz. As it is outside the USA phone allocation, '151 to

'200kHz is often used by DX stations particularly wishing to work Europe, including Canadians, Central and South Americans. When DX propagation is poor but short skip is possible this part of the band is used for inter-European working.

The USA phone segment commences at 21,200kHz and when conditions are good very strong signals are heard from USA Extra Class licensees who have the exclusive use of the first 25kHz in their country. The segment '250 to '350kHz is usually very crowded at weekends and tends to attract high-powered stations. The station with more modest means is therefore advised to operate in the '350 to '450kHz segment when working into the USA. The Advanced Class phone section starts at 21,225kHz and the General Class at 21,300kHz.

SSTV signals are occasionally heard around 21,340kHz and some 'phone patching' takes place in the area above 21,400kHz, the top 50kHz often being used by Americans living abroad to work stations back home.

Over the years both USA and non-USA DXpedition stations have tended to use 21,295–21,300kHz for their operations, but recently DXpeditions operating from areas other than those controlled by the USA seem to favour frequencies around 21,195kHz and 21,245kHz for this purpose, announcing their listening frequencies for various areas from time to time.

24MHz (12m) band

Allocated for amateur use at the 1979 World Administrative Radio Conference, this band is admittedly not very popular during years of sunspot minimum. Like the 18MHz band, it also suffers from a lack of beam antennas in use. However, it can provide communication on days when the 28MHz band is quiet, and should not be overlooked.

The IARU Region 1 Band Plan reserves 24.890–24.919MHz for CW operation, with data operation from 24.920–24.928MHz. Phone operation takes place from 24.931–24.990MHz.

28MHz (10m) band

The 28MHz band is on the borderline between HF and VHF. Indeed, some authorities allow the band to be used by operators who might elsewhere be regarded as licensed for VHF only. Of course the delineation between HF and VHF, specified by definition at 30MHz, is man-made and Nature draws no such firm division. It is this location in the spectrum which gives the band, sometimes described as "the band of surprises", the variability which is one of its attractions.

As at VHF, high power is by no means necessary to operate long ranges. It is generally accepted that if a path exists at all then 10W, say, in the CW mode and little (if any) more of SSB will achieve satisfactory communication. Indeed, contact with almost all the USA call areas has been made with 200mW. The smaller size of antenna elements for this band allows the construction of compact, efficient installations. It is interesting to note that the simple ground-plane performs well, especially for the sporadic-E (Es) or short-skip conditions which can produce good coverage of Europe from the UK during the summer (May–September). It will be seen that these features, coupled with the wide frequency range available, make it a very good band for relatively simple and inexpensive stations.

The band is much more dependent on solar activity than the 14 and 21MHz bands, but it is to be regretted that the majority of operators desert it during the years around sunspot minimum. Those who continue to use it through these periods are often surprised at the paths which appear from time to time. To work 100 countries during the lean years can be a stimulating

challenge. While, as in the lower HF allocations, propagation from the UK tends to swing from the east in the morning to the west in the afternoon, paths to many parts of the world will often exist simultaneously and WAC in five minutes working is by no means a rare feat.

Although, again speaking generally, propagation requires daylight over most if not all the path, DX contacts may still be made during the hours of darkness. It may well be that the few contacts recorded under these conditions would be increased in numbers if operators did not take such a dogmatic view of 28MHz propagation possibilities, but checked the band at times when experts say there will be no signals and also transmitted a 'CQ'. The same suggestion holds good also for the years around sunspot minimum. As an aside, evening propagation to the southern states of the USA can sometimes happen when the operators at both ends point beams to the South Atlantic. Frustration occurs when the distant station does not realise this is necessary and turns to the direct bearing, and then considers the contact lost. Apart from E and F propagation, the band performs in a similar manner to that of 50 and 144MHz and signals can be ducted over quite long distances under 'lift' conditions. Extended ground-wave contacts over distances of several hundred miles are commonplace via ducting.

The IARU Region 1 Band Plan for the 28MHz band follows a similar pattern to those for the other HF bands. That is to say, the lower frequencies from 28.0–28.05 and 28.15–28.20MHz are reserved for CW, with a band of 100kHz centred on 28.10MHz allocated for CW and data shared use. The remainder of the band, 28.20–29.70MHz, is available for both CW and phone, though, as might be expected, CW operation centres on the portion below 28.20MHz. A small 10kHz band centred on 28.68MHz is recommended for SSTV working. The band plan recommends that beacons use the 28.190–28.225MHz segment. This segment should never be used for normal communication. The FCC permits Novice and Technician licensees to use 28.1–28.3MHz for CW and data, and 28.3–28.5MHz for CW/SSB, and restricts other USA phone stations to above 28.30MHz. During years of high solar flux this last division causes non-American phone operators to spread either below 28.30MHz or well up the band, eg 28.90MHz and upwards, to avoid USA interference. Towards sunspot minimum, random phone operation tends to be conducted between 28.50–28.80MHz.

Stations using low-power AM and FM may be heard above 28.80MHz. The RSGB recommends that FM activity should take place between 29.60–29.69MHz, with 29.6MHz as the calling frequency. In the USA 29.6MHz is also the FM simplex calling frequency, and there are 29MHz FM repeaters with outputs at 29.620, 29.640, 29.660 and 29.680MHz (inputs are 100kHz lower in each case).

A specialist aspect of the 28MHz band is concerned with amateur space service communication and the sub-band 29.30–29.50MHz has been recommended for amateur satellite downlink use (see Chapter 7).

The availability of synthesised FM CB equipment that can be easily converted for 29MHz operation has encouraged many mobile operators to use the band both for DX and local working.

LOW-POWER DXING

In a real sense most amateur radio operation is low powered when compared against the usual commercial power allowances. The maximum power allowed varies from country to country and in some cases according to the class of the licence, amateurs in many parts of the world looking with envy on the kilowatt 'big guns' of the radio amateur world. However, there has always been within the hobby a group of amateurs who specialise in low-power (QRP) working. This aspect of the hobby has been increasing in popularity in recent years, as readers of the amateur radio journals will have noticed.

There are good reasons for this movement towards using low power. Running low power gives more challenge and increases the reliance on actual operating skills to achieve reasonable results. W9SCH has called QRP operation "the sportsman's amateur radio" and certainly many experienced DX operators have turned to low-power working for the challenge.

Some operators offer an ethical explanation for their low-power work. In these days of crowded amateur bands, it is more reasonable to use only the minimum power requirements to complete a contact. It is difficult to be a bully with only a few watts.

Finally, many amateurs see low-power DXing as an inexpensive approach to the hobby. Although the modern tendency is perhaps to consider spending a couple of thousands of pounds on commercial equipment, it is possible to achieve good results on the amateur bands by spending only a few pounds on low-power equipment. It must be admitted that there is a certain feeling of glee when working a station with a kilowatt and a quad antenna with an inexpensive 2W transmitter, but this is not to suppose that QRP operators rely upon the power and sophistication of the other man's equipment to maintain a solid contact. Many QRP operators are keen to work other low-powered stations and this type of contact forms a large part of such operators' aspirations.

What is QRP?

Opinion as to what constitutes low-power operation varies. In the USA powers of under 100W are considered to be QRP. The G-QRP Club uses 5W DC input as the power limit under which a station may be said to be QRP, while for contests IARU Region 1 defines QRP as 10W input and QRPp as 1W. In the USA the term 'QRPp' is often used for powers of 5W and less.

An input power of 5W or less would appear to place severe restrictions upon what might be achieved on the amateur bands, but the power level is not the disadvantage it may appear at first glance. Obviously the station is weaker, but in theoretical S-point terms the reduction is not so great. Assuming 6dB per S-point, a power ratio/dB chart will show that reducing power four times will only give a 6dB, or one S-point drop in signal level. Therefore a reduction from 150W DC input to 37.5W gives in theory only a single S-point loss. A station using 5W input can expect to be 15dB down, or about two and a half S-points, on a station using 150W input. Naturally these are only theoretical figures and are variable by such factors as efficient matching and high-gain antennas. In terms of increased signal strength a simple increase in power is therefore an inefficient method of obtaining results.

What can be achieved with such low power?

Recent results by low-power operators have shown that they consider their restricted power as no real barrier to real DX working. QRP awards are earnestly sought after and some individual results are worthy of mention. In the annual G-QRP Club Winter Sports between 26 December and 1 January 1992, Chris Page, G4BUE, operated as GB0QRP using 5W output from a Ten Tec Argonaut II. In that short period he had 476 two-way QRP QSOs, where both stations ran 5W or less. 62

DXCC countries were worked including: 8P, BV, HI, J7 (7MHz), KL7 (10MHz), KP4, SU (10MHz), VP5, VS6, VU and ZA. AA2U, NG1G, W3TS and N4AR were all worked two-way QRP on eight bands. No description of QRP DXing is complete without a mention of George Burt, GM3OXX, who has worked over 200 countries using less than one watt from all-home-built equipment with a simple wire antenna.

Equipment for low-power operation

It is probably true to say that the majority of QRP operators use home-built equipment. Circuits for such equipment appear in the various amateur radio journals, and especially in the G-QRP Club journal *Sprat*. Such equipment can be built to suit the amateur's expertise and pocket [30–36].

Low-power operation is mainly on CW, so simple equipment is capable of useful results. The serious operator, however, really requires a VFO-controlled transmitter and a good-quality receiver, if two-way QRP contacts are contemplated. He has to use extra cunning and skill to secure contacts, therefore simple-to-use equipment with full break-in facilities and incremental receiver tuning is ideal. Transceivers reduce the time required to call a station, and today's crowded bands demand a bandwidth filter, if only of a simple audio type. The low-powered station must not be hampered by difficult-to-use, inefficient equipment.

The recent increase in QRP operation has produced and even been fostered by several commercial transceivers. The Heath Company produced the HW7, HW8 and HW9 transceivers which are still available on the second-hand market. The Ten Tec Company in the USA produced a range of direct-conversion transceivers in the 'seventies with the 'PM' prefix coding. Ten Tec also produced the Argonaut range of SSB/CW transceivers and currently manufacture the Scout, a modular transceiver with a QRP option. MFJ Enterprises manufacture a small range of CW QRP transceivers and the Travel Radio, a 20m SSB transceiver. A new manufacturer of QRP equipment are Index Laboratories with their QRP PLUS, an all-band, all-mode, synthesised transceiver. In the UK many QRP operators used equipment built from kits produced by companies such as C M Howes, Lake, Kanga Products, Walford Electronics and Hands Electronics.

Antennas for low-power operation

In QRP circles the keenest discussion probably occurs on the subject of antennas and their matching. This subject should be close to the heart of all radio amateurs but, when using reduced power, valuable extra gain may be achieved by the antenna, and correct matching is essential to reduce losses of precious power. Anyone contemplating QRP operation is advised to read the standard works on antennas mentioned in Chapter 2.

An interesting fact about QRP operation is that most of the best-known and successful operators use only simple wire antennas. GM3OXX uses a dipole to work Australasia with 2W and G8PG and G3DNF have a history of good results only using various types of simple wire antenna. Good results have been obtained with random lengths of wire, but efficient matching between transmitter and antenna is essential. An antenna tuning unit is regarded as an important item for the low-power operator and many designs have been published in QRP journals, although circuits designed for high-power use are also used. The G-QRP Club have produced the *G-QRP Antenna Handbook*, available from the RSGB, which contains antennas and antenna matching circuits used by many QRP operators.

Another important item is an SWR meter or a meter for

Victor Brand, G3JNB, has this QRP station constructed from popular kits

indicating forward and reverse antenna current. There are several models on the commercial market, although this is an easy-to-build item of equipment. Solid-state transmitters are invariably difficult to tune to optimum output by metering the current input to the power amplifier. It is more usual in QRP work to tune for maximum output to the antenna and match the transmitter and antenna by reading the lowest attainable reflected power.

Low-power operating modes

Most QRP operating is CW, with its obvious advantages of simplicity and effective range-to-power ratio. SSB operation has, however, come into more general use with the production of commercial SSB QRP equipment. Equipment is readily available for SSB QRP operation and several operators have achieved DXCC with 5W or less.

In recent years many more constructors have built their own SSB equipment. Hands Electronics and Walford Electronics have both produced kits for building SSB transceivers. In the USA there has been considerable interest in the single-signal direct-conversion boards designed by Rick Campbell, KK7B. These use phasing techniques to produce good performance SSB transceivers for any band.

Operating with low power

All radio amateurs ought to study the propagation patterns outlined earlier in this chapter to make full use of prevailing conditions, but for the QRP operator these conditions may make the difference between establishing a contact or not. In fact low-power transmissions are used in some forms of propagation study.

A useful rule of thumb is to use the highest-frequency HF band that is open for which one has equipment and a good antenna. The adverse effects of absorption from the D layer is an inverse square of the frequency in use during the hours of daylight. After sunset the MUF (maximum usable frequency) falls, making 3.5MHz and 1.8MHz the most useful night-time and winter-evening QRP bands, although some useful work can be done if one dares to take low power on the crowded 7MHz band.

DX and long-range work bring into play the problems of radiation angles and skip distances from the very active F layers. Changes in the F layers as reflecting planes are very dynamic and only experience coupled with a general knowledge of propagation patterns can really determine the optimum paths for QRP work at various times on the HF bands. Although several paths may appear to be open from listening to incoming signals, many long-distance paths seem to show optimum propagation conditions in only one direction. The operator has to determine which outgoing path is open and this may well not be the one with the strongest incoming signals.

An example common to many operators is observed in the east-west path. On 14MHz, the 'your sunset, his sunrise' period appears to give the best results. However, the movements of the F2 layer appear to follow the Sun's path very closely. It is common to find that when the 14MHz band first begins to open to the west, the first weak signals appear to be the easiest ones to work. It is for example easier to work the first low-strength USA stations early in the evening with 2W on 14MHz, than to work S9-plus USA stations when the band appears to be really open (see also p48). It is also easier to work transequatorial than transpolar. Some QRP operators keep a propagation log – not a bad idea.

It might be said that operating technique and skill has to increase in inverse proportion to the available RF power. The key words for QRP operation are 'patience' and 'cunning' – the operator has to win his contacts. Like any good DX operator he must spend a lot of his time listening to the signals on the band, getting to know who is there and who they are working. A survey of DX operators conducted some time ago showed that they spent about 95% of their time listening and only 5% transmitting. Naturally this applies to operators who are looking for specific contacts, but the ratio of listening to transmitting should be high for reasonable results with low power. Another general tip is not to 'think QRP' and expect to do badly on the bands, but to assume that one is 'in with a chance' for most contacts.

Low-power operation often takes place around the international QRP frequencies of 3560, 7030, 14,060, 21,060 and 28,060kHz plus 1850kHz in the UK.

Calling CQ can be a waste of time with low signal strength; it is far better to call a specific station either in response to his CQ or at the end of an existing contact. When QRP is being worked both ways in skeds or on the international QRP frequencies, then calling "CQ QRP" is reasonable. Otherwise look for strong stations as they are probably the ones with the beams and sophisticated equipment best suited for the reception of low signal strength.

'Tail-ending' is a common practice for most QRP operators. Obviously it is wise to look for a station in contact with another station in a geographically close country. This indicates that a path does exist to your area and if a beam is being used it will be pointing in the right direction. Tail-ending involves speed, for the required station may decide to change frequencies and must be 'caught' while still listening on the frequency. Allow for the closing exchanges between the two stations in contact. The contact may close with an extra exchange of "73" or dit-dit, and if the station you are aiming for is working a local station, you may not be able to hear the local station due to the skip zone. This requires some judgement as to when to make the tail-end call. Full break-in facilities are a great asset in tail-ending. Breaking in to an existing contact is not advised. Not only is this bad manners, but the chances of a weak signal breaking through are slight. When calling the required station, either match his operating speed or send slightly slower to allow for clear reading of the signal. Sending above the speed of the other station is just 'showing off' and may frighten off the other station or render a weak signal unreadable.

It is not a good practice to use 'QRP' as a suffix when making a call. In the UK it is illegal to sign '/QRP'. If a specific station is required and is calling for DX, the technique of a rapid call followed by "QRP RPT PSE" sometimes brings results.

Conduct the contact in the usual way, but maintain only short overs, unless it is clear that one's signal strength is high with the other station. If possible avoid giving the other station information about one's power until his report has been received. It is surprising how much better reports are if the other station does not believe he is working a low-power station. Expect strength reports of S4 to 7 as normal – very few S9s will be given to QRP stations, except for the conventional and inaccurate 599 given in rapid contest working.

One of the real delights of QRP working is the kindly response it evokes from many operators. Remarks like "FB UR QRP SIGS" or "GUD SIGS FER QRP" are very common. Some operators are even known to 'turn down the wick' at their end and attempt to return the QRP signal! Do not be ashamed to be using low power as it usually gains respect from other operators.

Working DX in literal terms of 'long distance' is a matter of propagation study and use of conditions, dealt with earlier. DX in terms of rare stations is another matter in that the competition is greater. Rare stations attract a lot of attention and one may have to contend with the DX pile-up of calling stations. A station with low signal strength has obvious disadvantages in such situations, but may still be able to compete.

In a DX pile-up, the low-power station is probably at the end of the line, and must use all the usual techniques of frequency shifting and rapid calls. Many DX stations call by areas and this may give the QRP station a better chance. Do not call out of turn, which is not only bad practice but pointless with low power.

The DX pile-up can provide an extra bonus for the QRP operator. While half the amateur world is hunting after one station, move up or down the band and see which stations may be present on a clearer frequency. Some stations which are not DX for a normal station, but are DX for QRP, may be seeking contacts away from the pile-up.

'DX' may for the QRP operator take on the more literal meaning of distant stations or apply to prefixes yet to be worked with low power. This naturally begins with the extra patience required to seek specific stations or call areas. Look for the 'big' DX station, for he has the resources to work a low-power station. Listen to see if the required station is working other stations in one's own geographical area, and what sort of reports these stations are being given. Take into consideration that your signal will be two or three S-points down. In a band with a high noise level the problems are even more acute.

It is important to call the station on frequency, because a DX station with a 600Hz CW filter may not be able to hear a station calling off frequency. Try to zero beat with the station. This is a simple matter with independent transmitter and receiver systems, but with transceivers receiver incremental tuning (RIT) or VFO offset is important. It is then vital to know, by experience or experimentation, the degree of offset offered by such a control, which may vary from band to band. The careful operator will know where his signal is located in respect to the other signals he can hear.

Snappy operating procedure may be vital. Full break-in facilities can enable the operator to call quickly and gain the initial attention of the other station, and perhaps even monitor other calling stations. Imitate the speed and methods of the required station. If he is making quick calls such as "QRZ DE XXXX", reply with a simple "XXXX DE G3--- BK". Although a long slow call is suitable for low-power operation, in quick operating situations another station may have gained the contact before one's own call has been sent a couple of times.

Always note the time and frequency of a required DX station and try the same time and frequency again. This often seems to work. With low-power operation, one frequently has to weigh available time against probability in securing a contact with a particular station. Having failed to secure a contact after several attempts, realistically assess the chances of one against the possibility of finding other suitable contacts on the band. The QRP enthusiast must expect to use more time per contact than other operators, so available time for operating must be used to the best advantage.

QSL card returns may on the other hand be somewhat easier for the low-power station. Most DX stations are happy to work a low-power station and will be pleased to confirm the contact. Boldly mark the card "QRP" and "TWO WATTS INPUT" or whatever.

QRP organisations

There are many international clubs serving the low-power DX operator [37–40]. The G-QRP Club now has over 5000 members in 54 countries and publishes a quarterly journal, *Sprat*. In order to promote low-power operation these clubs also organise awards and contests – some further details are given in the relevant section of this chapter and in Chapter 5. *Radio Communication* has a bi-monthly QRP column.

HF AWARDS

As QSL cards from DX stations come flooding in (hopefully!) the operator naturally begins to consider progress towards one of the many attractive operating awards and certificates available from national societies and other organisations all over the world.

Depending on its 'difficulty', the acquisition of one of these certificates can be a real milestone in an amateur's operating activities, and something to display proudly on the shack wall for many a year.

The first step is to obtain a copy of the complete rules from the organiser of the award. If this is a national society then the addresses given in Appendix 2 may be used for this purpose. When requesting rules of overseas awards always include a large self-addressed envelope and three IRCs. All correspondence should include return postage. Allow a reasonable time for a reply, especially to a query about rules – the awards manager has to do this work in his spare time!

The rules should then be read carefully. Some awards require

```
John Smith, G9ZZZ
4 High Street
Notown
Blankshire
England
                         Application for the ZZZ award class 1

Endorsed all 14MHz, all 2X ssb

Date            GMT        Station     His signals    My signals    Band     Mode
13 August 99    1234       G7AS            59             59         14       2X ssb
15 August 99    0750       G7CX            55             46         14       2X ssb
    .            .            .             .              .           .        .
    .            .            .             .              .           .        .
    .            .            .             .              .           .        .
23 August 99    1453       G7NN            59             56         14       2X ssb

Certified that I have complied with my licence regulations

3 September 99                                            John Smith, G9ZZZ

                                                         John Smith
```

Fig 10. Suggested layout for awards application

special application forms but even if this is not necessary, a fairly standard sort of layout is always helpful to the awards manager dealing with the claim. He is invariably doing the job on a voluntary basis and a clear statement of exactly what is being claimed cuts down the amount of work involved. Always print your name and address in block capitals and if possible type the application. An easy and clear method of application is shown in Fig 10.

Full details of the RSGB HF awards and brief notes on some of the other popular DX awards are given below but it should be realised that awards are available from most national societies and a complete listing is well beyond the scope of this book.

There are a variety of certificated and trophy awards offered for the low-power operator by the G-QRP Club (see p57). The most popular of these are the QRP Countries Award, which begins with a basic 25 countries confirmed and the G2NJ Trophy, which is awarded on a three-year cycle for various QRP achievements. The awards and contest manager for the G-QRP Club is G8PG. The American QRPARCI also have an awards scheme, the most popular being the 1,000 Miles Per Watt Award. The awards manager is WA8CNN.

For details of VHF, UHF and microwave awards available to UK amateurs, see p80.

RSGB awards

DX Listeners' Century Award (DXLCA)

This award may be claimed by any shortwave listener eligible under the General Rules who can produce evidence of having heard amateur radio stations located in at least 100 DXCC countries. Stickers are available for every 25 additional countries confirmed. Submit a list in radio prefix order with the callsign and country name.

Endorsements are available for hearing 100 countries on 5, 6, 7, 8 and 9 bands (they need not be the same countries on each band).

Commonwealth Century Club (CCC)

This award may be claimed by any licensed radio amateur eligible under the General Rules who can produce evidence of having contacted, since 15 November 1945, amateur radio stations in at least 100 Commonwealth call areas on the list current at the time of application.

The certificate holder may claim, on payment of a contributory charge, a handsome plaque with a plate detailing name, callsign, date and number of the award. Additionally, an amateur providing evidence of having contacted all the Commonwealth call areas on the list current at the time of application may claim the Supreme Plaque in recognition of the magnitude of the achievement, again on payment of a contributory charge.

Notes:
(a) Credit for South Georgia and the South Sandwich Is will only be given for contacts with stations using a VP8 callsign. Credit for Antarctica and the South Orkney and South Shetland Is will only be given for contacts with stations using a callsign issued by a Commonwealth government.
(b) Where, very occasionally, a contact is made with a station using a callsign legitimately outside the geographical area to which the prefix normally applies, it will count for the actual area from which the operation took place. The evidence submitted will need to be clear.

5 Band Commonwealth Century Club (5BCCC)

This award, available in five classes, may be claimed by any licensed radio amateur under the General Rules who can produce evidence of having effected two-way communication, since 15 November 1945, with the requisite number of amateur radio stations located in the call areas listed, using all five bands, 3.5, 7, 14, 21, and 28 MHz. Each station should be located in a different call area per band. The five classes are for contacts as follows:

5BCCC Supreme	500 stations
5BCCC Class 1	450 stations
5BCCC Class 2	400 stations, with a minimum of 50 on each band
5BCCC Class 3	300 stations, with a minimum of 40 on each band
5BCCC Class 4	200 stations, with a minimum of 30 on each band

Certificates will be issued to winners of all classes. Additionally, as in the case of the CCC, winners of the Class 1 award will be eligible to claim a handsome plaque suitably inscribed on payment of a contributory charge, while winners of the

GENERAL RULES FOR RSGB HF AWARDS

The following general rules and conditions apply to HF certificates and awards issued by the Radio Society of Great Britain and should be read in conjunction with the conditions which govern the particular award programme:

Applicant eligibility

1. Claimants from the UK, Channel Is, and Isle of Man must be members of the RSGB and, as proof of membership, should provide a recent address label from *Radio Communication*. Applicants from elsewhere need not be members of the RSGB.
2. Claimants may be either licensed radio amateurs or short wave listeners. All certificates, but not special plaques, are available on a 'heard' basis to listeners.

Claim eligibility

3. Each claim must be submitted in a form acceptable to the HF Awards Manager. Where application forms are provided for particular award programmes, these should be used although a computer generated form including the same headings will generally be accepted. Each claim must include the following signed declaration: *"I declare that all the contacts were made by me personally from the same DXCC country and in accordance with the terms of my radio transmitting licence, and that none of the QSLs have been amended in any way since receipt. I accept that a breach of these rules may result in disqualification from the awards programme. I further accept that the decision of the HF Committee shall be final in all cases of dispute."*
4. All claims from within the UK, Channel Is and Isle of Man must be accompanied by QSL cards. Claims from elsewhere must also be accompanied by QSL cards but only in the case of those categories of award attracting a plaque. In all other cases a statement from the applicant's national society that the necessary cards have been checked will be accepted except that the HF Awards Manager reserves the right to ask to see some or all of the cards. For IOTA claims special rules apply (see the *IOTA Directory*).
5. Each claim must be accompanied by a fee of £3.00 or $US 6.00 or 9 IRCs per certificate or class of certificate. Applicants submitting cards for checking must include sufficient payment to cover their return. Cards will only be returned by air, recorded delivery (UK only), or registered mail (overseas) if adequate postage is enclosed. (For registered mail add US$ 4.50 or 7 IRCs).

Contact eligibility

6. All contacts must be made by the holder of the callsign.
7. Contacts may be made from any location in the same DXCC country.
8. Except where otherwise indicated, credit will be given for confirmed contacts made on or after 15 November 1945 on any of the 9 amateur bands below 30MHz.
9. Contacts with land mobile stations will be accepted, provided the location at the time of contact is clearly stated on the QSL card.
10. Credit will be given for two way contacts on the same mode and band, ie not cross-mode or cross-band. Certificate endorsements for single mode transmission and/or single band may be made on the submission of cards clearly confirming the mode or frequency of transmission, but the request must be made at the time of application. Special rules apply for IOTA.

Disqualification

11. The submission for credit of any altered or forged confirmations or, equally, bad behaviour on or off the air which is judged by the HF Committee to bring a particular programme into disrepute may result in disqualification of the applicant from all RSGB's award programmes. The decision of the HF Committee on this and other matters of dispute will be final.

Applications for awards (other than IOTA)

All claims, except IOTA, should be sent to:

> RSGB HF Awards Manager,
> F C Handscombe, G4BWP,
> 'Sandholm',
> Bridge End Road,
> Red Lodge,
> Bury St. Edmunds,
> Suffolk IP28 8LQ.

Prepare your application in accordance with the requirements of the award being claimed. Send QSL cards when required, and do not forget to enclose details of your name, callsign and full address as well as the certificate fee, adequate postage for the return of QSL cards, and for UK applicants, proof of RSGB membership. Payment may be made by cheque drawn on a UK bank or Eurocheque written in pounds sterling and payable to 'Radio Society of Great Britain'.

Supreme Award will be able to claim an engraved plaque on payment of a contributory charge.

WARC Bands Endorsement

A holder of the basic award who can provide evidence of contact with the required number of call areas on the 10, 18 and 24MHz bands may claim a WARC Band 'sticker' endorsement. This is available in five classes as follows:

5BCCC (WARC)	Supreme	300 call areas
5BCCC (WARC)	Class 1	275 call areas
5BCCC (WARC)	Class 2	250 call areas, with a minimum of 50 on each band
5BCCC (WARC)	Class 3	200 call areas, with a minimum of 40 on each band
5BCCC (WARC)	Class 4	150 call areas, with a minimum of 30 on each band

Note: on 10MHz credit will only be given for contacts on CW.

Top Band Endorsement

A holder of the basic award who can produce evidence of

contact with the required number of call areas on the 1.8MHz band may claim a Top Band 'sticker' endorsement. This is available in five classes for 30, 40, 50, 60 and 70 call areas.

Credit for deleted Commonwealth call areas

Credit will be given for contacts with stations in Commonwealth countries at the time of contact, and additionally, with stations using a Commonwealth callsign in Antarctic and the S Orkney and S Shetland Is. Since 1945 some countries have left the Commonwealth, while others have joined. The list of call areas specifies the relevant dates. For 5BCCC (including endorsements) contacts with 'deleted' call areas made at a time when the countries concerned were in the Commonwealth may count in place of 'missing' credits on any band up to the maximum possible for that band. Deleted call areas do not count for CCC.

List of deleted Commonwealth call areas

Contacts with the following may count for a 'missing' credit if made before the date specified. A contact after that date may still count for one of the Commonwealth call areas (see brackets).

AC3	Sikkim	1 May 1975 (India)
P2, VK9	Papua Territory	16 September 1975 (PNG)
P2, VK9	Territory of New Guinea	16 September 1975 (PNG)
VO	Newfoundland, Labrador	1 April 1949 (Newfoundland, Canada)
VQ1	Zanzibar	25 April 1964 (Tanzania)
VQ6	British Somaliland	1 July 1960
VQ9	Aldabra Is	29 June 1976 (Seychelles)
VQ9	Desroches Island	29 June 1976 (Seychelles)
VQ9	Farquhar Group	29 June 1976 (Seychelles)
VS2, 9M2	Malaya	16 September 1963 (W Malaysia)
VS4	Sarawak	16 September 1963 (E Malaysia)
VS9	Aden	1 December 1967
VS9	Kamaran Island	1 December 1967
VS9	Kuria Muria Is	1 December 1967
ZC5	British North Borneo	16 September 1963 (E Malaysia)
ZD4	Gold Coast, Togoland	6 March 1957 (Ghana)
ZS1	Cape District, SA	1 June 1961
ZS2	Cape Province (exc ZS1)	1 June 1961
ZS2	Marion, Prince Edward	1 June 1961
ZS4	Orange Free State, SA	1 June 1961
ZS5	Natal, SA	1 June 1961
ZS6	Transvaal, SA	1 June 1961
3D2	Fiji	15 October 1987
3D2	Rotuma Is	15 October 1987

Applications for CCC and 5BCCC

Applications for 5BCCC should use the special application form available from the HF Awards Manager. The form allows space for callsigns to be recorded for contacts on each band. A check list of current Commonwealth call areas is also available and can be used for applications for the CCC Award. Please send an A5 size SAE for the check list and application forms.

28MHz Counties Award

This award may be claimed by any licensed radio amateur eligible under the General Rules who can produce evidence of having effected two-way communication, since 1 April 1983, with amateur radio stations located in 40 counties/regions in the UK, Channel Islands and Isle of Man on the 28MHz band. Stickers are available for 60 and all 77 counties/regions confirmed.

Worked ITU Zones (WITUZ)

This award may be claimed by any licensed radio amateur eligible under the General Rules who can produce evidence of having contacted, since 15 November 1945, land-based amateur radio stations in at least 70 of the 75 broadcasting zones as defined by the International Telecommunications Union (ITU).

The certificate holder may claim, on payment of a contributory charge, a handsome plaque with a plate detailing name, callsign, date and number of the award. Additionally, an amateur providing evidence of having contacted all 75 ITU zones may claim the Supreme Plaque in recognition of the magnitude of the achievement, again on payment of a contributory charge.

5 Band Worked ITU Zones (5BWITUZ)

This card, available in five classes, may be claimed by any licensed radio amateur eligible under the General Rules who can produce evidence of having contacted, since 15 November 1945, the required number of land-based amateur radio stations located in the 75 ITU broadcasting zones, using all five bands, 3.5, 7, 14, 21, and 28 MHz. Each station should be located in a different ITU zone per band. The five classes are for contacts as follows:

5BWITUZ Supreme	350 zones
5BWITUZ Class 1	325 zones
5BWITUZ Class 2	300 zones, with a minimum of 50 on each band
5BWITUZ Class 3	250 zones, with a minimum of 40 on each band
5BWITUZ Class 4	200 zones, with a minimum of 30 on each band

Certificates will be issued to winners of all classes. Also, as in the case of the WITUZ, winners of the Class 1 award may claim a handsome plaque suitably inscribed, while winners of the Supreme Award will be eligible for the Supreme Plaque, both on payment of a contributory charge.

WARC Band Endorsement

A holder of the basic award who can produce evidence of contact with the required number of ITU zones on the 10, 18 and 24MHz bands may claim a WARC Band 'sticker' endorsement. This is available in five classes as follows:

5BWITUZ (WARC)	Supreme	210 zones
5BWITUZ (WARC)	Class 1	195 zones
5BWITUZ (WARC)	Class 2	180 zones, with a minimum of 50 on each band
5BWITUZ (WARC)	Class 3	150 zones, with a minimum of 40 on each band
5BWITUZ (WARC)	Class 4	120 zones, with a minimum of 30 on each band

Note: on 10MHz credit will only be given for contacts on CW.

Top Band endorsement

A holder of the basic award who can produce evidence of contact with the required number of call areas on the 1.8MHz band may claim a Top Band 'sticker' endorsement. This is available in five classes for 20, 30, 40, 50 and 60 zones.

Notes:

(a) The number of ITU broadcasting (ie land) zones recognised by the ITU is 75 zones (zones 1 to 75) and this therefore is the maximum score which can be claimed per band. However, the island of Minami Torishima (JD1) lies outside the 75 zones in sea zone 90. For 5BWITUZ (including endorsements) contacts with this island may count in place of one 'missing' credit on any band up to the maximum 75 for that band. Contacts with Minami Torishima do not count for WITUZ.

(b) In the case of the WITUZ and 5BWITUZ confirmations need not bear the appropriate ITU zone number but in order to count for credit they should give the location of the station in sufficient detail to place it clearly within one particular zone. Doubtful cases indicating possible overlap across two zones will not be given credit.

(c) The HF Awards Manager will use as his reference a list which is based on the *Radio Amateurs' Prefix Map of the World* published by Radio Amateur Call Book Inc, PO Box

2013, Lakewood, New Jersey 08701, USA. In the case of countries which encompass two or more ITU zones, eg USA, Russia and Brazil, zonal boundaries will generally follow the longitude/latitude grid lines as shown in the map. In the few instances of discrepancy between the map and the accompanying prefix/country list the decision of the HF Awards Manager will be final.

Applications for WITUZ and 5BWITUZ

Applications for WITUZ and 5BWITUZ should use the special application form available from the HF Awards Manager. A check list of ITU Zones and a map are included with the application form. Please send an A5 size SAE for the check list and application form.

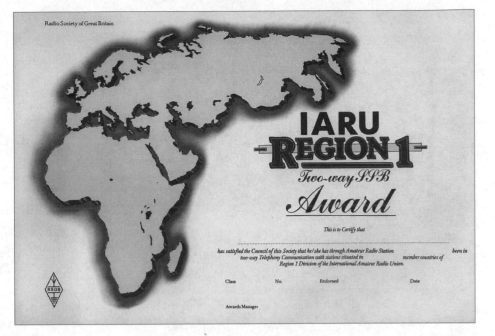

IARU Region 1 Award

This award, available in three classes, may be claimed by any licensed radio amateur eligible under the General Rules who can produce evidence of having contacted amateur radio stations located in the required number of countries whose national societies are members of the Region 1 Division of the International Amateur Radio Union (IARU).

The three classes are for contacts as follows:

Class 1   All member countries on the current list
Class 2   45 member countries
Class 3   30 member countries

Members of IARU Region 1 (as of April 1995) are:

Albania	Hungary	Norway
Algeria	Iceland	Oman
Andorra	Iraq	Poland
Austria	Ireland	Portugal
Bahrain	Israel	Qatar
Belarus	Italy	Romania
Belgium	Ivory Coast	Russian Federation
Bosnia	Jordan	San Marino
Botswana	Kenya	Senegal
Bulgaria	Kuwait	Sierra Leone
Croatia	Latvia	Slovakia
Cyprus	Lebanon	Slovenia
Czech Republic	Lesotho	South Africa
Denmark	Liberia	Spain
Djibouti	Liechtenstein	Swaziland
Egypt	Lithuania	Sweden
Estonia	Luxembourg	Switzerland
Faroe Is	Macedonia	Syria
Finland	Malta	Turkey
France	Mauritius	Ukraine
Gabon	Monaco	United Kingdom
Gambia	Mongolia	Yugoslavia
Germany	Morocco	Zambia
Ghana	Namibia	Zimbabwe
Gibraltar	Netherlands	
Greece	Nigeria	

Worked all Continents (WAC)

This award, issued by IARU headquarters, may be obtained by any licensed radio amateur in the UK, Channel Is or Isle of Man who is a member of the RSGB and can produce evidence of having effected two-way communication with amateur radio stations located in each of the six continents – North America, South America, Europe, Africa, Asia and Oceania.

Applicants should send QSL cards to the RSGB HF Awards Manager who will certify the claim to the IARU headquarters society (ARRL) for issuance of the award. They should also enclose a self-addressed stamped envelope for return of the cards, and proof of RSGB membership.

All contacts must be made from the same country or separate territory within the same continent. Various endorsements including 'all 1.8MHz' are available. In addition both a 5 and 6 Band WAC may be claimed.

Islands on the Air (IOTA)

The IOTA programme was created by Geoff Watts, a leading British short wave listener, in the mid-'sixties. When it was taken over by the RSGB in 1985 it had already become, for some, a favourite award. Its popularity grows each year and it is highly regarded among amateurs worldwide.

The IOTA programme consists of 18 separate awards. They may be claimed by any licensed radio amateur eligible under the General Rules, who can produce evidence of having made two-way communication, since 15 November 1945, with the required number of amateur radio stations located on the islands both worldwide and regional. Many of the islands are DXCC countries in their own right; others are not, but by meeting particular eligibility criteria also count for credit. Part of the fun of IOTA is that it is an evolving programme with new islands being activated for the first time (currently there are over 780 listed with reference numbers).

The basic award is for working stations located on 100 islands/groups. There are higher achievement awards for working 200, 300, 400, 500, 600 and 700 islands/groups. In addition there are seven continental awards (including Antartica) and three regional awards – Arctic Islands, British Isles and West Indies – for contacting a specified number of islands or

(a) **Mixed** (general type): Contacts may be made using any mode since 15 November 1945.

(b) **Phone**: Contacts must be made using radiotelephone since 15 November 1945. Confirmations for cross-mode contacts for this award must be dated 30 September 1981 or earlier.

(c) **CW**: Contacts must be made using CW since 1 January 1975. Confirmations for cross-mode contacts for this award must be dated 30 September 1981 or earlier.

(d) **RTTY**: Contacts must be made using radioteletype since 15 November 1945 (Baudot, ASCII, Amtor and packet radio count as RTTY). Confirmations for cross-mode contacts for this award must be dated 30 September 1981 or earlier.

(e-j) **160 metre, 80 metre, 40 metre, 10 metre, 6 metre, 2 metre**: Contacts must be made on the respective band since 15 November 1945.

(k) **Satellite**: Contacts must be made using satellites since 1 March 1965. Confirmations must indicate satellite QSO.

(l) **Five-Band DXCC (5BDXCC)**: This is available for working and confirming 100 current DXCC countries (deleted countries don't count for this award) on each of the five bands: 80, 40, 20, 15 and 10m. Contacts are valid from 15 November 1945. The 5BDXCC is endorsable for 160, 17, 12, 6, and 2m bands.

(m) **Honor Roll**. This top award, available in mixed, phone and CW variants, requires that you have worked and confirmed a number of DXCC countries within 10 of the total number on the current list, eg if there are 326 current countries, you must have 317 confirmed. There is an even more exclusive variant, the #1 Honor Roll – you must have *all* current countries confirmed!

Full details of the rules and an up-to-date country list are given in reference [43], obtainable from ARRL direct or from RSGB HQ. Note that QSL cards for this award have to go direct to ARRL and cannot be certified by the RSGB HF awards manager.

groups listed in each area. The IOTA Worldwide diploma is available for working a set number of islands in each of the seven continents. A Plaque of Excellence is available for confirmed contacts with at least 750 islands/groups.

The rules require that, in order for credit to be given, QSL cards need to be submitted to nominated IOTA checkpoints for checking.

A feature of the IOTA programme is the annual Honour Roll appearing in the RSGB's *DX News Sheet* which encourages continual updating of scores. This also appears also in *Radio Communication*.

If 'island chasing' appeals to you (and it can become compulsive), then write for the 60-page *IOTA Directory* which gives full information on the awards and the list of islands which count worldwide. This is available, price £6, US$10 or 15 IRCs (US$12 or 18 IRCs outside Europe) from:

Roger Balister, G3KMA, IOTA Director,
'La Quinta', Mimbridge,
Chobham, Woking,
Surrey, United Kingdom, GU24 8AR.

(A self-addressed adhesive label would be appreciated for replies. UK cheques should be made payable to R Balister – no foreign cheques please.)

Other awards
DX Century Club Award
This ARRL award is the best-known and most popular DX award in the world. It may be claimed by any ARRL member in the USA and possessions and Puerto Rico, and all amateurs in the rest of the world, who can produce evidence of two-way communication with at least 100 'countries' as defined on an official list. These DXCC countries are given in Appendix 4. Changes take place from time to time and these are noted in *QST*, *Radio Communication* and other magazines and DX newssheets.

There are 12 separate DXCC Awards available, plus the DXCC Honor Roll:

Worked (Heard) All Britain
This award is available to licensed amateurs (and SWLs on a 'heard' basis) for contacts with stations in 10km squares (National Grid), each square having a reference of two letters and two figures, eg SP99, TX34 etc. The award is divided into categories: 'Basic', 'Bronze', 'Silver' etc, depending on the number of squares and counties worked or heard. Full details of the rules and the form necessary are given in a special book which must be purchased first [45].

Worked All Zones
This award is issued by *CQ Magazine* in the USA for confirmation of contacts with stations in each of the 40 CQ DX Zones (these are given in Appendix 3). Full details of the award and a zone map are available from *CQ Magazine* [46], or from Dr E J Allaway, G3FKM, 10 Knightlow Rd, Birmingham B17 8QB. A five-band award is also available.

DX ON THE VHF AND UHF BANDS

A common belief seems to be that the HF bands are for DX working and the VHF bands are for local working – basically line-of-sight plus the odd 'lift' to perhaps the Continent. On a superficial and every-day level this view may be true, but further consideration shows how misleading it can be. Auroral contacts on 144MHz between the UK and Eastern Europe are quite common, Southern Africa has been worked from the Mediterranean on 144 and 432MHz, while the number of stations that have worked all continents on these bands by bouncing signals off the Moon, approximately 400,000km away, is gradually increasing. That is real DX by anyone's standards!

There is also an extra and fascinating dimension to DX work above 30MHz, this being the variety of propagation modes possible. HF band DX operation relies almost completely on ionospheric F-layer reflection, but on VHF/UHF modes used include tropospheric refraction, sporadic E-layer reflection, transequatorial E-layer reflection, auroral reflection, meteor scatter, field-aligned irregularity and moonbounce. The last four modes require special operating techniques to make full use of them, and have tended to attract enthusiasts accordingly.

In addition amateur satellites provide reliable intercontinental communication in the 145, 435 and 2400MHz amateur satellite bands (see Chapter 7).

Perhaps, however, the most enticing aspect of VHF/UHF DX is that it is still being explored. Countries continue to be worked for the first time from the UK and there is always a feeling that one might just be in the right place at the right time. This is especially true of the 50MHz band since it became available to all British amateurs on 1 February 1986.

BASIC EQUIPMENT CONSIDERATIONS

The power now used by serious DXers on VHF and UHF is comparable to that used on HF so, with the widespread use of beam antennas with 10–15dBd gain, really high ERP is possible. Consequently simple antennas such as dipoles or ground planes are rarely used, although sometimes conditions are so good that DX can be worked even with these.

Horizontal antenna polarisation has been used for most serious DX work since experiments carried out in the 'forties showed in general horizontal polarisation was superior (although just occasionally vertical polarisation was better). The use of vertically polarised antennas for DX work is confined to FM. Some stations have crossed Yagi antennas so that a choice of either polarisation is possible.

The siting of the antennas is just as important as the type of antenna used, and a ground-plane antenna sited on a chimney top clear of all obstructions may give better results than a beam antenna located indoors. The station site is much more important on VHF (and especially on UHF) than on the HF bands. Obviously a hill-top location is best but good results can be obtained in low-lying areas provided all directions are clear of obstructions. In general stations in reasonable locations should be able to work similarly located stations on SSB or CW at ranges up to 200km under any conditions unless there are significant obstructions in between, eg a range of hills. Results do depend on the band used, obstructions having considerably more effect at higher frequencies. A nearby hill which merely causes some attenuation on 144MHz may give rise to considerable difficulty on 432MHz and be sometimes almost an impenetrable barrier on 1.3GHz. However, too much should not be made of this as sometimes propagation is enhanced by 'knife-edge' diffraction round or over an object.

The feeder connecting the equipment to the antenna should have a low loss at the frequency in use, and this is very important at VHF and especially at UHF. For example, standard TV coaxial feeder has a loss of about 3dB per 10m at 433MHz while even UR67 (which is considered a high-quality cable at HF) will lose about 1.3dB per 10m at this frequency. Low-loss coaxial cables for UHF work are available and should be used if significant feeder lengths are necessary.

Because the external noise level is much lower on VHF and UHF than on HF, the noise factor of the receiver front-end is important if good results are to be obtained and many enthusiasts fit low-noise preamplifiers to their transceivers. However, this should not be done indiscriminately, because it may make the receiver more susceptible to cross-modulation from unwanted strong signals. Furthermore, the receiver noise factor may already be satisfactory, especially if the station is located in an electrically noisy urban area.

It must be emphasised that a beam antenna is the ideal form of noise-less RF amplifier, and therefore the best antenna possible should be erected before any money is spent on improving the receiver front-end (or buying an external amplifier for the transmitter).

OPERATING PRACTICE

In general this is not very different to that found on the HF bands. Pile-ups can occur in good conditions and because these can be short-lived it is good procedure to limit the contact to the exchange of signal reports and location details. Such details as equipment, name etc can be left to the QSL card. In this way more stations get a chance to work the DX station.

When conditions are good, call CQ sparingly, if at all, unless a very good signal is available. If a DX station does appear it will probably be called by a string of UK stations. A UK station with an average signal calling "CQ DX" will simply cause interference and not achieve the desired result. The old adage "If you can't hear 'em you can't work 'em" is just as true on VHF and UHF, and all too often one can hear stations calling "CQ DX" on the same frequency as distant stations which they cannot hear.

One feature of VHF/UHF operating which is rarely found on the HF bands is the use in Europe of *calling frequencies* specific to each mode. The idea is that these frequencies provide a 'meeting place' for operators using the same mode. In the UK, the 50 and 144MHz band plans identify particular calling frequencies (eg 50.200 and 144.300MHz for SSB, 50.090 and 144.050MHz for CW). Once contact is established, stations change to another frequency (the *working frequency*) so that others can use the calling frequency.

This system works well in poor-to-moderate conditions, when activity appears to be low. Operators leave their receivers tuned to the calling frequency, obviating the need to constantly tune the band as used to be the case in the distant past when transmitters were crystal controlled. But even though the band may seem empty entire contacts should not be conducted on the calling frequency as there may be other distant stations calling.

When conditions are good or a contest is in progress there is little point in using the calling frequencies, and in these cases it is probably better to call CQ elsewhere. For example, in a major sporadic-E opening on 144MHz the congestion around 144.300MHz is often so severe that it is difficult to complete an SSB contact. This is further aggravated by the poor operating procedures adopted by some amateurs, such as the use of unfamiliar phonetics.

Fig 11. The locator system

LOCATION INFORMATION

On the HF bands location details are given by reference to well-known cities but on VHF/UHF a locator system is used. This is necessary for contest purposes where scoring is based upon distance and similarly for awards and records. The approved IARU locator system was designed by Dr John Morris, GM4ANB [47, 48]. It was initially known as the *Maidenhead locator system* since it was tabled at a meeting of IARU Region 1 VHF managers in that town in April 1980. It came into official use on 1 January 1985.

The system is based upon three sizes of what are commonly (if incorrectly) called *squares*. The largest, called *fields*, are each 20° wide from west to east, and 10° high from south to north, thus dividing the Earth into an 18 by 18 grid. These fields are given two-letter indices, 'AA' to 'RR', with the first letter specifying the longitude and the second the latitude, the origin being at the South Pole at 180°W. Thus the field AA runs from 180° to 160°W, 90° to 80°S. North of this is AB, east is BA and so on. The field covering most of the UK (50° to 60°N, 20° to 0°W) is then IO. These fields are divided into 100 squares, each 2° wide and 1° high, labelled from '00' in the southwest corner to '99' in the northeast.

The final division is of these squares into a 24 by 24 grid of sub-squares, each one being 5′ wide by 2.5′ high. The sub-squares are labelled using two letters, again the first specifying the longitude and the second the latitude, starting from 'AA' in the southwest corner, and running to 'XX' in the northeast. A full locator thus consists of two letters, two numbers and two letters, with a typical reference being IO91IP.

Fig 11 shows how the locator is built up from fields, squares and sub-squares. It may be noted that all of the longitude-defining characters – the first, third and fifth – run from west to east, while the latitude defining characters – the second, fourth and sixth – go from south to north. In addition, at all levels the east-west size, in degrees, is always twice the north-south size.

In distance terms, each sub-square is about 4.6km from south to north. The east-west size varies with latitude, but in the middle of Britain (55°N) it is about 5.3km. If you take the

Table 1. Number-to-letter conversion table for hand calculation of a locator

0	A	4	E	8	I	12	M	16	Q	20	U
1	B	5	F	9	J	13	N	17	R	21	V
2	C	6	G	10	K	14	O	18	S	22	W
3	D	7	H	11	L	15	P	19	T	23	X

accuracy of the system as being the farthest you can get from the middle of a sub-square without actually leaving it, this gives a maximum error of about 3.5km (at 55° latitude), which is quite adequate for most normal operation.

The following step-by-step procedure can be used to calculate your locator from your latitude and longitude, using nothing more than pencil, paper and a simple calculator.

First of all you must find your latitude and longitude. These can be derived from the popular 1:50,000 series of Ordnance Survey maps but you should note that the blue grid lines do not run exactly north-south and east-west. Along the top and bottom margins of each map the longitude is given and along either edge the latitude, both at 1′ intervals. In the main body of the map the corners of 5′ by 5′ squares are identified by faint blue crosses. By pin-pointing your location within the appropriate square and pencilling in the sides you will be able to determine your latitude and longitude with great accuracy by proportion. The latitude should be rounded down to the next half of a minute south and the longitude to the next whole minute west.

Having established your latitude and longitude the procedure is as follows:

1. First deal with the longitude. Convert the longitude to decimal degrees. This is done by dividing the minutes part by 60 and adding the result to the degrees part.
2. If you are east of Greenwich, add 180.
3. If you are west of Greenwich subtract the value from 180.
4. Divide the result by two.
5. Now divide the value obtained by 10, and note the figures to left of the decimal point. These give the first letter of the locator, on the basis of 0 = A, 1 = B, 2 = C and so on, as shown in Table 1.
6. Multiply by 10, and note the single digit immediately before the decimal point. This is the third character of the locator.
7. Take just the fractional part of the value (the part to the right of the decimal point), and multiply by 24. The figures to the left of the decimal point give the fifth character of the locator, once again using Table 1.
8. Now follow a similar process for latitude. Convert the latitude to decimal degrees.
9. If you are north of the equator, add 90.
10. If you are south of the equator subtract the value from 90.
11. Divide by 10, and take the second letter of the locator from the digits to the left of the decimal point, using Table 1.
12. Multiply by 10, and note the digit to the left of the decimal point. This is the fourth character of the locator.
13. Take the fractional part, and multiply by 24. The figures to the left of the decimal point give the last letter of the locator, again using Table 1.

As an example, take Edinburgh Castle. From the map, its latitude is somewhere between 55°56.5′N and 55°57′N, and its longitude between 3°11′W and 3°12′W. Rounding to the next half minute south and whole minute west means that latitude 55°56.5′N and longitude 3°12′W are taken. Verify, using the above method, that its locator is IO85JW.

The intermediate results you should obtain are:

1. 3.2
2. No action
3. 1768
4. 88.4
5. 8.84, ie 'I'
6. 88.4, ie '8'
7. 9.6, ie 'J'
8. 55.94166667
9. 145.9416667
10. No action
11. 14.59416667, ie 'O'
12. 145.9416667, ie '5'
13. 22.59999984, ie 'W'

On the air the system should be called simply 'locator'. For example, you might say "My locator is IO83QP", or ask of another station, "What is your locator?". On CW the recommended abbreviation is 'LOC', so that the CW equivalent of "What is your locator?" is simply "LOC?"

The various divisions of the locator, fields, squares and sub-squares, have just those names. A VHF DX chaser might claim to have worked 300 'squares', or, for the real enthusiast, '20 fields'.

While the six-character locator system is accurate enough for VHF/UHF use more accuracy may be necessary for identifying locations and calculating distances and antenna bearings when operating in the microwave bands above 24GHz. At the IARU Region 1 conference in Belgium in September 1993 an RSGB proposal for an extended locator system was approved. The 5' wide by 2.5' high sub-squares are divided into 100 'micro-squares' each 30" wide by 15" high labelled from '00' in the southwest corner to '99' in the northeast. Thus a full micro-locator would be IO91IP37 and at 55°N latitude, the maximum error is reduced 10-fold to about 350m.

A short computer listing for determining locators is shown below. It is based on algorithms developed by GM4ANB and is written in Microsoft QuickBasic.

```
50 REM LOCATOR
100 pi = 3.14159265#
110 dr = pi / 180
120 DEF FNc (x) = x - INT(x)
130 CLS
200 PRINT "Please enter...."
210 PRINT
220 INPUT " Latitude deg,min,sec,n/s eg
    51,19,36,n   ", t1, t2, t3, T$
230 T$ = UCASE$(T$)
240 N = (t1 + t2 / 60 + t3 / 3600) * dr
250 IF T$ = "S" THEN N = -N
260 PRINT
270 INPUT "Longitude deg,min,sec,e/w  eg
    3,13,29,w   ", t1, t2, t3, T$
280 T$ = UCASE$(T$)
290 e = (t1 + t2 / 60 + t3 / 3600) * dr
300 IF T$ = "W" THEN e = -e
310 GOSUB 500
320 PRINT
330 PRINT "Maidenhead Locator is   "; LEFT$(q$,
    6)
340 PRINT " Microwave Locator is   "; q$
350 PRINT
360 INPUT "Another go <y/n>"; ch$
370 IF ch$ <> "n" AND ch$ <> "N" THEN 130
380 END
500 REM LATITUDE & LONGITUDE TO LOCATOR ROUTINE
510 T = 1 / 2 / pi: LO = e * T + .5: LA = N * T
    * 2 + .5: q$ = ""
520 T = 65: f = 18: GOSUB 570
530 T = 48: f = 10: GOSUB 570
540 T = 65: f = 24: GOSUB 570
550 T = 48: f = 10: GOSUB 570
560 RETURN
570 LA = f * FNc(LA): LO = f * FNc(LO)
580 q$ = q$ + CHR$(INT(T + LO)) + CHR$(INT(T +
    LA))
590 RETURN
```

THE VHF/UHF BANDS

The term 'VHF' applies to frequencies between 30 and 300MHz, and 'UHF' normally means 300MHz to 3GHz, but in amateur practice frequencies above 1GHz are normally included with microwaves.

The ITU VHF/UHF allocations for Region 1 are 144–146MHz and 430–440MHz. Most Region 1 countries permit 144–146MHz operation but there are several with restricted 430–440MHz Amateur Service allocations (see Appendix 9). Notwithstanding ITU allocations, national administrations may permit amateur service operation in additional bands. Starting with the UK in the early 'eighties amateurs in the majority of Region 1 countries have been granted permits to operate in the 50–52MHz band. In some countries, such as the UK, normal licensing conditions apply but in others there are restrictions on the width of the band, transmitter power, modes, antennas and times of operating.

Amateur allocations in Regions 2 and 3 are broadly similar to those in Region 1, with the addition of an ITU allocation between 50 and 54MHz. In Region 2 the bands 220–225MHz and 902–928MHz may also be allocated for amateur use. It should be noted that many of the amateur bands above 30MHz are shared with other services, as shown in Appendix 9.

The four VHF/UHF bands of particular interest to UK amateurs are those at 50, 70, 144 and 430MHz, commonly referred to as 'Six', 'Four', 'Two' and 'Seventy' respectively. The 70MHz band is a special allocation granted by the UK administration in the 'fifties. The initial allocation was only 200kHz wide, but was later increased, then subsequently decreased to the present 70.0–70.5MHz. The two higher bands are those allocated to the Amateur Service by international agreement.

Because of the wide variety of activities taking place on VHF and UHF, the band plans are necessarily much more complex than those for the HF bands. The main aim of the band plans is to separate incompatible transmission modes, and so let everyone get on with the business of communicating by his or her chosen method. The outlines of the 144 and 430MHz band plans are laid down by international agreement in the IARU after much debate and discussion. The 70MHz band plan was devised by the RSGB, and follows a similar outline to those for the higher bands.

Although the band plans are purely voluntary arrangements, it is in the interests of everybody to keep to them. Calling CQ on CW on 145.7MHz is quite legal within the terms of the amateur licence, but is very unlikely to result in a contact, and certainly will not make any friends. Similarly, the beacon sub-band may seem completely empty and an ideal spot for a contact, but even a short transmission there could well cause serious annoyance to somebody many miles away who is intently listening in the noise for a distant beacon. There is room on the bands for all of the many activities, provided a little care, consideration and respect for the interests of other operators is shown. The band plans act as a guide in this. For example, by having specific calling frequencies for data communications, packet operators can concentrate their listening and calling on known frequencies, and avoid interference both to and from other modes. All VHF/UHF users are recommended to keep a copy of the band plans to hand near the rig.

50MHz (6m) band

28MHz has already been described as having many of the characteristics of a VHF band. By the same token, 50MHz can take on many of the features normally associated with an HF band, especially at times around the sunspot maxima, when F2 propagation is often possible and worldwide contacts may be made. Just about every other type of propagation is also found occasionally at 50MHz. One phenomenon noted during the peak of sunspot cycle 22 was anomalous beam headings, particularly on the path between the UK and Japan. This affected both the short and long paths. 28.885MHz has become the recognized 'talkback' frequency on which the dedicated enthusiasts meet to discuss such phenomena, conditions and openings.

The IARU Region 1 Band Plan for 50MHz is given in Appendix 9, but it must be appreciated that amateurs in some countries cannot adhere to it due to local restrictions. Although 50.110MHz is the agreed intercontinental calling frequency, very many operators selfishly use it for more local contacts, often obliterating weak DX stations from outside Europe. Unfortunately newcomers to the band may pick up this bad habit from the more experienced operators who should know better.

70MHz (4m) band

It is unfortunate that because the 70MHz band is available in only a very few countries, its full potential cannot be recognised. However, there are several operators in other countries who have suitable receiving equipment and are interested in crossband working. Most commonly frequencies around 28.885MHz are used for talkback, but other bands have also been employed. There have been a few 70 to 144MHz crossband contacts made from the UK to the Continent by meteor scatter, where the more modest power and antenna gains in use on the lower band are compensated by the greater propagation efficiency. Skeds for MS contacts are usually made on the 14MHz VHF net, as described later in this chapter. The ultimate crossband achievement is to complete a 50 to 70MHz contact with a station on the other side of the Atlantic, and very few such contacts have been made.

When arranging crossband skeds, care should be taken over the choice of the 70MHz frequency as this band is used for broadcasting and other purposes in various parts of the world. The advice of the distant station should be sought on this point.

The future of the 70MHz band now looks brighter. In its review of the 29.7–960MHz part of the spectrum the European Radiocommunications Committee [49] concluded: "It would therefore seem possible to agree a limited amateur transmitting facility of at least 100kHz centred on 70.2MHz. It is also hoped that the existing beacon network between 70.0 and 70.15MHz can be maintained and extended". The time scale for adopting such proposals is likely to be long as the ERC has suggested its recommendations be implemented by 2008. However, as was the case with 50MHz, some countries may be prepared to grant special permits to their amateur licensees in advance of any general ITU agreement at a future World Radio Conference.

144MHz (2m) band

This is arguably the most popular of all amateur bands, largely because it is the lowest band allocated to 'VHF only' licensees

in many countries. Under good conditions it is possible to make contacts from the UK deep into Europe, to North Africa and down to the Canary Islands in the North Atlantic. When an opening of one sort or another occurs the high level of activity ensures there will usually be someone on the other end of the path keen to make a contact. As well as the normal CW, SSB and FM, many specialist communication techniques and propagation modes are in regular use, and this is reflected in the complexity of the usage part of the band plan.

The bottom 35kHz is devoted to moonbounce and it is important that this region be kept clear unless the Moon is well below any European horizon. It is in regular use by stations using high-gain antennas and sensitive receivers to copy weak signals which may be inaudible on most normal equipment. The CW-only segment extends up to 144.150MHz, with a calling frequency at 144.050MHz. Most CW activity takes place between 144.035 and 144.075MHz, and during openings, especially of the auroral type, there are usually many good DX contacts to be made in this part of the band. In particularly intense auroras the entire CW exclusive section can become quite congested. There is a CW activity period from 2000 local time every Monday evening.

The most popular DX mode is SSB for which the calling frequency is 144.300MHz. To avoid overcrowding a substantial change of frequency is recommended once contact has been established on 144.300MHz. When activity is high, such as during openings and contests, the concept of a calling frequency tends to be dropped and stations may be heard calling CQ anywhere from 144.15 up to 144.35MHz or higher. In these circumstances contacts are made in a similar manner to those on the HF bands. Cross-mode CW/SSB working is rare but can prove useful in getting through interference. The SSB and CW exclusive segment continues up to 144.5MHz, the higher frequencies being more popular for local SSB working and nets, such as those involving Worked All Britain enthusiasts. The bottom 500kHz of the band includes several meteor scatter and field-aligned irregularity calling frequencies and working segments, which should be avoided by stations not participating in such activities.

The non-channelised all-mode segment runs from 144.5 to 144.845MHz and it is here that the specialist communication modes, including RTTY, fax and SSTV, are to be found. Each of these modes has a specific calling frequency, which should be avoided by other operators. The sub-segment 144.5125 to 144.6875MHz is designated for data modes, mostly packet radio in practice.

Above the all-mode segment comes the beacon sub-band, 144.845–144.990MHz, and most European countries have one or more beacons in this region, as shown in Appendix 10. These beacons are used by keen DXers to help evaluate propagation conditions, and by careful monitoring may often give a valuable forewarning of an impending opening. This section should be regarded as strictly 'out of bounds' for transmitting.

The top megahertz of the band contains allocations for FM simplex, repeaters and satellite communications, which are dealt with in Chapters 6 and 7.

430MHz (70cm) band

This used to be very much an enthusiasts' band, most of the equipment being home-built, but now there is a wide selection of excellent commercial equipment available from all-mode transceivers, through high-power amplifiers to antennas. Although path loss, which is frequency dependent, is greater than on the lower bands, this is compensated by the higher antenna gains in common use. Most terrestrial contacts are made by tropospheric propagation, although the better-equipped stations complete auroral and meteor scatter contacts. Sporadic-E mode does not exist at 430MHz, the highest reported frequency being in the 220MHz region.

The anatomy of the DX section, 432.00–432.99MHz, is very similar to that of 144MHz, with CW, SSB, all-mode and beacon sub-bands, as well as special allocations for moonbounce and data modes. Many of the comments in the preceding section apply equally to 430MHz. Operating practice is also similar to that on 144MHz.

A common practice during lifts is for operators who are interested in 144MHz, 430MHz and perhaps 1.3GHz to call on the lower band and announce that they are "QRV on 70cm" or 23cm or both. If the other station is interested then a frequency on the higher band is agreed. This procedure has the advantage of allowing beam headings to be accurately determined, which is particularly useful when the narrow beamwidths in common use on the higher bands are considered.

1.3GHz (23cm) band

The 1.3GHz band is the lowest-frequency 'microwave' band but is included here as a borderline case, as it exhibits the characteristics of both the VHF/UHF bands and the higher bands. Propagation losses are higher than on 430MHz, and unless relatively efficient equipment is used results can be rather disappointing. Nevertheless, many dedicated 1.3GHz operators have made contacts of well over 1000km and some have worked over 100 locator squares.

Commercial equipment is readily available for this band but is of rather low power (a few watts). For serious DX work some form of PA is essential and raising the power output to 20–30W will effect a useful improvement in transmitter range in average conditions. Such power levels are easily obtained from the 2C39 family of planar triodes [56]. For the more ambitious the Siemens YL1050 can produce 600W RF output from 40W drive in linear mode [57].

On the receive side, commercial transverters usually have some form of RF preamplifier built in, but most converters do not, and certainly require an external preamplifier for good results. Many stations employ mast-head preamplifiers and these can often be of great benefit when long runs of feeder cable are unavoidable.

As with the lower bands, a good antenna system is of great benefit. Corner reflectors, and small Yagis and dishes, are unlikely to give very good results in average conditions. The more serious operators use multiple, stacked Yagi arrays or dishes (greater than 2m diameter). Since coaxial cables are considerably more lossy at 1.3GHz than on lower frequencies, the best-quality cable you can afford should be used. For example, an 11m run of RG214 cable will have a loss of 0.78dB at 144MHz, 1.52dB at 432MHz but almost 3dB at 1.3GHz. This means that only one-half the power generated by the PA will reach the antenna and that your receiver noise figure will be degraded by 3dB, too. So-called 'low-loss' UHF TV cable should not even be considered at 1.3GHz.

Operating on 1.3GHz is a mixture of making contacts directly on the band and setting them up from 432MHz. The newcomer is strongly advised to seek 1.3GHz contacts from 432MHz initially, as random calls on 1.3GHz outside contests, activity nights or lifts will most likely go unanswered. Also, arranged contacts have the advantage that antennas can be aligned accurately beforehand.

The IARU Region 1 band plan is quite detailed. As far as DX activity is concerned, most operation is around 1,296.200-MHz, referred to as the *narrow-band centre of activity*. Two points are important, however. The segment 1,296.000 to 1,296.025MHz should be left clear for moonbounce operating, and no transmissions should be made in the beacon segment (1,296.800 to 1,296.990MHz). Contrary to the practice on the lower bands, all activity, local or DX, SSB, CW or FM, is horizontally polarised.

More information on the 1.3GHz band is given in the microwave DX section on p78.

VHF/UHF PROPAGATION MODES

As mentioned previously, signals at these frequencies can be propagated a number of different ways and it is more convenient to discuss VHF/UHF propagation by mode rather than by band, especially as enthusiasts often tend to be attracted to particular modes rather than one particular band.

It should be noted that anomalous propagation conditions which affect one band will not necessarily affect the others. Furthermore, an 'opening' will usually have decreasing effect, the higher the frequency, but this is also not necessarily true and in many cases operators have found signals at 432MHz louder than the 144MHz ones during a 'lift'.

Knowledge of VHF/UHF propagation and when openings are likely to occur is essential for the DX operator.

Also most useful is an all-mode receiver which can tune the whole band for indications of good propagation. The following sections discuss briefly each mode from an operating point of view. A much more detailed account of the mechanisms of VHF/UHF propagation is given in [58] to which the interested reader is referred.

Tropospheric propagation

In the early days of VHF it was thought that propagation was only possible over line-of-sight paths and at distances beyond this attenuation was rapid; however, experience in the early 'thirties showed that this was not always so and sometimes much longer distances could be covered. These effects were soon related to atmospheric conditions and it was realised that radio waves were being bent back to Earth by the troposphere, hence the name.

The relation between weather and tropospheric propagation is complex but in general it may be said that the main requirement is a temperature or a humidity inversion. Normally the temperature of the atmosphere decreases with increasing height above Earth, but in abnormal circumstances it may increase over part of the distance so that VHF waves which are normally lost in space are bent back to Earth, sometimes at a range of hundreds of kilometres.

Since first published in the early 'seventies *Dubus Magazine* has included 'Top Lists' which now include the bands from 50MHz up. Examination of the 144MHz list for mid-1994 shows the average best distance claimed (usually known as 'ODX') by the top 80 stations to be just over 1500km, with four operators claiming contacts in excess of 2000km.

Clearly the DX enthusiast will wish to forecast the good conditions. Two essential aids are:

1. *Weather map (synoptic chart)*. This may be found on television or in a newspaper. The former is preferred as it is more likely to be up-to-date. Be careful to distinguish between actual maps showing the situation a few hours before and forecast maps, which are not necessarily accurate, as the weather is notoriously difficult to predict.

2. *Barometer.* Some means of observing changes in atmospheric pressure is required. A barometer, or better still a barograph, is suitable, though a surplus aircraft altimeter will be satisfactory, providing this is of the correct type (ie not a radio altimeter).

What to look for

Good conditions are usually associated with stable weather patterns and this means areas of high pressure (*anticyclones*). Therefore, look for anticyclones on the map and a barometer reading high. It will soon be found that the appearance of a high-pressure system does not produce good conditions, but when it starts to decline things may start to happen, especially if the anticyclone is short-lived. However, good conditions can occur when the atmospheric pressure is steady or even increasing.

It must be added that anticyclones may form over the British Isles and decline without any significant effect on conditions. Conversely DX can appear when the weather map appears to be a series of depressions, though an opening under these conditions is usually short-lived. A complete understanding would require a study of the atmosphere in impractically great detail.

How to identify enhanced conditions

The simplest method is to monitor known distant signals and the most useful of these are the beacons. Appendix 10 gives a list of European beacons in the 50MHz to 1.3GHz part of the spectrum operational at the time of going to press. A beacon list is also published in the annual *RSGB Amateur Radio Call Book.* A quick check of signal strengths of the beacons on the bands of interest will usually give a clue to the state of conditions. This is especially useful on 144MHz where many beacons are operating. It should be added that the beacons may be observed at enhanced strength when no other signals can be heard, either because there is no activity or because stations which are operating are beaming in other directions.

Other distant stations, eg television transmissions, may give a clue to conditions, though these can be difficult to identify. Sometimes unusual patterning on the screen of the domestic TV set or an announcement from the broadcasting organisation concerning 'Continental interference' may indicate that an opening is taking place.

Some points to observe:

1. All bands are not necessarily affected equally. It is possible for propagation to be enhanced at 144MHz but not at 432MHz and vice versa.
2. Propagation does not vary uniformly. It can be good to, say, the south but poor to the north simultaneously.
3. Skip effects are noticeable at times. It can be possible for a station 300km to the west to be working DX several hundred kilometres to the east which is quite inaudible. This is very frustrating and the only thing to do is to monitor carefully and hope for a change.

Sporadic-E (Es) propagation

This is the name given to intense ionisation of the E-layer which happens intermittently. The mechanism has been studied for many years and the general conclusion seems to be that there is no single cause of this phenomenon [59]. In the northern hemisphere, Es is most likely to occur between May and August with a minor peak in late December.

Es gives rise to propagation over distances from a few hundred to over 2000km at frequencies up to about 200MHz, so that it affects the 50, 70 and 144MHz bands. However, the ionisation has to be very intense for 144MHz propagation to occur such that on occasions when Es may be observed continuously on 28MHz for several days, it may reach 144MHz for only a few minutes during this time. Particularly in June and July, the 50MHz band is often full of Es signals on a daily basis, sometimes supporting multi-hop propagation from the British Isles to the Eastern Mediterranean, the Middle East and across the Atlantic to North America. For example, there was a superb multi-hop Es opening to Canada and North America on 7 July 1995 which lasted for many hours; it seems likely that the longest DX involved four hops! This event occurred within about a year of sunspot minimum so F-layer propagation can be discounted. The 70MHz band is often open for lesser periods in these months.

The most interesting Es band is 144MHz and since openings can be very short, from a few seconds to at most a few hours, it is desirable to know when Es is likely. This involves careful monitoring of signals in the approximate range 28–118MHz and a general-coverage receiver, preferably able to receive both AM and FM, is desirable. Programmable scanning receivers (eg Icom IC-R7100) are ideal for this purpose.

Various groups of signals can be monitored as follows:

28MHz band. European signals will always be audible when Es is around. When ionisation is intense, signals are extremely strong and the shorter the distance, the more likely it is that higher frequencies, such as 50MHz, are affected.

Band I TV signals (41–68MHz) can be useful but are often difficult to identify, especially the vision – though the sound channels can help. Small portable TV sets are useful monitors if you can get one but most modern British sets are UHF only, so useless. It is possible to buy multi-standard portable TV receivers in continental European countries where VHF TV services still exist.

68–73MHz. This band is still used by a few countries in Eastern Europe for FM broadcasting, but all have agreed to discontinue transmissions in the future. When Es is present, many of these stations may be heard (eg Radio Gdansk in Poland on 70.31MHz). If they are very strong, careful attention should be paid to 144MHz, especially if they are audible as early as 0630 GMT. If they are weak or fading, 144MHz is unlikely to open to these areas but it may do to somewhere else.

Band II (88–108MHz) is used by most European countries for VHF FM broadcasting. The sudden appearance of DX stations from Italy or Spain indicates that 144MHz may well open in those directions. In some cities in the British Isles several dozen UK FM stations are always audible and the appearance of a DX station may pass unnoticed. There can be some confusion since there may be local stations serving ethnic communities broadcasting in foreign languages (eg London Greek Radio on 103.3MHz).

Operating notes

As 144MHz Es openings are often very short-lived, efficient operating is essential and an exchange of report and QTH locator is the most that should be attempted. It is possible for a station to appear, calling CQ, be worked and disappear totally in less than a minute. Avoid using the SSB calling channels – there is no hope of establishing an Es contact and then changing frequency as is normal practice with other propagation. All too often a station fades out during a contact and there is usually nothing to be gained by waiting in the hope it will reappear – it is best to 'cut your losses' and look for someone else.

The ionised reflecting layer, which may be relatively small in area, can move very rapidly and also tilt. For example, Maltese stations may be very strong one minute then fade out to be replaced by Sicilians which are in turn replaced by Sardinians – all in the space of a few minutes.

CQ calls should be brief, perhaps 10–15 seconds, and used with discretion – if an operator is in an area of high activity, any DX station is likely to have many UK stations calling him and be unlikely to reply to a call. Conversely, if an operator is isolated, he may have an opening all to himself and a pile-up of DX may call him. In this case one will want to work as many as possible, so just exchange reports with each station but give the locator on every third or fourth contact – the waiting pile-up will have heard it already.

However, always remember that sporadic-E can be very localised and it is possible for a DX station which is S9 to one operator to be inaudible 30km away – and that a CQ call may well pay dividends, especially just as the band is opening.

Auroral propagation

The natural phenomenon known in Europe as the *northern lights* has been studied and used as a propagation medium by amateurs for more than 50 years. Radio auroral events cause great excitement among VHF operators, who are able to work DX stations at distances far exceeding their normal tropospheric range. During strong events stations located in southern England are often able to make contacts with Finland and Estonia by beaming their signals towards the auroral reflecting zones.

All auroral openings occur after a solar flare has released energy from the Sun. The GB2RS news bulletins in the UK often give details of sunspot activity and flares are usually associated with these eruption holes on the disc of the Sun. A solar flare releases tremendous amounts of energy across the entire electromagnetic spectrum from X-rays to radio waves.

The Sun emits ionised gas continuously and this is termed the *solar wind*. During flares bursts of energetic charged particles stream outwards from the Sun and spiral towards the Earth via the solar wind. These particles are divided by the Earth's magnetic field and then follow the field lines to regions known as the *auroral zones*. These zones are oval shaped and extend outwards from the poles to a radius of 23° on the night side of the Earth and to 15° on the daylight side. Visual auroral sightings indicate where the charged particles impinge on the Earth's upper atmosphere, ionising the E layer at a height of 110km.

The number of auroral openings in any year is dependent on the solar activity. Some areas of the Sun can remain active for several weeks, causing repeats of events 26 to 28 days after the initial aurora. This is due to the period of rotation of the Sun and events like these are known as *solar repeats*.

Warning signs of impending auroral events

Large increases in the solar noise levels on 95, 136 and 225MHz can be measured during flares. These sudden ionospheric disturbances are often followed by short-wave fade-outs on the 14–28MHz bands, causing disruption of amateur and commercial HF communication (see page 48). This is caused by cosmic particles and X-rays ionising the D-layer which absorbs rather than reflects radio signals. These particles complete the 150 million kilometre journey from the flare region on the Sun in less than 15 minutes. It should be noted that short-wave fade-outs occur which are not accompanied by auroral events, but fade-outs followed by large magnetic disturbances almost always signal an impending aurora.

A good and reliable indication of a forthcoming auroral event is known as *pre-auroral enhancement* and is familiar to HF band operators. This effect is particularly obvious during periods of poor propagation such as in the summer months at sunspot minimum. A typical example occurred on 6 April 1995 when, during a sustained period of mediocre conditions on 14MHz, the band became full of very strong signals from Australia and New Zealand with the propagation akin to that during sunspot cycle peaks. The following day HF band conditions had collapsed and there was a very intense aurora enjoyed by VHF operators on the 50, 144 and even 430MHz bands.

Changes in the Earth's magnetic activity are measured in three directions – horizontal, vertical and declination. All three change prior to and during auroral events but amateur observers have noticed that the angle of declination measurements give the first geomagnetic auroral warning signs. Declination is the angle measured between geographic and magnetic north. Fig 12 shows the magnetic disturbance recorded on 1 May 1978 on a chart recorder connected to a magnetometer set up in the garden of the home of Dr Gadsen of Aberdeen University. The chart shows a fairly quiet initial period with small normal daily changes in magnetic activity, and then at midday it shows the start of a *sudden commencement geomagnetic disturbance*. These magnetic effects are measured in professional observatories and a daily equivalent planetary amplitude figure (Ap) is issued which gives the average level at several different locations. These changes in magnetic activity which take place on a worldwide basis are caused by the slower-moving particles which take one or two days to complete the journey from the Sun to the Earth's magnetosphere. Large-scale radio auroral events took place on 1 May 1978 in three distinct phases – in the afternoon, late evening and again after midnight – the chart in Fig 12 shows the changes in magnetic activity preceding and accompanying the aurora.

It is quite easy to make a simple magnetometer to monitor deviations in the Earth's magnetic field using readily available components. The sensor can be accommodated in a 35mm film spool case containing a small bar magnet sitting in some oil and suspended by a cotton thread. Full details of the construction of a sensor and a simple magnetometer will be found in reference [60].

Shortly after the commencement of a magnetic storm the comparatively slow-moving particles ionise the E layers and align along the Earth's field lines. VHF radio signals beamed towards the auroral regions are reflected and refracted by the moving area of auroral ionisation. This moving reflector causes frequency shift and spreading, making all auroral signals sound distorted and difficult to copy. Morse signals are transformed into a rough hissing note and sideband voice transmissions vary from a growl to a whisper. The amount of frequency change on signals varies proportionally to the frequency band used – this effect is known as *Doppler shift* and can be as much as 1.5–2kHz HF or LF of the actual transmit frequency on 144MHz.

Auroral operation

The beacon stations closest to the auroral zones are usually the first auroral signals to be heard in the south. The Swedish beacon SK4MPI (144.960MHz) and the Lerwick beacon GB3LER (144.965MHz) in Shetland are good auroral indicators. Auroral events are usually first noticed by amateurs in Norway, Sweden, Finland and northern Russia, who will be on the band making contacts before the auroral reflections extend to the south. Due to their northerly locations, they see far more visual auroras and participate in more radio events than stations in

Fig 12. Magnetometer recording taken on 1 May 1978

southern England. Amateurs have noticed that the larger the change in geomagnetic activity, the further south the area of auroral ionisation extends, and stations as far south as Italy make auroral contacts in major events.

If you hear someone calling "CQ aurora" and you have not operated in an auroral opening before, resist the temptation to call indiscriminately, and listen only. There are going to be hundreds of future auroras and this is your chance to learn the entirely new operating techniques required for auroral contacts. First select horizontal polarisation and beam between north and east at 45°. Tune the beacon band between 144.845MHz and 144.990MHz; it will take some time to get used to the rough-sounding keying of the beacons which will be slightly off their usual frequencies due to Doppler shift. If you hear GB3LER and SK4MPI check whether DL0PR on 144.910MHz is readable. If these three beacons are heard the aurora is extending to at least as far as Germany, and is therefore a large-scale event which will probably last for a few hours and may repeat later in the evening. Turn the beam between north and east on each beacon heard and it will be noticed that different beam headings give peak signals for different countries. Generally the farthest DX is worked with the beam well to the east.

Next tune the SSB section between 144.160MHz and 144.490MHz and try listening to an experienced local station who is working auroral DX. Due to the distortion he will be speaking slowly, using phonetics and possibly end-of-transmission tones. Remember that you will hear the local station direct but the DX stations will be replying via the aurora and will be slightly off his frequency. A typical SSB auroral contact starts like this:

"CQ aurora, CQ Aurora, GM8LFB, Golf Mike Eight Lima Fox Bravo calling CQ aurora . . ." (repeated slowly several times) " and GM8LFB listening." pip (end of transmission tone). "GM8LFB, GM8LFB, LA2PT calling. Lima Alpha Two Papa Tango, LA2PT calling GM8LFB . . ."

End-of-transmission tones which give a low-frequency pip are very helpful in auroral openings when signals are weak – the tone readily identifies the end of each station's transmissions.

Independent receiver tuning (IRT) is a must for auroral reception as the amount of Doppler shift often changes in the middle of a contact. It will soon be seen that SSB contacts are difficult due to the distortion, and contacts tend to be limited to exchanging reports, names, and locators. Many amateurs also exchange and log the beam headings used at both ends of the contact as a study of these figures can reveal the particular area of ionised E layer being used. During weak auroral events SSB operators in England, Northern Ireland, North Wales and

Scotland can work each other and operators with better facilities can contact Norway and Sweden. During strong auroral events SSB stations all over the UK and north-west Europe can work each other.

A new operator listening in the CW section between 144.020 and 144.120MHz will hear a great many rough-sounding hissing CW signals during a strong event. Experienced operators are used to the strange AC sounding notes and contacts are completed quickly and efficiently. The letter 'A' is added when calling CQ and is also added after the readability and signal strength report, in place of the normal tone reports which are not sent during aurora openings as no signal sounds T9.

The best auroral DX is always worked on CW, just as on other propagation modes – CW is easier to copy in weak signal conditions and contacts are therefore completed much faster. Some auroral operators use full break-in technique on CW, allowing them to listen for stations breaking in during the sending of a CQ. During the large-scale aurora on 1 May 1978 GM4COK worked more than 150 stations in 20 countries on 144MHz CW.

Auroral openings can occur in three separate phases in a single 24-hour period. The first phase can start as early as 1300 GMT but usually takes place between 1500 and 1900 GMT. The second phase can occur between 2100 and 2300 GMT and a third phase can run from after midnight till 0600 GMT. Very few auroral contacts take place around 2000 GMT and there is often a fade-out between the evening phase and the after-midnight session. Some auroras have no afternoon phase and start in the evening, often continuing again after midnight. Some auroras have no afternoon or evening phase, only starting after midnight. These are almost always weak events, sometimes heralding a larger occurrence on the next day.

Due to the Doppler shift and distortion on signals, auroral contacts can only be made on CW and SSB. High power is not essential but helps greatly in weak events. During strong events almost anyone can participate – mobile-to-mobile contacts have been made from southern England to Scotland using halo antennas and 10W SSB transceivers.

Signals reflected from the auroral curtain on 144MHz do not change polarity, and high-gain horizontal antennas give the best results. Operators who are blocked to the south and south-east enjoy auroral openings as they can work stations, normally unheard due to the obstructions, by beaming well to the north of the direct path.

It has already been noted that the amount of Doppler shift is proportional to the frequency band in use. For this reason auroral signals on the 50 and 70MHz bands are easier to read and have less distortion than on the 144MHz band. Inter-UK

Fig 13. Example of 27-day auroral calendar

signals are generally stronger on 50 and 70MHz and the openings start a little earlier and finish a little later than on 144MHz.

Auroral contacts have been made on both CW and SSB on the 432MHz band but signals are about 40dB weaker than on 144MHz, and the Doppler shift can be as much as 4kHz. No auroral contacts have yet been made on the 1.3GHz band but as power levels increase and receivers improve this will doubtless occur soon. Professional studies reveal that radar reflections have been received at 3GHz.

Predicting auroral events

Before the advent of the packet radio network most operators relied on the telephone to alert others about auroral openings. These links were quite successful. Nowadays serious DXers monitor the DX PacketCluster which provides a real-time record of events as they happen.

Many operators keep special 27-day auroral calendars on which they record both the visual and radio events which are reported in *Radio Communication* and on the GB2RS news bulletins. The auroral calendar in Fig 13 which started on 1 January 1977 and records auroral events until 1 August 1978 shows the correlation between the visual and radio events and demonstrates the fact that auroras often repeat 27 days later. A study of Fig 13 shows that in the period 1 August 1977 to 1 August 1978 UK observers recorded 70 visual aurora and 100 radio events. These numbers are considerably higher than during the same period for the previous two years, thus reflecting the increase in solar activity as Cycle 21 got under way.

The auroral warning calendar is very easy to use – simply circle any radio events and dot any visual auroras. An operator who was on for the 21 September 1977 event would have been prepared for the repeats which occurred on 18 October, 14 November and 11 December 1977. As the calendar shows, many events repeat in 26 to 28 days, often three or four times, proving that this method can be used successfully. It is also interesting to look at the calendar with hindsight – with the exception of 8 December 1977 the aurora of 18 September

repeated consecutively 27 days later seven times. Did we miss an aurora on 8 December or was the event of 4 January and its subsequent repeats unconnected?

The fact that amateurs note, record and make radio contacts via the aurora is of great interest to professional scientists studying the auroral phenomenon. Predicting correctly the date of an aurora and analysing the ensuing results can be almost as interesting as working to Russia on 144MHz during an event. The fact no two auroral events are ever the same and that it is impossible to predict which countries will be worked are all factors which add to the attraction of working DX via the aurora.

Meteor-scatter propagation

Meteor scatter (MS) is a DX propagation mode which is open to exploitation by most serious VHF operators; it should not be regarded as the province of a few specialists. However, it does require a higher level of station organisation and operational competence than random tropo DX chasing. The information here should enable operators to fulfil the few special requirements to explore this very rewarding DX mode.

What are meteors? Meteors are particles of rocky and metallic matter ranging in mass from about 10^{-10}kg to larger than 10kg. About 10^{12} are swept up by the Earth each day. At an altitude of about 120km they meet sufficient atmospheric resistance to cause significant heating. At 80km all but the largest are totally ionised, and this ionisation can be used to scatter radio signals in the range 10MHz to 1GHz.

Amateur MS operation

Most amateur MS operation takes place on 144MHz although 28, 50 and 70MHz are also good bands. Operation on 432MHz is also marginally possible, but the path losses approach those experienced in EME operation. Commercial MS links tend to use the low VHF region, as the path availability is greater than at the higher frequencies.

The distances which may be covered by typical MS operation are similar to those possible via sporadic-E. Assuming most signals are reflected from a region at altitude 110km, the maximum range possible with an antenna exhibiting a main lobe at 0° elevation is about 2300km. Typical amateur antennas have a main lobe at 2–5° and thus the ranges to be expected are somewhat less.

Most MS contacts take place during periods of more-or-less predictable meteor activity – the so-called *showers*. Rather fewer contacts are made via sporadic meteors during the intervals between.

MS QSO procedure

The intermittent nature of MS propagation means that special operating procedures are necessary. Within IARU Region 1, they are the subject of international agreement (see panel on the next page), and should thus be employed. Failure to do so has resulted in not a few lost contacts.

On CW, high speeds are employed. During skeds, speeds from 200 to over 2000 lpm are in use. In random MS work 800 lpm is the recommended maximum speed. Most operators use memory keyers to send and tape recorders to receive but sophisticated computer software is also available to deal with these speeds.

Equipment

Meteor-scatter contacts are possible with low power, particularly on 50MHz but on 144MHz higher ERP is necessary for consistent success. 100W RF at the feed point of a 10–14dBd gain antenna should be aimed for.

A genuine system noise figure of less than 2.5dB is highly desirable. Many commercial transceivers, especially the earlier models, have inadequate front-end performance. However, a range of replacement front-end boards for several all-mode VHF transceivers is available which bring them up to competition grade. Masthead preamplifiers are used by serious operators but care should be taken to avoid too much gain which could degrade the performance of the transceiver.

Frequency setting is of paramount importance. A tolerance of ±500Hz is demanded on CW and 200Hz on SSB. A stability of better than 100Hz/h is also expected. This implies that no matter what technique is used for frequency calibration, the frequency standard employed should be standardised rather frequently; most of the crystals used in amateur frequency measurement systems are likely to vary over a range of about ±10ppm around room temperature.

Most MS signals will be quite weak so the antenna system should be as large as possible within environmental, structural and financial constraints. Long Yagis are popular, particularly the commercial 13- and 17-element models, although smaller antennas are capable of good results. With a high-gain array, such as a box of four 17-element Yagis, received signals will be much stronger than those from a single 9-element antenna. However, many MS operators have found that a too 'sharp' array often misses signals coming into the broader capture angle of a smaller single Yagi. Experienced operators tend to favour two or more stacked Yagis since these give extra gain while retaining a broader E-plane lobe.

The timing requirements of MS technique are stringent but not too difficult to meet. A quartz-controlled clock or watch is probably the most popular timepiece and even cheap ones achieve accuracies of one or two seconds per day. It is preferable to calibrate the timepiece at the start of an MS session; this can be done using the 'speaking clock', time signal pips, ticks from standard frequency transmitters, such as WWV or MSF, or the TV clock on the Teletext service. The prices of

clocks incorporating radio receivers phase-locked to radio transmitters such as MSF and Droitwich are now very reasonable. There are radio receiver boards available for plugging into your PC which will ensure the computer's clock is always spot on. Mains-driven clocks are to be avoided as they have poor short-term stability. On CW, two other items of equipment are required; a means of sending repetitive messages at the speeds involved and a means of decoding the received CW. For many years programmable electronic memory keyers have been used to store and send the various messages used during a sked. Cassette tape recorders, modified for variable speed, are used by most operators to record received bursts for play-back at readable speed during transmit periods. During 1995, some keen MS operators began using a digital tape recorder made by DF7KF which easily decodes CW at speed in excess of 2000 lpm.

Designs for memory keyers suitable for MS work have appeared regularly in amateur radio journals and literature. LA8AK has contributed circuit ideas to the 'Technical Topics' column in *Radio Communication* and commercial keyers are available. More recently dedicated MS operators have employed their station computer to control their MS activities. Some operators use their PCs to receive CW in WAV files which obviates the use of mechanical tape recorders. Modern MS operation is a far cry from the early days of multi-speed reel-to-reel tape recorders and endless tape loops for sending!

Arranging skeds

Once the procedures used for MS have been understood, and the necessary equipment gathered together, the intending MS operator has to find someone to work! There are really two choices: to make a first contact directly on the frequencies set aside for random MS operation, or to arrange a sked with an active MS station. Of the two, the latter is the approach most likely to be fruitful.

In order to maximise the chance of success, skeds should be arranged at optimum times. The sporadic meteor rate peaks at 0600 but with shower meteors it is possible to be more specific. A knowledge of the propagation mechanism and the astronomical co-ordinates of the individual showers makes its possible to calculate the optimum time for any given path.

An example of a computer listing for a meteor shower is shown in Fig 14. This gives at the top of the table the name of the shower. dates between which the shower usually occurs, approximate date(s) of the maximum, zenith hourly rate (the relative activity of the shower) and the astronomical co-ordinates (right ascension and declination). Explanation of these terms is given in reference [61].

In the body of the table, the information tabulated at each hour is the position of the radiant in the sky (in altitude and azimuth) and, for each of eight reciprocal bearings, the relative effectiveness (presented as a histogram normalised to a maximum of 10 units) and the optimum antenna offset in degrees in the direction indicated. This last parameter is the deviation required from the great-circle path for conformity to the correct reflection geometry, and is illustrated in Fig 15. It is the same for both stations. A complete set of such tables, covering all usable showers for locations in the southern part of the UK, is obtainable from RSGB [63].

An abridged version of these tables is given in Table 2. After the shower name the dates of the usual limits are given, followed by the date of the maximum and the zenith hourly rate. Optimum times are given for four pairs of reciprocal bearings. Although space does not permit the precise listing of the

IARU REGION 1 METEOR SCATTER PROCEDURES

Scheduled and random contacts

There are two types of meteor scatter contact, scheduled or random.

(i) A scheduled contact is where two interested stations have arranged in advance upon the mode, frequency, timing and duration of the test. This may be done by correspondence, or via the European VHF net which is active around 14.345MHz.

(ii) Non-scheduled contacts are made by calling CQ or responding to a CQ call and then following the IARU procedures. These are called *random contacts*.

Timing

It is recommended that stations use 2.5 minute periods on CW and one-minute periods on SSB. This period gives quite satisfactory results. However, improving technical standards make it possible to use much shorter periods. With scheduled contacts you can arrange for any time period you wish but it is recommended that the periods are kept to one minute or less, especially during major showers. The use of 'break' procedures within scheduled contacts is very effective. On SSB this could be every 15 seconds if so desired.

(i) All MS operators living in the same area should, as far as possible, agree to transmit simultaneously in order to avoid mutual interference.

(ii) If possible northbound and westbound transmissions should be made in periods 1, 3, 5 etc, counting from the full hour. Southbound and eastbound transmissions should be made in periods 2, 4, 6 etc. UK stations have chosen by default to transmit during the second period.

(iii) Start times should be arranged to be on the hour, eg 0000, 0100, 0200 etc. This makers the best use of everyone's operating time. It can indicate how much time a station may have before the next scheduled contact.

Scheduled duration

Scheduled contacts are usually of one or two hours duration although during shower periods this can be reduced to 30 minutes or less. Every uninterrupted schedule period must be considered as a separate test. It is not permissible to break off and then recommence at some later time.

Choice of frequency

(a) Scheduled contacts

The frequency selected for scheduled contacts should avoid popular transmission channels, taking into consideration the mode and band plan. For example CW schedules could be arranged to run between 144.130–144.150MHz, and SSB from 144.150–144.190MHz or from 144.410–144.450MHz.

(b) Non-scheduled contacts using CW

The frequency used for CW calls should be 144.100MHz. Contacts resulting from such CQ calls should take place in the range 144.101–144.126MHz. The following procedure should be used by the caller to indicate during the CQ on which exact frequency he will listen for a reply and continue the QSO.

(i) Make sure the selected frequency it is clear of traffic and QRM.

(ii) In the call, immediately following the letters 'CQ', a letter is inserted to indicate the frequency that will be used for reception when the CQ call finishes. This letter indicates the frequency offset from the actual calling frequency used: CQA = 1kHz from calling frequency; CQB = 2kHz from calling frequency; CQC = 3kHz from calling frequency, all the way to CQZ = 26kHz from calling frequency. For instance, "CQE G4ASR CQE G4ASR" would indicate that G4ASR was listening on the calling frequency plus 5kHz. In all cases the letter used will indicate a frequency *higher* than the CQ frequency. Contacts will therefore take place in the segment 144.101–144.126MHz.

(iii) At the end of the transmitting period the receiver should be tuned to the frequency indicated by the letter used in the CQ call. If a signal is heard on this frequency and identified as an answer to the CQ call, the transmitter should be moved to the *same frequency*. The entire QSO procedure will then take place there.

(c) Non-scheduled contacts using SSB

At the 1993 IARU Region 1 Conference it was agreed that 144.195–144.205MHz and 144.395–144.405MHz should be used for SSB operation. In an attempt to spread out activity no specific calling frequency has been mentioned. However, during non-shower periods it will generally be expected that stations will call on either 144.200MHz or 144.400MHz. During major meteor showers, operation should be anywhere within the 10kHz segments, having first ensured that the frequency is not in use.

CW transmission speed

Speeds up to 2000 letters per minute (400wpm) or higher are now in common use. For non-scheduled work a speed of more than 800 letters per minute is not recommended. In scheduled tests the speed should always be agreed before the test. Note that in some countries the national PTT requires that callsigns to be sent at a slower speed at the end of each transmission. Check that the message being sent is correct and readable before and during transmission.

QSO procedure

(A) Calling procedure

Scheduled contacts start with one station calling the other, eg "UV1AS G4ASR UV1AS G4ASR . . .". For non-scheduled operation the call is in the form: "CQ G4ASR CQ G4ASR . . .". On CW the letters 'DE' are not used unless required by the national PTT.

(B) Reporting system and procedure

The report consists of two numbers as shown below:

1st number (burst duration)	2nd number (signal strength)
2: bursts up to 5 seconds	6: up to S3
3: bursts of 5–20 seconds	7: S4 to S5
4: bursts of 20–120 seconds	8: S6 to S7
5: bursts over 120 seconds	9: S8 and stronger

A report is sent only when the operator has positive evidence of having received the correspondents or his own callsign, or parts of them. It is given as follows: "UV1AS G4ASR 38 38 UV1AS G4ASR 38 38 . . .", and should be sent between each set of callsigns, three times for CW, twice for SSB. The report must *not* be changed during a QSO, even though a change of signal strength or duration might well justify it.

(C) Confirmation procedure

(i) As soon as either operator copies *both of the callsigns and the report* he can start sending a confirmation report. This means that *all* letters and numbers have been correctly received. Confirmation is given by sending an 'R' before the report: "UV1AS G4ASR R38 R38 UV1AS G4ASR R38 R38 . . .". Stations with an 'R' at the end of the callsign could possibly send it twice, eg "UV1AS G4ASR RR38 RR38 UV1AS G4ASR RR38 RR38".

(ii) When either operator receives a confirmation message, such as "R38", and all other required information is complete he must confirm with a string of 'R's, inserting his callsign after every eighth 'R': "RRRRRRRR G4ASR RRRRRRRR G4ASR . . .".

When the other operator has received 'R's the contact is complete and he may respond in the same manner, usually for three periods.

(D) Requirements for a complete QSO

The requirements for a valid contact is that *both* operators *must* have copied *both callsigns*, the *report* and also an 'R'

(ROGER) to confirm that the other operator has done the same.

Missing information (CW)

If a confirmation report is received at an early stage in the contact, the other operator has all the information he needs. The following strings may then be used to ask for missing information:

BBB   Both callsigns missing
MMM   My callsign missing
YYY   Your callsign missing
SSS   Duration and signal strength report missing
OOO   Information incomplete
UUU   Faulty keying or unreadable

The other operator should respond by sending only the required information. This approach must be used with great caution to prevent confusion.

Meteor scatter using SSB

Contacts are conducted in the same way as on CW. Letters are generally spelt in the ICAO alphabet but may be spoken without phonetics during a schedule. The letter 'R' in confirmation reports is pronounced "Roger".

Procedures on 50, 70 and 432MHz

Most MS activity on the 50MHz band uses SSB. The MS calling frequency for SSB is 50.350MHz and that for CW is 50.300MHz. The standard periods of 1 minute for SSB and 2.5 minutes for CW are still used.

There is infrequent MS activity on the 70MHz band. The recommended MS calling frequency is 70.150MHz. However, most activity is with DXpedition stations who generally operate on pre-arranged frequencies in the SSB segment of the band.

Similarly, 432MHz activity is very low and all tests are scheduled.

antenna offsets given In Fig 14, a suitable approximation is to beam 10° off the great-circle path in the direction indicated in parentheses after the optimum times (see Fig 15).

One of the most comprehensive suites of public-domain MS software is that written by OH5IY [64]. It features the usual predictions of the peak times of the major and many minor meteor showers and times when reflections will be optimum for the required path. The program can be used to key the transmitter at speeds of 100–9999 lpm, receive and playback the CW if the PC has a sound card and Microsoft Windows operating system. It features a comprehensive sked editor, automatic logging and will even wake you up with an alarm call when it is time for a sked in the middle of the night! Like all such software, the various files are subject to continuing development and updating. Within days of a major shower, the observed radio data for it is posted on the Internet.

```
QUADRANTIDS        JAN 1-6       MAX. JAN 4.5    ZHR 110    RADIANT AT RA,DEC   232.0      50.0

HRS    ALT      AZ      N-S              NNE-SSW              NE-SW              ENE-WSW
 0    20.5    31.8E   XXX        7W    X        21WNW    X      16SE    XXXX       6SSE
 1    26.0    40.5E   XXXXX      7W    XX       15WNW    X      38SE    XXXX      11SSE
 2    32.5    48.7E   XXXXXX     8W    XXXX     14WNW    X      45NW    XXX       18SSE
 3    39.8    56.4E   XXXXXXX   10W    XXXXX    14WNW    XX     32NW    XX        32SSE
 4    47.8    63.8E   XXXXXXXX  12W    XXXXXX   16WNW    XXX    28NW    X         50SSE
 5    56.3    71.1E   XXXXXXXXX 15W    XXXXXX   19WNW    XXXX   28NW    X         52NNW
 6    65.2    78.7E   XXXXXXX   20W    XXXXX    23WNW    XXXX   30NW    X         46NNW
 7    74.4    87.5E   XXXXX     29W    XXXXX    31WNW    XXXX   36NW    XX        46NNW
 8    83.6   104.2E   XX        44W    XX       44WNW    XX     45NW    X         49NNW
 9    86.1   119.1W   X         50E    X        52ESE           55SE              56NNW
10    77.1    90.9W   XXXX      33E    XXXX     34ESE    XXX    39SE    XX        47SSE
11    67.9    81.1W   XXXXXX    22E    XXXXXX   23ESE    XXXXXX 26SE    XXXX      34SSE
12    58.9    73.4W   XXXXXXX   16E    XXXXXXX  16ESE    XXXXXXX 18SE   XXXXX     23SSE
13    50.3    66.0W   XXXXXXXX  13E    XXXXXXXXX 12ESE   XXXXXXX 13SE   XXXXXX    16SSE
14    42.1    58.7W   XXXXXXXX  10E    XXXXXXXXX  9ESE   XXXXXXXXX 9SE  XXXXXXX   11SSE
15    34.6    51.0W   XXXXXX     9E    XXXXXXXXX  7ESE   XXXXXXXX  7SE  XXXXXXX    8SSE
16    27.8    43.0W   XXXXX      8E    XXXXXXX    6ESE   XXXXXXX   5SE  XXXXXXX    6SSE
17    22.0    34.5W   XXXX       7E    XXXXXX     5ESE   XXXXXX    4SE  XXXXXXX    4SSE
18    17.4    25.5W   XX         7E    XXXX       4ESE   XXXXX     3SE  XXXXXX     3SSE
19    14.1    16.1W   X          9E    XXX        4ESE   XXXX      3SE  XXXXX      3SSE
20    12.3     6.4W              18E   XXX        5ESE   XXX       3SE  XXXX       2SSE
21    12.1     3.4E   X          29W   X          7ESE   XXX       3SE  XXXX       2SSE
22    13.4    13.2E   X          10W   X         14ESE   XX        5SE  XXXX       3SSE
23    16.3    22.7E   XX          8W             55WNW   XX        8SE  XXXX       4SSE
24    20.5    31.8E   XXX         7W   X         21WNW   X         16SE XXXX       6SSE

HRS    ALT      AZ      E-W              ESE-WNW              SE-NW              SSE-NNW
 0    20.5    31.8E   XXXXX      4S    XXXXXX    4SSW   XXXXXX    4SW   XXXXX      5WSW
 1    26.0    40.5E   XXXXX      5S    XXXXXX    5SSW   XXXXXXX   5SW   XXXXXX     5WSW
 2    32.5    48.7E   XXXXX     10S    XXXXXXX   7SSW   XXXXXXXX  6SW   XXXXXXXX   7WSW
 3    39.8    56.4E   XXXXX     14S    XXXXXXX  10SSW   XXXXXXXXX 8SW   XXXXXXXXX  8WSW
 4    47.8    63.8E   XXXX      22S    XXXXXXX  14SSW   XXXXXXXXX 11SW  XXXXXXXXX 11WSW
 5    56.3    71.1E   XXX       34S    XXXXX    21SSW   XXXXXXXX  16SW  XXXXXXXX  14WSW
 6    65.2    78.7E   X         46S    XX       30SSW   XXXXXX    23SW  XXXXX     20WSW
 7    74.4    87.5E             55S             43SSW   XXXX      34SW  XXXXX     30WSW
 8    83.6   104.2E   X         54N    X        55SSW   XX        50SW  XX        46WSW
 9    86.1   119.1W   X         53N    X        51NNE   X         49NE            49ENE
10    77.1    90.9W             56N    XX        46NNE  XXX       38NE  XXXX      34ENE
11    67.9    81.1W   X         49S    XX        46NNE  XXXX      32NE  XXXXXX    25ENE
12    58.9    73.4W   XXX       37S    X         50NNE  XXXX      28NE  XXXXXX    20ENE
13    50.3    66.0W   XXXX      25S             54SSW   XX        28NE  XXXXXX    17ENE
14    42.1    58.7W   XXXXX     16S    XX        38SSW  XX        30NE  XXXXXX    15ENE
15    34.6    51.0W   XXXXXX    11S    XXX       22SSW  X         39NE  XXXX      14ENE
16    27.8    43.0W   XXXXXX     7S    XXX       12SSW            49NE  XXX       14ENE
17    22.0    34.5W   XXXXXX     5S    XXXX       7SSW  X         20SW            18ENE
18    17.4    25.5W   XXXXXX     4S    XXXX       5SSW  XX         9SW            38ENE
19    14.1    16.1W   XXXXX      3S    XXXX       3SSW  XX         5SW  X         21WSW
20    12.3     6.4W   XXXX       2S    XXXX       3SSW  XX         4SW  X          8WSW
21    12.1     3.4E   XXXX       2S    XXXX       2SSW  XXX        3SW            5WSW
22    13.4    13.2E   XXXX       2S    XXXX       2SSW  XXXX       3SW  XX         5WSW
23    16.3    22.7E   XXXXX      3S    XXXXX      3SSW  XXXX       3SW  XXX        4WSW
24    20.5    31.8E   XXXXXX     4S    XXXXXX     4SSW  XXXXXX     4SW  XXXXX      5WSW
```

Fig 14. Example of the computer printout for a particular shower

Table 2. Principal meteor showers

Shower name	Limits	Max	ZHR	N–S	NE–SW	E–W	SE–NW
Quadrantids	1–5 Jan	3–4 Jan	110	02–06(W) 11–16(E)	11–17(SE)	23–03(S) 15–17(S)	00–05(SW)
April Lyrids	19–25 Apr	22 Apr	15–25	22–02(W) 06–10(E)	23–03(NW) 08–11(SE)	03–06(N)	22–01(SW) 05–08(NE)
Eta Aquarids	1–12 May	3 May	50	03–04(W) 10–11(E)	04–09(NW)	05–11(N)	08–12(NE)
Arietids	30 May–18 Jun	7 Jun	60	04–08(W) 11–15(E)	05–09(NW) 14–16(SE)	08–12(N)	04–06(SW) 10–14(NE)
Zeta Perseids	1–16 Jun	9 Jun	40	05–10(W) 13–17(E)	06–11(NW) 15–17(SE)	09–14(N)	07–07(SW) 11–15(NE)
Perseids	20 Jul–18 Aug	12 Aug	95	23–04(W) 09–13(E)	08–17(SE)	11–01(S)	18–04(SW)
Orionids	16–27 Oct	22 Oct	25	00–03(W) 07–09(E)	00–04(NW)	03–06(N)	05–08(NE)
Taurids S	10 Oct–5 Dec	3 Nov	25	02–05(E) 20–22(W)	20–01(NW)	22–03(N)	00–05(NE)
Geminids	7–15 Dec	13–14 Dec	110	04–09(E) 20–01(W)	22–02(NW) 05–09(SE)	01–04(N) 03–07(S)	03–07(NE) 19–23(SW)
Ursids	17–24 Dec	22 Dec	15	—	07–01(SE)	00–24(S)	16–09(SW)

There are several ways of making MS skeds. The most convenient method is to arrange a test via the European VHF Net on the 14MHz band. This is an informal meeting place for VHF DX enthusiasts and is centred on 14.345MHz. It gets very busy in the run-up to and during major showers. On Saturdays and Sundays 14.345MHz should be left clear for those arranging EME skeds (see following section). Another way is to communicate by letter or telephone with stations in the MS-Address-List published from time to time in DL8LAQ's 'Meteor Scatter' column in *Dubus Magazine*. The Internet is becoming a popular medium for making MS skeds and most useful are the various 'reflectors' to which requests for skeds, as well as general amateur radio topics, can be sent to scores of members for the cost of a single message.

When arranging an MS sked, a certain minimum amount of data needs to be exchanged:

(a) The date
(b) Times of start and finish (2h duration is usual)
(c) Length of transmit and receive periods
(d) The frequency
(e) Which station transmits first
(f) CW speed

Fig 15. Illustration of antenna offsets

Further reading

The discussion of MS propagation given here is necessarily rather superficial. Much has been written about MS propagation in both professional and amateur journals. Some sources are given at the end of this chapter [61, 62].

DX WARNING NETS

The most common lament heard on 144MHz in the aftermath of a sporadic-E or auroral opening runs along the lines: "Well, the band was absolutely dead and then I heard a very strong Italian station calling CQ. I called him, and we gave each other 5 and 9, sent our 73s, and signed off. I tuned around to see what else was about, and the whole band was full of 'G' stations calling CQ and working all of the DX! Where do they all come from?"

The second most common lament is heard from operators who have come on the air just after the end of the opening: "I missed it all as usual. It's very annoying, because I have been in the shack all day, tidying up but I didn't have the rig switched on."

While many operators still rely on the telephone to alert friends to an opening, the majority now watch the DX cluster on the packet network for news of tropospheric openings, sporadic-E and auroral events. This is a very efficient and informative use of packet radio as it gives a running commentary on what is happening.

MOONBOUNCE

Probably the most challenging type of VHF/UHF DX communication is that using the Moon as a passive reflector, popularly known as *EME* (Earth-Moon-Earth) or *moonbounce*. The first known use of the Moon as a relay was by the United States Navy which set up a circuit between Washington, DC and Hawaii using 400MW ERP. The first amateur EME contact was on 1296MHz in July 1960 between W6HB and W1BU. The majority of EME work takes place on the 144, 432 and

1296MHz bands although there is some activity on 50MHz. The microwave bands up to 10GHz are attracting more experimenters.

The logistics

The mean distance between the Earth and the Moon is 385,000km. The Moon's diameter is 3476km so a little simple trigonometry shows it appears a mere 0.52° wide as viewed from Earth. Bearing in mind the three-dimensional polar diagrams of typical amateur antenna arrays, it is obvious that only a very small amount of ERP will illuminate the disk. Moreover the Moon is a sphere, not a flat mirror, so only radio waves that hit the middle region will be reflected back to Earth. In other words, the path loss is enormous. To put some figures on it, the minimum round-trip path loss at 144MHz is 251.5dB rising to 270.5dB at 1296MHz. Even so, it is possible to work a few of the biggest EME stations on 144MHz using a few hundred watts and a single long Yagi under favourable conditions.

For stations without antenna elevation capability, EME communication is only possible around moonrise and moonset. At such times, depending upon the height of the antenna above ground, advantage can be taken of so-called 'ground gain' whereby the apparent gain of a horizontally polarised antenna can be up to about 5dB more than the free-space figure. This is equivalent to increasing the size of an array from a single Yagi to four – and all for free!

Arranging EME tests

The best time to arrange EME tests is when the Moon is nearest to Earth, known as *perigee*. At *apogee* (furthest from Earth) there is an extra 2dB path loss to overcome. However, this is not the only consideration since the background sky temperature and/or Sun noise at new Moon periods may mitigate against perigee operation. Unfortunately there can be periods lasting several years when conditions are far from ideal, particularly on 144 and 432MHz.

Publications such as *Dubus Magazine* and the *432 and above EME Newsletter*, edited by K2UYH [65], identify favourable sked weekends and include details of active EME stations. Skeds can be arranged by letter, telephone or e-mail, but most EME operators check into the EME net on 14.345MHz on Saturdays and Sundays. This starts around 1600 UTC for those interested in 432 and 1296MHz and from 1700 UTC the 144MHz devotees take over. A contact can only be attempted when both stations can 'see' the Moon over their radio horizons. These periods are known as *windows* and are best derived from computer programs such as those written by WA1JXN [66], VK3UM [67] and F1EHN [68].

EME QSO procedure

There are internationally agreed operating procedures for EME work and, as with MS operation, timing is all-important. On 144MHz 2min periods are used and on 432MHz and above, 2½min. The convention is that the station whose call appears first on a sked list transmits first then in following 'odd' periods. In the absence of a formal list the convention is that the furthest east station transmits first on 144MHz but on 432MHz it is the one furthest west.

There is a special TMOR reporting system for EME work. On 144MHz these letters denote the following:

T   Signals just detectable
M   Portions of calls copied
O   Both calls fully copied
R   Both calls and 'O' report copied.

On 432MHz and above, these reports have slightly different meanings

T   Parts of calls copiable
M   Both calls fully copied weakly
O   Both calls copied comfortably
R   Both calls and 'M' or 'O' report copied.

In favourable conditions RST reports are exchanged.

At the start of a sked both callsigns are sent for the complete period of 2 or 2½min, depending on the band. Only when both callsigns have been copied completely may you send a report which will be 'O' on 144MHz, and 'M' or 'O' on other bands. At this stage the first 1½min on 144MHz, or the first 2min of the period on other bands, will be devoted to sending callsigns and the final 30s the reports. Reports are acknowledged by sending "RO" on 144MHz and "RO" or "RM" on 432MHz and above and when this is received by the other station a series of 'R's is sent.

As in MS work, random EME contacts are made especially during contests. If you hear a station calling CQ, reply by sending his and your own calls. If the calling station does not copy your complete call he will reply with "QRZ", "???" or perhaps "YYY", the latter indicating he has not copied your call. In this case, send your call for the whole of the next period until you receive an 'O' or 'M' report. If you receive "GGG" it means the other station needs your grid, eg IO91, for scoring purposes in a contest.

Equipment

As mentioned earlier, on 144MHz it is possible to work a few of the stations using very large antenna systems with a few hundred watts and a single Yagi. However, if serious EME operation is contemplated you must be prepared to make a considerable investment in time and money. On the receiving side it is essential to achieve the lowest possible system noise figure and this usually means fitting a high performance low-noise preamp at the masthead. To avoid damage to the preamp it is vital to incorporate a properly-designed, fail-safe transmit/receive switching system.

The antenna array should have as much gain as possible combined with a clean polar diagram. On 144 and 432MHz Yagi antennas are the most popular because of their ready availability. Thanks to the research by DL6WU, DJ9BV, K1FO and others, the design of optimum performance Yagis is now available to anyone with a PC and there are several Yagi design and performance analysis programs in the public domain. This author uses DL6WU's doubly-optimised program to design Yagis to make use of available materials and K4VX's excellent YAGIMAX to analyse the performance and design matching systems. This software is listed in the catalogues of advertisers in *Radio Communication* and similar amateur radio publications. Collinear arrays have been used with success by some VHF operators and have the advantage of not being as 'deep' as an equivalent array of long Yagis. On the microwave bands dishes are favoured and there are plenty of graphs and tables in the handbooks to enable you to design your own.

Supporting a large EME antenna array should be regarded as an engineering project, the safety of the complete structure under all weather conditions being of paramount importance. A weak point can be the steering system, commonly referred to as the *az-el rotator*. Obviously the rotator(s) must be able to deal with the weight and inertia of the load imposed so it is essential to ascertain from the supplier that it/they will cope. The system will have to be carefully calibrated so the array can be aimed accurately at the Moon. Some operators adapt the screwjack systems from satellite TV dishes to elevate their EME antennas.

On the transmitting side the aim should be to deliver the maximum licensed power to the antenna array, usually the transfer relay at the masthead. The lowest loss feeder that can be afforded, for the power involved, should be used; there is not much point in generating lots of RF at the output of the PA then wasting 25% of it in the feeder! Such feeder and the appropriate connectors are not cheap if purchased new but sometimes surplus lengths become available from commercial sources. Some surprising bargains can also be found at radio rallies by way of hefty relays and connectors.

There are some proven designs of power amplifiers and associated power supplies and control circuits in the literature such as those by W1SL and K2RIW for 144MHz and 432MHz respectively [69, 70]. Commercial amplifiers are available capable of delivering many hundreds of watts, but if you have the time, skill and a proper understanding of RF engineering, it is very satisfying to build your own amplifier.

Summary

Interest in EME communication is growing steadily. Many regular operators are those who have been, and still are, MS enthusiasts. Both modes have similar equipment and operating requirements. However EME operation can be very frustrating. Having arranged a sked with a much sought-after station, conditions may be ruined by an unpredicted aurora, high winds or static rain. Or you can copy your sked partner perfectly but he hears nothing from you, and vice versa, due to Faraday rotation. Sometimes you hear nothing from your partner then learn later it was because he had a local power failure.

DX ON THE MICROWAVE BANDS

There are 11 internationally allocated amateur microwave bands extending from the 1.3GHz (23cm) band to the 241GHz (1mm) band. Most, but not all, of these bands are available in the UK. All the bands below 24GHz are Amateur Secondary, shared bands, whilst many of the bands above this (including part of the 24GHz band) are Amateur Primary or Amateur Primary (Exclusive).

Since most of the microwave bands are many tens (and sometimes hundreds or thousands) of megahertz wide, is difficult to tune the whole of the band in order to find stations to work. This has led to the use of 'preferred' frequencies or 'preferred' sub-bands and, just as there are voluntary bandplans in all the bands below 1GHz, so there are similar bandplans in all the amateur microwave allocations. The narrow-band sub-bands (or 'segments') were, at one time, based upon either multiples of 144MHz or multiples of 1152MHz, since the microwave frequencies were derived either by multiplying from 144MHz or 1152MHz. It is becoming increasingly difficult to use some of these harmonic relationships, as they no longer lie within the amateur allocations in many countries.

Full details of the current microwave band usage (such as calling and working frequencies for terrestrial and space/EME use) are given in Appendix 9 and are generally very similar to those in the VHF and UHF band plans given there.

Nowadays, modern microwave equipment uses mixing and linear amplifying techniques (as well as multipliers in local oscillator chains) in both receivers and transmitters – *transverters*. Multimode transceivers at 28MHz, 144MHz or 432MHz (or occasionally at 1296MHz) are used as very sensitive and stable intermediate frequency receivers and transmitter signal sources. It should be noted that the direct use of 28MHz as an intermediate frequency is not recommended because the small frequency separation between the local oscillator injection frequency and wanted and unwanted mixing products makes it extremely difficult to produce a 'clean' output signal by filtering the mixer products to suppress both the LO and unwanted (image) product. In this case, it is usual to introduce a 28/144 or 28/432MHz low power transverter between the 28MHz transceiver and the microwave transverter.

MICROWAVE PROPAGATION

Ionospheric propagation never occurs above 1GHz. Indeed, the upper limit appears to be somewhere around the amateur 70cm band (432MHz). There are a few isolated reports claiming to have observed ionospheric propagation at 1.3GHz but these are unconfirmed and very doubtful.

Free-space transmission losses, measured in decibels, increase with the square of the frequency (in megahertz) as well as with the square of the transmission path distance (in kilometres). In addition, above about 23GHz, atmospheric absorption by water, water vapour and oxygen peak in certain frequency bands, adding greatly to the free-space losses. As a consequence, some microwave bands are useable for contacts over very limited distances.

All the tropospheric propagation modes observed at VHF and UHF occur at microwave frequencies. It is becoming apparent, as more regular fixed-station activity takes place, that 'lifts' or 'openings' may occur more frequently than at VHF or UHF because the vertical extent of the tropospheric anomaly can be smaller to have the same effect. That is, the ability of a 'duct' of a particular thickness to propagate radio waves with low-loss (attenuation) is related to frequency – amongst other things! DX of 1000km or more has been worked quite frequently.

In addition, over-the-horizon forward-scatter propagation occurs all of the time because of normal atmospheric irregularities (turbulence) and, often spectacularly, by cloud, rain, hail, snow and aircraft scatter, most of which are on too small a scale to noticeably affect VHF/UHF propagation. Another propagation mode, allied to tropospheric ducts, is the formation of a low-level *super-refraction* layer over large stretches of water, for instance across the North Sea.

It can be seen, therefore, that there are several apparently conflicting factors affecting microwave propagation. On the one hand, settled weather conditions can lead to the formation of ducts and, on the other, turbulent, unsettled weather can enhance scatter modes. Again, at higher microwave frequencies, atmospheric water vapour absorption can increase attenuation and yet super-refraction layers over water (where the humidity is obviously high) can enhance propagation! It is these apparent contradictions which perhaps add to the fascination and challenge of microwave operation.

MICROWAVE EQUIPMENT

Unless efficient equipment is employed – and operated well – results on the microwave bands can be disappointing in terms of distance worked. Until a few years ago, 100km was considered DX on the 23cm band, for instance. There is still very little commercial amateur gear designed to operate on the microwave bands and what there is appears to be relatively inefficient in terms of low power output and sub-optimal receiver sensitivity. There are also few commercially available high-gain

G3PHO/P at Alport Height, near Matlock, Derbyshire operating on 10GHz narrow band

microwave antennas, with the exception of parabolic dishes designed for satellite TV.

Man-made noise and noise emanating from natural sources such as thunderstorms, electrical discharges and sparking decrease in intensity as the frequency increases. This makes it possible to use microwave receivers with very low noise figures to detect really weak signals: this is simply not possible at HF and VHF because the noise 'heard' by the antenna is greater than the noise generated within the receiver itself. A few years ago microwave receivers were very noisy, completely masking the fact that noise levels drop with increasing frequency. Modern gallium arsenide field effect transistors (GaAsFETs) produce so little noise that many decibels of thermal noise emanating from the Sun, Moon or Earth can be detected by amateur receivers, even as high as the 10GHz band, where sub-1dB receiver noise figures are attained. This is a level of performance which could not have been dreamed about 10 years ago, let alone in home-built equipment!

Because of these factors, a well-equipped amateur microwave station will generally consist of home-built, optimised receive and transmit converters operating in conjunction with a good, all-mode VHF or UHF transceiver used as the intermediate frequency, usually at 144MHz but occasionally at 432MHz. Transmit power amplifiers and low-noise receive pre-amplifiers are usually mounted at or very close to the antenna in order to minimise feeder losses and the degradation of receiver noise figure resulting from these feeder losses. The antenna system itself will invariably be designed and constructed to give as much gain as can be engineered and managed: fortunately high-gain microwave antennas are neither unmanageably large nor obtrusive.

Since the advent of satellite TV broadcasting in Ku-band (11 to 13GHz), GaAsFET devices and other components, such as microwave monolithic integrated circuits (MMICs) and surface mount devices (SMDs), as well as complete low-noise amplifiers, block converters and 'set-top' tuners, have become readily and cheaply available. Since Ku band is close to the amateur 10GHz band, the dish antennas, feeds and low-noise block converters can be easily modified to operate in the latter band. Similarly, the set-top tuners cover the range 950 to 1700MHz, which encompasses the amateur 1.3GHz band, and can also be quite easily adapted to amateur use. Such equipment is,however, better suited to amateur wide-band operation, such as ATV, rather than narrow-band operation.

Having said that amateur construction and operation can be greatly aided by the availability of components and equipment, it is still quite difficult to construct or modify equipment for either band, since most modern equipment is constructed on printed circuit board using components which are, in conventional terms, very small. They are thus fairly easily damaged by excessive heating (whilst soldering) or static voltages (whilst handling), although many amateurs new to microwave construction and operating have successfully built, aligned and are operating quite elaborate equipment with a minimum of resources.

THE MICROWAVE BANDS
The 1.3GHz (23cm) band

Solid-state transmitters up to 40–50W, or valved amplifiers to full allowed amateur output, are in common use. Antenna gains, from Yagi or quad-loop Yagi arrays up to about 26dBi are in use for terrestrial QSOs whilst dish gains up to 35dB or more are in common use for EME contacts. Receiver noise levels are well below 1dB.

Terrestrial DX up to 1000–1200km by tropospheric propagation is possible and not uncommon. With the exception of over-water super-refraction paths (West Coast USA to Hawaii, or across the Great Australian Bight), longer paths are easier via the half-million mile Earth-Moon-Earth path! Future uses include amateur satellite Mode L operation where the Earth-to-space uplink is in the 23cm band and the space-to-Earth downlink is in the 70cm (433MHz) band.

The band is popular for ATV and there are growing numbers of ATV and speech repeaters in this band. There are also quite a lot of propagation beacons (between 1296.800 and 1297.000MHz) which help to indicate when tropospheric propagation is good.

Some further information on the 1.3GHz band is given in the VHF/UHF section of this chapter.

The 2.3GHz (13cm), 3.4GHz (9cm) and 5.7GHz (6cm) bands

These three 'intermediate bands' are considered together since comparatively little use has been made of any of them. Transmitter power output levels drop with increasing frequency, either because solid-state power devices become progressively more expensive for a given power output, or because conventional disc-seal valves become less efficient and are definitely 'running out of steam' above 3.4GHz. Receiver noise levels are below 1dB.

At 2.3GHz, distances up to around 860 to 900km for terrestrial contacts are possible, beyond which the EME path is easier! The corresponding terrestrial distance for the 3.4GHz band is a little less, between about 820 and 840km: at 5.7GHz it is about 800 to 820km.

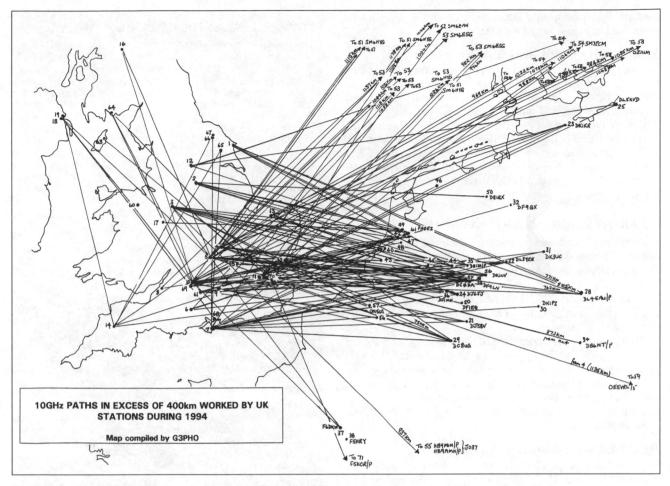

Fig 16. Paths in excess of 400km worked from the UK during 1994

Loop-Yagi antennas are practical up to about the 3.4GHz band. Beyond this, dimensions and constructional tolerance become too critical to make them worthwhile. Consequently, above 3.4GHz, parabolic dish antennas predominate.

Present uses are limited. 2.4GHz and 10GHz beacons have been 'flown' on amateur satellites Oscar 9 and 11 (UOSATs): it is intended that some of these bands will be used for amateur satellite communications, probably starting with the Phase 3D satellites, the first of which is to be launched in early 1996. The next two bands up, 10 and 24GHz, are also likely to be included in these packages which are intended to be in highly elliptical orbits, in order to mimic 'near-geostationary' communications capability (see Chapter 7).

The 10GHz band

This has, for many years, remained a very popular microwave band. This is mainly because very simple, low-powered, wideband FM (speech) transceivers are very easy and inexpensive to construct. These have been based on surplus intruder-alarm doppler units used as both the receiver local oscillator/mixer and the transmitter at power levels in the range 1mW to 30 or 40mW. The techniques are simple and serve as an admirable introduction to microwave operation over short distances from fixed locations, or longer line-of-sight paths when operated portable.

A small dish antenna, typically 600mm diameter, may have a gain of 35dB or more and a beamwidth of one or two degrees. This makes accurate antenna pointing important: at the same time, the antenna gain on both receive and transmit is such that a 10mW station 'sounds' like a 10W station.

Since the advent of satellite TV broadcasting (at 11 to 13GHz), much surplus equipment has appeared on the amateur market. This has proved to be very easily modified for ATV use at 10GHz and so the band is much used for this mode. Normally distances of up to 150km, line-of-sight, with either WBFM speech or ATV, are possible.

At the same time as satellite TV broadcasting started to expand, amateur-designed narrow-band (linear) transverter designs, suitable for all-mode transmission and reception, appeared. In the UK, the local oscillator designs of G4DDK, the transmit and receive converters and power amplifiers of G3WDG and the transverter control circuits of G3SEK or G4JNT have enabled the home construction of very effective equipment for this band. Transmit powers up to 1W, solid-state, or 5 to 30W using travelling wave tube amplifiers (TWTAs) are within the grasp of many home-based stations. Receiver noise figures can, again, be below or around 1dB. Coupled with enough antenna gain (say a 4 or 5m dish), EME contacts are possible.

Under good tropospheric propagation conditions, even a modestly powered home station with, say, 1W output power, a 2dB receiver noise figure and a small (600mm) dish antenna can work distances up to around 1000km. Fig 16 shows some of the paths worked from the UK, on the 3cm band, mainly due to favourable tropospheric conditions in late October 1994. There have been similar openings since, and the world record for terrestrial tropospheric DX is almost 2000km. The USA to Australia has been worked by EME.

The 24GHz band and higher

Not enough work has yet been done to prove the real worth of these bands, although fairly long-distance terrestrial communications ought to be possible on the 24 and 47GHz bands and worldwide ranges, via amateur satellites, will be possible. Although the technology exists, most amateurs are several years away from being able to afford the devices or learn the skills necessary to exploit the 'millimetre' bands. Work has started, with low powers (currently well below 1W), high antenna gain, narrow-band (CW) techniques and is yielding promising results!

VHF/UHF/MICROWAVE AWARDS

Naturally the awards and certificates for HF operating (see p57) can also be gained for work on the higher frequencies, though this is usually much more difficult. For example, a Worked All Continents award is easy for the average 14 or 21 MHz operator to acquire, but a 432MHz WAC is another thing altogether, implying the use of moonbounce techniques, and possibly years of technical refinement.

There are, however, some awards available specifically for the VHF, UHF and microwaves. In the UK the RSGB issues various awards which are also available to non-members. The rules, current at the time of going press, for these are shown below but please remember they are subject to change and before applying you should check wth the RSGB VHF/UHF Awards Manager.

RSGB 50MHz Countries Award

The initial qualification for this certificate is proof of completed two-way QSOs on 50MHz with 10 countries. Stickers will be provided for increments of every 10 countries worked. Only contacts with countries permitting 50MHz operation can be considered.

Rules
1. All contacts must have been on or after 1 June 1987.
2. QSL cards submitted must be arranged in alphabetical order of the countries claimed, and a checklist enclosed.
3. Stations are eligible for awards in the following categories:
   (a) Fixed stations.
   (b) Temporary location or portable operation (/P).
   Categories cannot be mixed.

RSGB 50MHz DX Certificate

This certificate takes into account the considerable potential for cross-band working when transmitting in the 50MHz band. There is therefore no stipulation on the band used for the incoming signal. The initial qualification is confirmation from 25 different countries of a successful QSO with transmission from the applicant's country taking place within the 50MHz band. Stickers will be provided for increments of 25 countries confirmed.

Rules
1. All contacts must have been on or after 1 June 1987.
2. QSL cards submitted must be arranged in alphabetical order of the countries claimed, and a checklist enclosed.
3. Stations are eligible for awards in the following categories:
   (a) Fixed stations.
   (b) Temporary location or portable operation (/P).
   Categories cannot be mixed.

GENERAL RULES FOR RSGB VHF/UHF AWARDS

1. Awards are available to licensed amateurs and listeners (on a heard basis). All claims must be fully supported by QSL cards. For the various squares awards, these cards must also bear the IARU (Maidenhead) locator details. A card without an IARU locator originally printed on it is acceptable provided that it bears some adequate form of positional information (for example old QTH locator or latitude and longitude), in which case the IARU locator square designation should be clearly added to the card by the award claimant.
2. For all awards with a fixed station category, the applicant must state that all the contacts were made from the same location. In the case of an amateur moving home location he/she may apply for the award using QSL cards gained from more than one location, but the award will be endorsed as 'gained from more than one location'.
3. Endorsements such as all CW, all SSB, all auroral contacts, or all contacts made during the first year of being licensed may be made on application. The appropriate information must be contained on the QSL cards and a declaration signed when applying for endorsements.
4. The charges for awards in 1995 were: RSGB members £3, US$6 or 12 IRCs. UK residents who are not RSGB members £6, US$12 or 24 IRCs. Overseas applicants who are members of their national society £6, US$12 or 24 IRCs. Other overseas applicants £9, US$18 or 36 ircs. Where applicable proof of membership of their national (IARU approved) society is required, eg recent *Radio Commmunication* label or photocopy of membership card. There is no charge for stickers to update levels of achievement, however, if a new certificate is requested, the charges above will apply.
5. All claims must be submitted to the RSGB VHF/UHF Awards Manager, Ian L Cornes, G4OUT, 6 Haywood Heights, Little Haywood, Stafford, ST18 0UR. Application forms may be obtained from this address by sending an SAE.
6. For the safe return of the QSL cards, adequate postage and a self addressed envelope must be sent with the application.

RSGB 50MHz Squares Award

The 50MHz Squares Award is intended to mark successful VHF achievement. The initial qualification needed for this certificate is proof that 25 different locator squares have been worked with complete two-way QSOs within the 50MHz band. Squares in any country will qualify provided that operation from that country is formally authorised. Additional stickers will be provided when proof is submitted for increments of 25 squares.

Rules
1. All contacts must have been on or after 1 June 1987.
2. QSL cards submitted must be arranged in alphabetical order of the QTH squares claimed, and a checklist enclosed.
3. Stations are eligible for awards in the following categories:
   (a) Fixed stations.
   (b) Temporary location or portable operation (/P).
   Categories cannot be mixed.

4-2-70 Squares Award

The 4-2-70 Squares Awards are intended to mark successful VHF/UHF achievement. Initially, a certificate and one sticker will be issued. Further stickers will be issued as additional locator squares are claimed. The title of each award gives the number of locator squares and countries needed to qualify for the award. For example, to obtain the 144MHz 40/10 award you must have QSL cards confirming contact with 40 locator

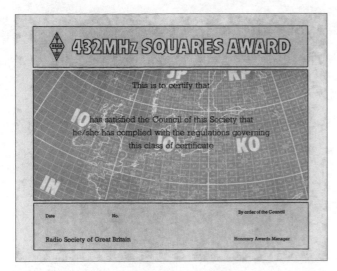

squares including 10 countries on 144MHz. The following awards are available:

70MHz	20/4	144MHz	40/10	432MHz	30/6
70MHz	25/6	144MHz	60/15	432MHz	40/10
70MHz	30/8	144MHz	80/18	432MHz	50/13
70MHz	35/8	144MHz	100/20	432MHz	60/15
70MHz	40/8	144MHz	125/20	432MHz	70/15
70MHz	45/8	144MHz	150/20	432MHz	80/15
70MHz	50/8	144MHz	175/20	432MHz	90/15
		144MHz	200/30	432MHz	100/15
		144MHz	225/30	432MHz	110/15
		144MHz	250/35	432MHz	120/18
		144MHz	275/35	432MHz	130/18
		144MHz	300/40	432MHz	140/20
		144MHz	325/40	432MHz	150/20
		144MHz	350/45		
		144MHz	375/45		
		144MHz	400/50		
		144MHz	425/50		
		144MHz	450/50		

Rules
1. All contacts must have been after 31 December 1978.
2. Eligible countries are those shown in the countries list printed in the 1995 edition of the *RSGB Amateur Radio Call Book*.
3. Stations are eligible for awards in the following categories:
   (a) Fixed stations.
   (b) Portable stations, any location.
   (c) Mobile stations, any location.
   Categories cannot be mixed.
4. QSL cards submitted must be arranged in alphabetical order of the QTH squares claimed, and a checklist enclosed.

VHF Countries and Counties Awards
The following awards, intended to mark successful VHF/UHF achievements, are available:

Title of Award	Requirement Countries	Counties
50MHz Standard Transmitting	12	40
50MHz Senior Transmitting	20	60
50MHz Standard Receiving	12	40
50MHz Senior Receiving	20	60
70MHz Standard Transmitting	3	30
70MHz Senior Transmitting	6	60
70MHz Standard Receiving	3	30
70MHz Senior Receiving	6	60
144MHz Standard Transmitting	9	40
144MHz Senior Transmitting	15	60
144MHz Standard Receiving	9	40
144MHz Senior Receiving	15	60
432MHz Standard Transmitting	3	20
432MHz Senior Transmitting	9	40
432MHz Standard Receiving	3	20
432MHz Senior Receiving	9	40
1296MHz Standard Transmitting	3	20
1296MHz Senior Transmitting	6	40
1296MHz Standard Receiving	3	20
1296MHz Senior Receiving	6	40

Supreme Award (for fixed stations only) For holding: 3 Senior awards or 2 Senior + one 1296MHz Awards.

Rules
1. All contacts must have been made after 1 January 1961, in respect of old UK counties, or after 1 January 1975, in respect of new counties. Scotland revisions with effect from 1 January 1976. Start date for 50MHz contacts 1 June 1987.
2. Eligible counties are those listed in the 1995 edition of the *RSGB Amateur Radio Call Book*.
3. Stations are eligible for awards in the following categories:
   (a) Fixed stations;
   (b) Portable stations (/P any location);
   (c) Mobile stations (/M any location).
   Categories cannot be mixed.
4. Each different confirmed contact with a station in a Scottish region counts up to a maximum of three per region.

Microwave Award
The following awards, intended to mark achievement on the microwave bands, are available. Successful applicants will initially receive a certificate and one sticker; further stickers will be issued as later claims are received.

Locators:

Award	Two-way contact with locator squares
1.3GHz / 5	5
1.3GHz / 10	10
1.3GHz / 15	15
1.3GHz / 20	20
1.3GHz / 25 etc (up to 80)	80
2.3GHz / 5	5
2.3GHz / 10, 15, 20, 25 etc	as 1.3GHz
3.4GHz / 5	5
3.4GHz / 10, 15, 20, 25 etc	as 1.3GHz
5.7GHz / 5	5
5.7GHz / 10, 15, 20, 25 etc	as 1.3GHz
10GHz / 5	5
10GHz / 10, 15, 20, 25 etc	as 1.3GHz
24GHz / 5	5
24GHz / 10, 15, 20, 25 etc	as 1.3GHz

Countries + Counties:
Two-way contact with three countries and 20 UK counties on 1.3GHz, 2.3GHz, 3.4GHz, 5.7GHz, 10GHz and 24GHz. For the purposes of the Award a county is defined as that current at the time of introduction of the award.

Rules
1. All claims must be fully supported by QSL cards carrying the relevant IARU Locator information or Country-and-County information.
2. All contacts must be made after 31 December 1978.
3. Eligible countries are those listed overleaf.
4. Stations are eligible for awards in the following categories:
   (a) Fixed stations;
   (b) Portable and mobile stations. (The applicant must state that the operation was from one site, defined as being anywhere within a 5km radius of the point.)
   Categories cannot be mixed.
5. QSL cards submitted should be listed and arranged in IARU QTH locator alphabetical numeric order.

Microwave Distance Award
The following distance awards, intended to mark achievement on the microwave bands, are available.

1.3GHz	for the first contact made beyond a distance of 600km
2.3GHz	for the first contact made beyond a distance of 500km
3.4GHz	for the first contact made beyond a distance of 400km
5.6GHz	for the first contact made beyond a distance of 300km
10GHz	for the first contact made beyond a distance of 150km (Basic Class)
10GHz	for the first contact made beyond a distance of 300km (Intermediate Class)
10GHz	for the first contact made beyond a distance of 600km (Advanced Class)
24GHz	for the first contact made beyond a distance of 25km (Basic class)
24GHz	for the first contact made beyond a distance of 75km (Intermediate class)
24GHz	for the first contact made beyond a distance

Rules
1. Stations are eligible for awards in the following categories:
   (a) Fixed stations;
   (b) Portable stations (/P any location);
   (c) Mobile stations (/M any location).

FURTHER INFORMATION
SWL clubs
[1] International Short Wave League; details from Mrs E May, G0OZI, 10 Clyde Crescent, Wharton, Winsford, Cheshire CW7 3LA.
[2] International Listeners' Association; details from Trevor Morgan, GW4OXB, 1 Jersey St, Hafod, Swansea, SA1 2HF.

HF antennas
[3] 'HF DX – the inside story. Part 1: Antennas, rotators and towers', Ian Buffhan, G3TMA, and Bob Whelan, G3PJT, *Radio Communication* June 1992.
[4] *Radio Communication Handbook*, 6th edn, ed Dick Biddulph, G8DPS, RSGB, 1994, Chapter 12.
[5] *Practical Wire Antennas*, John Heys, G3BDQ, RSGB, 1989.
[6] *HF Antennas for All Locations*, 2nd edn, Les Moxon, G6XN, RSGB, 1993.
[7] *HF Antenna Collection*, ed Erwin David, G4LQI, RSGB, 1991.
[8] *ARRL Antenna Book*, ARRL.

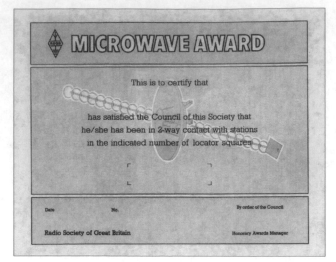

[9] *The ARRL Antenna Anthology*, Vols 1–3, ARRL.
[10] *All About Beam Antennas*, Bill Orr, W6SAI, and Stu Cowan, W2LX, RPI.
[11] *All about Cubical Quad Antennas*, Bill Orr, W6SAI, and Stu Cowan, W2LX, RPI.

HF receivers etc
[12] 'HF DX – the inside story. Part 2: Receivers and transmitters', Peter Hart, G3SJX, and Ian White, G3SEK, *Radio Communciation* July 1992.
[13] 'Dynamic range, intermodulation and phase noise', Peter Chadwick, G3RZP, *Radio Communication* March 1984.
[14] 'Modern receiver front-end design', Ian White, G3SEK, *Radio Communication* April-July 1985.

HF DX information
[15] 'HF DX – the inside story. Part 3: Information and software', Don Field, G3XTT, *Radio Communication* August 1992.
[16] *The DX Magazine*, produced by VP2ML, PO Box 150, Fulton, CA 95439, USA.
[17] *DX News-Sheet*, produced weekly by the RSGB, is an up-to-date tip-sheet of special and rare station activity, plus propagation data, edited by G4BUE. Subscription details from RSGB HQ.
[18] *Les Nouvelles DX*, produced (in French) by F6AJA, 515 Rue de Petit Hem, F-59870 Bouvignies, France.

Propagation
[19] 'HF DX – the inside story. Part 4: Operating and propagation', Martin Atherton, G3ZAY, *Radio Communciation* August 1992.
[20] *Radio Communication Handbook*, 6th edn, ed Dick Biddulph, G8DPS, RSGB, 1994, Chapter 11.
[21] 'Some new insights into the mechanism of the sunspot cycle', F M Smith, G8KG, *Radio Communication* July 1976.
[22] 'The DXer's crystal ball', *QST* June/August 1975.
[23] 'A breakthrough in simplifying ionospheric propagation forecasts', *CQ* March 1975.
[24] *The Shortwave Propagation Handbook*, George Jacob, W3ASK, and Theodore J Cohen, N4XX, CQ Magazine.
[25] *Radio Wave Propagation*, F C Judd, G2BCX, Heinemann.
[26] *Radio Propagation Handbook*, Peter N Saveskie, Tab Books.

General HF DXing

[27] *Secrets of Ham Radio DXing*, Dave Ingram, K4TWJ, Tab Books.

[28] *The Complete DXer*, Bob Locher, W9KNI, Idiom Press, Box 583, Deerfield, IL 60015, USA.

[29] *Low Band DXing*, John Devoldere, ON4UN, ARRL.

QRP

[30] *Solid-state QRP Projects*, W3FQJ, Editors and Engineers.

[31] *G-QRP Club Circuit Handbook*, 1983.

[32] *G-QRP Club Antenna Handbook*, 1992.

[33] *Solid State Design for the Radio Amateur*, Wes Hayward, W7ZOI, and Doug DeMaw, W1FB, ARRL, 1977.

[34] *QRP Notebook*, Doug DeMaw, W1FB, ARRL, 1991.

[35] *W1FB's Design Notebook*, Doug DeMaw, W1FB, ARRL, 1990.

[36] *QRP Classics*, ARRL, 1990.

[37] The G-QRP Club. [Up to 5 watts] c/o John Leak, G0BXO, Flat 7, 56 Heath Crescent, Halifax, HX1 2PW.

[38] QRP Amateur Radio Club International, c/o Michael Bryce, WB8VGE, 2225 Mayflower, N W Massilon, OH 44647, USA.

[39] CW Operators QRP Club, c/o Kevin Zietz, VK5AKZ, 41 Tobruk Ave, St Marys, SA 5042, Australia.

[40] OK QRP Klubu, c/o Petr Doudera, OK1CZ, Ul Baterie 1, 16200, Praha 6.

Awards

[41] *Amateur Radio Awards*, 3rd edn, Cris Henderson, G4FAM, RSGB, 1988 (out of print).

[42] RSGB HF Certificates and Awards leaflet.

[43] ARRL DXCC List (CD216) and form (CD164).

[44] RSGB Countries List leaflet.

[45] Worked All Britain Award, c/o Keith Draycott, G3UQT, 28 Ladywood Road, Kirk Hallam, Ilkeston, Derbyshire.

[46] Worked All Zones Award, CQ Magazine, 76 North Broadway, Hicksville, NY 11801, USA.

VHF/UHF

[47] 'Locator system for VHF and UHF', J Morris, GM4ANB, *Radio Communication* November 1980.

[48] 'The new locator system', J Morris, GM4ANB, *Radio Communication* October 1984.

[49] Detailed Spectrum Investigation Phase 2, 29.7–960MHz,

Section 10.4.3 Spectrum Issues, European Radiocommunications Committee. See also *Radio Communication* June 1995, pp30–31.

[56] *VHF/UHF Manual*, 4th edn, ed G R Jessop, G6JP, RSGB, Chapter 9.

[57] '1kW power amplifier for 23cm', Karl Schötz, DL9EBL, *Dubus Magazine* 3/1993.

[58] *VHF/UHF DX Book*, ed Ian White, G3SEK, DIR Publishing Ltd, 1992, Chapter 2.

[59] 'Sporadic E studies', Jim Bacon, G3YLA, *Radio Communication* May–August 1989.

[60] 'Plotting of magnetic deviation and aurora', D J Smillie, GM4DJS, *Radio Communication* February and March 1992.

[61] 'Meteor scatter: theory and practice', T Damboldt, DJ5DT, *VHF Communications* 4/1974.

[62] 'The astronomy of meteor scatter', J R Matthews, G3WZT, *Radio Communication* May 1981.

[63] *Meteor Shower Data*, RSGB (a computer list).

[64] MS-Soft suite of meteor scatter programs written by Ilkka Yrjölä, OH5IY, Jukolantie 16, FIN-45740 Kuusankoski, Finland. Available on the Internet at ftp.funet.fi in the pub/ham/VHF-work/ directory. The current filename is mssof42f.zip.

[65] *432 and Above EME News* edited by Allen Katz, K2UYH, Engineering Dept, Trenton State College, Trenton, NJ 08650-4700, USA. E-mail address a.katz@ieee.org.

[66] MOON.BAS High Performance Moon Tracking Program written by Lance Collister, WA1JXN. CP/M and PC versions available.

[67] EME.EXE Moon tracking suite of programs written by Doug McArthur, VK3UM, 'Tikaluna', 26 Old Murrindindi Road, Glenburn, Victoria, Australia 3717. Versions written for PCs with and without math co-processors.

[68] TRACKING.EXE and SETUP.EXE written by Jean-Jacques Maintoux, F1EHN, 24 rue de Villacoublay, F-78140 Velizy, France. Now ported to Windows 3.x. Ready-made tracking interface board available.

[69] 'The W1SL 144MHz power amplifier', John Nelson, GW4FRX, in *VHF/UHF DX Book*, ed Ian White, G3SEK, DIR Publishing Ltd, 1992, Chapter 8.

[70] 'The K2RIW power amplifier', John Nelson, GW4FRX, in *VHF/UHF DX Book*, ed Ian White, G3SEK, DIR Publishing Ltd, 1992, Chapter 10.

5 Contests

CONTESTING is one of the most popular activities in amateur radio, and has been for a very long time. For many amateurs, it is a real incentive to improve their operating skills and station efficiency, for others an enjoyable chance to be part of a team competing with antenna arrays and equipment which they could only dream about in a home environment.

In this chapter HF and VHF/UHF contest operating are discussed separately but there is of course much in common and the would-be contest operator will benefit by reading both sections. There is also a section on amateur radio direction finding, an increasingly popular form of contesting which combines physical effort and radio skills, and which can be enjoyed by young contestants without transmitting licences.

HF CONTESTS

Most national societies around the world organise HF contests for their members, catering for all levels of operating ability and sophistication of equipment, and several societies also organise international contests.

The prime object is to encourage entrants to develop their operating skills, study and obtain a better understanding of propagation and experiment with equipment and antennas with a view to improving the overall performance of their stations. A contest is, by definition, a competitive activity but there is a wide range of different scoring schemes so that it is not always the entrant with the greatest number of QSOs who wins. Many events use a system of 'multipliers' so that, for example, the final score is made up of the QSO points multiplied by the number of countries worked on each band. Some RSGB contests use bonus points for new countries rather than multipliers.

Most modes, frequencies and power levels are catered for, with the exception of 10, 18 and 24MHz which it has been agreed through the IARU shall remain free of contests. Almost without exception the prizes offered for these events are non-monetary, usually consisting of certificate or a trophy that the winner holds for one year.

During international HF contests, stations will be active all over the world, which provides a unique opportunity to test new antennas and equipment. If one is working for an award that requires contacting stations on islands, in countries or rare locations then these events do offer an excellent opportunity to establish contact with such places. There is no doubt that the main international events create a lot of worldwide interest and band activity. Under these circumstances, confirmation of a contact can take longer as the contestant will have to write out his log before tackling QSL cards and may have had in excess of 1000 contacts.

Contests fall broadly into two categories – single operator and multi-operator. The former, as its name implies, is for

stations operated by one person only for the duration of the contest. Most organisers define this quite closely, insisting that all of the station operating including logging and check listing is done by one person only. Forward planning is essential and is dealt with in detail later. Some people can operate for 48 hours without sleep, while others find difficult to concentrate after operating for 18 hours. Most experienced contest operators can operate for a 24 hour period with only brief breaks to attend to nature's demands! It is important that anyone intending to enter a major contest on a serious basis should develop the ability to do this.

Multi-operator contests usually include a separate section for group entries which are particularly well supported in Eastern Europe where the pattern of club operating activity is well established. However in recent years this mode of operation has become increasingly popular in the West, and in particular in the USA. Callsigns belonging to the different contest groups are regularly heard in all the major events. While multi-operator contests may lighten the load on the individual, they bring fresh problems of their own – particularly organisation. The majority of contests specify CW or SSB, with many the major events having separate sections on different weekends catering for each mode. There are differing opinions on the relative merits of CW and SSB in contests. Many people find that higher scoring rates can be achieved on SSB, while to others CW is more personal, less tiring and more of a test of individual skills. Certainly SSB contests tend to require more extensive equipment and antenna systems than CW events.

RSGB HF contests

The policy of the Society's HF Contests Committee is to organise events that cater for all sections of the membership – annual calendars of both RSGB and international contests are shown on the next page.

Although quite a number of contests do require contacts outside the operator's own country, there are several of the RSGB events that feature inter-UK working. For RSGB events the contest exchange usually consists of a signal report followed by an incrementing serial number – though there are exceptions.

Among the most popular events are *The Affiliated Societies Contests* (AFS) which take place annually in January. Members of RSGB affiliated societies operate from their own homes but their logs are grouped together into teams and submitted as a combined club score. In the CW event five members constitute a team, and for SSB there are three in a team. Each AFS contest lasts for four hours.

An ideal series of contests for potential contest operators wishing to gain experience and improve their operating skills are the *Cumulatives*. Out of a series of three sessions, two count for points. Logs from all sections are always welcomed by the adjudicator for checking purposes. These events start early in

HF CONTEST CALENDAR

Month	RSGB contests	International contests
January:	Cumulatives on 1.8, 3.5 and 7MHz Affiliated Societies Contest	CQ 1.8MHz CW DX Contest REF CW Contest
February:	First 1.8MHz Contest 7MHz CW Contest	ARRL DX CW Contest VERON CW and SSB Contests REF SSB Contest
March:	Commonwealth Contest	ARRL DX SSB Contest Bermuda CW and SSB Contest CQ WPX SSB Contest
April:	Ropoco 1 Low Power Fixed	Helvetia (USKA) CW and SSB Contest European Sprint SSB
May:	—	ARI International CW and SSB European Sprint CW CQ WPX CW Contest
June:	National Field Day Summer 1.8MHz	All Asia DX SSB Contest IARU HF Championship
July:	Low Power Field Day IOTA Contest	—
August:	Ropoco 2	All Asia DX CW Contest DARC European DX CW Contest
September:	SSB Field Day	DARC European DX SSB Contest Scandinavian Activity Contests
October:	21 and 28MHz SSB Contest 21MHz CW Contest	CQ DX SSB Contest VK/ZL Contests European Sprint SSB European Sprint CW
November:	Second 1.8MHz Contest Club Calls Contest	CQ DX CW Contest
December:	—	ARRL 28MHz CW and SSB Contests Canadian CW and SSB Contests

January on weekday evenings on 1.8MHz and at the weekends on 7 and 3.5MHz – all on CW. As there is a training element to these events, when checking is completed, the adjudicator may write to entrants who have lost a number of points offering constructive advice. Contestants with considerable experience of contest operating are encouraged to offer advice on-air during the event.

Some contests allow separate entries for the specialised interest of QRP and the RSGB recognises this group by running special QRP contests. The *RSGB Low Power Fixed Contest* is a two band event run in April on 3.5 and 7MHz CW, as is the *Low Power Field Day* in mid-July. Another QRP contest is organised by the German DLAGCW CW activity group which takes place twice a year in January and July. This group also runs a short 'Happy New Year' on 1 January which features a QRP section.

Worthy of special mention are the *RSGB ROPOCO Contests*. In these events accuracy of information in the exchange is of primary importance rather than operating speed. The contest exchange consists of RST plus the postcode. It is essential to ensure that codes are copied correctly at the time that they are sent, for the code received in one contact is passed on in the next contact, and so on. The postcodes thus rotate, hence the name: ROtating POst COdes.

In contrast another spring event is the *RSGB Commonwealth Contest* (formerly BERU) where the accent is more on quality than quantity. This contest is limited to 24 hours and is a fascinating contest with its requirement to 'dig out' various Commonwealth call areas on different bands.

During the summer months two events – *RSGB National Field Day (NFD)* and *SSB Field Day* – take place. The former ranks as one of the Society's major events. The contest has evolved from a low-power event which encouraged the use of home-brew transmitters and receivers to one designed to recognise the use of modern commercial equipment but at the same time retaining the requirement to operate under emergency conditions, ie without mains power supplies and away from permanent buildings. NFD is split into two sections, giving scope for both large and small groups to compete. In the open section the only limitation on antennas is that they must not be higher than 65ft whereas in the restricted section only one antenna is permitted with no more than two supports up to 36ft high. The general strategy remains the same for both sections. Carefully study the rules to allow maximum latitude of operation. Learn as much as possible from the results of previous years – this is important to a club trying to improve its overall position in the results table. For example, it is apparent that the outright winners of NFD rarely win an individual band award. This leads to the conclusion that some equality of operation between different bands must be established, although in some instances the leading station on 14MHz has also been the overall winner due to the large potential score that can be realised from contacts with North America.

September's SSB Field Day is a rather more recent addition to the contest calendar. In the open section there are no restrictions on antennas and it is left to the ingenuity of individual groups to set up the most extensive effective arrays possible, though complexity does not always pay off!

Following the example of NFD a restricted section has been introduced, again catering for the smaller group. The dates and times of both field days are co-ordinated within IARU Region 1 and the key to success is to work a high proportion of European portables.

The *Club Calls Contest* (CCC) is a club-based contest in November in 1.8MHz, designed to encourage use of this band and also to allow clubs to 'air' their distinctive club callsigns. Class B members also have an opportunity of entering a club HF event under supervision.

International contests

Turning now to the international scene, the main event of the spring is the *ARRL DX Contest*. The object here is to contact only stations operating from Canada and the USA, which at first sight may not seem terribly interesting. However, this is not the case – American states and Canadian provinces on each band provide multipliers which adds a great deal of interest. Furthermore, it is apparent that North American stations comprise probably the most efficient contesters in the world and this makes contacting them in quantity a real pleasure. Quantity it

Chris Swallow, G3VHB, operating as G3VHB/P in the RSGB National Field Day Contest, June 1994

really is too. In this event, 3000 QSOs on one mode is quite normal and there is every prospect of higher totals to come with improved band conditions, antennas, receivers and the availability of computers to a growing number of licensees. Yet another major spring event is the *WPX Contest* sponsored by CQ Magazine in which prefixes serve as multipliers. There are separate CW and SSB events which are very good for multi-operator participation.

Undoubtedly the biggest event of the year is the *CQ Magazine World Wide Contest*, with the phone event being held on the last full weekend in October and the CW section on the last full weekend in November. This is a contest where you contact anything and everything. There are separate sections: single-operator with or without packet, multi-band, multi-operator or single band – in other words there's something for everybody.

Organisation and strategy
Whatever the mode, whatever the contest, the key to success lies in detailed preparation, with the emphasis on detail. This really does mean thoroughly going through everything which is associated with the contest. Some first-time participants do not pursue contest operating further because during their first event they find their scores are low compared with the other UK stations. What they do not realise is that the leading stations may have well spent a whole year preparing for that single event, testing equipment and antennas, analysing results and planning strategy.

What is meant by 'strategy'? Basically this is the combination of operating technique, band changing, multiplier hunting, timing of meals, shack organisation, sleeping arrangements and a host of other factors which, when taken together, mean that you will at least make one more point than your nearest rival and thus win the contest. Take a look at the results of a few contests. It is surprising how often there is a very narrow margin between first and second place. Although 'Murphy's Law' can play its part, the difference is usually due to attention paid to relatively small details in station performance.

Rules
Contest rules for individual events are published by the organisers and are summarised in magazines such as *Radio Communication*, *QST*, *CQ*, *NCJ* (National Contest Journal) and various DX news-sheets. (Details of the subscription rates for these other magazines and news sheets appear regularly in *Radio Communication*).

Contests organised by the RSGB are shown in *Radio Communication* in the regular feature 'Contest Classified', while a

summary of some other events appears in 'HF News'. There is also the RSGB Contesting Guide which appears in the September issue. It is recommended that a full set of rules be obtained by any competitor considering a serious entry.

It may seem obvious to say "read the rules", but many participants do not *read* them, they glance through them or read them after the event! Read carefully so that a clear understanding is obtained of exactly what the organisers require as well as what is not required! For example, some contests automatically disqualify entrants with more than 2% duplicates. Make sure the points and multiplier system is understood. Some contest organisers request copies of an entrant's dupe sheet if the number of contacts exceed a specified number. It is always helpful to the adjudicator to include it – it does make checking considerably easier. Note the closing date for submitting entries and to whom the log has to be sent. Again organisers vary, some request that the log be posted by a certain date, others that the entry must be received by a certain date. In the latter case it is important to check that the mailing method will ensure that the entry arrives in time. The post office can give you an *approximate* time that a letter will take. Having taken the trouble to participate and write up your log, it may be worthwhile including a stamped self-addressed post card (airmail if abroad, with IRCs rather than stamps) acknowledging that your entry has arrived safely and in time.

Propagation
For HF contests, knowing when bands are likely to be open to various parts of the world at different times is a basic necessity and the reader is advised to become familiar with the information presented in Chapter 4. A set of detailed predictions for the month of the contest is ideal. A variety of computer programs are available for propagation predictions, for example Mini-Prop, which allows you to enter radiation angle, estimated solar flux number and a choice of either long-path or short-path predictions. Use may also be made of the grey-line DX path. Originally this method was developed for 3.5 and 1.8MHz DX but the principle applies equally well to the other HF bands. There are both computerised and manual methods of calculating the path parameters. These calculations can be given visually using a DX Edge available from the RSGB (see Chapter 4). Referring to last year's copies of the RSGB *DX Newsheet* can be very enlightening for obtaining a weekly analysis of the DX worked and heard from the UK. Remember that 28, 21, 14MHz, and to a certain degree 7 and 3.5MHz, all follow a similar pattern, but the lower the frequency, the shorter the opening. Note that European contacts can sometimes be made more easily by beaming due south, particularly on 21 and 28 MHz. The frequencies of the 28MHz beacons should be known for they can be an excellent guide to conditions on that band. Don't forget the 14.1MHz worldwide beacon service (see Chapter 4). Beacon frequencies are given in Appendix 10.

Antennas and equipment
Antennas are a crucial part of the contest station, the one item that offers the greatest scope for ingenuity and experimental work. The antenna used must be suitable for the particular contest in mind; for example, it's no use trying to work a lot of Europeans on 7MHz with a ground plane. A dipole fairly close to the ground would provide a greater contact rate. Conversely the low dipole would be of little use in trying to work into Australia where a good low-angle radiation pattern is required. Similarly, forward gain might be beneficial under some circumstances, but a good front-to-back ratio could be just as

important to reduce European QRM for DX contacts. The subject is vast and there are several excellent books available from the RSGB dealing with all aspects of the subject.

During the contest there may be several stations using high-gain antennas, erected just for the event, that can overload your receiver. Even with a top-grade receiver a step attenuator in the receive antenna line can make all the difference between 100% copy and none at all, particularly on 7 and 3.5MHz. Experiment with equipment layout to find the arrangement that suits you best. It is apparent from viewing several top contest stations that none are exactly the same. The arrangement of receiver, transmitter, keyer, clock and check lists so that operating is comfortable and everything comes to hand easily is very personal.

Multi-operator, multi-band contests have one additional facet. *All* of the equipment must be capable of operating simultaneously without degrading receiver performance on each band. Commercial filters are available which will help to cut down inter-station interference, or they may be home-brewed.

Many operators enter their first contest from their home station only to find shortcomings in the station configuration. It is important that the station equipment is capable of virtually continuous operation for the duration of the event. Other shortcomings may become very apparent during a long period of operating. For example, the keying monitor may be too loud or too soft. The antenna rotator may go out of sync. The VFO tuning knob may be just a little too high from the operating table for comfort during a long spell of operating. The chair which for occasional sessions in the shack seemed ideal can become very uncomfortable after 36 hours. It is surprising how few chairs are really comfortable for long periods. The operating table may be just a little too narrow, so that check lists keep dropping onto the floor.

It must be the aim of every serious contest operator to use the best possible equipment available. A thorough examination of all the equipment should be made in the months prior to the event – do not leave everything to the last minute! If the station for the contest station is to be made up of equipment borrowed for the occasion from friends or club members, check that the system works well in advance and that everything is compatible.

Regular maintenance is also very important. Most serious contesters maintain and experiment with antennas during the summer months and service all their equipment during the winter. If there is the slightest doubt about an item of equipment - check it. It may take a whole day to bring down and check a beam only to find that everything is working fine but at least your mind has been put at rest and the confidence that everything is working well is worth many extra points.

Some maintenance procedures that should be carried out regularly are to examine all coaxial fittings and ensure that the weather-proofing is still intact, and to check all feeders for excessive loss. Checks for any EMC problems on all bands should of course be made regularly.

Contest operating can be an enjoyable club activity – potential exists for large antenna arrays to be used that would be impossible from most amateurs' home locations. Even a modest operation will depend for its success on the planning and organisation that is applied prior to the event.

Organisation of club entries

One of the first decisions to be made is the attitude of club members – do they want to enter for the fun of the event and gain contest experience or are they entering as a dedicated band

Using a trailer-mounted telescopic tower and beam will greatly simplify antenna erection. This is G3VHB (left) and G3LNS raising the TH7 beam for G3VHB/P in NFD 1994

of enthusiasts who are prepared to go to some lengths to win? Entering to win can be very hard work, requiring a lot of time and dedication. Entering for fun is as easy as you make it, but more ambitious members of the group may not be satisfied. Achieving a balanced approach is a special skill required of a club contest manager.

The most difficult problem that groups always have to face is the question of operators. A club may for example have two really proficient CW contest operators, but many a lengthy committee meeting has been held to try and decide how long these two should operate when balanced against the need to placate say 30 other members who have come along to help put the station on the air and provide equipment. One person should have overall responsibility for the group effort. It is up to him or her to ask other members to take on particular aspects of the organisation as needed. Responsibilities can be divided in several ways, eg site and accommodation, transport, power, eating arrangements, antennas, antenna erection and equipment for use on each band. Decide on how big a contest you are going to tackle. A multi-band 48 hour contest needs a lot of operators and equipment for a successful entry. A more modest effort to gain experience is advised for a group just embarking on contest operating as a club activity. Next find a good site and obtain permission to use it. There is no doubt that location and type of soil does play quite a significant role in the efficiency of an HF installation.

Produce a budget of the expected cost of participation. Hire of generators and the fuel to run them can be quite expensive. Some groups are able to meet these additional expenses from their subscription income but often an extra levy will be needed on those taking part – make sure that this is acceptable before proceeding. All the 'gear' that is to be used should be tested as an entity before the contest. This often shows up surprising problems which can be dealt with in advance. Accommodation for equipment and people should be considered, especially if you are operating from an exposed site. Tents may not be adequate under severe weather conditions – would it be possible to hire or borrow a caravan? If so how will you get it on site and retrieve it later?

Safety

Portable operating generally means that antennas really want to be erected as high as possible, usually supported by means of a tubular mast. Select the antenna you intend to use carefully – small tri-band beams can give quite good performance but for superior gain the quad is hard to beat.

Now for the mast itself, the erection of which may well be the most dangerous activity contemplated in the contest – so do have sufficient help and plan carefully exactly what you are going to do and make sure everyone helping understands what is expected of them. If you have not erected a mast before or have a limited amount of help, do not be too ambitious. Choose thick-wall scaffolding poles, *not* the thin-wall TV antenna masts which tend to buckle very easily. The tubular section should be joined with external sleeve clamps, *not* the interior expanding type of connector. When using a sleeve with a bolted flange (like the Jaybeam type) arrange the flanges to oppose the bending during lifting, or better still weld two more ribs at 90° to the bolt flange to provide additional rigidity. The person in charge of the group erecting the antennas should check personally that all of the bolts have been tightened. It is worthwhile using shakeproof washers. A gin-pole is practically essential, and if properly constructed will simultaneously ease erection of the mast and increase the overall safety of the operation (Fig 1).

As a rule of thumb, the gin-pole should be a quarter to a third of the length of the mast. If a base plate is being used it should be securely fixed to prevent slipping when lifting the mast. The use of four sets of mast guys is recommended because this will ease lifting. There should be a ring of guys for each section of the mast. Calculate the length of guys beforehand and have them already prepared and clearly marked – allow a reasonable amount of spare for handling and tying off. The guy stakes should be placed on a circle with a radius not less half than the height of the mast. Use substantial lengths of angle iron driven into the ground at an angle away from the mast. The depth required will depend on the soil composition but usually if they are driven in about 60/90cm they should be adequate for most installations. Strips of reflective material to mark the low end of guys and stakes may prevent one of the helpers driving or walking into them in the dark. Be especially careful in placing guys and stakes if you are on public property and near to public footpaths.

If there is a wind blowing always raise and lower the antenna into the wind. The force that can be applied to a beam at 15m by a strong breeze may take the guys right out of everyone's hands. Be prepared to accept reduced height rather than risk the loss of the entire installation to a powerful gust of wind.

Use gloves to handle rope. Those members working near the base of the mast should wear some form of protective head gear – a motor cycle crash hat or a recognised safety helmet. If the mast does get out of control and you cannot catch it with the guys, call your assistants to stand clear and try and let it drop gradually. Heroics could mean a trip to the hospital – antennas are easier to mend than bones!

Electrical safety is also very important when using mains-powered equipment literally 'in the field'. Check the earth continuity of all earth leads on distribution boards and cables that are likely to be used. Do not rely on the generator frame sitting on the wet grass as the safety earth return – use a proper earth spike and bond it to the generator – this can also reduce interference. All gear should be fully enclosed against misplaced fingers.

Never erect masts near overhead power lines.

Finally, remember that weather can play strange tricks on high exposed locations. Go prepared with plenty of warm clothing as well as some in reserve, sleeping bags and the means of obtaining some hot food under extreme conditions.

More information on the safety aspects of contesting is given in the VHF/UHF contest section later on.

Strategy

Having understood the rules, studied propagation for the period in question and sorted the equipment aspect out thoroughly, it is advisable to ask oneself the following questions.

1. When will I start and finish; when will I take rest periods?
If the contest is over a short period with no restrictions on minimum periods of activity in the rules, the answer is simple. Where a 36 or 48 hour DX contest is being considered a careful study must be made to determine the time that will be most productive for contacts and multipliers. It is impossible to give advice on exactly how long to allow for sleep as people vary in their requirements, some requiring only two hours, others needing a minimum of four hours.

If you plan a single-band entry on either 21 or 28MHz this really does not pose a problem for these bands usually close in winter by 2000 GMT. At the height of the sunspot cycle both of these bands are capable of remaining open beyond that time. 14MHz is a little more tricky for it may be open from 0400 GMT and with reasonable conditions will remain productive until 0000 GMT. The contact rate will start falling on 7 and 3.5MHz between 0200 and 0400 GMT.

2. When will I change bands?
The majority of 'big guns' and DXpeditions change bands either on the hour or the half-hour. After studying the propagation forecast a plan can be drawn up with the object of obtaining as many multipliers or countries on each band and being on a band at the right time to yield a maximum number of contacts. Having prepared a band plan, stick to it as far as multipliers are concerned, even if it means leaving a pile-up on 14MHz to look for multipliers on 21MHz. Conversely be prepared to take advantage of short openings on 28MHz.

3. Who has won the contest over the past two years? What equipment and antennas were used?
Detailed results are always published and additional information can usually be obtained by writing to the operators concerned enclosing a stamped addressed envelope. After a big event, the top contesters often get together to exchange notes on equipment, antennas and propagation. Do not be disheartened if for example G4 . . . has a four-element wide-spaced Yagi on 7MHz at 50m – obviously he will be able to work DX that others cannot hear – but even the best operators make mistakes. While he is pounding away on 7MHz an opening may occur on 21MHz which yields an even higher scoring rate! There is much that can be done with experimental wire antennas and phased arrays on 3.5 and 7MHz to bring up the station rating. Pay particular attention to receiving antennas on these LF bands. If you have the space, Beverage antennas can give very useful front-to-back ratios. RSGB events, which usually require a running serial number, do give you the opportunity to see how last year's leaders are doing compared to your score.

Fig 1. Erecting a mast using the gin-pole method. The mast typically consists of three scaffold poles giving 60ft, with another pole for the gin-pole. Guys are 8mm polypropylene. (a) Overhead view showing the mast and gin-pole laid out on the ground prior to erection. (b) Setting the pre-bend; the amount varies the top load. (c) Side view showing the gin-pole being raised using the block and tackle. (d) As the guys take the strain, the mast should be slightly bent as shown. The antenna can now be fitted to the top of the mast. (e) With the mast in position, the gin-pole guys are transferred to stakes and adjusted to remove the bend (The other two sets of guys are not shown for clarity.) (f) The mast in final position. Note the procedure should be reversed to lower the mast, ideally lowering *away* from the wind

4. What was the winning score? How many contacts and multipliers? What were conditions like? How did other UK stations fare?

Again, the majority of this information will be published and a few hours studying the results will usually produce the information required. As well as the leaders the other top 10 entrants are worth examining closely, particularly if one of them

is known personally. In this case a detailed knowledge of both equipment and planning can be gleaned. Scoring rate targets can be calculated as an incentive during the contest. Tables 1–3 and Fig 2 show typical scoring plans and rates.

5. What should I do about meals?

Food and non-alcoholic drinks are important. A lot of contesters

Table 1. 1989 RSGB 7MHz CW Contest

Time	GW3YDX QSOs	Mult	G3FXB QSOs	Mult
1200–1300	68	16	63	16
1300–1400	30	3	29	4
1400–1500	28	3	39	4
1500–1600	41	5	29	1
1600–1700	43	6	36	7
1700–1800	37	5	27	3
1800–1900	29	2	23	2
1900–2000	20	2	16	4
2000–2100	38	—	22	1
2100–2200	35	6	15	3
2200–2300	29	4	23	1
2300–0000	28	5	25	6
0000–0100	41	8	27	7
0100–0200	34	1	36	—
0200–0300	37	—	27	1
0300–0400	32	—	36	—
0400–0500	34	—	18	—
0500–0600	40	1	34	—
0600–0700	27	5	13	4
0700–0800	32	1	22	1
0800–0900	20	—	12	—

Table 2. 1989 Commonwealth Contest band plan – G3FXB

Time	Band	QSOs	Prefixes
1200–1245	28	13	VE2, VE3, VS6, VU, Z23, 9J2, 5N2, ZD8, VO, GB5
1246–1415	21	31	VK2–6, VK9, VE2, VE3, VE4, VS6, GB5, ZL1, ZL2, 5N2, VO, 6Y5
1430–1515	14	22	VK2–6, VK9, VS6, VE1, VE4, VE7, ZL1
1515–1540	28	5	VE2, VE3
1550–1605	14	6	VE1, VE7, ZL3
1621–1713	28	15	VE1–4, VE6, VE7, VP2, 5N2
1720–1815	21	22	VE2, VE4, VE6, VE7, 9J2, VQ9, ZC4
1820–1822	28	1	VE7
1828–1836	21	5	VE2, VE3, VE7, ZL1
1850–1908	14	5	GB5, VU, ZC4, 9J2
1916–1932	21	7	VE1, VE2, VE6, VE7
1932–1955	7	1	VK2
2000–2003	21	3	VE1, VE3, ZD8
2005–2010	14	2	VK5, ZD8
2012–2015	21	2	ZL3, VE1
2015–2100	7	8	VK3, VK5, VK6, VK7, VE1, VE2
2101–2200	14	26	VE2–6, 6Y5, VO
2208–2253	7	13	VQ9, VE1–3, VK6, VU, ZD8
2300–2305	3.5	3	GB5, VE1, VQ9
2325–2335	14	4	VE2, VE3
2345–0047	7	14	VO, 9J2, 6Y5
0050–0055	3.5	1	VE3
0110–0112	14	1	VP5
0120–0159	7	8	VO, VE4, VE7, 5N2
0200–0220	3.5	4	VO, VE1, VE3
0300–0305	7	3	VO, VE2, VE3
0330–0331	3.5	1	VO
0335–0428	14	8	ZL1, ZL2, ZL3, VK3, 5N2
0430–0445	7	2	VE2, VP2
0450–0455	3.5	1	VP2
BREAK			
0510–0511	3.5	1	6Y5
0530–0550	7	4	ZL1–3
0551–0553	14	2	ZL1, VK3
0557–0607	7	5	ZL2, VE4, VE6
0612–0630	3.5	2	VE3, ZL3
0645–0656	14	4	VK2, ZL2, 5N2
0700–0710	7	4	VK4, VE4, VE7
0715–0750	14	5	VK3, VK6, VK7, ZL1, VE3
0800–0820	21	3	5N2, ZL1, ZL2
0821–0825	14	1	ZL2
0830–0840	21	1	VK2
0850–0900	14	2	VK3, VK7
0901–1028	28	11	ZL1, ZL3, VK2, VK4–6, 9V1, VU, VS6
1100–1105	14	1	A35
1120–1159	21	5	ZL1, VK2, VK3

Table 3. 1988 CQ Contest CW single band (21MHz) – G4CNY

Time	First day QSOs	Zones	Countries	Second day QSOs	Zones	Countries
0513–0600	6	5	6	—	—	—
0600–0700	7	5	6	—	—	—
0700–0800	28	5	14	19	1	6
0800–0900	63	2	10	56	1	1
0900–1000	67	2	6	45	—	—
1000–1100	34	3	10	36	—	2
1100–1200	52	4	7	28	1	2
1200–1300	93	1	1	32	—	—
1300–1400	76	1	2	36	1	1
1400–1500	53	1	2	38	—	—
1500–1600	87	—	1	70	—	—
1600–1700	62	—	3	44	—	1
1700–1800	78	—	1	46	—	1
1800–1900	27	1	3	42	—	1
1900–2000	26	—	3	1	—	—
2000–2100	3	—	2	2	1	2

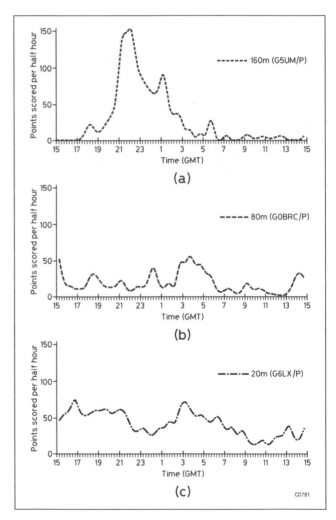

Fig 2. Scoring rates for three stations in NFD 1988

have fizzy drinks or tea and coffee. Sandwiches for breakfast and lunch are a good idea so that you can continue operating on CW and listening on SSB. Light snacks are better than large meals. It is useful to start the contest with a large vacuum flask of coffee.

6. What check lists do I need?

Duplicate contacts are always a problem in contests where valuable time may be wasted making them. Operators have

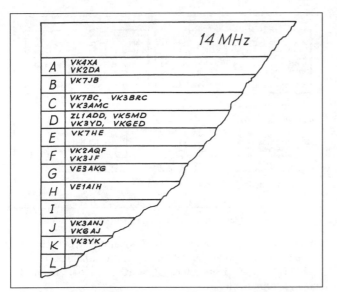

Fig 3. Check list suitable for contests with low QSO totals

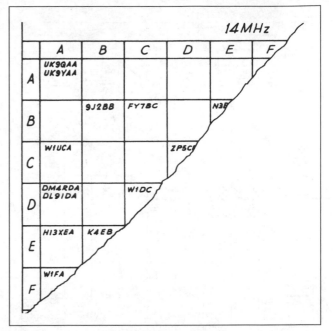

Fig 4. Check list suitable for contests with high QSO totals

devised various forms of check or dupe sheets to overcome this problem but this is one area where the computer really helps.

In an event such as the Commonwealth Contest check sheets are essential (one is available from the RSGB) as it is normal practice to call stations as opposed to calling CQ. As the contact total in this event is quite small the form of check sheet shown in Fig 3 is quite suitable. In this example stations are entered by the last letter of their callsign, which some find an easier way of spotting a callsign on a check sheet. On the other hand, many use the first letter of the suffix, so that the checker can scan the correct part of the check list as soon as the first suffix letter is copied. This type of dupe sheet is satisfactory for any contest with low contact totals.

In contests where the contact total is high (such as the CQ, ARRL and WAE Contests), if the check is to be of any use for reference during the event itself, the listing can be sub-divided. If this is not done, there may be so many calls listed under each heading that it will be impossible to find a particular call quickly and maintain a reasonable contact rate. Fig 4 shows an alternative to meet this need. It should be mentioned that this type of check list is unsatisfactory for high-contact-rate contests, as the requirement of entering each call down on the list can be self-defeating. In this case it may be preferable to contact everyone and sort out the duplicates after the contest. Before things get really hectic programmable keyers can help in giving a little time to keep on top of the paperwork but it is in this situation where the computer really comes into its own (see below).

In some contests where almost all of the contacts are made in response to CQ calls such as the ARRL Contest a check list can probably be dispensed with, it being quicker to work the occasional duplicate than to check every call. Of course duplicates in the log must be clearly marked after the contest. These problems do not exist in multi-operator contests when a log keeper will keep all the paperwork up to date. However, if only one second op is available then they can be more productively employed looking for multipliers, especially if a second receiver is permitted in the rules.

In contests such as CQ World-Wide a check list of the zones and countries is essential. Fig 5 shows such a system.

An all-purpose check card suitable for most contests designed by G3HCT is shown in Fig 6. This is printed on light card measuring 292 by 216mm. The top section shows the card being

used as a country check card. A horizontal line separates the two days. The centre section demonstrates a check list for duplicate contact analysis. Note that in this system the calls are sorted by the letter following the numeral so that if one is looking over the check list while a station is calling, checking can commence before it finishes sending its call.

Computers

It is important not to get the idea that one must have a computer to compete in contests. Several top-flight operators use paper in the major contests and compete on equal terms with those using computers. Perhaps the main advantage is that, when the contest is over, the entry can be printed (or copied onto disk) and sent off immediately, thereby doing away with the need to spend many hours writing up the entry by hand. In the past, many high-scoring contest entries have failed to appear in the results listings because after all the hard work of the contest itself, the entrant ran out of time doing the paperwork.

Fig 5. Check list for multipliers

NOV 30
DATE 1976   TEST CQ   14 MHZ BAND
1st day   482 QSO's   23c   14z

ZONES	A	B	C	D	E	F	G	H	I
1	A4	BV	CX	DL	EI	FY	G	HA	IS
2			CO	DM	EA	FP8	GU	HB9	I
3			CT1	DU	EA8	FM	GM	HC	
4			CT3		ET3	FO8	GD	HP	
5							GI	HK0	
6							GJ	HI	

	J	K	L	M	N	O	P	Q	R
	8JP	3KD8	3LN5	3MXK	4NCY	130QR	2PU	2QT	3RMF
		2KK	3L0E	2M1	3NAS				
		6R1	2L8		3NKS				
		2KK	4LR						

S	T	U	V	W	X	Y	Z	Numbers

Fig 6. All purpose check card designed by G3HCT

The EI5DI Super-Duper contest logging program in action

There is a number of well-established contest logging programs which, between them, support the wide range of differing scoring schemes in today's contests. The first program to gain wide acceptance was CT, written by K1EA, which has been joined by programs by K8CC, W5XD and N6TR to handle most of the major international contests. There is a choice of two programs tailored for the RSGB contest programme: Super-Duper by EI5DI and LOG by G3WGV. All the programs have developed a high degree of sophistication and can keep the log, enter the time of QSO using the computer's internal clock, update the outgoing serial number automatically and check for duplicate contacts in milliseconds. They include a CW sender which (with the addition of a simple interface) will key the transmitter and send the outgoing exchange, as well as CQ calls and other programmable messages. The more sophisticated programs offer statistical analysis of your performance as it happens, often on a band-by-band basis. If your software is programmed with the scoring rules for the contest all you have to do is enter the callsign and exchange. The computer determines whether it is a bonus or multiplier contact, works out the points to be claimed and often updates a running total display on

screen. For multi-operator (or single-operator 'assisted') categories, the computer can be connected to a packet TNC to enable DX 'spots' from a local PacketCluster to be fed to the screen automatically.

Using a computer to log contest QSOs in real-time can provide all the above benefits but there are a number of potential problems. For example, computers and displays can radiate RF interference and may be sensitive to the field from your transmitter – you may well need to do some screening and filtering, and cables should be kept as short as possible. Power cuts and hardware faults are not uncommon – make sure that the program you want to use writes contact data to disk after every QSO, be prepared to disable any disk caching utilities and copy the data frequently to floppy disk. You need to be fairly proficient in using a keyboard: 'hunt and peck' is usually not fast enough. Also, everyone makes keyboard errors and in the heat of a contest these may be worse than normal, bringing the possibility of mis-typing or even accidentally deleting information. Take time to learn how to use the program you finally choose and become completely familiar with it, before the contest starts. Try to start off in one of the smaller events.

Some contesters prefer to log on paper during the event but use a computer for dupe-checking and printing afterwards. Most of the programs mentioned have a 'post-contest' mode. This avoids many of the problems of real-time logging, but can introduce another – transcription errors. Ensure you enter the callsigns correctly, as mistakes here cost points. Duplicate contacts may not be picked up because a zero was typed the first

This is the CT contest logging program, written by K1EA

time, and a letter 'O' the second. Not all the programs check callsigns for validity as they are entered. If the program prints a dupe sheet, please remember to send it in with the log. Finally, always double-check the printed log against the original. Time spent doing this is well worthwhile.

Increasingly, contest organisers accept contest entries on disk or via the Internet. This cuts down on postage costs but be sure to include all the information required by the organiser.

Operating technique

This is something that cannot be learnt just by reading a book; theory may help but there is no substitute for practice. With experience you get the 'feel' of a band and can predict whether it will open to a particular part of the world or not. Some operators, especially those with good signals, may prefer to choose one spot frequency and stay there. If this is done some care must be taken in choosing the frequency. There is a natural tendency to move up the band to avoid what appears to be an area full of interference. Tighten up the selectivity and you will be able to find a clear spot. When looking at the lower portions of the bands do not forget that the lowest sections are restricted to those holding Extra Class licences in the USA.

A conscious decision must be made about when to call and when not to call CQ. A general rule of thumb is that more points will be made calling CQ and getting replies, than by calling stations. This obviously presupposes that you have a reasonably commanding signal or that you are operating from a rare spot and that everyone will be looking for you. There are however exceptions to these rules. The aim of some contests is to work stations in one particular region and only these should call CQ. Furthermore under some band conditions, or towards the end of a contest, there may be little response to CQ calls. These are the times when it is necessary to systematically search a band for multipliers or for additional points. Remember it is extremely bad practice to find an apparently clear frequency and start calling CQ. Listen on the frequency for at least 10 seconds and then ask "Is this frequency in use?" on SSB or send "QRL?" on CW. Only if no one replies can a short CQ be tried. If the frequency is in use then move away and repeat the procedure. While no-one has an absolute right to occupy a channel it is generally understood that the station who was using the frequency first has the right to remain there. For this reason it is unwise once a frequency has been found and contacts are being made to give it up, unless changing bands or looking for multipliers.

As already mentioned, in most contests there is a bonus or multiplier system, often based on the number of countries worked. It is always useful to have in mind before the contest starts just how much value in time (or contacts lost) each multiplier has. For example in the ARRL DX Contest, one multiplier is equivalent in terms of points to about 15 contacts, or at a peak scoring period to about seven to eight minutes operating time. In the CQ DX Contest where multipliers are countries and zones, each multiplier is worth about eight contacts or roughly five minutes operating time. These figures give some idea of the 'worth' of a multiplier and at peak contact times it does not pay to take time off to look for multipliers. With an event lasting longer than 24 hours then it is sound advice to go for contacts the first day and concentrate a little more on quality during the second day. Scoring rates or the number of contacts you should achieve each hour will vary from contest to contest and from year to year. However, it is helpful to establish a target to try and achieve per hour. Probably the maximum scoring rate using a 'G' call is in the region of 120–150

per hour on CW and maybe twice that on SSB. These rates apply to the peak periods when the band is open to the USA. Again, most logging programs display the current rate.

The scoring rate is not necessarily directly proportional to the speed of sending – QRS for slow stations will save time in the end. The degree of abbreviation and callsign repetition enter into the equation. The speed of sending should be such that contacts are dealt with efficiently but not at the expense of having to meet continual requests for repeats from other stations. The more a callsign is repeated, the more stations hopefully will join in the 'pile-up' waiting for a QSO. The bigger the 'pile-up', the harder it becomes to pick out calls – so there is a question of balance with the aim to just keeping the 'pot' simmering and not boiling vigorously! Time spent listening to well-run DXpeditions can be very instructive in learning techniques for handling pile-ups whilst maintaining some semblance of order. Large pile-ups from Japan can be a problem both on SSB (with the difficulty of phonetics) and on CW with weak signals. Do not be tempted to withhold your callsign in an effort to control the pile-up.

Often operators can benefit by considering if all parts of their transmissions are really necessary. It may be polite to say "73 and good luck in the contest" but it will certainly lower your scoring rate without adding any essential information to your or his log. After all, the other side of a contact knows the number that he sent and does not want it repeating back to him unless there is a doubt. Accuracy is of great importance and should not be sacrificed in the interest of speed – again it is a question of striking the right balance. Note that in CW contests it is quicker to send at 20wpm giving all the information once than to repeat everything at 35wpm. Many operators are now using memory keyers or DVKs to give CQ calls and reports. At first sight these may appear to be gimmicks but they do save time and give an extra few seconds to deal with the log and check lists.

Listen to the top contest stations working and note their style and the number of contacts that they achieve in an hour. If possible arrange for a local operator to record you operating in a contest so that you can analyse your own technique. Listening to a recording highlights the mistakes that you may be making. You can only work stations one at a time but it is essential that you work them faster than the opposition!

Finally, know and observe the IARU Band Plan – do not call non-contest stations for points and remember at the end of the day it is only a hobby – apply the rules of sportsmanship to your operating.

Analysis

Within 24 hours of completing a contest, make notes for next year while everything is still fresh in your mind. It is indeed a rare person who can recall months later *all* the little details which need to be improved to make the operation more comfortable and efficient. Indeed, you may prefer to keep a sheet of paper handy during the contest so that any thoughts can be jotted down immediately.

Graphical analysis of the scoring rate can also highlight peak times and enable you to examine the times when the scoring rate plummeted – this is where the analysis of one contest merges into the preparation for the next. The rate at which contacts are made is of prime importance; if displayed graphically it is easier to get an overall picture of your operation. See Fig 2. If graphs are drawn for several years then you have a better base on which to formulate a contest plan showing when to change bands and look for multipliers. It is interesting to plot a contact rate graph and a scoring rate graph. This will illustrate the importance of concentrating on high-point-value QSOs, and may suggest when the best time to sleep is during a 48-hour contest.

Sending in an entry

Official forms should be used if specified, as it does make the adjudicators work so much easier. Don't forget the cover sheet and declaration. Like the rules, these two points may seem obvious but adjudicators – no matter how impartial they try to be – tend to be biased against the log submitted on narrow lined absorbent paper written with a green felt tip pen! It is imperative that duplicate contacts are clearly marked and that points are not claimed for them. The check list or dupe sheet should be included with your entry to assist the adjudicator. Also if you get someone else to type your log – do check for transcription errors. Transcription errors are also common in computerised logs – at the very least make a cursory examination for nonsensical callsigns. Comments and helpful suggestions for improving the contest are always welcome, while the odd anecdote makes a welcome break for the adjudicator. Last, but not least, ensure that you have put sufficient postage on your entry and that it is sent to the correct address. It would be a pity to see all that time and effort wasted.

VHF/UHF CONTESTS

Contesting on VHF is essentially great fun, just as it is on HF. It also poses a great many challenges for us, both as individuals and in working together as a team. Experience can only be gained through practice, improvement and refinement. It involves learning from failure and being sufficiently self-motivated to keep on going when the going gets rough and the odds are apparently stacked against you, particularly when it's wet, windy, you're tired, no one will do it the way you want and you know that you're right, the equipment's failed yet again and somebody forgot to pack the milk for the coffee and the bottle opener too! If it can go wrong, it usually will and does. But when it does go right, it's one of the best feelings in the world. You know that you have worked well and rightly deserve your success. You don't have to actually win a contest to feel like this – simply seeing your scores and placings improve, overcoming practical problems or exceeding personal goals can provide an enormous amount of satisfaction.

Contesting is very much about being in competition with yourself, rather than just being about beating fellow contesters. Don't expect to beat the major groups on your first attempt. They have worked hard to get to where they are and invariably possess the resources and experience which you are hoping to gain. However, always remember that they can, and at sometime in the future will, be beaten. Select the bands, contests and sections which are of interest to you and carefully maximise your available resources. Set yourself realistic targets and gain the satisfaction of seeing a steady improvement.

The first thing you need to do is to prepare. Read the rules which for RSGB contests are published each year in the September issue of *Radio Communication*. These rules tell you what is and what is not acceptable in the operation and paperwork requirements associated with the wide variety of contests throughout the year. Then, read the individual contest rules. Alright? Now read them again. Have you noticed, for example, that the third and fourth sessions in the Backpackers require Rule 14e and not Rule 14c as applied in sessions one and two? It is small, subtle changes like this which facilitate the

RSGB VHF/UHF CONTEST CALENDAR	
January	144MHz CW, 70MHz Cumulatives
February	70MHz Cumulatives, 432MHz Fixed/AFS
March	March 144/432MHz, 70MHz Fixed
April	144MHz Fixed Station Cumulatives, 1.3/2.3GHz Fixed
May	432MHz–238GHz, 432MHz Trophy, 10GHz Trophy, 144MHz, First 144MHz Backpackers
June	IARU 50MHz, 50MHz Trophy, 1st 50MHz Backpackers, 70MHz CW, 2nd 144MHz Backpackers, 432MHz FM
July	VHF NFD, 3rd 144MHz Backpackers, 2nd 50MHz Backpackers, 144MHz Low Power, 432MHz Low Power
August	432MHz Fixed
September	144MHz CW Cumulatives, 144MHz Trophy, 4th 144MHz Backpackers, 70MHz Trophy
October	144MHz Cumulatives, 432MHz–238GHz IARU, 1.3/2.3GHz Trophies, 1.3/2.3GHz Cumulatives, 432MHz Cumulatives, 1.3/2.3GHz Fixed
November	1.3/2.3GHz Cumulatives, 432MHz Cumulatives, 144MHz CW Marconi, 6h 144MHz CW
December	144MHz Fixed/AFS, 70/144/432MHz Christmas Cumulatives

smooth running of contests, particularly when there may be more than one event taking place simultaneously.

As you read through this chapter you will, we hope, receive a great deal of information. In fact, there may be too much information to take in on a single reading and so we recommend that you return time and again and consider the issues raised. These may also form the basis for group or club discussions to see how they effect your decisions and reasoning in how you actually go about entering contests. Indeed, this is the main purpose of this section. There are many excellent books which deal with the theory, design, construction and operation of equipment and readers are advised to refer to these for further reading.

Sites

At VHF there is something of a myth that height above sea level is everything, but this is far from being the complete story. What is more important than plain elevation is whether the site has a clear unobstructed take-off in the important directions. This can mean that even a small rise of a few tens of metres can be a very good location if the surrounding land for a good number of miles is essentially flat. If you happen to live near to the coast, a site on or very close to the water can be excellent, particularly on 70cm and higher since you will be able to take advantage of the fragile marine ducts which sometimes form over water and break up very quickly when they hit land. This said, nothing is ever hard and fast, and these sorts of conditions are not present for so very much of the time, so under normal circumstances you could well be better off on a site which is further inland but higher. If, like many people, you are planning to use a site which is some way inland, then height certainly seems to become more important and you ideally want to be a good few hundred feet above the surrounding terrain. However, even away from the coastal plains of the country there are many flatish parts of the country where sitting on top of a relatively small dimple will pay big dividends.

Since there is no 5000ft mountain in the UK which has a clear shot for 360°, and which is only 10km from the coast in all directions – and even if there was it would already be well and truly booked by a major contest group – it is very important to try and decide what directions are important to you, and these may vary from contest to contest. For a major Europe-wide contest, the bulk of activity is likely to be in Central and Southern England and of course in the rest of Europe – for this sort of event you will want to pick a site with a good take-off in those directions. However, a UK-only contest with county multipliers will lead you to wanting a different site, with a good take-off to most of the UK, and you may be prepared to sacrifice some performance into Europe. If you are planning to travel any distance, you will probably make your initial choice of site from looking at the OS maps; however, you cannot rely on this alone – you really need to go and take a look at your proposed site before the contest to check out how to get access etc. At this point a good hint is to take a small station with you – perhaps even just a mobile – and make sure that the beacons or even repeaters are as loud or louder at your proposed site than in the rest of the surrounding area. If you do not have any amateur station with you, you can get a fair idea from just using ordinary broadcast VHF stations on the car radio.

So, we've discussed how to find your ideal site – now how do you go about getting it? Unfortunately, the obvious technique of just driving to the site on the day of the contest and setting up is the wrong one. First you need to check that the site does not have anyone who regularly uses it for contests – contesting etiquette and common sense says that you do not just turn up and use someone else's site without first making contact with them to see if they are planning to use it. Just turning up very early at a site and claiming it on the basis that "I was here first" is a guaranteed technique for not winning friends and influencing people! Equally, don't pick a site that is only a few kilometres down the road from a site which is likely to be used by another group – you are only going to cause both of you a lot of heartache and shortened tempers with all the mutual QRM which will be present during the contest, no matter (within sensible practical limits) how clean your transmitters are or how good your receivers are. The sensible exclusion zone around the 'big gun' portable stations is probably a few tens of kilometres in directions where they are likely to spend a lot of time beaming – even at 20km, these stations can be well in excess of 100dB above noise with you, and hardly any VHF receiver will take kindly to this level of abuse.

While on this subject, if you are going somewhere new, then you should also be conscious of the locals who live near your station. Particularly if you are travelling somewhere remote, many of them may not be accustomed to big signals on the band and may not have engineered their stations to cope with this much RF. Equally, the attitude "Well, it's not my fault – get yourself a decent receiver" will do nothing to further the general cause of contesting, or indeed your or anybody else's ability to use the site in the future. Some pre-contest planning, perhaps by contacting the locals, maybe via the local club, in order to explain to them what you are planning to do and perhaps to invite them to come and see the station could go a long way to turning a potentially unpleasant situation around. They will then feel more involved in the situation and also if you understand the potential problems, you may be able to avoid beaming your eight Yagis over the top of a particular local station's house more than absolutely necessary.

In all likelihood, the site you have chosen to use will be on private land – obviously you need to obtain permission from

A typical VHF contest scene!

the land owner to use it. Even if the site is public land, be sensible – don't obstruct gateways and paths, and don't damage any of the surroundings – basically, observe the Country Code.

Operating

Operating techniques vary enormously between individuals and between different contests and there is no single right and wrong way to do things. For example, 2m contests at busy times tend to be relatively frantic affairs, but 23cm events are usually quite relaxed. First read the rules and make sure that you know what is required of you during the contest. Check out what the exchange is and ensure that you have all the relevant information to hand. It is also worth knowing what the WAB details are for your site because there are almost bound to be a number of people who will ask you for these.

Throughout the event, you have a basic choice between calling CQ and tuning around for calls, and the relative amount of time you spend on each activity will depend upon what band you are using, how big your signal is, whether it is a multiplier contest, what conditions are like and what time it is in the contest, to name but a few factors. Certainly for the main contests on 2m and 70cm it is likely that, unless you have a very small station indeed, you will want to call CQ for some of the time. When you call CQ, choose your frequency carefully – obviously make sure that you aren't sitting too close to one of your local stations from whom you could suffer heavy QRM, but equally, make sure that you aren't going to have heavy QRM at the DX end of the QSOs. For example, if you are expecting to make a lot of contacts into Germany, don't sit 1kHz LF of one of the big German portable stations. If you find a particular frequency doesn't run well, then try another – you may well have some QRM at the far end which is too distant for you to hear.

While calling CQ make sure that you sound enthusiastic and that you are enjoying yourself even if you are frozen to the bone and finding it slow going – remember that you need to attract that casual station just tuning the band and make him/her just want to call you. Don't leave too long a gap between CQs – this author feels two to three seconds is usually about right – this is long enough for anyone who is a bit slow off the mark to go over to transmit, but not so long that someone who just catches the end of your call and who wants to know who you are before calling, gets bored and tunes onto the next station. When

The new Backpackers mini-contests enable you to have fun contesting with the minimum of equipment over a four-hour period. Here Backpackers trophy winner Julian Ross is operating G0LBO/P from the summit of Coniston Old Man

someone answers your call, say "Good morning" or whatever and pass the exchange clearly and concisely. If signals are reasonable, it usually isn't necessary to send the information more than once. It is worth passing the information in the same order as the columns appear on the log sheets (callsign, report, serial number, locator, county etc), and do spell out your locator phonetically. If you miss any bits, or are unsure that you have copied it correctly, do ask for a repeat or confirmation – it is better to take a little longer to get it right that to lose the points for the QSO. Finally, when all is done, say thanks and move onto the next QSO. There is a fine balance to be drawn between making the QSO very quickly and needing lots of repeats, and making the QSO too slowly so that if anyone is waiting to call you they will get bored and tune off. If more than one station replies to a CQ call it is worth asking the other caller to stand by – more often than not, they will do so. If you are uncomfortable with any of these ideas, before you call CQ, take a listen around the band, particularly to the big stations, and see how they handle their QSOs. As you are calling CQ, keep the antenna moving around – don't forget that VHF/UHF antennas often have quite narrow beamwidths and the more distant QSOs rely upon both your and the far ends' antennas being in the right directions.

At some point you may feel the need to stop calling CQ and take a tune round the band. This is likely to be when your QSO rate from calling CQ drops too low. This author usually starts from one end of the band, with the antenna pointing in one direction and works his way to the other end of the band; then nudges the antenna round a bit and starts at the bottom of the band once again. As you tune through the band you'll come across various stations that you may or may not have worked already. Pay particular attention to the weak signals – these may well be the DX and of course are worth more points. Turn the antenna enough towards the station you are calling to make the signal reasonable, but don't worry about getting it all the way round if you don't need to. Do check your dupe sheet or computer before calling them to make sure that you haven't had a previous QSO. A dupe sheet is just a list of callsigns of stations you have already worked on the band in a form which you can look up very quickly. If you are logging by computer you won't need to use one of these – the software will have a substitute function built-in – but if you are logging by hand, you will need to maintain a manual dupe sheet as well as your log. A popular way of making a dupe sheet is to have a piece of paper (preferably A3) ruled into 26 columns headed A-Z, and

maybe even with a couple of spare overflow columns. As you work people, not only do you enter them in your log, but their callsigns also get entered onto the dupe sheet – in the column determined either by the first or last letter of their main callsign. It doesn't matter which option you choose – just so long as all the operators know which you are using. Don't forget the final suffix has no bearing on whether the contact is a duplicate – eg a contact with DB8KJ and DB8KJ/P are duplicates.

When you call a station, do use phonetics for your call, even if they are strong – of course you know what your callsign is, but they may not be quite sure. If you don't get a response immediately try again a couple of times – making sure that you don't have the RIT in, split VFO enabled, repeater shift enabled etc, and do try calling on CW if you are just too weak for SSB. If nothing succeeds at making a particular station hear you, it can be worth either storing their frequency in the other VFO or a memory (if you have these facilities), or simply writing the frequency down on a piece of paper and trying again from time to time in case they conditions improve, they turn their antenna more towards you, or maybe they have less QRM. It is often worthwhile alternating calling CQ and tuning over periods of some tens of minutes. After all – while you are tuning the band some new casual operators will have come on and you may want to net them with a few CQ calls. Equally, it can take some time for both your antennas and a particular DX station's antennas to become properly aligned.

One topic which arises from time to time in discussions between contesters is that of what to do when someone who you have worked before calls you. If you are using a computer to log, you will have immediate notification that he/she is a 'dupe' and will have to decide what to do about it. Some people take the view that it is always quickest just to work them again. Personally, this author is less convinced and, certainly for SSB contests, will say something like "G0ZZZ, sorry we've worked, G4PIQ Contest". On CW the decision is less easy – it takes a bit longer to send an appropriate message, and he generally sends something like "G0ZZZ QSO B4 TU G4PIQ TEST". If all goes smoothly and the recipient of this message understands, this is definitely quicker than working the station again. However, this all comes horribly to grief in those 10% of cases where either the other operator doesn't understand what you sent or, even worse, enters into a debate with you as to whether you really have worked before or not, and what was the previous QSO number and what was the time, and so on . . . ! When this happens you immediately regret not just working them, since the rhythm of the pile-up has been broken and the QSO rate has been smashed by this long QSO. This author also finds that, just sometimes when a 'dupe' calls him, a second sense says "This one is going to be trouble" and he works him anyhow but, to say the least, this is a somewhat unscientific criterion!

Paperwork

Any contest entry consists of the logs themselves and some supporting summary information. Of these two parts, writing up the logs themselves is by far the most time-consuming part. There are two main options for doing the logs – either use a computer or do it by hand. We'll cover the computing option in more detail later but, if you are forced to write up the logs by hand, please use the standard RSGB log sheets – LSVHF for VHF contests (25 contacts per page), and use separate sheets for each band. Also, please *do* take the time to write the logs up after the event. Even if you use these forms to scrawl on during the contest, unless you are a really remarkable operator, they will be full of crossings-out, corrections, illegible scribblings, and so on. It doesn't do anything for the image of your log (not to mention the adjudicator's sanity and patience) if he/she receives a log like this. If your log is neat and tidy, you are much more likely to be given the benefit of any doubt when it's 3am and the adjudicator is struggling to finish the checking before the next committee meeting!

The other part of the entry is the supporting information. The most obvious piece of this is the summary sheet – RSGB Form 427 (one needed per band, and any version from 1986 onwards is acceptable). However, for some contests, additional information is required. If the contest is a multiplier event, you also need to submit a list of the multipliers worked on each band, along with the callsign and serial numbers of the QSOs for which multipliers were claimed. In case one of the contacts you have claimed as a multiplier is disallowed, where you have them, you should include details of more than one QSO with each multiplier. The RSGB VHF Contest Committee have a form MUL1 which provides a useful template if you wish to use it. For multi-band VHF contests, there is no longer a requirement to submit a 4422 Summary Sheet. For cumulative contests, please include a note of your scores from the individual days either on the back of the cover sheet or on a separate piece of paper. There is no problem with using computer-generated forms in the same format as the official ones. Sample forms are given in references [1] and [2].

If, once the contest is over, you switch off brain, automatically churn out the paperwork, and just put it in the post without checking it, you are doing your entry a grave disservice. Dave Lawley, G4BUO, former Chairman of the HF Contest Committee, has said that in his experience about half the points lost by people are given away after the contest has finished, often through careless writing-up of the log. The classic mistakes are made in mis-reading other people's handwriting – 'P's for 'D's, 'L's for 'C's etc, and anyone who has every tried to decipher one of this author's hand-written logs will know exactly why he prefers a keyboard! These sorts of mistake can only really be avoided by careful checking of the logs afterwards, and preferably by the generators of the spider-scrawl handwriting themselves. Other errors are just plan silly though – watch out for F stations in JO16 (the oil and gas fields in the North Sea) instead of JN16 (Central France), or UK stations in IO01 (about 400 miles off the west coast of Ireland) rather than JO01 (eg Essex). Slightly more subtle, and even more common examples are PA stations in parts of JO31 which are definitely in Germany, or ON stations in parts of JO10 which are in France. After adjudicators have been on the band a few years and have checked a few contests, they develop a sixth sense of spotting these sorts of errors (even the subtle ones), so it is worth your while taking the time to check your log carefully.

Finally, the ultimate sin must be mentioned – that of having unmarked duplicates in your log. We all end up making more than one contact with a few stations on each band in a contest, but it is essential to the health of your score that you mark them in the log as duplicates and claim zero points for them. If you don't, you will loose 10 times your claimed score, and indeed if there are an excessive number (five or more) in the log you can be disqualified. Also, don't forget that DB8KJ and DB8KJ/P count as duplicate contacts. You may think it unlikely that anyone, and particularly the top contest groups, would allow these to creep into their logs. However, astonishingly, in VHF NFD during two recent years, the claimed scores in one or other of the sections in VHF NFD have been very close, and the winner has been decided by one station having unmarked duplicates

CODE OF PRACTICE FOR VHF/UHF/SHF CONTESTS

1. Obtain permission from the landowner or agent before using the site anfd check that this permission includes right of access. Portable stations should observe the Country Code.
2. Take all possible steps to ensure that the site is not going to be used by some other group or club. Check with the club and last year's results table to see if any group used the site last year. If it is going to be used by another group, come to an amicable arrangement before the event. Groups are advised to select possible alternative sites.
3. All transmitters generate unwanted signals; it is the level of these signals that matters. In operation from a good site, levels of spurious radiation which may be acceptable from a home station may well be found to be excessive to nearby stations (25 miles away or morel).
4. Similarly, all receivers are prone to have spurious responses or to generate spurious signals in the presence of one or more strong signals, even if the incoming signals are of good quality. Such spurious responses may mislead an operator into believing that the incoming signal is at fault, when in fact the fault lies in his own receiver.
5. If at all possible, critically test both receiver and transmitter for these undesirable characteristics, preferably by air test with a near neighbour before the contest. In the case of transmitters, aim to keep all in-amateur-band spurious radiation, including noise modulation, to a level of −100dB relative to the wanted signal. Similarly, every effort should be made to ensure that the receiver has adequate dynamic range.
6. Above all, be gentlemanly and polite at all times. Be helpful and inform stations apparently radiating unwanted signals at troublesome levels, having first checked your own receiver. Try the effect of turning the antenna or inserting attenuators in the feed line; if the level of spurious signal changes relative to the wanted signal, then non-linear effects are occurring in the receiver. Some recent synthesised equipment has excessive local oscillator phase noise, which will manifest itself as an apparent splatter on strong signals, even if there is no overloading of the receiver front-end. Preamplifiers should always be switched out to avoid overload problems when checking transmissions. If you receive a complaint, perform tests to check for receiver overload and try reducing drive levels and switching out linear amplifiers to determine a cure. Monitor your own signal off-air if possible. Remember that many linear amplifiers may not be linear at high power levels under field conditions with poorly regulated power supplies. The effects of overdriving will be more severe if speech processing is used, so pay particular attention to drive level adjustemnt. If asked to close down by a government official or the site owner, do so at once and without objectionable behaviour.

in their logs. On a third occasion, the only reason that it did not happen was that the first and second placed stations *both* had unmarked dupes!

Computers

Computers are perhaps the area in which the greatest development has occurred in contesting in the last few years. It is by no means essential to use one, but more and more people are doing so and reaping the benefits. Perhaps the first question to ask is – what does computer logging give me which paper logging doesn't? The cynic may reply – nothing other than more equipment, something else to learn about, and more boxes to blow up! This author takes rather the opposite viewpoint to this and finds that the little extra effort required to organise computer logging for a contest pays big dividends both during and after the event – he is pretty reluctant to enter any event without the aid of a machine now. The biggest bonus from using a computer must be that you don't have to spend hours after the event transcribing your real-time logs into something which is acceptable to the contest adjudicators. This author hates doing any form of paperwork and finds it almost impossible that to believe that he used to write up 500+ QSO contests by hand. Now at the end of the contest, all that is required is to make a fairly careful examination of the contacts in the file on the computer – make sure that everything looks sensible, and then print out the logs – this should take minutes instead of hours.

The computer is also a big help during the event. Search-and-pounce operation is much easier than with a paper-based dupe sheet. All you have to do is to type a part of the callsign of the station you have heard into the computer, hit the appropriate key, and the machine will show you whether you have had a previous contact or not. Speaking as a single operator who cannot write in two places at once, keeping a paper-based dupe sheet while making contacts at a reasonable rate was always a difficult exercise. This problem is of course eliminated with the computer where the dupe sheet is automatically generated as you log the contacts you make. Keeping track of multipliers is normally a similar problem, and again the computer can keep track of this for you automatically, with screens to indicate what multipliers are still required. The ability to send appropriate automatically generated CW messages from the keyboard is a great aid to keeping down the stress level in CW contests too.

You can get computer logging packages for many different types of computer, but here we are going to concentrate on those available for the PC. One of the accusations often levelled at computer logging is that you need to spend a lot of money on the computer. This is not necessarily the case, with the packages commonly being used at VHF being able to run on a simple XT. Old XTs can be picked up second-hand very cheaply, and there are also some very cheap 'surplus stock' 286s around. What is probably more important than the raw power of the computer is whether it is quiet from an RF point of view. Machines vary greatly in this respect, both between models and with frequency for an individual computer. Unfortunately, the only really sure way to find out if a particular machine is going to cause a problem is to try it in the situation in which you intend to use it. There are quite a number of techniques for reducing the noise, much of which tends to escape on the connecting leads, and these solutions have often been covered in *Radio Communication* and elsewhere over many years. Do, however, make sure that the screening in your own receive system is up to the job – this author has certainly experienced instances where he was getting more grief from computer QRM than he felt he deserved, and it was all because the braid of a piece of coaxial cable was open at one end. Immunity to transmitted RF also needs checking – some monitors have a crisis with large quantities of RF, and keyboards have been known to take on ghostly self-typing properties too. In one case, on 80m, you just had to lay your hands above the keyboard to make it start typing of its own accord!

Software is the other important consideration for computer logging. Assuming that you are not going to write your own, there are a large variety of possible packages to use, some freeware, some shareware and some commercial. Having taken a look at many of the alternatives, there are two packages which

stand out as being the most developed and suitable for VHF contesting in the UK. Both have their good and bad points – you have to make a decision on what you want. These are both commercial packages and are LOG by G3WGV, and SDV by EI5DI. LOG is a package which covers both HF and VHF contests, while SDV is a VHF variant of SD (Super-Duper – the HF version). You can check the September 1993 issue of *Radio Communication* for more details on Super Duper in a review, but its great virtue is the ease of use and one can well believe the various stories told of complete beginners to computer logging being very comfortable with the software within minutes. There is full window editing, so it is just a matter of moving the cursor keys up and down to change the details of a previous QSO, and SD is somewhat unique in that it won't let you do anything inconsistent, by, for example logging G4PIQ in Essex on 2m, but in Suffolk on 70cm. The automatic display of bearing and distance is particularly useful with the narrow antenna systems in use at VHF/UHF. Some VHF contests now use a multiplier scheme which consists of locator squares, counties and countries, and the latest versions of SDV have the option to cope with all of the variants. Some of the VHF contests which are co-ordinated with Europe (the 2m Trophy and the 70cm section of the October UHF event) require scoring in both radial rings and at 1pt/km if you are going to enter both the IARU event and the RSGB one. SDV supports this well, with both kilometres and radial rings on the log. SDV supports all the usual features which help search-and-pounce operation such as 'check partial' (eg enter 'IQ' and it will list all the calls worked containing 'IQ') and a nice touch here is the ability to search either by suffix or prefix. Also, the normal counties and countries worked lists are well implemented, making it easy to keep and handle on your multiplier situation. The standard CW keying functions are all there too, and it all appears to require very little in the way of computer power since it is claimed that it will even run fine on an XT.

LOG by G3WGV has a more difficult user interface, but one which is based upon the 'standard' of the HF CT package by K1EA, making it easier for those accustomed to CT and its clones, but not necessarily simpler for beginners. One big difference between CT and LOG is the lack of a full window editor in LOG with the process for editing a previous QSO being rather messy. Most of the functionality is very similar to Super Duper although implemented differently but LOG supports some nice extra features for multi-operator contests, enabling you to look at the statistics of the operating, and it has a good front-end for the filing system. LOG is also able to support most of the RSGB events and will run on a simple computer platform. It does have a couple of omissions though – it cannot use locators as multipliers and so, during such events, you will have to keep track of squares worked manually, and edit the LOG file afterwards to show these multipliers. The current version cannot score contests at 1pt/km – this author uses a BASIC program to write kilometres into the comments field.

For multiplier contests, the entry needs to include a summary list of multipliers worked. LOG automatically creates such a list (although excluding locators), while you will have to do this manually with the present release of SDV. If you have a large log and have to do it entirely by hand, this can be a bit of an arduous task, however, one solution would be to use a spreadsheet/database program such as Microsoft Excel to make light work of the job – another alternative would be to write a BASIC or other language program to do the job.

Neither SD or LOG support PacketCluster access, but this can be circumvented by running the applications in a DOS window inside Microsoft Windows and having a separate terminal emulator window open for packet access. It cannot be guaranteed that this will work on all machines although EI5DI does support this function in his latest versions. The other downside of doing this is that you require at least a 386 machine, and this author has found that, to get adequate speed in LOG, a 25MHz 486 seemed to be about the minimum requirement when running inside Windows.

Please bear in mind that the above description of the programs relates to the versions available at the time of going to press (1995) – you should of course get current information from EI5DI and G3WGV before making a choice.

Safety

This section attempts to shed some light on aspects of safety which both prospective and experienced contesters should consider. It is weighted towards portable operation but remember that many of the points, especially those addressing the erection of antennas, apply equally as well when operating from home or a club shack. Most new contest operators operate from home or their local club shack and it is important to think about safety in these cases: bad habits are difficult to break when operating in the field, so have fun and be safe.

What does 'safety' mean? Some people might think it means erecting and collapsing masts and antennas without anyone getting hurt. Others may think it applies to the possible use of high voltages in amplifiers on site. Similarly some consider that insurance policies form a safety net if things go wrong. The simple answer is 'safety' means all this and more.

First things first: this section is written from hands-on experience and hopefully covers most of the salient points, but please bear in mind safety and common sense cannot be separated. If you do not feel happy about something on a contest site, either tell someone or do something about it. Above all, if you are unsure about the safety of any aspect of your contesting activities don't do it: antennas, masts, tents, expensive radio equipment and even cars are all replaceable – lives are not. Please be careful in your contesting activities: your first mistake could be your last – don't fool around when someone's safety is involved.

Picture the scene: there you are, sitting on your 3000ft hill in Scotland with a superb take-off in most directions. You are congratulating yourself and your colleagues with your choice of site and how everything seems to have got off to an excellent start. The problem is you may have already made your first and most important mistake. Always remember to tell someone where you are going and for how long. It really is not too surprising how amateur radio kit doesn't work very well under a foot or more of snow. We are trying not to be too patronising here – you may think that with all that radio kit you could summon help in an instant. That may be true but think of it this way – a member of your team who has been injured could be in quite a bad way by the time the local mountain rescue team get him to the ambulance at the bottom of the hill. In other words, summoning help by radio is a cure but it is not a prevention. Note that if using private land it will always pay to seek the permission of the landowner – your health could suffer otherwise (but that's another story!).

So you have let somebody know where you are and when you should be back, now on to the weather. High pressure is forecast so there shouldn't be any problem with the weather. Wrong! Temperature generally falls by 1° C per 300ft height gained and that is without wind chill. No need to bother you with the sums, but you can see that the summit of the hill will be a lot colder than the track running in the valley below. Add the wind chill and you would be amazed at just how easy it is to get caught out. So remember to take cold and wet weather gear with you, even if you are just out for a Sunday afternoon. Naturally, you cannot always rely on the British weather, the rain may not be belting down and sometimes it does get quite sunny. Therefore in addition to your cold weather gear, don't forget the sun cream. Most people have a good idea of how their own skin copes with the sun, but don't forget you could be out it the sun for many hours. Something else that you should consider: it is possible to get sunburnt in all seasons, and especially in winter, wind burn leading to accelerated dehydration can be a problem. So always lean on the side of caution – this author would rather look silly wearing a floppy sun hat than get burnt on his bald spot!

Hopefully most readers will be well aware of the potential problems the weather can throw at you, but please remember that the weekend isn't over until you are tucked up safe and sound in bed at home. Please try to remember your journey home. For some this might be a five-minute stroll down a leafy lane in pleasant sunshine. But for others it could be a nine-hour drive from one end of the country to the other. So take it easy – don't spoil the weekend by crashing the car on the way back because you are too tired.

Back to our mountain top. You can now start to put the station together, erecting masts, putting antennas together, erecting tents, connecting every bit of radio kit in site to your earth. "Earth?", you say. Yes, even in the middle of nowhere you should take an earth spike and connect the chassis of your precious radio to it. This will not only help to protect you from nasty RF burns, but also help to maintain a Faraday cage to prevent static build-up (or worse, static discharge).

Now to the antennas and masts. Before you do anything, look and think. Obviously no one in their right mind would put up a mast near overhead power lines, would they? This author was reminded at this point of someone he saw flying a kite only 20 or so yards from a three-phase overhead power line! No, of course we are all too sensible to do anything like that. However, don't forget to think about the worst case: what would happen if the mast did come crashing down? Is it near a road? Is it near a building? What about the car park? Is there a footpath nearby – the general public may not appreciate a stake with several guys lashed to it knocked into the path. Is there likely to be any livestock roaming about? Sheep, cattle and other animals can be quite destructive; it's not their fault, they just see a new tree with funny branches that just has tested by rubbing against it or by nibbling at the guys. You might think that your presence on site would deter any of this activity – not so: one group I know was operating from a farmer's field when someone spotted the rear end on a cow sticking out of an unmanned tent. The 4m gear inside was rather messy by the time the cow had finished.

Other points to think about: many good sites are on coastal cliffs, with obvious dangers. One point might, however, be worth noting: when operating from a coastal cliff you should consider informing the coast guard. Low-flying helicopter training sorties can't be ruled out. Also take time to think about the lights in use at night from such sights – it is easy to misinterpret coastal lights from off shore.

Inland there are different problems. Some National Parks have military training ranges and the local soldiers are not likely to take to kindly to a strange antenna, generator and tents overlooking their firing range. Check the local firing range timetable before setting out.

"But I thought *you* were giving the orders!"

Now to the mast and antennas themselves. Do you have the right tools for the job? Nothing is worse than slipping with a screwdriver that is too big and putting it through your hand. What about heavy duty footwear? Trainers and the like do not provide much protection from a sledge hammer; heavy walking boots are better but steel toe-capped boots are best. Hard hats are cumbersome but could just save you from a nasty head injury. They are available with chin straps for those who might have them blown off in a gale or to stop them falling off when bending over to work on something at ground level.

Erecting the masts could and should be the subject of many more words than this section can cater for. Just remember that guy ropes can stretch, stakes can loosen, knots can untie themselves. Always watch the mast, guys, stakes and other people. Never fool around when lifting a mast into the sky – this is potentially the most difficult and dangerous time of the whole weekend.

Should there be any children, cats, dogs, or other unwanted distractions about, assign somebody to look after them during this time. If they want to get involved, tactfully point out the dangers but don't allow inexperienced people to get involved.

Always discuss the details before erecting the mast. Nominate someone (who should know what they are doing) to oversee the operation. This person should stand back so he or she can get a good view of the shape of the mast. Try to agree a set of simple instructions that are short but meaningful, eg "Pull in on your bottom guy, Richard . . . OK" instead of "Erm . . . I think that bottom one needs to be a bit tighter, hmmm maybe if the wind shifts . . . just a minute, I'll check . . . oh yes, but not too much now".

When lifting masts using gin-pole methods, remember the forces exerted on the top guy to the gin-pole. This guy can easily stretch, causing the mast to sag under its own weight, leading potentially to catastrophic consequences. If erecting a mast taller than 45ft, with antennas mounted close to the top, this author recommends using steel guy wire to the gin-pole. This doesn't stretch, but does have safety implications all of its own. If you use steel securing wires, ensure that they are fastened off properly with shackles and turn-buckles.

Never use steel rope to pull the gin-pole or any other lifting arrangement. Always use good-quality rope, and always wear gloves. Even in the height of summer, a pair of thick industrial gloves or heavy-duty leather gloves are essential for handling ropes. Don't worry about feeling daft, or anybody making fun – always wear gloves when handling ropes. Naturally the gloves should not remove all sensitivity from your hands because you will still need to tie knots, but fingerless gloves are in general not recommended.

Once your mast with antenna(s) has been lifted into place and secured you can breathe again. No apologies for repetition – operations involving masts and antennas needs careful thought and planning. The front cover of *Radio Communication* a while back showed a picture of a substantial mast with antennas in the process of falling over. Talking sometime later to the team involved, they said that the only explanation they had was that as the mast went up a guy rope had snagged on a bench. This caused it to stretch, the mast went out of true and the rest is history. Luckily this group are amongst the most experienced in the UK and were able to cope with the problem, though not without damaging elements of the mast and several antennas. Even more luckily, as the photograph confirms, nobody was under or near the mast and everybody was watching it. The point of highlighting this is not to embarrass the group in question, but to emphasise that erection of masts can go wrong, even with the best groups. Do take care when erecting your mast and antenna.

So now your mast is up, the antennas are fine, the radio equipment is ready, so off you go . . . well not quite yet. The generator, if not already fired up, needs some thought. Generators should be relatively straightforward, but not always. Always use a funnel to fill the generator, even if it is diesel, but especially if it is petrol. Of course if you are using a petrol generator ensure that strict fire precautions are observed. Always use high-quality mains cable to connect to the equipment. This will not only ensure less losses, but is less likely to suffer from someone accidentally driving over it. Don't forget that generators are heavy beasts – if you are having one delivered to site try to get it in the correct place first time. Nobody wants to put their back out by moving a generator a few yards.

That's enough about the safety aspects of generators – what happens if you are using batteries (for low-power or Backpacker-type contests)? Most batteries these days are intrinsically safe, but it always pays to check. Try to ensure that there is no possibility of an accidental short-circuit as some batteries can leak toxic gases or even explosively vent electrolyte if a short-circuit is applied.

So now your masts are safely up in the sky, equipment working nicely, generator humming away well and you're 100 QSOs in front of the next station on the band. That's just how it should be. You can relax and enjoy a nice beer or two. Fine, but please remember the effects of alcohol. This is not the place to preach about the latter, but one major UK VHF contest group insists on a 'dry' site. This is because they nearly dropped a mast on someone a few years ago after one too many pints in the pub. Of course we all like the odd pint or two, but be sensible. Think of the dangers, and remember the law.

Has all this sounded rather negative? It is difficult to treat a subject such as safety in anything but a serious manner. Above all safety on site is the application of common sense. Being aware of the potential dangers and doing something about them can help to ensure an enjoyable and successful weekend.

Further information on the safety aspects of contesting is given in the HF contest section.

Generators

Finding a source of power at any portable site is a major consideration, particularly at VHF where good sites may be quite some distance from a mains electricity supply. If you are just running a few tens of watts you may well be able to get away with battery power, but more substantial stations require an inordinate amount of effort to ensure a ready supply of battery power – particularly if you are at the top of a mountain! The obvious alternative is a generator, and these can be extremely reliable and behave just as you expect. However, equally, they can be an immense source of frustration and the cause of hours of lost operating. Chris Parry, G8JFJ, has sent these very useful thoughts on this subject, focusing some of the problems which can (but don't always) occur!

The basic choice is between diesel or petrol (although gas power is also feasible) but nevertheless all the options are expensive to buy or hire! Most sets produce 220VAC or 240VAC, although battery charging 12VDC or 24VDC sets produces an attractive alternative solution for modest power stations. Petrol or gas engines can both stop in driving rain, and have been known to lose regulation upwards, which is potentially dangerous. (This author can vouch for this, having used one petrol generator which suffered from major overshoot on its throttle control loop – as you went back to receive and the main load came off, it would shoot up to 350V – this destroyed a rig and bits of an amplifier very quickly!) Putting a box in line between the generator and equipment which will cut the load if voltage outside the limits 200-270V is detected is an excellent insurance policy.

You should bring the generator up to its governed speed before connecting the load, and also isolate the load before stopping the generator. One computer PSU failure was definitely traced to waveform stretching as the machine slowed down. Again, an automatic switchbox would have avoided this situation. 10% voltage regulation is an everyday problem for portable contest groups, and both the receiver and the transmitter reservoir capacitors need to be rated to cope with the potentially high voltage on receive. An alternative is to switch in a fan heater on receive (a popular winter-time solution).

Both petrol and gas engines use spark-ignition which can cause potential EMC problems, and the storage and transport of upwards of 20 gallons of petrol needs to be considered. 'Hot' filling of petrol generators can be very hazardous, especially in windy weather. At least one station recently lost many hours of operating recently with a trip down the mountain to hospital after an operator split petrol all over a hot generator. The flywheels of Japanese sets are often inadequate for smoothing the pulsating torsional load presented by a big SSB transmitter, and this causes poor voltage regulation at syllabic rate.

Diesel sets can be difficult or impossible to start after long periods of storage unless they are 100% healthy, and summer-grade fuel can freeze in March. Diesel is very prone to develop bacteriological contamination during storage, particularly in the summer, and especially when stored in clear or white vessels/pipework. Diesel sets are bigger and heavier than similarly-rated petrol sets, but are far more economical and, as an extra bonus, fuel can be tax-exempt 'red' diesel, available from boatyards etc. Anything bigger than 5kVA is best trailer-mounted in order to reduce the manhandling hazards in rain or snow. Generators of all types need to be sited away from the main antenna lobe, downwind, and where cables do not cross footpaths.

However, the big issue is how big a generator do you need? In general, a much bigger one than you might at first expect! This because most transmitters have capacitor-input power supplies which draw current only on waveform peaks, causing high copper losses in the alternator. As a 'sizing' guide, aim for a generator with a VA rating fourfold greater than the required transmitter output PEP. Even with a generator significantly bigger than this, with most valve amplifiers you should not expect to see the same power output on the generator as you do at home, mainly because the HT will be down. As an example, on a 240V mains supply this author's K2RIW supply sits at 2.6kV off load, and the amplifier will deliver about 600W – on a 9kVA 230V generator it is down to 2.3kV, and will only deliver 450W, and on a 2.5kVA petrol generator you are down to 300W out! The only real solution to this problem is either to have much bigger amplifiers than you need, or to use those with choke-input supplies which take current over the whole mains cycle. A good example of an amplifier with a choke input supply is the old Tempo 2002 which is almost as effective on a generator as it is on the mains – it isn't known what the newer 2002A is like, however. Some forms of switched-mode supplies can also be a good option.

Cable size may be less significant than expected, because of the high source impedance of the generator as compared with domestic mains. Ex-building-site alternators are often 220VAC brushless types and produce a square-wave EMF. Better types with proper sinewave output exist, but these have brushes, and may therefore be less reliable and present possible EMC problems. Beware of heavy oil consumption – smoky generators could seize if run continuously for 24 hours. Also beware of vibration – avoid the temptation to get 240VAC out of a 220VAC mechanically governed set by raising the governed speed by 10%. The engine mountings etc may have a high Q and be ineffective (or worse) at anything other than the intended mechanical frequency.

Many alternators have the neutral connected to the frame, but others have the L-N output fully insulated. Chalk hilltops in summer present earth conductivity problems, even assuming it is possible to drive in an earth stake, and in all cases it is necessary to think carefully about safety in terms of fusing and RCCB/ELCB performance, especially if using multiple generators as part of a single installation (see previous section). If you don't fully understand this side of the system, get good advice from someone who really does!

One final point is that of physical safety – when using a crank handle, fingers and thumb must go on the same side to avoid risk of injury in event of kickback, and all belts, chains and shafts must have guards.

Equipment

Contesting provides an ideal opportunity to develop a wide range of personal skills by encouraging innovation and experimentation. You may, perhaps, have constructed your rig, antenna, preamp, feed system or mast support; be a QRP enthusiast, a QRO specialist 'having a day off'; have an interest in alternative power sources or may just want to see how you and your trusted rig will perform in a different environment to the shack.

Although this is not a technical book, some basic points will be discussed here as, unlike better-quality HF gear, VHF equipment 'off-the-shelf' is often unsuitable for contest operation and may need some modification.

Receiver basics

There are too many factors to consider when looking at receivers in detail, but two of them are most significant in the context of a simple contest station; how well you can hear very weak signals and how well the receiver copes with very strong signals. The following notes are a very simplified view of these two factors, as they apply to a 2m SSB receiver.

Weak signal reception

Weak signal reception is ultimately limited by the background noise, (sometimes called the 'noise floor') of the receiver system. This noise comes from two sources; the inherent noise in the receiver and both man-made and atmospheric noise picked up by the antenna.

The noise from the antenna varies with frequency (eg 6m is noisier than 2m) and quite dramatically with location. On 2m a reasonable antenna can pick up enough noise to over-ride the inherent noise in the receiver. In this case, weak signal reception is limited by the signal strength arriving from the ether and even the very best preamp will make only a slight improvement. A larger antenna will pick up both more signals and more noise, so there is no overall improvement.

As a simple test, switch to SSB and connect a good dummy load to the antenna socket. Connect an AC voltmeter to the speaker socket and set the volume control so that the meter indicates about 50% full scale (which might not be steady). Replace the dummy load with the antenna, tune to a quiet spot and read the meter. If the reading has increased by more than 20%, then weak signal reception is limited by the antenna noise and a preamp will be of little or no use.

A smaller antenna (dipole, halo, HB9CV or small Yagi) will collect less noise and the inherent noise in the receiver then becomes very significant. Many modern receivers are well designed and very little improvement is possible, but equally many can benefit from a *modest gain* preamp. The has the effect of improving the signal-to-noise ratio (making the signal more readable), even though the speaker and S-meter may indicate that the noise level has increased.

Try some organised tests with a local station who can reduce power to give you a barely readable signal (this avoids propagation variations). If there is no clear improvement from adding a preamp, leave it out!

Strong-signal problems
The first draft of this section quickly assumed the proportions of a book, discussing IMD, intercept point, reciprocal mixing, cross modulation and blocking. This indicates the complexity of the subject, and this section is, therefore, extremely simplified. Those people who wish to pursue the matter further are advised to consult the amateur press which contains numerous articles giving greater detail.

Unfortunately, most reasonably priced multi-mode VHF transceivers have been designed with little consideration for the need to work in the presence of off-channel strong signals. When such signals are present, such as on a crowded contest band, various symptoms can occur. This includes strong signals appearing to splatter widely (even over the whole band), the receiver not working when tuned near a strong signal, the background noise jumping up and down or just being much higher than normal. All of these can be caused by a faulty transmitter, but they are almost always due to the receiver being overloaded.

How to spot overload? Firstly, look at the S-meter when tuned to a strong signal. If it is pinned on maximum, then the receiver is likely to be overloaded. Change the antenna direction, antenna or use attenuators to reduce the signal strength to S5–S6. If the problems reduce a lot, or disappear, then the problem is receiver overload. If the problems remain, then call the station and politely explain the problems and the tests carried out at reduced signal strength, and ask that the transmitter be checked. If the problems persist, write to the contest adjudicator.

What to do about it? Overload problems escalate dramatically with signal strength and most solutions will involve reducing the level of the interfering signal. Some tests can be

G8ZRE shows all the equipment needed for a successful Backpackers operation

improved by modification or replacement front-end units (see below). The inherent problems of a poor receiver cannot be placed on anyone except the manufacturer, so other solutions have to be pragmatic:

(a) Live with it.
(b) Make sure that any preamp is really needed and be prepared to live without it.
(c) Make a more directional antenna so that the wanted signal can be peaked and/or the unwanted signal nulled out.
(d) Find another site.
(e) Modify your existing radio.
(f) Buy a new (more modern) radio, having checked with the manufacturer that the receiver has been designed to avoid or significantly reduce such problems.

Commercial transceivers
The power limits for the Backpackers series of contests were largely dictated by the power output from a wide range and variety of commercial rigs which have been or are currently available. The ubiquitous FT290 (Mk1) will, if operated correctly, perform well. However, it should be borne in mind that this radio, like many others of this generation, can possess a relatively high level of synthesiser noise in comparison to more modern radios. Under normal conditions operating from home, there may have been no previous problems noticed but as soon as you venture to a good location with anything like a reasonable antenna under contest-style conditions, you will notice that very strong signals may appear to either spread across the band or may be audible on more than one frequency. This fact is compounded if a high-gain preamp is placed in series with the rig. This is not an attempt to play down what has been an enormously popular radio. What we are trying to do is to give you some idea of the type of phenomena you are likely to experience on this and similar radios when a really strong signal appears on the band. If you do experience these problems, firstly make sure your noise blanker is switched off, disconnect your preamp, then your antenna and tune across the 'offending' station to confirm the effect before rushing in and making a complaint.

Unfortunately, it takes a lot of time and effort to build a receiver which will cope with strong signals as it is usually the mixer or IF stages which easily become overloaded. Even the 'big boys' get it wrong occasionally and if you genuinely believe that a station is too wide, politely make a complaint and make appropriate notes in your log book. The other station must do the same and checks are made by the adjudicator. If the problem persists, ask other stations, particularly those who are not so local, to listen to confirm the effect. If they do, they should also make and log a similar complaint. These will be discussed at future VHFCC meetings and a decision will be made.

If you are in the fortunate position of needing to buy a radio (and being able to afford it!), it may be worth reading the various equipment reviews in the excellent *Buyers' Guide to Amateur Radio* (sadly now out of print) written by Angus Mckenzie, G3OSS. This book gives an excellent account of a wide range of equipment which has been available over the last 15 years or so. Again, this is where your local club could assist by sourcing a copy for you to borrow for a short time. Among the several VHF transceivers reviewed many are often seen advertised in the 'Members' Ads' column of *Radio Communication* or turn up from time to time as trade-ins on retailers' shelves – but they don't stay there for long! A visit to one of the larger radio rallies held most weekends across the country may prove more successful with rigs on offer ranging from the TS700, TS7010, TS780, FT221, FT225, FT726, IC275, IC251, C58 to the elusive IC202. Many of these radios can be updated by fitting the appropriate, now very popular MuTek front-end board. Undertaking such a modification will make a significant improvement to both the sensitivity and strong signal handling performance, making the radio more competitive.

Another way round the problem is to transvert, usually from 28MHz, thereby making use of the excellent technical characteristics and features of most of the more modern commercial HF transceivers. When you read about the superb technical specifications on offer, it's a great shame that these are not generally replicated in standard VHF equipment. At the end of the day it is all about cost, market forces and the numbers of units sold. It has always been assumed that the average VHF operator (if one exists) is likely to be less demanding about his equipment as a talk-box to work across the other side of town, particularly as the generally low levels of activity do not place the same rigorous demands on performance as they do on HF. It is only when people like you, me and the rest of the VHF DX/contesting community who are actually placing increased performance demands on our equipment does this limitation become a problem. In real terms, we are generally a low percentage of the amateur market and must therefore be regarded as being economically non-viable. However, there is increasing demand and this is why firms like MuTek who design replacement RF and mixer boards have been so successful in filling a niche in an otherwise extremely competitive market.

There are several excellent commercial transverters currently available, particularly the SSB Products range with designs extending into the microwave region. The LT series are among some of the best around and variants of these are available in kit form. These are not cheap but you do get what you pay for in terms of performance capability. The MuTek range also have a good reputation with the Mark II series of transverters in particular being specifically designed to be 'bomb-proof'. Of course, you can build your own and there are several very good designs available in the amateur press, particularly those published in *VHF Communications* where kits may also be available. Always take care to ensure that the design will cope with strong signals. High-level ring mixers, including the SRA1-H or variants, correctly terminated and injected with around 15mW of local oscillator RF are now usually standard. Again, there are some really excellent transverter designs in the *VHF/UHF DX Book* [3].

Out of all the current batch of commercial transceivers currently available, the TS850s has the advantage of being able to

program the main display to read either 50MHz, 144MHz or 432MHz which makes transverter operation very user-friendly. When combined with all the additional facilities, including voice memory, electronic keyer and CW filters down to 250Hz, you begin to wonder how you ever managed to operate without it! However, not all HF transceivers allow you to extract the low level of RF required to drive the transverter so easily. Many have no low-level output socket which necessitates some form of internal modification, making interfacing that much more difficult. If you undertake such a modification (thereby invalidating the warranty) you will have to ensure that the PA is suitably disabled or you're likely to send 100W into the back of your transverter – not a wise move! However, once you have interfaced everything correctly you potentially have access to better performance and a wider range of facilities which could give you that extra edge in contests, if not only by the increased ease of operating facilitated by such a system.

Modifications

A little has already been mentioned about replacement front-end boards in VHF transceivers which, because of their increased performance, in most circumstances, can do away with the need for a preamp. Assuming you are using an unmodified radio of vintage years and you believe it to be a little 'deaf', the addition of a preamp can work wonders. There is, however, the considerable drawback that the dynamic range of your radio, that is, its ability to perform under strong signal conditions, will almost certainly suffer quite badly. Those of you who are more technically minded may wish to modify the first stage of their radio by doing away with lossy diode switches, slug-tuned cores and rather dated front-end devices possessing high noise figures. As a first step, consult the circuit diagram and try replacing the first RF device (if a dual-gate FET) with either a BF988 or BF981. This should lower the level of internal receiver noise, making weak signals more audible. Then, bypass the antenna switching diodes and note a further improvement (don't transmit!). If you are suitably impressed, like many of those who have successfully completed similar modifications, purchase a miniature change-over relay and wire it in place of the existing components. Of course, don't even think of delving into your rig if you are not confident about what you are doing. Needless to say, any warranty previously given will no longer be valid. Another way round the problem is to use a mast-mounted preamp, but this can lead to increased expense, problems in switching and additional weight. They are also prone to blow at the most inconvenient of times, particularly when you do something stupid in the middle of nowhere! However, if you can interface and sequence everything correctly they can be of enormous benefit, if not essential, particularly on the higher frequencies.

Linearity and output power

It should be remembered that a radio advertised as producing 10W output will in fact often produce considerably more. All too familiar are the horror stories of the 10W radios (producing anything up to 16W) driving '10W input' solid-state amplifiers into distortion and non-linearity. This is mentioned in case those of you with 3W output rigs intend to increase power to enter the higher output section in the Backpackers or intend to drive the ubiquitous black-box 'brick'. What you need to do is to measure the input versus output power of your amplifier. In doing so you will notice how little power it will require to drive it to something like 70% of its stated output power – it will probably require a further doubling of the previously measured drive

A typical 10GHz Cumulative Contest portable scene. G4EQD/P (left) and G3PHO/P on Houndkirk Moor, near Sheffield

power to produce the stated output. Probably even this power is lower than the stated amplifier input. In the meantime, driving your amplifier to around 70% of its rated output will almost certainly give you one of the cleanest signals on the band. This is even more important given that on battery power you will not be able to realise the 13.8V that your radio was aligned on. Given that the gain and linearity of a transistor amplifier is affected by variations in voltage, you should always run your equipment below its rated output to maintain a level of clean output.

As far as valve linears are concerned, it is beyond the scope of this book to discuss the various issues and particular advantages these have to offer – suffice to say that they are invariably the norm in high-power contests. At full legal output, they offer the most cost effective and efficient way of generating high power levels and are far superior, when driven correctly, than any solid-state alternative that is generally available to the amateur. However, great attention must be paid to voltage generation, regulation and associated issues which have been discussed earlier. Readers are invited to read the excellent sections written by John Nelson, GW4FRX, on the design, building and operating of valve linears as published in reference [3].

Feeders

At the end of the day you can only work what you can hear. Losses encountered before the receiver will limit its ability to hear weak signals. Therefore, use a good-quality feeder between your antenna and radio. Don't be fooled – many of the cheaper cables marked as 'RG58U' are rather thinly braided – fine if you're working on HF but particularly lossy even with short runs on VHF. UR67 is certainly better, even more so when terminated correctly with good quality N connectors. There are several alternative low-loss cables currently being advertised which have significantly lower loss than UR67 while still maintaining much of the latter cable's flexibility. It is certainly worth considering these, particularly when feeding single or group antennas from a common feed point above the rotator. Its also worth checking to make sure that there are no special connector requirements and that every effort is taken to ensure a good waterproof bond with the cable. One very popular brand was nick-named 'hosepipe' because it carried water almost as efficiently as RF!

Look out at rallies and radio car boot sales for some LDF250, or even better, LDF450 coaxial cable. These cables are of particularly low loss, meaning that more of your valuable transmit power reaches the antenna and that more of those incoming weak DX signals make it to your receiver. Unfortunately, they are not very flexible and even in medium-size lengths can be a little on the heavy side. The cost of these cables new is highly expensive and such an heavy financial commitment would be unrealistic for the majority of amateurs. It is because these cables are used so extensively commercially that odd runs do thankfully appear on the amateur market at prices comparable to new UR67. Don't forget that open-wire feeder, when correctly terminated, can be of particularly low loss and is very light weight (ask the 70cm EME enthusiasts). Again, this is where there is considerable scope for experimentation. Read the amateur press for further information.

Antennas

This is probably going to be one of the main areas were contests are either won or lost. Quite simply, the more metal work that you can get airborne to capture/radiate those precious radio waves, the more effective and competitive your station is likely to become. However, herein lies the problem – you'll have to compromise between performance and what you can actually carry, erect, and support safely and keep in the air under windy conditions.

There are numerous designs available for the constructor as well as several commercial models. Gain, directivity, front-to-back ratio, matching, feeding, stacking, baying, weight, length and rotation techniques will all have to be considered when deciding on the optimum arrangements. In the Backpackers series of events, we are not expecting massive, multiple arrays which require several acres of land and an army of workers. The 'no tower' and support restrictions will have told you that, but it is perfectly within reason to be able to run two or more antennas or to erect long-wire directional arrays, particularly if you are operating from the extremes of the country. Alternatively, a single nine-element Yagi will perform well, particularly from a high spot with a good take-off. It is always highly interesting to note in the results what stations have been using and to observe changes in fashion, particularly when new designs are either published or come onto the market. Off-beat designs such as collinears, quagis, slopers, and rhombics can also work very well. Look out for details in the amateur radio press, particularly some of the American publications. There's even a lot of fun to be had by stacking a couple of HB9CV antennas a half wavelength apart. In fact, this aspect of stacking and baying antennas is of particular interest to contest stations.

Quite simply, the stacking and baying of antennas is a highly effective way of increasing gain. However, this increased gain is at the expense of concentrating greater energy into the main lobe of the antenna, thereby reducing its beam width. However, if you reduce size of the forward lobe, either in the vertical or horizontal plane, you are restricting the area of its overall coverage and will therefore have to turn the antenna more frequently to beam-up on the weaker stations. This is particularly the case if you bay two or more antennas side by side. One way round the problem is to stack the antennas above each other, thereby reducing the vertical beamwidth. In fact, this makes a great deal of sense because you are concentrating more ERP back towards the horizon where it's going to be of greater use rather than firing a proportion your valuable radiated energy into the sky or ground where it will be wasted, while at the same time still retaining the original (wider) horizontal beam width. Stacks of up to eight antennas high, correctly phased, are common practice in major events, particularly on UHF.

Some groups prefer to stack and bay their antennas in a box-of-four formation. This arrangement is certainly popular when up to eight big Yagis are used, say on 2m, particularly with groups who have access to mobile towers as this formation is more easily accommodated above the head unit bearing. Another way around the problem is to use more than one mast support, effectively creating two or more independent antenna systems. However, even as this increases the flexibility of the system allowing the antennas to be beamed in different directions, it requires extra care in phasing the systems correctly, general layout and a great deal more hardware and man-power to erect and maintain the system. In addition to the main forward lobe, all antennas possess side and back lobes. With careful stacking it is possible to achieve a little more than the theoretical 3dB additional increase in gain as these lobes are either nulled or combined. However, the more antennas you have, the greater the feeder loss, which, it may be argued, is likely to be so high that it outweighs the apparent advantages any increase in antenna gain likely to be achieved. In any case, all antennas perform better the higher they are able to radiate in free space. In this way you may find that a smaller, light-weight antenna appears to out-perform one with a higher quoted gain mounted at a lower height. Don't forget that given half a chance, strong winds will do nasty things to large antennas mounted high above the ground! The whole operation is something of a balancing act between what is desirable and what is achievable given the available resources and the nature the environment and local conditions. However, there is little doubt about the overall effectiveness of big arrays when correctly matched as they really do give added fire-power (reciprocated on receive) to a contest station.

With a little reading you'll soon become more familiar with the basics of antenna performance and design. However, a word of warning: be suspicious of many of the high gain figures quoted in both amateur and commercial literature. Often, gain is quoted as a single point or isotropic radiator, rather than gain over a dipole giving rise to some confusion. To convert, subtract 2.1dB from the isotropic figure. Also, running some of the more recent computer simulation software reveals that some of the quoted gains are impossible to achieve on the specified boom length. For further proof, ask the 'big boys' what antennas they use and you will almost certainly find that, commercial or home-brew, they are based on the DL6WU designs which have superseded the older NBS types. It should be borne in mind that many of the more recent published designs are attempting to squeeze the last fraction of a decibel and are primarily aimed at those whose main interest is EME. Quite frankly, although desirable in terms of performance, these types of antennas are by no means mandatory for a good contest station. The older designs work very well and it is highly unlikely that you would be able to perceive the difference of one decibel, let alone fractions of one, during the general noise and confusion of a contest. However, there is still considerable scope for experimentation, particularly in the areas of manufacturing for portability and in the combining, stacking and baying of more than one antenna. For more information, consult references [3] and [4], and also the DUBUS publications.

AMATEUR RADIO DIRECTION FINDING CONTESTS

There is one sphere of amateur radio activity that offers a unique opportunity for combining radio skills with the diverse skills of navigation and (for those so inclined) cross-country running, made the more interesting by a competitive atmosphere. These are the elements which combine to make amateur radio direction finding (ARDF) contests, and those who respond to the challenge of ARDF find themselves taking part in a most enjoyable activity. This section seeks to explain how these contests are organised and the techniques which are used by those taking part in them.

More comprehensive information can be found in the *Amateur Radio Direction Finding Manual*, which is published by the RSGB – see reference [5]. The following pages summarise ARDF activities in three parts: 1.8MHz, 144MHz, and IARU Rules contests.

1.8MHz contests

Historically, ARDF in the UK has developed mainly on the 1.8MHz band and regular contests have taken place since the 'twenties. Currently, there are several clubs which organise programmes of events – on Sunday afternoons, weekday evenings, and even at night. These may involve finding just a single hidden transmitter, but sometimes there are up to four. Each year, the RSGB sponsors a series of qualifying events leading to the National Final in September, and much of the following reflects these events. The general principles apply equally, however, to other 1.8MHz contests which various clubs organise under local rules.

An attempt to summarise the main points of a set of rules is made below.

1. Starting and finishing times are quoted.
2. The number of hidden transmitters, their callsigns and frequencies should be given.
3. The transmission schedule should be specified, and if 'random' transmissions are used the minimum duration of each transmission and maximum gap between transmissions should be given. If morse signals are to be used as an aid to transmission, this should be stated.
4. Provision should be made for approximate bearings to be given in the event of transmissions being inaudible to some competitors at the start.
5. The power input to the PA of each transmitter should remain constant throughout the contest. The antennas will be directly connected to the transmitters, which will not be operated by remote control.
6. The hidden stations should be located at least 50 yards (46m) from any inhabited building and must be directly accessible to competitors without them entering, crossing or trespassing upon property in private occupation.
7. The hidden stations must be at least 50ft (15m) from any public highway.
8. Transmitter locations and the start should be covered by a specified map sheet, details of which are published before the event.

9. A competitor may be accompanied by a team, providing it does not consist of more than three others.
10. Only one portable receiver capable of being tuned to the 1.8MHz band may be carried by any competitor's party during the event but a second portable receiver may be available for use only as a reserve.
11. The rules must state how the winner is to be determined. Usually this is the first contestant to locate all stations, in any order, but there may be variations. In some contests, bearing accuracy and other factors are taken into account.

The competitor's equipment

Obviously, the first item of equipment required is a suitable receiver. The main features of a 1.8MHz ARDF receiver are listed here, but the reader who wishes to consider detailed circuit layouts is advised to consult the various articles in which such circuits have from time to time been published [5–7].

To be suitable for 1.8MHz contests a receiver should:

1. Cover the frequency range 1.8–2.0MHz.
2. Have a directional antenna (frame or ferrite rod).
3. Have a telescopic vertical antenna for 'sense' purposes (more about this later).
4. Have the circuitry effectively screened, so that the signal pick-up is on the antennas only, and not on the internal wiring.
5. Be capable of handling a wide range of signal strengths. This is because the directional antenna will only pick up a small signal from a distant transmitter – thus requiring a substantial amount of gain – but there must be adequate gain control or attenuation to prevent the receiver from overloading when it is operating in close proximity to the transmitter.
6. Be reasonably selective.
7. Incorporate a BFO.
8. Be portable and preferably of rugged construction.

The competitor will also need a compass, which is normally mounted on the receiver (care being taken to keep it well away from any ferrous components, and especially any loudspeakers or meters which may be carried). He will also require a map of the area covered by the contest (normally a single sheet of the Ordnance Survey 1:50,000 series) with a board to rest it on, a 360° protractor, ruler and pencil. Unless the range of the contest is very limited, as in pedestrian events, some means of transport will of course be essential.

Competitor technique

Some competitors say that direction finding is a science; others assert that it is an art. The truth probably lies somewhere between!

At the start of a contest, each competitor is given the frequencies and callsigns of each transmitter. He will also be advised of the transmission schedule, and whether morse signals will precede telephony signals as an aid to identification. If this is the case, he will use his BFO to identify the stations but will probably wait for the continuous carrier of the telephony transmission before attempting to take an accurate bearing – still using the BFO.

It has already been mentioned that a DF receiver should incorporate two antennas. The main directional antenna (frame or ferrite rod) is capable of giving quite accurate bearings (to within a degree or two) but, as the set is rotated through 360°, the operator will note that there are *two* positions at which the received signal falls to a minimum (these are referred to as *null*

The start of an event with competitors trying to get their first bearing

points). If a frame antenna is used, the null points occur when the frame is at right-angles to the bearing from the transmitter, and if a ferrite rod is used they occur when the rod is in line with the bearing from the transmitter. Using the directional antenna alone, the operator cannot tell in which of two directions (180° apart) the hidden station lies. However, if he now switches in a signal from the vertical antenna and combines this with a signal from the main antenna, there will be only *one* signal maximum and one null as the set is rotated through 360°. The receiver is thus able to *sense* the direction of the transmitter positively, so the vertical antenna is referred to as a *sense antenna*.

The null point which occurs with the sense circuit in operation will be at 90° to the null points observed when using the directional antenna alone. With experience of a particular receiver, the operator can tell the direction of the transmitter with respect to the maximum and null positions.

Note that the competitor, having used the sense facility to determine the general direction of the transmitter, will not attempt to obtain a precise bearing in this mode, but will disconnect the sense circuit and obtain an accurate bearing using the appropriate null with the directional antenna alone. This is because the maximum and null obtained with the sense circuit in operation are very broad, unlike the nulls obtained with the directional antenna alone, which are quite sharp.

Finally, after carefully positioning the receiver to take the bearing (and preferably after two or three attempts, to reduce the chance of errors) the competitor can read the compass and note the bearing. It will be easier if the operator has an assistant (or navigator) to record the bearing, especially in multistation contests where the bearings of the other stations have to measured in a similar fashion. The navigator can then transfer the bearings to the map, using the protractor and ruler.

Assuming that there is only one hidden station to find, the competitor now has a line on the map indicating the direction of the transmitter. What he does not know is how far along the line the transmitter lies, or how accurate the bearing is. He might make an estimate of the distance based on the strength of the signal, but this is far from reliable since cunning organisers will often arrange for a very weak signal from a station within a few hundred metres from the start, or equip a distant station with a very effective antenna to ensure a strong signal. As regards bearing accuracy, errors of 2° or 3° may normally be expected, but occasionally quite large errors may arise. Much can be done to reduce the risk of serious error by choosing a good spot to take the bearing, as far as possible from any metallic objects which will re-radiate the signal. Wire fences, telephone wires and, above all, overhead power lines should be avoided like the plague!

How then does the competitor close in on the transmitter? The standard technique is to select a point some distance to one side of the plotted bearing, and take a second bearing on a subsequent transmission. In choosing the site for the second bearing, the seasoned competitor will probably make an estimate of where he thinks the transmitter lies and will choose a spot which will give him a good (ideally right-angled) cross on the original bearing. If he has a reliable crystal ball, he may perhaps notice that his bearing passes through a patch of woodland that looks a promising site from the map, and may even risk going there without taking a cross bearing. It is usually advisable, however, to take two, three or even more bearings before becoming sure that the area of the hidden station has been pin-pointed.

Note that as the competitor takes bearings on subsequent transmissions, the relative signal strengths of the received signals at different locations can be used as a guide to the proximity of the transmitter – though caution must be exercised in case the transmitter antenna has marked directional characteristics. Also, as the competitor nears the transmitter the effect of bearing errors becomes less significant. For example, a bearing error of 5° results in a bearing which passes 2.6km from a transmitter at 30km, but an error of less than 0.2km when the transmitter is 2km away.

If the transmissions are on a random schedule, it is of great benefit to the competitor if he has some means of listening for transmissions while travelling in his car. The ideal arrangement comprises a loaded whip antenna and a monitoring loudspeaker amplifier which can be used in conjunction with the DF receiver. The RSGB rules also permit the use of a fixed monitoring receiver in the competitor's car.

There is an additional technique which can sometimes be very useful if the receiver operator has a driver. If, for example, the transmitter is hidden in a wood with a road passing alongside it, the competitor can use his receiver, on its directional antenna, to follow the bearing as he is driven past. Such bearings taken inside a car are of course not accurate – but as the vehicle passes the transmitter the operator will note that the bearing 'turns'. This tells him the best point at which to enter the wood, and furthermore by noticing how sharply the bearing turns he may deduce how far inside the wood the transmitter lies.

When the competitor has located the area of the transmitter with sufficient confidence to abandon his car and set off on foot, the way in which his receiver is used changes since there is no longer much point in taking compass bearings and plotting them on the map. The main priority is to get to the transmitter as quickly as possible, so if the competitor can run rather than walk, so much the better! It will probably be obvious in which direction the competitor should go when leaving the road, but in some instances he will need to wait for a transmission and take a 'sense' before setting forth. He will then run towards the transmitter as directly as he can, while taking maximum advantage from any paths which may exist. He may leave his sense circuit switched on, or alternatively may run forward in the direction indicated by the null of the directional antenna, in which case he will be conscious of the turning of the bearing if he runs along a path which passes fairly close to the transmitter,

thereby indicating the point to leave the path and dive into the undergrowth.

In any case, the signal strength will increase perceptibly as the transmitter is approached, and most receivers will probably overload as they reach the transmitter antenna. The competitor now knows he has arrived – well, almost!

Almost, because the transmitter and its operator are probably well concealed, and because the organiser may have deliberately provided it with an antenna several wavelengths long, in which case the receiver will lead him to the points of maximum radiation which occur every half-wavelength along the antenna. He may therefore have to resort to a detailed search of the area, or to find the antenna wire and follow it to its source.

Sometimes, especially if an elaborate antenna system has been used, the receiver will lead its operator time and time again to a particular spot where the transmitter is obviously not sited. The trampled undergrowth may well indicate that other contestants have suffered the same problem. The best avenue open to the competitor is to control his frustration and try another approach from a new point some distance away on the next transmission. If that fails, methodical searching is the only alternative.

When the transmitter has finally been located, the competitor hands his entry paper to the operator, who will record his time of arrival. The competitor then leaves the site, taking care not to disclose its whereabouts to any other competitors in the vicinity.

So far only a single-station contest has been discussed. When two or more transmitters are involved the basic technique is of course unaltered. However, the contestant has to decide in which order to hunt the stations. There can be no set guidelines here – every contest situation is different. A competitor may decide to play for safety and select for his second bearings a site which is likely to give reasonable cross bearings on all the transmitters. Alternatively, he may 'play a hunch' on the location of one particular transmitter, and give scant attention to the others until later. The worst situation which can arise is to discover, on the second transmissions, that none of the stations can be heard. The competitor is then on his own since all the others have dispersed to different points, and he has to decide a new policy. When this situation arises, it is most likely that at least one station is near the start.

Transmitting equipment

Attention will now be turned to the other aspects of ARDF contests, as viewed from the organisational side. The main item of equipment is the transmitter, and basically any transmitter which is capable of operating in the 1.8MHz band and being powered from a battery may be used. The elaborate apparatus used in the shack is not, however, appropriate and it is normal practice to use a fairly simple transmitter.

The emphasis should be on portability and reliability. To achieve this, attention should be given to weather protection. Rechargeable batteries, housed within the transmitter case, are practicable and crystal control is desirable. It needs to be capable of transmitting speech modulation (A3E) and morse (A1A); this can be achieved with a conventional microphone and key, though more sophisticated equipment using electronic keying and stored speech is also used.

Contest organisation

When setting out to run a contest, the organiser has to bear in mind the standard of difficulty which is appropriate. If the contest will attract an entry of novices, a fairly simple standard is needed – but the organiser of a three-station national final should make it tough. Several factors combine to determine the overall difficulty of a contest, and careful consideration must be given to each one.

The first things to fix are the start and the transmitter site or sites. These cannot be decided in isolation since the distances between the start and transmitters, and between the transmitters themselves, as well as the nature of the route between them, must all be considered. It is necessary to ensure that the transmitters will be able to radiate adequate signals to the start.

The start itself should be arranged off the public highway, with adequate parking space for the expected number of competitors' vehicles, and somewhere which will not inconvenience members of the public. A large open space, free of overhead wires and fences, will help competitors to get good bearings – but a start which lies beneath high-voltage power cables may be deliberately chosen if it is desired to make the contest more difficult.

The selection and arrangement of the actual transmitter sites is the most important part of contest organisation, and is the main factor by which a contest will be judged. It is most important, however, that the sites chosen are directly accessible to competitors without them entering, crossing or trespassing on property in private occupation. Access via public rights of way is, of course, permissible. In some circumstances it will nevertheless be courteous for the organiser to advise local residents of his plans so that they are not alarmed when a horde of strange characters wearing headphones descends on the area!

A good transmitter site will be well away from the road and well hidden. A long antenna or one with several spurs off it will make the site much more difficult for the competitors, but things will be made easy for them if a simple vertical wire going straight up into a tree is used, as this will lead them directly to the transmitter. There are many ruses which the transmitter operator can deploy to hide himself and his equipment – probably the most common is to crawl into a thicket. Other ideas which have been exploited are holes in the ground, boats moored to river banks, stations in trees etc. Sometimes a transmitter operator need not be hidden at all – he may be disguised as a fisherman (with the antenna connected to the end of his rod and the transmitter in his basket), or the transmitter may be operated by a 'courting couple' in the back of a car. The contestant needs adequate skill to be confident of any decision to challenge in the latter case!

The broad principles of setting up a hidden station have been outlined above, but there are of course many finer points which will help to ensure a good contest. For example, a station may be on a river bank but far from a bridge – very frustrating for the competitors who arrive on the wrong side, unless they are good swimmers and have come prepared with a plastic bag which will keep the receiver dry!

The transmitter operator should always ensure that he leaves no obvious tracks leading to his hide, and the antenna itself should be concealed as far as possible. Fine wire is difficult to follow through woodland but care must be taken with the lead-in to the transmitter so that arriving competitors will not inadvertently break it. Care should also be taken that the operator's car is not parked conspicuously by the approach to the hidden site – this is a certain give-away. Arrangements should be made for someone else to drive him and the equipment to the spot and then drive off again.

In an important contest, it is worth arranging for radio contact between the hidden stations and the start officials, so that signal strengths may be checked prior to the start and also so that all parties may be kept advised of the progress of the contest. Ideally, a frequency band other than that in use for the contest should be chosen for control purposes. It is a wise precaution for a spare transmitter and power supply to be on hand during the setting up of a contest so that these can be rushed to the site in the event of an equipment breakdown.

144MHz contests

VHF direction finding, or *foxhunting* as it is more popularly called, is fun – the ultimate game of hide and seek! The participants (known as the *hunters* or the *hounds*) have to locate a hidden transmitter (known as the *fox*) by using a receiver and a directional antenna. The person who finds the transmitter or transmitters first wins the contest.

Anyone can take part in foxhunting: you do not need an amateur radio licence, since participants are only operating a receiver. VHF foxhunting also has advantages over other forms of amateur radio direction finding: both classes of full licensees can operate the hidden transmitter, and unattended transmitter operation is allowed without restrictions. More importantly, VHF foxhunting can be accomplished using ready-made receivers. The majority of amateurs own a 144MHz transceiver and most of these are suitable for use on foxhunts.

Types of events

Newcomers to foxhunting are recommended to attend events organised by the many established local DF groups throughout the country. There are also a number of annual VHF foxhunts designed to encourage national and inter-club competition, and some foxhunting weekends with organised camp sites. You could, however, set up your own foxhunting group. As a minimum for a competitive hunt, you would need two teams prepared to do the hunting and someone to hide and operate the transmitter.

Usually, VHF foxhunts are organised with one or two transmitters hidden in an area covering part, or all, of an Ordnance Survey Landranger map. This can cover an area of 40×40km, but is usually much smaller. Transmissions are made at regular intervals and the hunters take bearings on the signals using directional antennas. This is done by rotating the antenna while observing the receiver's S-meter and using a compass to measure the direction the antenna is pointing. This bearing is plotted on a map and the hunter then proceeds to another location somewhere along this plotted line to take another bearing.

The first few bearings will indicate the general area of the transmitter. Further bearings will lead either to the discovery of the transmitter which may be in a vehicle, or will indicate a particular area into which the hunter must enter on foot. Sometimes the transmitter can be cleverly hidden in dense woodland, or disguised as an innocent-looking object. The team that finds the transmitter (or both transmitters in the case of a 'double fox' event) in the shortest time, wins the contest.

Although most VHF foxhunts require the use of a car, some events are designed to be 'walking only' contests, in which case the designated search area is reduced appropriately. There are some events where searching in cars is practised over a relatively small area with very regular transmissions and low power. These are ideal for beginners.

Equipment required

Any 144MHz FM transceiver can be used for the hidden transmitter. All the operator has to do is either operate the transmitter manually or to arrange for the PTT connection to be

"Now where's that fox?"

controlled by a microprocessor or timer unit. Any legal level of power can be used (but note the licence conditions regarding unattended operation) and the type of antenna is optional.

As for the hunter's receiver, most people will use commercially available transceivers such as FM handhelds or small mobile/base station transceivers rigged for portable use. These should have an S-meter, although those without S-meters can still be used with some modification, or with the use of additional devices such as noise generators. If the rig has CW/SSB capability, these modes will help to give more accurate bearings on very weak signals. The ubiquitous Yaesu FT-290 has all these features and is a popular and successful foxhunting rig.

Dual-band 144/430MHz handheld transceivers are also popular. These sets can be used to take bearings on the third harmonic of the fox frequency as the hunter gets close to the transmitting antenna. As harmonics are relatively weak, they are easier to take bearings on.

While these transceivers are certainly practical for foxhunting, problems can occur when you try to locate a powerful transmitter that may only be a short distance from you. This is because commercial transceivers are designed for long-distance communication where signals are expected to be very weak. As an RF gain control is absent on most modern 144MHz transceivers, the extremely strong signals near a transmitting antenna can overload the receiver and prevent you from seeing any movement of the S-meter. One remedy is to build a simple attenuator that can be switched into the antenna coaxial line.

Some hunters have also built devices known as *sniffers* which are often just 144MHz crystal sets with a DC amplifier and meter. They are basically very insensitive receivers that cope well within strong RF fields and can be switched into the directional antenna line when the hunter gets close to the fox.

Another serious problem is the breakthrough of strong RF signals directly into the receiver or through the antenna coaxial cable and connections. This can often be solved by placing the receiver in a metal container or wrapping it in aluminium foil. Anti-static component bags also work well. There is a solution for most problems, so almost any receiver can be used successfully – it's just a matter of experimenting and finding the best solution for your rig.

As for the directional antenna, a small beam such as the two-element HB9CV is highly recommended, since it has good gain for weak signals and is small enough to be taken through dense undergrowth and stored in a small car full of foxhunters!

You will also need a car (or team up with someone who has transport), a map, compass, ruler and pencil etc for plotting bearings.

With this basic equipment, you can start practising by taking bearings on local repeaters or amateur stations. You should also try taking bearings on a transmitter which is only a few metres away from you, so you can identify any problems your equipment might have when operating in a strong signal environment.

Advanced hunting

After participating in a few competitive hunts, you will appreciate fully the technical nature of VHF foxhunting and the problems that can occur. In theory, your bearings should point directly at the transmitter, but factors such as the accuracy of the compass, antenna, and even the hunter himself can lead to errors! Also, VHF signals tend to reflect easily off hills and buildings, so you may end up taking a bearing on one of these 'bounces'.

One of the least understood problems of VHF foxhunting is that of *local phasing*. This occurs when a bearing is taken in a built-up area, and it can be caused by the signal bouncing off nearby objects like houses, cars and hedgerows.

The effect of receiving these numerous bounced signals varies. If you are lucky, the main signal will still be stronger than the bounces, but usually they will show up as several peaks on the S-meter, or they will 'combine' and give an S-meter reading that barely moves as the antenna is rotated. Very often, the bounce signals will 'phase' with each other so that a maximum S-meter reading is observed when the antenna is pointing at a reflected signal. This could lead the hunter off in the wrong direction.

One way to avoid this problem is to walk a few metres when taking a bearing, as this will help to average out the phasing effects and a predominant bearing should be observed, indicating the direction of the transmitter. However, the only reliable way around the problem is to move away from the area completely and find somewhere else, preferably high and in the open, and take another bearing.

You should always bear in mind that most bearings will not be completely accurate; you only use each bearing to indicate the general area to proceed to. To find the transmitter, you simply keep taking additional bearings, preferably at right-angles to previous readings, and continually narrow down the possible area for the fox to be in. Make a mental note of the maximum S-meter reading for each bearing. This will indicate that you are getting closer to the transmitter.

Do not be daunted by these problems, as they actually add to the interest of a foxhunt. You will be able to overcome these technical hurdles by experience and possibly by developing some additional equipment such as 'sniffers' and attenuators. Some ingenious work has been done by foxhunters and there is still scope for more development of DF hardware and techniques. Apart from being an absorbing and competitive challenge, foxhunting is also an ideal outlet for design and construction skills. This is an area where the average radio amateur has the chance of contributing some original and useful answers to technical problems. Computer buffs may be interested to know that any application of PCs to amateur radio direction finding problems will probably be pioneering work.

The future

At the moment, the rules used for a local VHF foxhunt depend on the club that is organising the event. However, it would be an advantage if all clubs could aim towards using standard rules. For example, if a standard frequency is used, then participants would be able to develop simple, lightweight receivers with a minimum of components. This could help more people get involved in the sport, particularly young people. To this end the RSGB ARDF Committee has adopted a set of simple rules to be used as a recommended standard. These were published in the January 1995 issue of *Radio Communication*.

VHF foxhunting is steadily growing in popularity. Although still predominantly a local club activity, there are now some nationally advertised hunts held every year and even a foxhunting weekend which is held every July in the Forest of Dean. This event has a number of advanced foxhunts, a beginners 'walking only' session and even experimental hunts for IARU foxhunting (see next section).

IARU Rules contests

As stated earlier, ARDF in the UK began on the 1.8MHz band and later evolved to include the 144MHz band. In other parts of the world ARDF has developed along different lines, and a form of contest which is formalised in a set of IARU rules has become established in most other European countries as well as the Far East. These contests, also known as *foxhunting*, take place on the 3.5MHz and 144MHz bands. National societies organise their own programmes of events leading to championships (sometimes open to members of other IARU societies including the RSGB), there are IARU Regional Championships, and a World Championships series is held every two years.

There are several major differences between these events and those UK activities described above. For those familiar with the sport of orienteering, there are a number of similarities. The contest takes place entirely on foot, normally in forested terrain, and is confined to the area of a special large-scale map (usually on a scale of 1:15,000) which is issued to competitors at the start. There are five transmitters, or foxes, located within the area. These use the same frequency, but each transmits for one minute in five in sequence. Thus, Fox 1 transmits for the first minute, then Fox 2 for the second minute etc until it is the turn of Fox 1 again. The transmitters are unattended, and identify themselves simply by repeating their callsigns in morse code.

Non-directional antennas are used for the transmitters, and their locations are marked by a red and white marker flag, of the type used in orienteering competitions. Normally, there is a marking device attached, which is used to 'clip' a card carried by the competitor to prove that he has visited that fox. Alternatively, electronic devices are sometimes used to log progress on 'smart cards' carried by competitors.

Competitors participate in four classes: Seniors, Juniors, Women, and Old Timers (over 40). Groups comprising not more than one from each class start at five-minute intervals, at the same point in the transmission cycle. Whereas seniors are required to hunt all five foxes, the other classes search for only four, but the fox to be omitted is different for each class. Certain rules specify the spacing of the foxes, and they should be

arranged such that a line taking the shortest possible route from start to finish via all five foxes will be in the range 4 to 7km.

The location of the finish is shown on the map, and is also marked by a beacon which transmits continuously, sending its callsign on a different frequency to that of the foxes. Each competitor is timed at the finish, and the winner in each class is the one who has visited all the appropriate foxes in the shortest time.

There are other factors to consider, too. A maximum time limit is specified – typically this is two hours. A competitor who is approaching the end of the time limit may have to decide to head for the finish before finding all the foxes, or risk being 'out of time'. There are no restrictions on the order in which the foxes may be visited, but clearly there is an optimum order, and the determination of this order is a most important requirement for the contestant.

All the equipment carried is influenced by the need to use it during an energetic run through the forest, probably a wet forest(!), and participants dress accordingly. As well as an appropriate receiver for the band in use, most competitors carry a compass and pen, a means of keeping the map dry, and sometimes a map board and protractor arrangement.

Receivers can be relatively simple affairs, since the limited competition area means that signal strengths are fairly strong. However, a good dynamic range is necessary to cope with the dramatic increase in signal strength on final approach to the fox. For 3.5MHz, ferrite rods used in conjunction with short sense antennas are popular. There is more variety for 144MHz: many prefer the compact HB9CV antennas but Yagis are also used. Some receivers are actually built into the central spar of a Yagi. Whatever arrangement is preferred, it is never ideally suited for running through a forest. One method of easing the problem is to construct Yagi elements from some flexible material, such as steel rule tape. However, this has the problem of affecting compass readings if care is not taken.

The reader may have gathered from the above description that the ethos of IARU contests is very much about fairness, and there is no intention of deliberately hiding the foxes or using trick transmitting antennas, which often feature strongly in the 'fun' ethos of ARDF in the UK. Despite this, the basic techniques of taking bearings are just the same as described in the 1.8MHz and 144MHz parts of this section. Bearings and signal strength assessments on 3.5MHz are generally a fairly reliable guide to direction and distance, but on 144MHz it is a very different story since reflections due to the terrain and vegetation can lead the competitor astray, especially in wet weather. Coping with these difficulties is just another part of the skill required.

The major Championship events are excellent international social occasions as well as providing competition of the keenest standard. The 3.5MHz and 144MHz contests take place on different days, and there are usually social functions associated with prize-giving ceremonies. It is clear that several countries have well-managed and successful national teams, whose members benefit from selection procedures followed up by regular training sessions to develop and perfect their techniques.

FURTHER INFORMATION

[1] *RSGB Amateur Radio Call Book*, ed Brett Rider, G4FLQ, RSGB, published annually.
[2] *VHF Contesting Handbook*, ed David Johnson, G4DHF, RSGB, 1995.
[3] *VHF/UHF DX Book*, ed Ian White, G3SEK, DIR Publishing, 1992.

[4] *VHF/UHF Manual*, 4th edn, ed George Jessop, G6JP, RSGB, 1983.

[5] *Amateur Radio Direction Finding*, ed George Whenham, G3TFA, RSGB, 1994.

[6] 'HF direction finding', Chris Plummer, G8APB, *Radio Communication* June/July 1991.

[7] 'DF receiver for 160m' and 'DF transmitter for 160m', Peter Asquith, G4ENA, *Radio Communciation* May 1993.

[8] 'VHF direction finding', C J Seymour, G4NNA, *Radio Communication* October 1983.

[9] 'Foxhunting in the 2m band', Phillip Smith, GW1XBG, *Radio Communication* July 1995.

6 Mobile and portable operation

OPERATION away from the home station has always been an enjoyable aspect of the hobby – for some it offers an escape from EMC problems and indoor antennas, for others the excitement of using a really good site or a DX callsign. Today's radio amateur can use the same equipment at home, in the car, or out in the middle of a meadow, such has been the progress of miniaturisation and operating convenience. Each year this process continues, with more and more sophistication in smaller and smaller equipments. Truly, this is the age of 'go anywhere' amateur radio!

MOBILE OPERATION

About half of all amateurs in the UK operate stations fitted into their cars, and all bands from 1.8MHz to 1.3GHz are in use, with AM, SSB, FM and even occasionally CW! Mobile operating has particular attractions for those amateurs making regular car journeys to and from work, for gradually the companionship of a group of fellow travellers is formed which can ease the tedium of the journey and bring fresh interest to the hobby. Most local mobile-mobile work is carried out on VHF/UHF FM.

Alternatively some HF enthusiasts have fitted 100W SSB transceivers and loaded whip antennas to their cars, and can make intercontinental contacts while driving to work! The social side of amateur mobile radio is well catered for in the UK with many mobile rallies held during the summer months.

Equipment and antennas

Mobile transceivers have to contend with relatively inefficient antennas, high electrical noise levels and rapidly fluctuating signals. A high-sensitivity receiver is required, with efficient AGC and a noise blanker (SSB) or with excellent limiting characteristics and a correctly adjusted squelch (FM). The acoustic noise level will be high and a reasonable audio output of at least about 2W will be found necessary.

Adequate protection of the RF power amplifier against high VSWR is essential. Many mobile antennas exhibit high VSWR when wet, and if a loaded whip is used this may well have a narrow bandwidth, giving a high VSWR when out-of-tune. Many modern HF transceivers feature automatic ATUs which can be very useful in allowing the matching of a mobile whip which is slightly off-resonance.

Mobile safety is paramount, and this demands a minimum of easy-to-operate controls with clear and unambiguous dials and meters, preferably illuminated at night.

The 12V power requirements should not exceed the spare capacity of the vehicle generation system. In practice this may, for example, confine the use of a 100W HF transceiver to daylight hours when the vehicle lights are not required. The average vehicle voltages fluctuate considerably and are 'spiky'; therefore internal transceiver voltage regulation and overvoltage protection are very desirable. Vehicle interference may be a problem and require suppression [1, 2].

A mobile transceiver should be small enough to fit in or under the dashboard – such transceivers are available in HF as well as VHF/UHF models from all the major manufacturers. Some HF transceivers are available with a remote head for the dashboard, allowing the rest of the rig to be tucked away out of sight. No matter what the attractions of larger equipments are, they will demand special mountings which will spoil the car interior and may lack operating convenience.

Rugged mechanical construction is essential, because a great deal of vibration will be encountered. Note that extremes of temperature and humidity are common in vehicles.

When planning a mobile installation, consideration should be given to the possibility of using the transceiver in other modes of operation, particularly as a portable station, for in this case requirements are in many ways similar. For example, if a hand-portable SSB or FM transceiver is available, all that needs to be done is to obtain an add-on RF amplifier and antenna, and leave these permanently in the vehicle (see later).

Recent editions of the UK Highway Code [3] state (rule 43) that "You must exercise proper control of your vehicle at all times. Do not use a hand-held telephone or microphone while you are driving. Find a safe place to stop. Do not speak into a hands-free microphone if it will take your mind off the road." The Department of Transport, in a letter to the Society, adds: "The Highway Code is an advisory code of practice in that a failure to observe any of its provisions is not in itself an offence. Such failure, however, may be used in any court proceedings which may arise. Current legislation already places the responsibility on drivers to have proper control of their vehicles at all times. A motorist who fails to do so as a result of distraction or lack of concentration is liable to prosecution". It follows that radio amateurs who operate mobile stations while actually driving should not use hand-held microphones and take great care not to be distracted by the radio.

The basic necessity is to leave both hands free for driving and to allow the driver's head unrestricted movement, while keeping the mouth-microphone distance roughly constant. A boom microphone with headset has two disadvantages – it is conspicuous and the ear muffs will seriously impair the driver's hearing. One solution is to use a miniature condenser-type microphone with a tie clip or alternatively mounted on a lightweight boom from spectacle frames. A suitable control circuit can be found in reference [4].

Whichever alternative is chosen, operators should bear in mind the recommendations of the Highway Code and the need to maintain good audio quality. This can only be achieved by making sure that the microphone is reasonably close to the operator's mouth and that the audio gain is not excessive. It may be that if the vehicle is excessively noisy the audio gain must be kept low and the operator must speak more loudly to

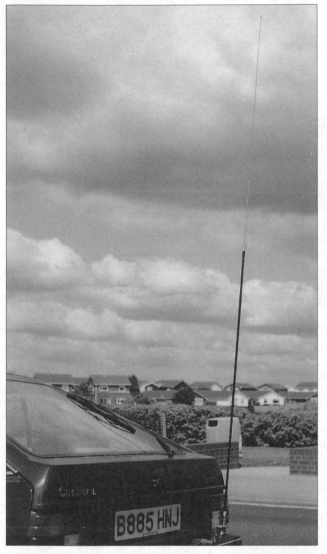

An HF mobile antenna doesn't have to be too obstrusive. This is the Pro-Am antenna

compensate. It must be borne in mind when making adjustments in the relative quietness of a stationary vehicle that we all tend to speak more loudly when the vehicle is moving. There is a need to ask for reports over the air and to take action to improve the quality if unfavourable ones are received. It may not be possible to operate in a noisy car or lorry travelling at 70mph with all the windows wide open as the readability of the signal can become R3!

The best positions for HF mobile whip antennas are the rear wings or the rear bumper bar. Commercially made bumper mounts are available and can considerably lessen the risk of unsatisfactory mounting. If the car is fitted with a towing hitch, this can also serve as a very effective mounting point for a HF antenna. The ideal position for VHF or UHF mobile antennas is the centre of the roof, but this is not always possible or desirable for other reasons. Various types of mounting are available for those who do not wish to drill the car metalwork. These include gutter mounts, window-clip mounts, magnetic mounts and bootlip mounts.

Whatever antenna is chosen, the fixing must be mechanically strong enough not to be damaged when the vehicle is travelling at high speed, or succumb to a blow caused by a low-hanging branch or other obstruction. Care should also be taken that the antenna does not project horizontally from the vehicle, even at speed, in such a way that it becomes a danger to other vehicles or pedestrians.

On the HF bands, the antenna system is the most critical component in any mobile installation, even more so than with fixed stations. The whip antenna with loading coil normally used has a low feedpoint impedance and a narrow bandwidth, and this involves careful tuning and matching for optimum results [5].

Most VHF FM operators use a $5\lambda/8$ or $7\lambda/8$ whip mounted on the rear wings, although in some cases this may have only marginal advantages over a $\lambda/4$ whip mounted on the roof. The most popular UHF antenna is the collinear, usually roof mounted. However, dual or even triple-band antennas are growing in popularity as they can cover two or three bands with only one mounting. All popular VHF and UHF mobile antennas are a good match to 50Ω coaxial cable, and no special matching circuit is necessary.

Expensive radio equipment left permanently attached to the vehicle should always be insured against theft, and the driver's ordinary insurance may not cover this eventuality. A burglar alarm should always be fitted and, if possible, the transceiver disguised or removed completely when not in use. Information on insuring equipment can be obtained from specialists such as Amateur Radio Insurance Services [6].

Operation

Mobile operation on the HF bands (and in the DX portion of the VHF and UHF bands) is little different to normal SSB fixed-station operation in that there are no specific mobile calling frequencies or sub-bands allocated. The HF SSB mobile operator is usually more interested in working DX stations in fixed locations rather than other mobile stations, and mobile-mobile contacts are fairly rare, except perhaps on 1.8MHz SSB and 29MHz FM.

As the frequency is raised, the effects of the terrain through which the vehicle is passing become more pronounced. On the HF bands this is usually confined to a relatively slow variation in signal strength but on VHF, and especially UHF, individual buildings and trees will markedly affect the radio path, giving rise to a rapid and characteristic signal 'flutter' when the vehicle is on the move. Sometimes a poor VHF signal may be obtained when the car is parked in an apparently good position on the side of a hill. This may be caused by the vehicle being in a 'null', and the solution may be to move the car forward a few metres and try again.

Most mobile-mobile working takes place on the FM sections of the 144 and 432MHz bands. 50 and 70MHz are also becoming increasing popular, especially as there is the prospect of 50MHz repeaters soon. Operating in these sections is channelised, which is a considerable safety and convenience advantage for the mobile operator. Instead of fine tuning a VFO dial, he or she can click a rotary switch round to change frequency, and with practice this can be done without taking the eyes off the road. Many HF and VHF/UHF transceivers feature memories and these are extremely useful for mobile operators in that they allow fast, accurate frequency changes while on the move.

The use of FM is convenient in this case because one of its characteristics is that strong signals will completely obliterate weak ones in the receiver (the so-called *capture effect*). Therefore operation on the same channel (termed *co-channel working*) is often possible with two pairs of stations only 20km apart, without the annoying heterodynes typical of AM operation.

The channels are spaced 25kHz apart in IARU Region 1, and to avoid the necessity of giving long strings of digits when specifying frequencies on the air, they have been numbered. Channel 0 on the 144MHz band corresponds to 145.000MHz; channel 0 on the 432MHz band corresponds to 433.000MHz. Channel 1 (144MHz band) is 145.025MHz and channel 1 (432MHz band) is 433.025MHz, and so on.

To distinguish between simplex (non-repeater) and repeater channels the channel numbers are prefixed 'S' and 'R', and 'U' is added to denote the 432MHz band. The repeater channels are discussed in more detail later.

The normal way to set up a simplex contact while operating VHF/UHF mobile is to make (or answer) a CQ call on the mobile calling channel and to change frequency as soon as contact is made to one of the 'working' channels. For example, the mobile calling channel on the 144MHz band is S20 (145.500MHz) and the working channels are S10, S11, S13–S19 and S21–S23 (S12 is reserved for local RTTY). This procedure does have its difficulties. One or more of the working channels may be occupied, but sometimes this is not apparent to both stations.

Using the standard 10–25W transceiver and a 5λ/8 whip it will usually be found that the range for mobile-mobile simplex work is very unpredictable in low-lying urban areas, and that mobile 'flutter' is a problem, particularly when both stations are on the move. Of course, one solution is to fit an add-on RF amplifier to boost the transmitter power, and perhaps also a preamplifier to improve the receiver sensitivity. Although these measures can give a useful increase in range, the extra expense, spectrum pollution and power consumption involved have led to a different and much more sophisticated technique being preferred – the use of *repeaters*.

| Coverage of repeater | Coverage of station A | Coverage of station B |

Fig 1. The improved range of communication available between mobile stations using a repeater. The simplex coverage areas of stations A and B shown are constantly changing shape as the two vehicles pass through different terrain, and thus the two stations would have to be quite close before reliable simplex communication was possible

REPEATER OPERATION

A repeater is a device which will receive a signal on one frequency and simultaneously transmit it on another frequency. Thus a low-power transmitter in a vehicle can transmit on the repeater's *input channel* and the signal will be faithfully reproduced on the repeater's *output channel*. Careful design has meant that repeaters can receive and transmit in the same band. This means that the same antenna on the car can be used for both reception and transmission.

In effect the receiving and transmitting coverage of the mobile station becomes that of the repeater and, since the latter is favourably sited on top of a hill or high mast, the range is usually greatly improved over that of unassisted or *simplex* operation (see Fig 1). Typically the effective range is increased from the order of 10–25km from the mobile station to something like 50km in any direction from the repeater, depending upon terrain and band used. Another advantage is that contact with other stations becomes more predictable. The coverages of stations A and B in Fig 1 continually change shape as the two stations pass through different terrain. Thus it is never easy for the mobile operator to estimate his or her simplex range. In contrast, the repeater service area is a known and much less variable factor. One further advantage is that mobile 'flutter' is usually diminished due to the superior antenna location at the repeater site.

How a repeater works

A repeater is an unmanned relay station and therefore requires an automatic system to control its operation. This logic system must ensure as far as possible that the repeater only relays signals intended for that repeater, and that those signals it does relay come up to an acceptable standard in respect of frequency, strength and deviation. For example, there is little point in the repeater relaying a signal which is so weak that it is unintelligible.

It would be very wasteful of power to have an FM repeater transmitter left on continuously if there were no signals being relayed, and so it is arranged that it is only switched on when a signal for relaying is present on the input channel. To ensure that signals which are not intended for relaying cannot accidentally switch on the repeater transmitter, UK repeaters, which conform to IARU Region 1 specifications, require a short audio tone *(toneburst)* to be sent by a user at the start of a transmission *(tone access)*. This tells the repeater to switch on its transmitter. Once this has been done other stations may *carrier re-access* the repeater indefinitely until it is no longer required. It will then automatically switch its transmitter off and another toneburst will be required if further use is to be made of it.

In order to make the best use of a repeater it is desirable to have knowledge of how the repeater control logic works in outline, and a typical sequence of events during a transmitting over is as follows. The repeater receiver is switched on continually and monitors the input channel, using a squelch system. When a signal appears on the input the control system determines if:

(i) the signal has tripped the squelch (ie it is of adequate strength);
(ii) there was an audio tone (toneburst) of correct frequency and duration present; and
(iii) the received signal is correctly deviated.

If these initial conditions are satisfied (known as a *valid access)* the control system will switch the repeater transmitter on and allow the receiver audio output to modulate it. During the over, the control logic continuously monitors the incoming signal level, and if it falls at any time below the standard required for valid access, may switch off the transmitter or disconnect the receiver audio from the modulator. When the over is finished and the incoming signal disappears from the input channel, the repeater squelch will close and indicate to the control logic that it must ready itself for the next over. After a short delay the repeater will signal it is ready by transmitting either a 'K' or 'T' in morse code.

The short delay between the end of an over and the 'K' (or 'T') is quite important. During this interval the repeater will still relay any new signals on the input channel. Consequently this interval may be used by a third station to quickly announce its presence by giving its callsign. The use of 'Break' is unnecessary as the repeater users will already be listening for such a call. This practice is termed *tail-ending* and is a good way of inserting urgent or emergency messages between overs.

If the repeater has relayed a signal for more than a certain period of time (typically 2min on 144MHz and 5min on 432MHz) the control system may go into a *time-out* mode, close the talk-gate, and possibly transmit some form of *busy* signal until the incoming signal disappears off the input channel. This is done primarily to prevent overs from being too long, but is also a useful anti-jamming measure. It should be noted that some repeaters do not incorporate time-out devices. It is good operating practice to keep repeater overs to less than a minute whether or not time-out is fitted.

Equipment considerations

UK repeaters use the standard IARU Region 1 toneburst frequency of 1750Hz. The tolerance of this frequency is nominally ±25Hz and an accuracy of ±10Hz should guarantee satisfactory operation in all cases. Likewise the duration requirement varies but 500ms will satisfy all UK repeater requirements. The toneburst deviation should be set to ±2.5kHz. If you are using a modified PMR or a homebrew transmitter, do ensure that the transmitter, receiver and toneburst are operating correctly before you try use a repeater – *do not align equipment through a repeater.*

UK 144MHz repeaters have their inputs 600kHz lower than the outputs according to IARU Region 1 recommendations, while the 432MHz repeaters have their inputs 1.6MHz higher than the outputs (see later). Most modern commercial transceivers have the useful ability of being able to reverse this frequency shift at the touch of a button. For example, assuming the transceiver was set to channel R7 (145.175MHz transmit, 145.775MHz receive) the frequencies would be reversed as soon as the REVERSE-REPEATER switch was depressed, becoming 145.175MHz receive, 145.775MHz transmit. It thus allows the operator to listen on the repeater input channel (the ability to listen on any frequency in use for transmission at the station is required by UK licence regulations).

CTCSS repeater tones

CTCSS is now being permitted in the UK as an optional feature on 144MHz and 432MHz repeaters to improve the effectiveness of the network.

The principle of CTCSS (continuous tone-code squelch system) is that a sub-audible tone is continuously transmitted in addition to the usual signal. Being below the normal speech frequencies, it does not affect the received signal.

A repeater user who is on the border of more than one repeater's coverage area can now be selective. By transmitting the appropriate CTCSS tone, only one repeater will be activated rather than all the others on the same channel. The system operates in parallel with the usual 1750Hz access tone – either can be used to access a repeater.

In addition, a repeater only transmits its CTCSS tone when relaying speech, but not with its periodic idents. A suitably equipped amateur station can screen out the annoying idents, so making it more convenient to monitor the repeater.

The UK has been divided into 23 different CTCSS regions using 10 different tones, so that repeaters in the same area share the same CTCSS tone. The scheme is optional and will not be used to form 'closed repeaters'. Repeaters with the CTCSS facility available transmit the appropriate letter in morse code after the callsign.

See Appendix 11 for a map of CTCSS regions and tone frequencies in the UK. The *Radio Communication Handbook* [5] gives more technical details of the CTCSS system and the circuit of a simple tone generator.

Using a repeater

The proper use of a repeater requires a high standard of operating ability and courtesy. Knowledge of the way in which repeaters work and confidence that one's own equipment is 'spot-on' does help, but also required is an ability to express oneself concisely; this being especially important on a repeater with a high level of activity. It must also be remembered that the purpose of repeaters is to facilitate mobile communication, and therefore mobile stations should be given priority at all times.

If it is required to test access into a repeater, the callsign and purpose of the transmission should be stated, eg "G1XYZ testing access to GB3ZZ". The repeater will respond with a 'K' or 'T' if access has been made. CQ calls are not normally made through repeaters; instead stations usually announce they are "listening through" the repeater, eg "G1XYZ listening through GB3ZZ". One such announcement is sufficient.

If it is apparent after setting up a contact that the stations are likely to be within simplex range of each other, the input channel should be checked. If signals are reasonable, the repeater should be vacated and the contact completed on one of the

CODE OF PRACTICE FOR REPEATER OPERATION

1. Avoid using a repeater from your base station; it is really for the benefit of the local mobiles. If you really must use it, use the lowest possible power and a directional antenna to avoid interfering with other repeaters on the same channel which you may not be able to hear. To be sure, use a CTCSS tone to access only the repeater you want.

2. Listen to the repeater before you transmit to make sure it is not in use. If you hear a local station you wish to call, listen on the input frequency to check whether the station is within simplex range before calling.

3. Unless you are specifically calling another station, simply announce that you are "listening through", eg "G1XYZ listening through GB3ZZ". One announcement is sufficient. If you are calling another station, give its callsign followed by your own callsign, eg "G2XYZ from G1XYZ".

4. Once contact is established:
   (a) at the beginning and end of each over you need give only your own callsign, eg "From G1XYZ";
   (b) change frequency to a simplex channel at the first opportunity (especially if you are operating a fixed station);
   (c) keep your overs short and to the point or they may time-out, and do not forget to wait for the 'K' or 'T' (if used);
   (d) do not monopolise the repeater as others may be waiting to use it;
   (e) if your signal is very noisy into the repeater, or if you are only opening the repeater squelch intermittently, finish the contact and try later when you are putting a better signal into the repeater.

5. If the repeater is busy, emergency calls may be made by tail-ending before the 'K', and announcing (a) that you have emergency traffic, and (b) which facilities you wish a station to provide. This will normally in most 'risk-to-life' situations be a telephone so that the other station can alert the emergency services. Do not reply to an emergency call if you cannot provide the services requested.

simplex channels. This is especially important if both stations are fixed.

Sometimes stations outside the repeater's service area will access the repeater successfully, but their signals will be very noisy and they may only open the repeater squelch intermittently. If this is the case, the contact should be terminated and another attempt made when a better signal into the repeater can be obtained.

If you wish to join an existing contact on the repeater then you should transmit your callsign in the gap immediately after one of the participating stations drops carrier but before the 'K' or 'T'. Don't worry if you are a little slow in doing this as the repeater will inhibit the 'K' or 'T' as soon as it realises another transmission is taking place. The use of "Break" on its own is unnecessary and illegal as an amateur should always identify his/her transmission using a callsign. To insert emergency or urgent messages, use the time before the 'K' or 'T' to announce your callsign and the problem, eg "G4AFJ/M emergency road traffic accident A46/A606 junction".

Because many UK repeaters will time-out after a few minutes, lengthy repetition of callsigns wastes the time available for each transmission. For example, "From G1XYZ" is quite sufficient at the beginning and end of each over.

A spell of listening will soon show that two common operating errors are timing-out and forgetting to wait for the 'K'. As a result, the repeater may eventually interrupt communication and the user, quite unaware of this, may spend up to a minute or so blocking the repeater to no avail. A simple time-out warning device may therefore prove useful.

There are two selfish attitudes which should be discouraged. The first is the practice of "taking another 'K'". This defeats the idea of sharing out the available air time to all users, ie it defeats the time-out of the repeater. The second bad practice is to use the gap before the 'K' to make a comment about the previous over. A good operator waits for his/her over before commenting because they realise that otherwise they are preventing the proper use of the gap to allow others to join in by inserting their callsign.

Certain repeaters, especially those outside the UK, may have different requirements, but if the rule 'listen before transmitting' is followed this should present no particular problem. Repeater groups usually have available literature with full details of their repeater and its facilities, which is well worth studying. Contact the keeper (see Appendix 11 for lists of keepers).

The UK repeater network

UK FM repeaters are operational in the 144, 432MHz and 1.3GHz bands, giving coverage of most of the country. All repeater callsigns are in the series GB3-plus-two-letters, and callsign identification is regularly given in morse code at 12wpm.

All UK repeaters are designed, built and maintained by groups of enthusiasts under the overall control of the RSGB Repeater Management Group which has full responsibility to the licensing authority for all aspects of repeater operation, including technical standards and frequency allocation etc. There are no 'closed' or private repeaters in the UK – all are available for general use. The annual cost of a repeater is some £250 and every regular user of a repeater should join the repeater group to support it and contribute to its funds.

Over 80 144MHz FM repeaters are licensed, using IARU Region 1 repeater channels R0–R7. The network was originally planned on a basis of non-overlapping service areas, but additional repeaters have been brought into service to cope with the increasing popularity of FM mobile operation, especially in the major cities where the amateur 'population density' is high.

432MHz repeaters far outnumber those on 144MHz in the UK. The IARU Region 1 frequencies are used, but the input and output channels have been transposed to avoid placing the output adjacent to the amateur fast-scan TV band. The channel number prefix 'RB' is used instead of 'RU' to denote the UK system. Some channels were originally not allocated to avoid interference with foreign repeaters using RU channels. UK 432MHz repeaters are planned on a grid basis, each one nominally serving a 33km square. Consequently each has more of a local and community character than the VHF repeaters.

Several 1.3GHz repeaters are currently licensed. These use channels RM0 (input 1291.00MHz, output 1297.00MHz) to RM15 (input 1291.375MHz, output 1297.375MHz), ie 25kHz spacing and 6MHz shift. These repeaters mostly use horizontal polarisation and radiate a continuous carrier (to act as beacons) when not being used for talkthrough.

Details of all the above repeaters are given in Appendix 11. It should be emphasised that repeaters are experimental devices subject to modification and improvement, and therefore these details are subject to change. In addition new repeaters are being brought into service from time to time. Further details of these are published in *Radio Communication* and up-to-date lists including proposed repeaters are available as computer print-out from RSGB HQ [7].

Problems with repeaters

From time to time in urban areas there is abuse or jamming (mostly on 144MHz band repeaters). The best advice is:

- Do not respond in anyway at all on the air to unlicensed transmissions or abusers.
- Do not approach suspected offenders as this can encourage further abuse and may prejudice investigations already underway.
- Help to gather as much information about the problem as possible.

For example, write down dates, times, and frequencies when the interference took place. Note any pattern of operation, suspected location of offenders, details of any bearings obtained with DF equipment etc. Tape recordings of the interference can be useful. Also details of other callsigns, names and addresses of those who have heard the interference as well.

A copy of this information should be sent to the repeater keeper (see the list in Appendix 11 for the callsign of the keeper). If problems persist, then copies of all correspondence and information should be sent to the Repeater Management Group Chairman c/o RSGB HQ. Further information on procedures to be followed can be obtained by contacting the Zonal Repeater Manager or the RMG Abuse Co-ordinator c/o RSGB.

MARITIME MOBILE OPERATION

For the fortunate operator who combines an interest in amateur radio with boating, it is possible to become an almost permanent one-man DXpedition, girdling the world and sharing the experience with friends back home and in the many countries visited. Even a yachtsman whose cruising aspirations take him no further than English coastal waters can sample the experience of being a rare call for, in spite of a considerable increase in the popularity of maritime mobile operating over the last few years, the /MM suffix is still sufficient to create additional interest at the 'other end'.

Before one can join this exclusive fleet, there are a number of obstacles which are peculiar to maritime operation to be surmounted, and here a look will be taken at one or two of the major ones.

Licensing

The current UK licence now permits operation in any vessel or vehicle, requiring the suffix '/M' or '/MM' to be added to the callsign. Written permission is required from the Master of a ship for the installation, use or modification of a station.

Before the proposed station can be operated, British Telecom International may have to inspect it. This inspection is done by the Ship Radio Inspection Officer and normally has to be arranged at or near a major commercial port. The licensee must have on board the same power- and frequency-measuring equipment as he is required to have at home.

Apart from inspecting the station and requiring the would-be operator to give an on-the-spot demonstration of the accuracy of, and his ability to use, the test equipment, BTI may also need to establish that the amateur station does not interfere with the ship's main transmitters and receivers. BTI may also require to see the ship owner's written agreement to the establishment of an amateur station on his ship. Not much of a problem when the owner is also the skipper and operator, but possibly more so if the ship happens to be a supertanker. As far as BTI are concerned, the same regulations apply to all kinds of ship. Their inspectors may well also bring their own equipment to check

compliance with licence conditions and levels of harmonic radiation, spurious emissions and unwanted sidebands etc.

The Class A licence allows operation on all bands but does not permit operation by anyone other than the licensee, even under supervision, unless the other person is in possession of an Amateur Radio Certificate. Radio silence must be observed if requested by the ship's Master.

Finally, when operating with a licence which does not permit third-party message handling, or with shore stations similarly restricted, do remember the terms of your own (and your friends') licences. When a long way from home it is all too easy to risk infringing your licence and embarrassing friends, not to mention the risk of losing for the boating fraternity a very valuable privilege – UK amateurs have only been allowed to operate /MM in the last few years.

Reciprocal licensing

The UK licence does not authorise use while ships are alongside in foreign ports or in foreign territorial waters (unless the country authorises UK radio amateurs to operate under CEPT TR61/01 – see later). Maritime mobile operation has become much more popular in recent years, and on several occasions yachtsmen in particular have found themselves in trouble with local overseas radio regulatory authorities or police as a result of them using amateur band transmitters in foreign ports without prior permission.

Before operating, it is wise to make contact with the local amateur radio association in the country concerned. In smaller countries, quite often it will be found that they either operate the amateur licensing system on behalf of their telecommunications authority or certainly can arrange personal introductions which help avoid administrative delays. Experience has proved that advance application in writing (other than to the USA and major European countries) tends to be unsuccessful as many countries have no fixed policy on amateur maritime licensing, and the granting of permission to operate is dependent upon the reaction of the individual official on the spot. See the 'Operation in foreign countries' section at the end of this chapter for further information.

Equipment

Favoured equipment, both by yachtsmen and ships' radio officers, is the smaller portable transceiver which will operate on 12V DC. While not a problem in a large ship's wireless room, the climatic conditions encountered on board a small yacht, especially in the tropics, were certainly not envisaged by the manufacturers of the rig, who thought their equipment was destined to be tucked, warm and dry, beneath the dashboard of a car. Initially many yachtsmen make the mistake of locating the rig among their other radio gear around the chart table. Such a position is almost inevitably going to expose the equipment to a splash of sea water sooner or later. Better to put it inside a locker next to the chart table, and run a multi-way cable to a remote alternative operating position in the cockpit.

Spares

If a yachtsman is going to set off across the Atlantic working regular skeds with friends back home it is irresponsible to do so without both spares and some knowledge of the potential weaknesses of the particular 'black box' that will be aboard. While retailers and manufacturers will normally maintain that the gear they are selling just never goes wrong, they will usually become a lot more helpful if approached with a full explanation of just why the enquiry is being made!

If a /MM station goes suddenly off the air with equipment failure in mid-ocean (as this author's did), great concern is likely to be caused to friends who have been keeping skeds. Certainly, they know that the most likely cause is radio equipment failure, but when it actually happens they can hardly be blamed for fearing worse. In this case, the problem was transmitter PSU failure and, as the receiver section was still working, we could hear our friends becoming more worried as each missed sked went by, wondering whether to report our disappearance to the appropriate authorities. We were able to get back on the air by cannibalising other electronic equipment that was on board but ever since then we have shipped a small 'floating junk box' and also a spare transceiver.

Power supplies

Even a modern 150W PEP transceiver will represent quite a considerable drain on a yacht's batteries and at sea it is easy to become involved in quite long operating periods without thinking. Ideally a separate accumulator should be carried specifically for the rig, with suitable means to isolate it from the ship's main batteries. Here again, not a 'big ship' problem for in that case the ship's 110V AC supply will be available.

Antennas and earths

Due to its ability to operate with a perfect earth system a boat will put out a remarkably good signal with quite modest power. For instance, when working the UK from the West Indies, a yacht running 150W to a vertical dipole may well be given the same report as a shore station on an adjacent island which is running 500W to a two-element cubical quad! The problem is more that of the antenna being non-directional, and with the pile-up of callers who may be anxious for a contact there is no way to notch out any of the interference. In these circumstances the infallible solution is to plead a sudden navigational problem and switch off!

Shipboard antennas are normally vertically polarised and radiate an excellent low-angle signal. The favourite seagoing antenna is normally a vertical λ/2 dipole although if the boat is of steel construction then a λ/4 ground plane driven against the ship's hull may be better. This author has a 'floating antenna farm' with a three-way rotary coaxial switch giving access to

(a) a λ/2 dipole;
(b) a 1λ ground plane (yes, full wave on 14MHz – the back stays to the mast are just 19.8m [65ft]);
(c) a λ/4 ground plane.

This makes it possible to change in mid-contact. It is quite often found that there will be long slow fading on one antenna and not on the other, and clearly there is quite a lot of interesting experimenting to be done.

Whatever the antenna it is essential to ensure a good match and an SWR of 1:1, as with limited power available it is essential that it all gets radiated. With a high SWR, transmitters with transistorised output stages having high-SWR protection will not function at all.

Seagoing RF

On a merchant ship the antenna is usually well elevated and the operating position is adequately screened, but on a yacht the reverse is true and everything can easily become 'humming' with RF. Even if a linear amplifier can be powered, the stray resonant circuits provided by the stays, rigging and wiring on a yacht can be positively dangerous when excited by a

Table 1. Maritime mobile nets

Net name	Frequency (kHz)	Time (UTC)	Controller
Jerry's Happy Hour (US)	21,402	0100	
Travellers	14,116	0300	Roy, VK6BO or Peter, VK6HH
Pacific	14,313	0400	Terry, ZL1MA
Canadian	14,115	0400	
Kenya	14,345	0500	Tony, 5Z4FZ
Anzus	21,205	0500	
South African	14,316	0630	Davina, ZS5GC
German	14,313	0700	Various
Pacific Inter Island	14,315	0800	Rick, NH2F
United Kingdom	14,303	0800	Bill, G4FRN or Ernie, G8OS
German	14,313	1030	Various
Indian Ocean	14,332	1115	Roy, VK6BO or Peter, VK6HH
South African	14,316	1130	Alistair, ZS5MO
Mississauga Canadian	14,121	1145	Various
Seanet	14,320	1200	
JA Okera	21,437	1220	
Transatlantic	21,400	1300	Trudi, 8P6QM
German	14,307	1630	Various
Swedish	14,303	1630	
United Kingdom	14,303	1800	Bruce, G4YZH, Sue, G0OEP, Rudi, G4FTO, or Tony, G0IAD
SW Pacific	14,315	2100	Tony, ZL1ATE
Indonesian	7090	2230	
United States	14,300		Various

strong RF field. It is therefore far better to keep the power level down and make a really serious effort to get maximum radiation and minimum reflected power. If part of a boat's rigging is used as a radiator, remember that rigging usually comes in symmetrical pairs. For example, if one of the mast stays is a convenient 15m long, its opposite number must be detuned- the favourite technique is to bridge across about 500mm with 1.2mm (18swg) copper wire with a 500pF mica capacitor in the middle.

Even with low power, other electronic equipment on board may seriously misbehave when subjected to RF fields – remember, the makers of equipment used in small yachts never had it in mind that their gear would have to tolerate a 14MHz SSB signal in close proximity. Electronic speed/distance logs and quartz crystal clocks should be carefully checked out for RF tolerance before setting out on any major voyage.

Operating frequencies

Throughout the world, most /MM operation is carried out on the 14MHz band, irrespective of the stage in the sunspot cycle. Each region has its own net frequencies and sked times. Most English-speaking maritime mobiles in Region 1 and 2 check into a net on 14,303kHz at 0800 and 1800 (see Table 1). Other nets to note include the Indian/Madras stations operating between 0700 and 0800 on 7080kHz and at 1900 on 14,150kHz (all times Indian local), offering information for yachts approaching India. It has also been reported that a medical information net operates from Germany as a listening watch daily between 0645 and 0715 UTC on 14,332kHz (callsign DL0MAR), with two doctors available to give medical advice to maritime mobiles.

If you are neither /MM nor keeping regular skeds with a /MM station, a wanted contact and subsequent card will be more readily forthcoming if it is borne in mind that the net operations should be allowed to proceed without interruption to their natural conclusion before an attempt to contact is made.

Table 2. Choice of mobile and portable equipment in the UK

Operation	Power output range (continuous)	Power supply	Transportation	Alternative operation
Hand-portable (pedestrian)	Low (50mW–5W)	Dry batteries or nicad rechargeable batteries (6–12V DC)	Pocket or shoulder	Mobile (add-on PA) Base station (add-on PA)
Fixed portable (vehicle mobile)	Medium (5W–50W)	Vehicle battery (12V or 13.8V DC)	Vehicle	Base station (12V or 13.8V DC PSU)
Fixed portable (110–250V AC)	High (50W–100W)	Petrol generator	Vehicle	Base station

This author (and most other /MM operators) is always delighted to chat and reciprocate a card provided he is not interrupted when talking to his friends in the Mediterranean after all, exchange of information about harbours, fishing and RF in the rigging is to the /MM operator what life is all about!

PORTABLE OPERATION

'Going portable' single handed is one of the most interesting and satisfying challenges of amateur radio. To set up a completely self-contained station in the middle of nowhere is somehow to go back to fundamentals and rediscover the hobby anew. Each expedition is an adventure and, irrespective of whether the station is 'black-box' or 'homebrew', much will be learnt about radio communication, probably more than is realised at the time. The temptation to throw the rig and a makeshift antenna into the back of the car at the last minute should, however, be resisted. Some forethought and planning will pay great dividends – probably only owners of hand-portable stations can contemplate 'instant' activity!

Transceivers

Table 2 shows the three main classes of portable transmitting equipment as used in practice. The first class consists generally of completely self-contained equipment in one enclosure and specially made for that particular type of operation. The second class covers a wide range of equipment, but the most suitable will often be mobile transceivers with add-on preamplifiers or power amplifiers if required. The third class comprises main station equipment generally delivering close to the maximum permitted power. The power supply to be used is an important factor. The low-power equipments with under 5W input can be run off lantern batteries, but those contemplating this are reminded that mains electricity costs far less than battery electricity (up to about 1,000 times less in the case of a PP3!) and therefore a set of nicad batteries and charger will prove a good investment. The larger nicad batteries can be used up to about 20W peak transmitter input, and it is therefore quite feasible to run a 10W PEP SSB transceiver from this type of power source.

Higher powers will demand lead-acid batteries or a portable generator, neither of which are particularly convenient to carry about single-handed. If these power sources are chosen they should be maintained regularly. Generators should get the manufacturer's recommended maintenance and be exercised during lay-off periods. During the winter wet batteries should be exercised and a freshening charge given each month. Discharge them into a load at a measured rate every so often, and then recharge at a known rate. All very elementary but all too often this can be overlooked.

Careful thought should be given to which type of portable operation is really intended and, if possible, equipment chosen that can also be used at the home station. For instance, if

high-power portable operation (eg for contests) is the eventual goal, it may be worth considering purchasing a generator and using base station equipment from the outset, rather than wasting time and money building up a system of low-power transmitters and power amplifiers. On the other hand, if the main interest is in hand-portable operation with occasional mobile work, an attractive possibility is an add-on power amplifier, which may be left permanently connected in the vehicle ready for service.

Antennas

Antennas used for single-operator portable operation must be simple to transport and put up, robust, easy to tune, efficient and, perhaps surprisingly, occupy little space, for sometimes the roadside is the only accessible land.

Three popular antennas for HF portable work are the inverted-V dipole, the short loaded vertical and the ground plane. The dipole [8] takes up the most space, but on flat ground is a good high-angle radiator and on steeply sloping ground can give excellent DX results [9]. The short loaded vertical is similar to the mobile antennas from which it was derived. Its main advantage is that it can be made into a multi-band system by various combinations of coils and antenna sections [8, 10]. The use of HF ground-plane antennas is somewhat controversial, with some operators claiming they give poor DX results, but nevertheless they continue to enjoy much popularity [11]. They are simple to make and erect, can be made self-supporting and require little space.

On VHF, omni-directional antennas are usually useless when located on top of a hill, for they will pick up all the locals as well as the DX. Far better results will be obtained with even the simplest beam antenna located a couple of metres high. The Yagi is easily the most popular beam antenna for portable VHF work, and usually the five-or six-element 144MHz versions are the largest that can be carried inside the average car, the boom length being the limiting factor. Other more portable antennas worth considering are the instant cubical quad [12] and the two-element HB9CV antenna [5]. If a roof rack is available, larger antennas can be carried, but high-gain systems are by nature heavy and unwieldy, and therefore not a good choice for the single-operator station. One tip when transporting the commercially available Yagi antennas having wing-nut element fasteners is just to loosen these rather than taking them off altogether. The elements can then be pivoted along the boom axis, which saves car space and leads to much quicker assembly once the destination is reached. Portable masts can be obtained ready-made or alternatively made up out of sections of aluminium tubing (see Chapter 5 and reference [13]).

Setting out

It is recommended that the portable station be completely assembled at home and soak-tested before any excursions are made. Remember that access to all the home station test

A 6m guy-less mast in position. For construction details see [14]

Pan-handle steady for mast. Make sure the roof-rack is well secured

equipment will not be available while out portable. Critical control settings should be noted down. Make sure the equipment will operate satisfactorily down to about 10V – sometimes relays are sticky at less than the ideal 12V.

Practise erecting the antenna in the garden several times until the routine is learnt, and test it using the transmitter if this is possible. Draw up a check list of items required for the portable station, so that these can be ticked off while loading the car. Make sure the equipment will not slide around and get damaged while in transit – an old rug or blanket laid over the car paintwork will protect it and the equipment from scratches. The load must be secure, even in an emergency stop or in sharp cornering, otherwise this could be dangerous. Do not neglect the 'inner man' when going out on a prolonged expedition. Comfort is an important item, and a car tends to get much colder

than a tent at night. Even in the summer months the early mornings can be very cold in the UK, especially on high ground, and a sleeping bag and hot food is a necessity, not a luxury, in such circumstances.

Selecting a site

HF stations will probably work reasonably satisfactorily at most locations providing there are no significant obstructions within about 100m. Those using ground plane antennas should try the marshy ground near rivers which ensures good earth conductivity, while users of horizontal dipoles are recommended to try hillsides sloping in the desired direction [9]. VHF stations are best located on top of an open hill with a steep slope in the direction of the likely DX.

A few likely sites in the area of interest should be selected from maps before setting out, for most of these will be found to be unsuitable for various reasons (see Chapter 5) once they have been reconnoitred. With experience comes a feeling for good sites which will save much time. Once a suitable site is selected find out who owns the land and call on the owner to get permission to set up the station: quite apart from being common courtesy this may bring to light any local ordinances or restrictions. It may result in an even better spot being discovered as local knowledge is tapped. A side effect of such calls can be freedom from interference by authority in any of its uniformed guises since the residents will know what is happening. In the latter connection, it is recommended that the validation document be carried at all times to avoid possible misunderstandings.

Callsigns and logkeeping

The UK licence regulations require that the suffix '/P' be added to the callsign when a fixed station is sited at a temporary location or '/M' when a pedestrian is operating a hand-portable station. In the case of fixed stations, either (i) details of the temporary location to an accuracy of 5km must be given every 30min or (ii) prior written notice of the location must be given to the local RIS office.

A normal log must be kept, similar to that for the home station, and details of the temporary location must be entered.

OPERATION IN FOREIGN COUNTRIES
Reciprocal and unilateral licensing

Since the time in 1965 when the first UK reciprocal licensing agreement was approved, the facilities available to persons wishing to operate from foreign countries have become numerous. It is generally recognised that in Europe the Belgian national society, UBA, was the first to commence the pattern which today is commonplace. With the increase in business travel and the desire to visit foreign countries on holiday the demand for reciprocal arrangements has multiplied. A list of the countries with which the UK has a reciprocal agreement is given in the UK section of Appendix 2.

There are also countries whose legislation does not permit the conclusion of a formal agreement, or whose conditions for licensing are to a lower standard than that in the UK, but who are prepared unilaterally to grant temporary amateur licences; therefore UK amateurs visiting countries not listed and wishing to operate an amateur station there should write to the administration concerned well in advance of their visit to ascertain whether a licence can be obtained. Again, these possibilities are noted where known under the relevant country section in Appendix 2.

It is essential that the applicant should allow plenty of time for the issue and despatch of a reciprocal or unilateral temporary licence. There may be queries from the administration concerned which will take additional time to resolve. This does mean that a suddenly arranged business trip may not be the time to seek a reciprocal licence in the country concerned.

Typical documents that *may* be required when applying in person are:

- Your amateur radio licence (take a photocopy or two in case they wish to retain a copy).
- Your passport.
- A completed application form giving your temporary address.
- Details of amateur radio equipment to be used, eg brand, serial number, frequency coverage and power output.
- Proof that your stay is temporary, eg a visa.
- The current licence fee.

In some cases, you may even be required to supply a letter written by your own local police attesting to your good character. Follow particularly carefully any instructions provided by the issuing administration regarding payment.

If you are applying by post you may need to photocopy your licence and passport and in some cases get these notarised as true copies. In the UK the RA will issue, on request, a short letter confirming the existence of a current licence.

In some cases a reciprocal licence will be accompanied by a document showing the regulations for the amateur service in the country concerned. These should be carefully studied and strict compliance with the regulations is obviously required. Particularly do not assume, even in a Region 1 country, that the band allocations follow those of the UK.

Operation under CEPT T/R 61-01

In Europe a significant and welcome development has been the introduction of a scheme whereby amateurs from countries which have implemented CEPT Recommendation T/R 61-01 can temporarily operate with the minimum of formality in any of those countries (see Chapter 1). CEPT licensing does not replace reciprocal/unilateral operation, as it is a short-term solution for portable or mobile operation, eg holiday operation from a hotel; however, it does also authorise operation from the station of a radio amateur in the host country. If you wish to operate from a permanent address or for over three months, you still need to apply for a reciprocal/unilateral-type licence.

Operating privileges under CEPT are the lowest common denominator of both the UK and the host country so, for example, you cannot operate on 70MHz from the Netherlands because Dutch amateurs do not have that band. (Remember that even if the host country has the same band, it may not be the same frequency range!) Conversely you cannot operate on higher power than the UK, even if the host country's own amateurs are allowed to. UK Class B licensees are not allowed operation on bands below 144MHz and Novice licensees are not allowed to operate under CEPT at all.

The callsign that you use is your own, preceded by the host country prefix, eg PA/G4FTJ. However, you may need to vary the host country prefix depending on your location (just as in the UK), and in some countries, such as Italy, it is dependent on whether you are operating a CEPT Class 1 station (UK Class A) or a CEPT Class 2 station (UK Class B). As you are mobile or portable, you probably need to add the appropriate suffix '/M' or '/P'.

If you are interested in operation under CEPT in a particular country you should:

- read the CEPT sections of BR68 and Chapter 1 of this book;
- send for the RA information sheet RA247;
- write or telephone the licensing administration of the country to ascertain the current licensing conditions for CEPT operation (and how to import amateur radio equipment). Addresses are given in RA247 and also in Appendix 2 of this book. Many countries have helpful leaflets in English on this topic.

More countries are expected to implement CEPT T/R 61-01, giving an even wider range of countries where you can operate with the minimum of formality. In IARU Region 2, the equivalent is the International Amateur Radio Permit (IARP). Hopefully, one day these two systems will merge.

Importation of amateur equipment

The customs treatment of amateur radio equipment varies not only between countries but also between different ports of entry or border crossings. A carnet covering the equipment may be required and it is recommended that due to the continuing changes regarding carnets that up-to-date information be obtained from the AA or RAC. A number of countries will accept equipment in transit provided that it can be sealed and inspected when it is exported from the country.

CEPT operation does itself not cover the importation of amateur radio equipment, although in practice there are minimum customs formalities between EU countries.

Most non-EU countries will allow the temporary importation of a transceiver, power supply and antenna as part of your personal effects, but you should carry receipts and an inventory, complete with serial numbers. If in any doubt, contact the relevant embassy, licensing administration or national amateur radio society.

FURTHER INFORMATION

[1] 'Going HF mobile – some experiments in vehicle suppression methods', R V Heaton, G3JIS, *Radio Communication* October 1981, p920.
[2] 'Suppression of vehicle interference for mobile radio operation', D Morris, G3AYJ, *Radio Communication* May 1976, p336.
[3] *The Highway Code*, HMSO, 1993.
[4] 'A transmit control for mobile operation', J M Bryant, G4CLF, *Practical Wireless* July 1989, p24.
[5] *Radio Communication Handbook*, 6th edn, ed Dick Biddulph, G8DPS, RSGB, 1994.
[6] Amateur Radio Insurance Services, Shepheards Hurst, Green Lane, Outwood, Surrey, RH1 5QS.
[7] *UK Repeater List,* RSGB (up-dated frequently).
[8] 'Aerials for portable operation', J E Hodgkins, G3EJF, *Radio Communication* May 1971, p319.
[9] *HF Antennas for All Locations,* 2nd edn, Les Moxon, G6XN, RSGB, 1993.
[10] 'A six-band portable aerial', H S Brown, G3RFG, *Radio Communication* May 1973, p329. Also appears in [11].
[11] 'Portable operation with ground planes', J B Roscoe, GM4QK, *Radio Communication* March 1972, p150.
[12] 'The G8ENN instant beam', D A Tong, G4GMQ, *Radio Communication* April 1976, p270.
[13] *HF Antenna Collection*, ed Erwin David, G4LQI, RSGB, 1991.
[14] 'Take to the hills', I J Kyle, GI8AYZ, *Radio Communication* July 1972, p436.

7 Amateur satellite and space communications

ONE of the most interesting and exciting operating activities is communication via satellite, which also offers many possibilities for technical experimentation, including the use of low power. Amateur satellites have come a long way since the relatively primitive devices launched in the 'sixties, and those currently in orbit include sophisticated communication and research satellites which would have cost millions of dollars if constructed on a commercial basis.

The main organisation involved with the launch of amateur satellites is the Radio Amateur Satellite Corporation (AMSAT-NA) with its headquarters in the USA [1]. It has groups affiliated groups across the globe, including AMSAT-UK [2]. At the time of writing (July 1995) several other AMSAT groups have been actively engaged in the design, building and launch operations with over 30 launches to date.

Russia (and the former USSR) has also launched several amateur satellites, co-ordinated by the Radio Sport Federation in that country.

The satellites constructed by AMSAT Groups in USA, UK, Germany, Mexico, Israel, South Africa, Japan, and Russia, loosely known as *AMSAT-International*, are generically known as *OSCARs* (Orbital Satellites Carrying Amateur Radio). These OSCARs will have their own name in their own countries and organisations, but in general all amateur satellites now have an OSCAR numbering, ie Oscar 17 is called also *Dove* (Peace) by the Brazilian owners. Oscar 16 is called *Pacsat*, and so on. These two satellites were part of a clutch of micro-satellites launched in a batch of six from the same spacecraft in 1993. To date we are up to number 28 (Portugese POSAT). These, added to the Russian series, make the above total.

There are currently 18 active amateur satellites. These have been classified into three *phases*:

- Phase 1 – experimental (Oscar 1–5)
- Phase 2 – long-life, medium-orbit, satellites with transponders (linear repeaters) allowing two-way communication (Oscars 6–8, 16, 18, 19, 20, 22, 23 etc)
- Phase 3 – high-altitude (DX) orbit satellites with sophisticated transponding and control systems (Oscar 10 and 13).

PHASE 2 SATELLITES

Oscar 9 (which has now re-entered Earth orbit), 11 and 17 are Phase 2 research satellites and do not contain an amateur-usage transponder.

The USSR/Russian satellites (RS1–RS15) have all been of the Phase 2 type, allowing two-way analogue communication. RS5/6, RS7/8 and RS9 and RS14 are now defunct. RS10/11 and RS12/13 are still currently functioning. A new launch, RS15, took place on 29 December 1994 – this had some defects during the first few months in orbit, but now appears stable and giving good amateur-type analogue communications. It has been suggested that the on-board batteries were not fully charged prior to launch in Russia. This may well be the last Russian satellite to be built for some time to come.

However, during April 1995 two launches took place from Russia. These were the Technion (Israel) and University of Mexico satellites. Unfortunately both satellites were lost when the rocket launch vehicle failed to ignite on the fifth stage of flight over Eastern Russia. These satellites would have been numbers 29 and 30 if placed into Earth orbit.

In the Phase 2 designated satellite generation there is the Japanese JAS-1 and 2 series.

JAS-1 is now defunct, although still in orbit. Reports have been received of intermittent operation but this is not substantiated. JAS-2, named Fuji (Oscar 20), is currently in operation with the usual beacon on 437.795MHz CW and with communications taking place in digital and analogue modes between various defined *channels*. (There are reports of JAS-3 being designed as we go to press.) See Fig 1.

Also using Phase 2 type orbits are the purely digital satellites: Oscars 22 (Uosat 5), 23 (Kitsat A) and 25 (Kitsat B). These three satellites are used in 9600 baud mode for message handling with a computer (high-speed packet). Specific frequencies with uplinks on 2m and downlink on 70cm are available with orbits mostly available early morning and evening over the UK. Oscar 22 is now used almost exclusively as a *satgate* store-and-forward device. This means that an amateur who has no satellite equipment can place a message to his local packet station for onward transmission to GB7LAN or GB7LDI (in the UK) for onward transmission via Oscar 22 to any other packet station on the system. Full information is well beyond the scope of this chapter and the reader is referred to the many books written on all satellites, modes, and frequencies obtainable from AMSAT and the RSGB. AMSAT-UK [2] also carries a wide range with full coverage of the subject.

Phase 2 and 3 satellites require a different approach in their use, and are considered separately in this chapter. Since Phase 2 satellites are low-orbit devices, their communication range is restricted and they move across the sky quite quickly (approximately every 100 minutes in time per orbit). Therefore considerable attention to tracking them is required. Phase 3 satellites are in a higher orbit and appear to move very slowly when at apogee (the highest point of the orbit). Tracking is not then a particular problem but, due to the increased range, more attention then needs to be given to the efficiency of the user's station, in particular the receiving antenna and the receiver. High-efficiency front-ends should be the aim of the satellite user.

Uosat-Oscar 11, 22, 23, 25

Designed and constructed at the University of Surrey, Uosat 2 (Oscar 11) is a research satellite which also has an amateur satellite transponder. Oscar 11 does not now offer two-way amateur communications, but is currently used for two-weekly updates of news and information on the whole satellite hobby.

SATELLITE FREQUENCY GUIDE.
AMSAT-UK
[All frequencies in Mhz]

OSCAR 25 (KITSAT-B)

Downlinks	436.500 (9600bps)
	435.275 (9600bps)
Uplinks	145.870 (FSK/FM)
	145.975 (FSK/FM)

OSCAR 26 (ITAMSAT)

Downlinks	435.867
	435.822
Uplinks	145.875,145.900
	145.925,145.950

OSCAR-27 (EYESAT)
(Provisional)

Downlink	436.800
Uplink	145.850

OSCAR-28 (Posat)

Downlinks	435.275
Uplinks	145.980

RS 10

	Freq	Mode
Beacon/ROBOT	29.357	(CW)
Beacon/ROBOT	29.403	(CW)
Mode A Uplink	145.860 - 145.900	(SSB,CW)
Mode A Downlink	29.360 - 29.400	(SSB,CW)
ROBOT A Uplink	145.820	(CW)
ROBOT A Downlink	29.357 or 29.403	(CW)
Beacon/ROBOT	29.357	(CW)
Beacon/ROBOT	29.403	(CW)
Mode K Uplink	21 160 - 21 200	(SSB,CW)
Mode K Downlink	29.360 - 29.400	(SSB,CW)
ROBOT K Uplink	21.120	(CW)
ROBOT K Downlink	29.357 or 29.403	(CW)
Beacon/ROBOT	145.857	(CW)
Beacon/ROBOT	145.903	(CW)
Mode T Uplink	21 160 - 21.200	(SSB,CW)
Mode T Downlink	145.860 - 145.900	(SSB,CW)
ROBOT T Uplink	21 120	(CW)
ROBOT T Downlink	145.857 or 145.903	(CW)

RS 11

	Freq	Mode
Beacon/ROBOT	29.407	(CW)
Beacon/ROBOT	29.453	(CW)
Mode A Uplink	145.910 - 145.950	(SSB,CW)
Mode A Downlink	29.410 - 29.450	(SSB,CW)
ROBOT A Uplink	145.830	(CW)
ROBOT A Downlink	29.407 or 29.453	(CW)
Beacon/ROBOT	29.407	(CW)
Beacon/ROBOT	29.453	(CW)
Mode K Uplink	21 210 - 21 250	(SSB,CW)
Mode K Downlink	29.410 - 29.450	(SSB,CW)
ROBOT K Uplink	21.130	(CW)
ROBOT K Downlink	29.407 or 29.453	(CW)
Beacon/ROBOT	145.907	(CW)
Beacon/ROBOT	145.953	(CW)
Mode T Uplink	21 210 - 21 250	(SSB,CW)
Mode T Downlink	145.910 - 145.950	(SSB,CW)
ROBOT T Uplink	21.130	(CW)
ROBOT T Downlink	145.907 or 145.953	(CW)

RS 12

	Freq	Mode
Beacon/ROBOT	29.408	(CW)
Beacon/ROBOT	29.454	(CW)
Mode A Uplink	145.910 - 145.950	(SSB,CW)
Mode A Downlink	29.410 - 29.450	(SSB,CW)
ROBOT A Uplink	145.831	(CW)
ROBOT A Downlink	29.408 or 29.454	(CW)
Beacon/ROBOT	29.408	(CW)
Beacon/ROBOT	29.454	(CW)
Mode K Uplink	21.210 - 21 250	(SSB,CW)
Mode K Downlink	29.410 - 29.450	(SSB,CW)
ROBOT K Uplink	21.129	(CW)
ROBOT K Downlink	29.408 or 29.454	(CW)
Beacon/ROBOT	145.912	(CW)
Beacon/ROBOT	145.959	(CW)
Mode T Uplink	21.210 - 21 250	(SSB,CW)
Mode T Downlink	145.910 - 145.950	(SSB,CW)
ROBOT T Uplink	21.129	(CW)
ROBOT T Downlink	l45.912 or 145. 959	(CW)

RS 13

	Freq	Mode
Beacon/ROBOT	29.458	(CW)
Beacon/ROBOT	29.504	(CW)
Mode A Uplink	145.960 - 146.000	(SSB,CW)
Mode A Downlink	29.460 - 29.500	(SSB,CW)
ROBOT A Uplink	145.840	(CW)
ROBOT A Downlink	29.458 or 29.504	(CW)
Beacon/ROBOT	29.458	(CW)
Beacon/ROBOT	29.504	(CW)
Mode K Uplink	21 260 - 21.300	(SSB,CW)
Mode K Downlink	29.460 - 29.500	(SSB,CW)
ROBOT K Uplink	21.138	(CW)
ROBOT K Downlink	29.458 or 29.504	(CW)
Beacon/ROBOT	145.862	(CW)
Beacon/ROBOT	145.908	(CW)
Mode T Uplink	21.260 - 21 300	(SSB,CW)
Mode T Downlink	145.960 - 146.000	(SSB,CW)
ROBOT T Uplink	21.138	(CW)
ROBOT T Downlink	145.862 or 145.908	(CW)

Published by AMSAT-UK London E12 5EQ
Tel: (081)989 6741. Fax: (081) 989 3430. Compuserve 100024,614

SATELLITE FREQUENCY GUIDE.
AMSAT-UK
[All frequencies in Mhz]

OSCAR 10 (Phase 3B)

Mode B

General Beacon	145.809 (Carrier)
Engineering Beacon	145.987
Uplink	435.030 - 435.180
Downlink	145.975 - 145.825

OSCAR 19 (Lusat)

Uplinks (AFSK/FM)	145.840 145.860
	145.880 145.900
Downlink (PSK)	437.150 (BPSK/SSB)
Downlink (RC)	437.125 (BPSK/SSB)
CW Beacon	437.125 (CW)

OSCAR 11 (UoSat 2)

Beacon	145.826(AFSK/FM)
Beacon	435.025(AFSK/FM)
Beacon	2401.500(AFSK/FM)

OSCAR 20 (Fuji)

Beacon	435.795 (CW)
Mode JA Uplink(SSB,CW)	145.900 - 146.000
Mode JA Downlink (SSB,CW)	435.900 - 435.800
Mode JD Uplinks (AFSK/FM)	145.850 145.870
	145.890 145.910
Mode JD Downlink (BPSK/SSB)	435.910

OSCAR 13(PHASE 3C)

Mode B

General Beacon	145.812 (PSK,CW,RTTY)
Eng. Beacon	145.985 (PSK,CW,RTTY)
Uplink	435.423 - 435.573 (SSB,CW)
Downlink1	145.975 - 145.825 (SSB,CW)

Mode S

Beacon	2400.325 (PSK,RTTY)
Beacon	2400.664 (PSK,RTTY)
Uplink	435.603 - 435.639 (SSB,CW,FM)
Downlink	2400.711 - 2400.747 (SSB,CW,FM)

OSCAR 21 (RS14)

Beacon	145.819 (CW)
Beacon	145.952 (BPSK/FM)
Beacon	145.987 (BPSK/SSB)
Mode B	(SSB,CW)
Uplink 1	435.022 - 435.102
Downlink 1	145.932 - 145.852
Uplink 2	435.043 - 435.123
RUDAK 2	145.946 - 145.866
Uplink 1	435.016 (AFSK/FM)
Uplink 2	435.155 (BPSK/FM)
Uplink 3	435.193 (BPSK/FM)
Uplink 4	435.041 (Various modes)
Downlink	435.987 (Various modes)
Beacon	145.948 (CW)
Beacon	145.838 (BPSK/FM)
Beacon	145.800 (BPSK/FM)

OSCAR 16 (Pacsat)

Uplinks (AFSK/FM)	145.900 145.920
	145.940 145.960
Downlink (PSK)	437.025 (BPSK/SSB)
Downlink (RC)	437.050 (BPSK/SSB)
Downlink S	2401.143 (BPSK/SSB)

OSCAR 22 (UoSat-5)

Downlink	435.120 (9600 FSK/FM)
Uplink	145.900 (FSK/FM)
Uplink	145.975 (FSK/FM)

OSCAR 17 (Dove)

Beacon 1	145.82516 (AFSK/FM,Dig voice/FM)
Beacon 2	145.82438 (AFSK/FM,Dig voice/FM)
Beacon S	2401 .2205 (BPSK/SSB)

OSCAR 23 (KITSAT-A)

Downlink	435.175 (9600 FSK/FM)
Uplink	145.850 (FSK/FM)
Uplink	145.900 (FSK/FM)

OSCAR 18 (Webersat)

Downlink(RC)	437.102 (BPSK/SSB)
DownLink	437.075 (BPSK/SSB)
Uplink	145.900
Uplink ATV (NTSC)	1265.00 (TV/AM)

Fig 1. Both sides of the *AMSAT-UK Satellite Frequency Guide*, much reduced in size. This is available from AMSAT-UK on laminated A4 card, full size, for easy reference

Table 1. Transponder mode designations

Mode	Uplink	Downlink	Satellites
A	145MHz	29MHz	RS10–13
B	435MHz	145MHz	Oscar 10, 13, 21
J	145MHz	435MHz	Oscar 20, 22, 23, 25–28
JA	145MHz	435MHz	Oscar 20 analogue
JD	145MHz	435MHz	Oscar 20 digital
JL	1.2GHz/145MHz	145MHz	Oscar 13
K	21MHz	29MHz	RS10–13
KA	21/145MHz	29MHz	RS10–13
KT	21MHz	29/145MHz	RS10–13
L	1.2GHz	435MHz	Oscar 13
S	1.2GHz	2.4GHz	Oscar 13
T	21MHz	145MHz	RS10–13

Many research satellites have been organised by scientific bodies and the layman only has slight knowledge of the full details of construction and use when in orbit, and of the results obtained.

Oscars 22, 23 and 25 were also designed and built by the University of Surrey Space Department. Oscar 22 is owned by the University, while Oscars 23 and 25 are owned by the Korean space authorities. These satellites have store-and-forward amateur packet with 9600 baud transponders on board, and have given excellent service since launch.

Uosats are research tools that the radio amateur and the layman can use, with the professionals also interested because of the several experiments they carry. Full details of the satellites are available in book form from AMSAT-UK [4] but, to whet one's appetite, here are a few details: 145MHz enthusiasts can tell, by interpretation of their radiation counter readings, if an aurora is likely; UHF/microwave enthusiasts have the 2.4 and 10GHz beacons to use in propagation studies; scientists are using the radiation detectors and the three-axis magnetometer (the first time one of these has flown in near-Earth space); computer buffs can feed the telemetry, in ASCII code, straight into their machines. The telemetry (and other data) is received by voice as well as RTTY and CW. The primary frequencies are 145.825 and 435.025MHz; other frequencies can be seen in Fig 1.

RS10–RS15

Unfortunately, for various reasons, less detail was made available for the Soviet amateur satellites than for their western brothers, although more information is forthcoming now for RS15 since the Cold War ended. It is known that RS satellites are partly pressurised and heated in order to maintain frequency stability. The satellite 145MHz antennas, from their pictures, look like canted turnstiles, although no requirement for circular polarisation on the uplink has been publicised. Power output is in the 500mW to 1W PEP range. The previous satellites, RS1 and RS2, are known to have been about 2m by 1m in dimension.

A very useful device carried on RS satellites is known as the *robot*. One can actually have a contact with, rather than through, the satellite when the correct procedure is used, CW (morse code) only. The robot communicator calls CQ, expects to be called back with its own callsign (and yours) and then responds with a sequential serial number; to use RS12 as an example:

CQ CQ CQ DE RS 12 QSU ON 29454 KCS

RS12 DE G3AAJ $\overline{AR}$ *(not K)*

DE RS12 QSO NR 1645 G3AAJ DE RS12 QSO NR 1645 OP
   ROBOT TU FR QSO 73 $\overline{SK}$

Morse code speed can vary between about 12 and 40wpm, and the calling station can be heard coming back from the robot

making it sound a little like a CW repeater; in fact some stations have used it as such. The robot also has a limited vocabulary when it is not sure; it can send:

QRM, QRZ, QRS, QRQ and RPT

as dictated by circumstances. Later on the callsigns of stations worked are dumped, by ground command, and a QSL card can be expected for the contact from the QSL bureau in Moscow.

Locating Phase 2 satellites

Since radio communication via an amateur satellite is essentially line-of-sight, it follows that it can only take place when the satellite is above the user's horizon, and it is therefore necessary to determine the periods when this occurs. In addition, if beam antennas are in use it will be necessary to ascertain the beam headings of the satellites during these periods. Furthermore, some sophisticated satellite stations use antennas capable of variable elevation as well as azimuth rotation (az-el antennas), and in this case it is also desirable to know the approximate elevation of the satellite above the horizon at any time.

All this information can be derived quite simply from daily orbital data which is available from a number of sources, but in order to do this it is first necessary to have a basic understanding of the terms involved. These will therefore now be described briefly as they directly affect locating the satellite – much more complete orbital information concerning amateur satellites is given in references [4] and [5] to which the interested reader is referred.

Orbital data

The simplest way to understand satellite orbits is to imagine one is out in space observing the Earth rotating on its axis from west to east with the north pole at the top (Fig 2). If an object as small as a satellite could be detected it would be seen coming from behind the Earth over the Antarctic region, proceeding northwards across the equator, then disappearing over the north polar region. This part of the orbit is known as the *ascending node*. The remaining half of the orbit, when the satellite travels from north to south, is called the *descending node*.

It will be noticed that the orbit is tilted anti-clockwise from the north-south line, or is *retrograde* in space terminology. The satellite never goes right over the poles. The time which a satellite takes to make its orbit is known as the *period*, during which the Earth will have rotated eastwards. The satellite will therefore cross the equator at a different longitude, the difference being the *longitude increment*.

An orbit is said to commence when a satellite crosses the equator travelling north. All orbit predictions consist of this time in Universal Clock Time (UTC), and degrees west of the

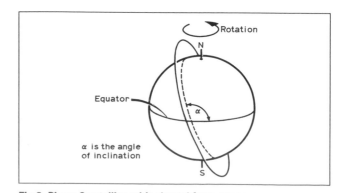

Fig 2. Phase 2 satellite orbit viewed from space

```
OSCAR11   20-08-95   03:06:52   143.0<   09:39:07   241.1<   19:27:29    28.2>
OSCAR16   20-08-95   00:13:30    14.1>   15:20:21   240.8<   23:44:09     6.8>
OSCAR17   20-08-95   09:52:22   158.3<   14:54:37   233.9<   23:18:22   359.8>
OSCAR18   20-08-95   01:04:56    26.5>   14:30:57   228.0<   22:54:43   353.9>
OSCAR19   20-08-95   09:54:55   158.6<   14:57:09   234.2<   23:20:52     0.1>
OSCAR20   20-08-95   00:45:08    30.5>   11.58.46   199.0<   23:12:24     7.4>
OSCAR26   20-08-95   00:52:03    33.2>   12:38:27   209.8<   22:43:56     1.2>
OSCAR27   20-08-95   00:24:29    26.4>   12:10:55   203.0<   23:57:22    19.6>
RS10-11   20-08-95   01:34:12   339.7>   10:19:09   111.5<   15:34:07   190.6<
RS12-13   20-08-95   01:34:17   298.1>   12:03:26    96.2<   22:32:35   254.2<
RS15      20-08-95   00:10:05   178.6<   12:56:24    11.6>   23:35:00   172.4<
```

Fig 2. Satellite predictions for 20 August 1995 as listed in the orbital calendar produced by AMSAT-UK. Only three orbits are given for each day – these will normally be the first, last and mid-orbits within range of some point in the UK, but there will be exceptions. Subsequent or previous orbits can be calculated using data shown in the calendar. The times given are those that the satellite crosses the equator (EQX). At the time the satellite crosses the equator it will either be moving north (ascending node >) or south (descending node <)

Greenwich meridian where it occurs. This method of stating longitude often confuses the uninitiated, more used to degrees east and west of Greenwich, but it is really quite simple; up to 180°W there is no problem, after that 170°E is equivalent to 190°W, 160°E equates with 200°W, and so on round to the Greenwich meridian again; hence 5°E is given as 355°W.

The first orbit each day is called the *reference orbit*; these orbits are usually out of range of the UK. Future orbits can, however, be calculated with fair accuracy, given any reference orbit information. This may be obtained from the calendar available from AMSAT-UK [2] (see Fig 2). Alternatively predictions are available for the week ahead on Teletext, news bulletins such as GB2RS, the UK packet BBS, and all AMSAT and AMSAT-UK nets. In addition AMSAT-UK run a telephone BBS on +44 (0)181 547-1479 (Kingston-on-Thames area) and up to 28kbaud rates are catered for. Latest Kepler elements from NASA are normally posted on this telephone BBS within a day of them being released by NASA. Kepler elements can of course be fed into the many satellite prediction programs now available for most computers [2].

Using the predictions

Having obtained the time of equatorial crossing and corresponding longitude for a suitable orbit from one of the above sources, this has to be converted into acquisition-of-signal (AOS) and loss-of-signal (LOS) times, and possibly beam headings and elevation if directional antennas are in use, as noted previously.

Numerous ingenious ways of deriving this information have been published. These fall broadly into three types: (a) the use of a special map with a rotating cursor which represents the satellite track; (b) the use of 'look-up' tables or charts; (c) computer programs.

Method (a) was developed by G2AOX and K2ZRO and uses a device which is now universally known as the *Oscarlator*. It consists of a polar projection map of the northern hemisphere, a small section of which is shown in Fig 4, and a transparent acetate overlay (Fig 5). The small circle is cut out of the latter and stuck on the map with its centre at the user's location and its straight line pointing towards the North Pole. The large circle is cut out and placed over the map so that its centre corresponds with the north pole, and the 'O' mark corresponds with the point at which the satellite crosses the equator going north.

The curved line across the circle denotes the satellite track, and the point where this intersects the small circle is the AOS. The time after EQX (equatorial crossing) that this occurs can be found by reference to a time scale printed on the curved line. The approximate direction can also be ascertained from

the map. The details for LOS and in fact any intermediate point can be determined in the same way.

The map and transparent overlays are available from AMSAT-UK at a small charge [2].

Method (b) utilises a table of satellite paths calculated for every 2° of EQX longitude (ascending node). Strictly speaking, the tables are only applicable for the location for which they were calculated but in practice the error is small at other locations up to 200km away. The time is given in minutes after ascending node and beam headings are true bearings. The tables are again available from AMSAT-UK [2].

Computer programs for method (c) are available from AMSAT-UK in IBM PC, BBC and Acorn Archimedes formats. One of the most popular suite of PC programs is AMSAT-UK Satscan II. This has full map and prediction screens and is very accurate (see Fig 6).

Equatorial crossing times for most satellites are broadcast on the various AMSAT-UK nets every Sunday, Monday, Wednesday and Thursday.

Receiving satellite signals

Reception in the 29MHz band from RS satellites differs from normal reception from distant ground stations in that it is basically line-of-sight, and it is also usually necessary to be able to receive the satellite's signals while the user's transmitter is on the air. Furthermore, as the satellite's power has to be shared between all the relayed signals, it is likely that only a few milliwatts is being radiated by the satellite for each signal. The performance of many amateur-band receivers and transceivers falls off at 29MHz, particularly at the satellite end of the band. Consequently a simple low-noise preamplifier to provide about 10dB gain will often bring about a dramatic improvement in reception.

A simple dipole or ground-plane antenna will enable good signals to be heard from the nearer satellite passes but for serious DX work at maximum range, a low-angle beam antenna of some kind should be considered, mounted in the clear as far as possible from local noise sources. Simple and compact beams with good gain for their size are the HB9CV and ZL-Special designs. To cope with the nearly-overhead passes, a fixed horizontal dipole (16ft overall) running east-west is sufficient since the satellite will be north-south or south-north on such orbits.

Transmitting to the satellite

The uplink passbands for all modes of the Phase 2 low-orbit satellites are given in Fig 1.

In the case of the RS satellites the maximum recommended

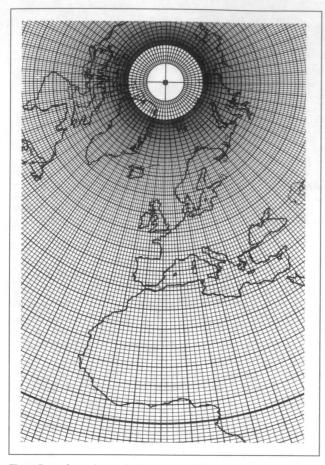

Fig 4. Part of a polar projection map of the northern hemisphere. The line near the foot of the map is the Equator, which is a complete circle on the whole map

Fig 5. Typical Oscarlator for RS15 satellite, much reduced from actual size. The large circle corresponds to the equator on the polar projection map; the small circle to maximum satellite range when pasted on to the map

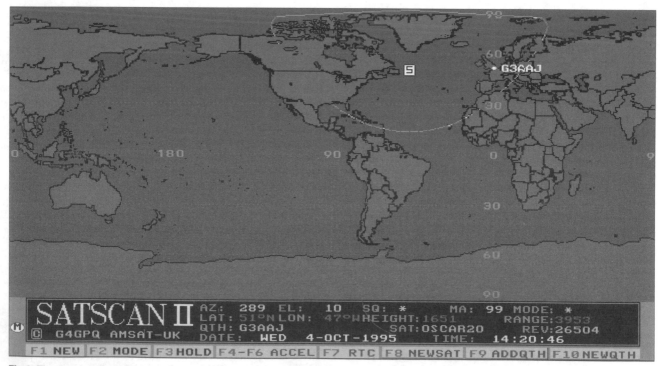

Fig 6. The Satscan II world map showing the selected satellite and its communication 'footprint' moving in real time. Lunar and solar displays are also available

SATELLITE BAND PLANS

Band plans have been adopted by all IARU countries as the recommended operational usage of all Oscar satellite communications. It conforms to the accepted 'one-third' rule in terrestrial amateur band plans, ie lower end CW, middle phone/CW, upper SSB. The plan, which has been agreed since 1979, allocates a percentage of the available radio frequency spectrum as seen on the downlink to different modes of communication. The relative amount of spectrum for each mode is thus the same for any transponder in any satellite. Irrespective of the current use of channels on some satellites the thirds rule has been a success in the majority of cases. The allocations are as follows:

Notes:
1. Guard area to avoid interference to beacons.
These frequencies are available for emergency and bulletin stations.
2. RTTY and SSTV, if permitted and included within the capability of the satellite. are placed at the edge of the CW and SSB passbands, conforming to their usage at HF where RTTY is present within the CW space and SSTV is transmitted in the SSB sub-band.
3. Mixed mode area. This is recommended for crystal controlled stations, or dxpedition stations, or anyone wishing to work both CW and SSB stations.
4. Mode A guard channels 5kHz non-inverting pass band. Mode B guard channels 2–5kHz inverting passband Mode J guard channels 5kHz inverting passband.

The plan is always based on percentages of the downlink passband. It applies to both inverting and non-inverting transponders. The allocations of frequency for Oscar satellites are as follows:

ERP at horizon ranges is 50W. However, it has been frequently proved quite possible to access with less than 1W to a dipole, provided the other users are keeping to low power.

Band plans

As with other amateur allocations, there are band plans for the orderly use of the space sections of the amateur bands. These are as detailed by international agreement at ITU and IARU conferences and are shown on this page for Phase 2 satellites. It should be noted that where the transponder passband is inverted then HF becomes LF, USB becomes LSB etc. This plan applies to all future spacecraft, at all times, except when special trans-satellite tests are being held. It should be remembered that all band plans only work for the good of every user of a band of frequencies on a gentlemens' agreement basis. However, if you transmit outside recommended band use, you would not expect to get a reply from another satellite user.

Huge antenna arrays are not required for satellite operation, although beams with az-el rotation are desirable. This photo shows a typical small installation in a garden

Reason: as is well known, all satellite users are gentlemen (or ladies), or should be!

Range of communication

For a station at sea level in the British Isles the horizon distance to Oscar 11 is about 3800km, equivalent to a ground distance of about 3950km. It follows that the maximum ground range is twice the latter, or 7600km; however, the 2m range can be exceeded considerably when there is anomalous propagation on 145MHz. For example, E-layer ionisation will enable a VHF or UHF signal to be received by the satellites when they are below your horizon. This is part of the hobby that a few enthusiasts obtain great DX contacts by studying and using the outer edges of both the received and transmitted 'footprints' of stations.

Polarisation

Imagine a satellite in orbit without a sophisticated stabilisation system. That satellite is likely to roll and tumble according to minute external influences of solar and terrestrial origin, and so the orientation of the satellite's antennas, as seen from the ground, could (and does) change in direction. The polarisation to cater for all orientations (except when the antenna is end-on to the observer) is circular but one then suffers a 3dB penalty (from cross-polarisation) as the price of consistency. Satisfactory results can be obtained with horizontal or vertical polarisation alone for most of the time but fading will be troublesome occasionally; better results can be obtained by having both polarisations available and switching between them to select the strongest signal.

Some satellites' antenna systems are themselves circularly polarised (on VHF and upwards) and some advantage can be gained by ground stations using the same sense of circular polarisation, but only when the satellite antenna system is pointing towards the observer. At other times selected linear polarisation will be better so the best all-round results will be achieved by the station who can switch between horizontal, slant, vertical, left-hand circular and right-hand circular polarisations; a means of obtaining these options from a crossed Yagi array is

Another satellite array mounted on an outbuilding

detailed in reference [5]. Right-hand circular polarisation (RHCP) is also known as *clockwise* polarisation and is used on Oscar 10.

Doppler shift

This is a frequency- and velocity-related effect readily noticed in amateur satellite observations (typical speed of a satellite is about 17,000mph); it appears, under normal circumstances, as if the satellite is drifting lower in frequency. To use Oscar 8 (now defunct) mode A as an example: Doppler shift on the 145MHz uplink added, via the linear transponder, to that on the 29MHz downlink to give a cumulative 'drift' of up to 5 or 6kHz per pass. As frequency increases, so does the amount of Doppler shift and so use of higher frequencies, such as 435 and 1,270MHz, would result in a total amount that could get extremely large; remember that the shift of both links has to be taken into account and, in the case of Mode A, the 4 or 5kHz of 145MHz added to the 1kHz of 29MHz to give the total amount.

Designers of transponders, however, can in a mixer stage extract a negative component rather than a positive component (or turn it upside down) such that one Doppler shift is subtracted from another. As an example, Doppler shift on the 145MHz uplink (4–5kHz) is subtracted from that on the downlink (about 12kHz) resulting in only 6 or 7kHz instead of the 18kHz which would result if the positive component were used. This is why the transponder is called *inverting* – frequencies at the top of the uplink band come out at the bottom of the

downlink band and vice versa; consequently the convention of transmitting lower sideband results, through the translation process being inverted, in upper sideband being received.

Telemetry

It is hoped that the foregoing will have enabled a newcomer to amateur satellite communication to understand the subject sufficiently to at least calculate when and where to listen for amateur radio satellites. Short-wave listeners will be able to hear many countries via satellite and it is interesting to copy the telemetry sent down continuously on the beacon frequencies.

The morse code telemetry from Oscar 11 consists of figure groups, while RS12–15 telemetry is made up of letters and figures in a variable format; morse code speeds can be between 12 and 20wpm. Telemetry values, when decoded, give details of such parameters as battery voltage, current and temperature, power outputs etc, ie the 'housekeeping' data. Telemetry is an essential feature of satellites as it enables the ground control stations to take appropriate action if, for example, excessive battery current is being drawn or if the PA stage of the transmitter is becoming overheated.

RTTY and ASCII telemetry carry similar parameters to the CW telemetry and, with up to 60 channels available, much information can be transmitted.

Speeds and formats are detailed in the handbook mentioned previously. The tone frequencies transmitted by frequency modulation from Oscar 11 conform to the once-popular Kansas City CUTS system and can be received on a home computer with a suitable interface.

In addition to telemetry formats requiring some skill or machinery, Oscar 17 (Dove) contains a speech synthesiser which can be used to 'speak' short messages which have been inputted from the command station.

Practical communication

Undoubtedly the most common abuse of a satellite is the use of far too much power. The operating schedules for all satellites allow them to be used whenever heard except that if you use the satellite while an experiment is in progress you could upset the whole experiment.

The use of excessive power seems to be due to the rather inferior receiving systems employed by some operators and this causes these stations to run a lot more power than necessary before they can find their own signal; as previously mentioned this causes problems to other users. This is 'undue interference' according to the terms of the UK amateur licence, and cases have occurred where stations have lost their licence because of this. The receiver sensitivity required is 0.1μV for 5dB over the noise and this will enable weak signals to be heard. There are few amateurs fortunate enough not to be troubled with RF interference from switched-mode power supplies and line time-base oscillators in TV sets, faulty thermostats and sundry industrial and domestic noises. Much of this interference can be dealt with by a good noise blanker as opposed to a noise limiter.

To illustrate how to communicate through an amateur satellite, let us take a step-by-step example for RS12 in Mode A. It is assumed that you have a separate receiver and transmitter.

1. From the orbital calendar, or other published orbital data, check when a convenient orbit will occur and calculate AOS/ LOS times and any beam pointing information needed. There are approximately 12 orbits per day on the LEO (low Earth orbiter) type satellites.

Fig 7. Relationship between uplink and downlink bands for RS12/13 (see text concerning effects of Doppler shift)

2. Tune up your transmitter in the 145.96–146.00MHz segment before the calculated AOS time, using a dummy load (do not tune up 'on-air').

3. If your transmit and/or receive antennas are rotatable, point them in the general direction from whence the satellite will come over the horizon. Keep the beam-pointing information where it can be seen at a glance.

4. Set up your receiver to cover the 29.4–29.5MHz section of the band, and make sure that the receiver is not muted or desensitised when the transmitter is used, and also that the squelch control, if fitted, is fully open.

5. Listen for the telemetry on 29.408MHz but remember that the satellite is travelling towards you at an orbital velocity of about 4.5 miles per second, causing a Doppler shift upwards in frequency of about 700Hz at the start of the orbit.

6. Having established that the satellite is within range and functioning, you should hear a number of mainly SSB and CW signals as you tune across the passband, so the next goal is to find out if your signal is being relayed by the satellite. What you must not do is to transmit a powerful carrier, 'swishing' your VFO across the whole passband trying to hear yourself. This is anti-social and unfortunately all too prevalent with newcomers who have not paid attention to getting the best possible *receive* system from the antenna through to the loudspeaker.

   You can quickly calculate where your signal ought to be within a few kilohertz on 29MHz. For example, if you transmit on 145.925 MHz on the uplink, your 29MHz signal would be at the edge of the downlink passband, ie 29.425MHz. Fig 7 should make this relationship clear. Again, due to the cumulative effects of Doppler shift on both 145 and 29MHz, you should tune up 4–5kHz away from the calculated frequency, higher in frequency if the satellite is approaching you or lower if it is receding from you. It is then permissible to 'swish' the VFO for fine adjustment of frequency, but better to swing the receiver tuning. (Now read this again!)

   It is also suggested that newcomers to the satellite scene spend at least a few sessions of shack time in listening mode only. This time will be well spent, and will help you to get a feel for the band. More importantly, you will not be known as a 'lid' to fellow enthusiasts who will be pleased to help you if you ask. Most satellite radio amateurs have had to learn the new techniques and are ready to help you get the most out of this hobby.

7. If you put out a CQ call, monitoring your own signal on 29MHz, be prepared for someone breaking in; that is the beauty of satellite working – it is the ultimate 'break-in' system of operation. Some CW stations are crystal controlled so you should tune around in case anyone is answering on other than your own frequency. Once contact is established a QSO would proceed in the usual way but, as the maximum 'visible' time of the satellite is between 15 and 35 minutes, most contacts are 'contest-style'. Maximum visibility occurs on overhead passes.

CODE OF PRACTICE FOR SATELLITE OPERATION

Naturally the same ethics of amateur conduct and behaviour apply as they do to normal terrestrial communication on both the HF and VHF bands but, because each satellite is a DX 'band' with limited and power-sharing openings, certain additional points should be observed.

DO NOT turn on your carrier, whistle, send CW or otherwise until you can hear the satellite beacon. If you have a poor downlink receiver and a good uplink, as most European users seem to have, the chances are that someone else's DX contact will be ruined by your signal.

DO NOT run more than the recommended EIRP at any time (if you don't know what 'EIRP' and other buzz words mean why not try and find out?), or you will ruin contacts for those who are 'playing the game', and give them grounds for the same irresponsible behaviour. Calculate your EIRP, don't guess it.

DO NOT call stations in your own area when the satellite is near the horizon – they have but a few seconds a day to work DX stations but most of any orbit to work you.

DO NOT call Satgate incessantly. The old-time operators' 3 times 3 de K is really the way to call CQ these days as well on a satellite. Short bursts are enough, then listen, otherwise you are just depressing the satellite's AGC and using its battery power unnecessarily. Many of the rarer stations are crystal controlled so it is necessary to listen for them.

DO pay maximum attention to your receiving system – when it is good enough you will hear returns from even 100mW uplink power, and hence work much more DX for less power. Attention to higher gain, lower angle and less noise on your downlink reception is cheaper and far more productive than anything else you can do.

DO use the outer limits of the passband, thus avoiding the overcrowded centre, and encouraging others to spread out and avoid mutual interference.

DO listen to Codestore bulletins (on the beacon frequency). Use or at least listen to the AMSAT nets, and benefit by applying the updated operational information heard.

DO let people know if you are crystal controlled so that they move off your frequency after the contact.

DO try to have proper amateur contacts via amateur satellites, rather than merely exchanging a few numbers contest-style. Try spreading the word about new stations, schedules or other satellite-interest information.

DO pay attention to special service channels and avoid transmitting on these. They may be required at that time to control the spacecraft for your better enjoyment.

DO NOT work stations obviously using more power than required for a reasonable signal. These stations are stopping the enjoyment of all other users of the satellite and they degrade the transponder efficiency. If they are louder in your receiver than the beacon (telemetry) they are in excess of design parameters for the transponder. This is a fact, not a myth, and can be easily proven by you the listener.

Do persuade all stations to reduce power to the minimum for a satisfactory QSO.

8. If you generate the required ERP by a low-power transmitter feeding a high-gain beam, do not forget in your initial enthusiasm to turn the antenna from time to time. Accurate time-keeping is necessary to have the antenna pointing in the right direction at the right time. A convenient approach is to turn the array in increments equal to the half-power beamwidth, say 45° for an eight-element Yagi, although you may find in times of good tropospheric and ionisation propagation that the 'true' path is not necessarily the best.

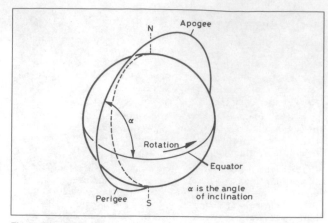

Fig 8. Elliptical orbit viewed from space

9. After you have made contacts, if you wish to send a QSL card, mark the card with "145/29MHz via RS12 orbit No xxx etc" in the frequency space on the card.

PHASE 3 SATELLITES
Oscar 10 (P3B)
Launched in June 1983, it was the first Phase 3 satellite be placed in orbit (an earlier attempt was made in 1980 but the launch vehicle malfunctioned). Unlike the Phase 2 satellites, it is in a highly elliptical orbit with a much longer period, allowing worldwide VHF/UHF communication for hours at a time (Fig 8).

Oscar 10 contains two transponders, the U transponder (Mode B) (input 435MHz, output 144MHz) and the L transponder (Mode L) (input 1269MHz, output 436MHz). Currently, it is still in operation on Mode B only. It also has two beacons, the engineering and general beacons, active on both transponders. The general beacon transmits CW and 400 baud PSK – a special decoder is required for the latter mode, and a circuit and PCB is available from G3RUH.

Ground-station requirements
All ground-station antennas should have right-hand circular polarisation (linear polarisation will result in signal flutter and loss of at least 3dBi). The recommended receive antenna gains are 13.5dBi for the L transponder (3dB receiver noise figure), while the corresponding transmit antenna EIRP is 28.8dBW.

Normal SSB receivers having the above noise figures will be suitable – accurate frequency readout is a distinct advantage.

For the U transponder (Mode B), ordinary SSB transmitters should prove satisfactory, as will a 28 to 5MHz transverter. A power amplifier is unlikely to be required, with the high antenna gains possible today, unless feeder losses are significant.

As an example, a typical station using SSB through the U transponder (Mode B) could consist of the following:

- 435MHz 'black box' transceiver, providing 20W PEP SSB.
- 10-element crossed Yagi, for 435MHz, right-hand circular polarised.
- 145MHz converter, feeding 28–30MHz HF receiver.
- Six-element crossed Yagi, right-hand circular polarised for 146MHz.
- Manual az/el adjustment. A Trackbox or Kansas City Tracker [2] can of course be used for automatic tracking

The Phase 3C satellite being packed for transit to the launch site

with a computer interface. You will also need an orbital calendar.

This station should have no difficulty hearing itself for 75% of the satellite's visible time. CW and SSB communication should present few problems provided that both transmitter and receiver are accurately calibrated. The limiting factor is the requirement to aim the antennas at the satellite, and the absence of high-power antennas on the uplink.

Oscar 13 (P3C)
Oscar 13 was launched in June 1983 from Kaurou (Devil's Island) by ESA. The operating information contained in the Oscar 10 section above is similar to that required for this satellite. The basics are the same, and the 'Code of practice' given earlier should certainly be used in the same context. The bands currently in use are as per the *AMSAT-UK Satellite Frequency Guide* (Fig 1).

Tracking
Because Oscars 10 and 13 are in an elliptical orbit, tracking is a little difficult, and much benefits from automated assistance. However, at apogee the satellites have a very slow motion relative to the ground, and these satellites will appear to hang in the sky at the same position for hours on end, preceded and followed by a much faster motion. Tracking methods available are:

1. The very easy way. Listen to the AMSAT nets which will probably provide local AOS and LOS (acquisition and loss of signal) predictions. If you are very lucky they will also provide antenna aiming (azimuth and elevation) information. (AMSAT-UK will always provide this information.)
2. A more reasonable way. Use the orbital calendar that is produced by AMSAT-UK. This is a bi-monthly calendar, available at low cost to members.)
3. Use an elliptical tracking computer program, and AMSAT-provided Keplerian orbital elements. Keplerian orbital elements are published in *Oscar News*, *Orbit*, *ASR* etc, and on the UK packet network by AMSAT-UK (G3RWL).

Transmitting through the satellite

A variety of communication modes can be used – CW, SSB (LSB, received by ground stations as USB), and DPSK/PSK (data). FM and AM telephony, RTTY, SSTV and other high-duty cycle modes of transmission are should *not* be used. The frequency chart above gives full details of up/down frequencies.

The receiver and transmitter should be left on continuously (full duplex). The transmitter power and bandwidth should not be greater than necessary to achieve reliable communication – no SSB telephony transponded through the satellite should return a peak strength stronger than that of the general beacon (transponded CW signals should be less than 9dB below that of the general beacon).

The Doppler shift experienced by ground stations varies according to the frequency in use, the position of the satellite in its orbit, and the position of the ground station. Maximum figures for stations located at latitude 50°N are ±2kHz (145MHz), ±6kHz (435MHz). As well as Doppler shift, there is a small time delay due to the distance involved – the round trip can take up to 250ms at apogee, and the receiver audio should then be turned down while transmitting to avoid 'echo'.

In general, operating through the satellite is similar to using Phase 2 satellites and the reader is referred to advice given earlier under 'Code of practice for satellite operation'. Further information and technical data is also available from AMSAT-UK [7] (stamped, addressed envelope or three IRCs, please).

MIR

One exciting possibility is that of communication with a manned spacecraft. This is because the Russian cosmonauts on Mir have been encouraged to make use of amateur radio in their off-duty periods. The equipment carried on board currently is a 2m FM transceiver and a packet TNC. The packet equipment is usually left on in beacon/PMS mode, allowing 'connects' with amateur radio operators on the ground. Messages may be left for the cosmonauts and any replies or bulletins read. Packet format is AX.25 1200bps AFSK.

When time and workload allow, the cosmonauts may use 2m FM phone and call CQ. Voice contacts are often by pre-arrangement; it is discourteous and pointless to interrupt. Casual calls to the spacecraft are useless – wait for a prompt.

The operating frequency for both packet and phone is 145.550MHz. Accurate antenna tracking is imperative. The spacecraft receiver is 'bombarded' by many stations at the same time, resulting in only 'noise' being received. Stations using highly directional antennas and accurate tracking have more chance of penetrating the 'noise' and making contact.

Callsigns are in the UxMIR series, recently RxMIR, and change with fresh crew. PMS access is via one of the on-board calls with '-1'.

Remember that the cosmonauts tend to work on Moscow time, say 0500–2000 UTC.

Mir's orbit is at 350–400km altitude with a period of 92 minutes. The ground track covers the whole of the Earth's surface between latitude 51.6°N and S with a footprint radius of a little over 2000km. There are at least 15 orbits a day of which five to seven successively pass in range of a given location, two or three being at reasonable elveations. The passes are from west to east with rapid transit and maximum duration of 11 minutes, of which only the central part is useful for contacts. Accessible UK contacts arise from equatorial crossings (EQX)

At the time of going to press, the Phase 3D satellite is undergoing construction. Here Dick Jansson, WD4FAB, applies epoxy resin to the edge of one of Phase 3D's flight model solar panels in the P3D lab at Weber State University, Ogden, Utah (AMSAT-NA photo by Keith Baker, KB1SF)

between 25 and 150°W. EQX of about 80° gives acquisition near 260°W, maximum elevation (central UK) 80°, loss at 90°E.

FUNDING THE SATELLITE PROGRAMME

Membership of AMSAT-UK is open to anyone, including SWLs; there is a minimum donation and extra donations are always welcomed. Members receive *Oscar News* approximately six times per year which keeps them in touch concerning past achievements, present activities and future plans.

AMSAT-UK also runs several nets (which are open to non-members) where news is disseminated and questions can be asked. The most regular of these is on 3780kHz (± QRM) every Sunday morning at 1015 UK local time (G0AUK). Other, more local, nets take place from time to time; usually weekly and mostly on 144.28MHz. There is also a half-hour information net on 3780kHz on Monday and Wednesday evenings at 7pm. Sunday and Thursday nets are run on 144.280 at 7pm clock time.

AMSAT-USA also runs nets on Sunday evenings on 14.282 and 21.280MHz (usually at 1800 and 1900 GMT respectively). These nets, from the USA, are more of a worldwide news service than a place for questions but there is, occasionally, time for these. Further details of AMSAT-UK activities can be obtained from [2] for the courtesy of a self addressed and stamped envelope (9in × 6in) or three IRCs.

THE FUTURE

Now preparing for launch in mid-May 1996 is the heaviest (at half a tonne), the most complicated, and the most sophisticated satellite ever built by radio amateurs. Built jointly by teams in Germany and USA by AMSAT International, and with equipment designed and built by groups across the world including AMSAT-UK, this satellite should satisfy every kind of mode of amateur operation for a long time. Expected life span is 15 years at least.

You are invited to send a small donation to assist in the launch, and more importantly to assist in the upkeep of the command stations once the satellite is finally in orbit and operational. Donations should be sent to [2] below.

Full details of P3D operations are beyond the scope of this chapter, if only because the satellite is not in orbit at this date. Full information will be the subject of technical books from AMSAT groups after lift-off. An eight-page technical paper is available now for a small donation to AMSAT-UK funds.

FURTHER INFORMATION

[1] AMSAT, PO Box 27, Washington DC 20044, USA.

[2] AMSAT-UK (R J C Broadbent, MBE, G3AAJ), London, E12 5EQ, England.

[3] AMSAT-UK – a series of A4 technical, PVC-laminated, information sheets.

[4] *The New Guide to Amateur Satellites*, AMSAT-UK.

[5] *VHF/UHF Manual*, G R Jessop, G6JP, 4th edn, RSGB, 1983.

[6] *Space Radio Handbook*, J Branegan, GM4IHJ, RSGB, 1991.

[7] *AMSAT-UK Oscar 10 & 13 Handbook*, AMSAT-UK. (Now out of print).

[8] *AMSAT-UK Satellite Frequency Guide* showing all current satellites. PVC laminated on A4 card.

8 Data communications

DATA communication is one of the fastest growing operating modes in amateur radio. No longer confined to sending simple text messages, amateurs are hooking into worldwide DX information networks using complex software and hardware. Most data communications take place on VHF and UHF using packet radio but, in spite of slower data rates, HF digital communications are also popular and have led to some sophisticated new modes being developed to cope with typical HF band conditions.

The present chapter reflects this emphasis, with an outline of the various HF modes followed by a more detailed discussion of how to get going on VHF packet radio and use its network facilities. The sections on message writing and operating guidelines which complete the chapter are of course broadly relevant whichever mode is in use.

HF DATA COMMUNICATIONS

From mechanical teleprinters to sophisticated microprocessor-based error-correcting systems; from simple two-tone FSK to complex modulation systems like QPSK; from nothing more than printed paper output to a Pentium computer as user interface with on-line databases and every conceivable extra; the world of amateur radio HF data communications has seen great changes over the years. What is more, these changes seem to be occuring at an accelerating rate.

It can be hard enough for the seasoned data enthusiast to keep abreast of the latest modes – how much more confusing it is for a newcomer, trying to decide what mode might be suitable for him or her?

RTTY

Perhaps fortunately for the newcomer, interest and activity in the most basic digital mode, RTTY, is as high as ever. Many DXpeditions nowadays include operation in digital modes, and in most RTTY will be represented. BARTG's monthly news broadcast regularly bristles with reports of exotic callsigns heard in the RTTY band segments.

RTTY can be found on most of the HF bands, especially during contests which are well supported. On 20m, look around 14,080–14,095kHz. RTTY signals are characterised by a continuous warbling sound, as alternate high and low tones are sent, representing one and nought data bits (*mark* and *space*). Part of RTTY's appeal is its essential simplicity, and hence the simplicity of the equipment needed. Originally, RTTY was operated using mechanical teleprinters. These are rarely encountered nowadays as the mode usually involves a personal computer and multi-mode data controller – a 'black box' encompassing a microprocessor and a modem.

Many home computers have been programmed for RTTY, such as the Sinclair Spectrum and the Commodore 64, and these are usually used with a 'dumb' modem whose task is to

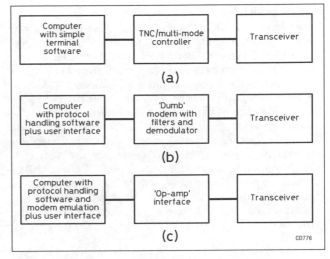

Fig 1. Equipment needed for HF digital modes

convert the mark and space tones to voltage levels suitable for the computer to read. The computer's task is to assemble the incoming bits into Baudot characters, and convert these to ASCII for the video display. Today the PC is becoming a standard accessory in the amateur's shack. These can similarly be programmed for RTTY, and numerous shareware or more commercial programs are available. Associated interfaces can range from nothing more than a simple op-amp circuit to provide the PC with square-wave audio, to state-of-the-art DSP (digital signal processing) based modems with unrivalled performance and flexibility.

One benefit of this general approach is the scope for experimentation and DIY. If you are interested in doing some home construction and tinkering with op-amp or DSP filter design, then a modem that can be used with RTTY and perhaps Amtor and Pactor software on a PC is an ideal project. If you are interested in trying your hand at some real-time programming, then an RTTY program on a PC is an ideal place to start.

The popular alternative is to use a multi-mode TNC such as a PK232 from AEA or the KAM from Kantronics to handle all the RTTY and other protocols, leaving the PC simply to act as a user interface. On its own, this can be seen as a waste of the power of a PC, but when the PC is simultaneously used for other tasks such as logging with database facilities, this approach can make a lot of sense. RTTY has a limited character set, so messages are generally restricted to just text and numbers. It is ideal for live keyboard chat QSOs, with a data rate of about six characters per second – quite adequate for most people's typing.

These options are summarised in Fig 1. Sometimes option (c) is extended to include a stand-alone DSP filter between op-amp and transceiver – a strange mixture of technologies!

A typical multimode data controller (AEA DSP-2232) which uses DSP technology

General principles

All the popular HF digital modes use a simple two-tone modulation system. One tone represents a certain signal state (perhaps a 'one' bit in computer talk) and a different tone represents an alternate state (eg a zero bit). Precisely what a particular tone represents depends on the particular digital mode in use. Because signals are to be received via an HF SSB radio, the absolute pitch of the *transmitted* tone is not important – what is important is the separation (shift) between the tones. The signals must be accurately tuned in at the receiving station, to arrive at tones which match the modem used for reception. Originally the standard shift used for RTTY was 170Hz, but increasingly 200Hz shift is used for RTTY and the newer digital modes. In practice, the difference between these two shifts is not important and they are not incompatible. (Wider shifts such as 425, 850 and 1000Hz are used by commercial stations).

For all digital modes, a stable receiver is needed. Receive filters narrower than those used for speech are to be preferred. A rough guide to the required bandwidth is:

$$\text{Bandwidth} = \text{Frequency shift} + (2 \times \text{Baud rate})$$

For 100 baud, this computes to 400Hz, and a 500Hz filter will be a good choice for the popular HF digital modes.

Tuning to within 50Hz is required, so a slow tuning rate such as 1kHz per revolution of the tuning knob is helpful, together with fine resolution on the dial read-out.

In Europe, modems are normally designed to receive tones centred on 1360Hz ('low tones'), using USB – the higher-pitched tone in RTTY is referred to as the *mark* tone, and the lower tone is *space*. In the USA, 'high tones' are used, centred on 2210Hz and the standard is to use LSB. The higher tone is then *space* and vice versa. As the shift between the tones in either case is the same, there is no problem of compatibility between USA and European standards. The operator at each end tunes his receiver so that the tones heard match those expected by his modem (as indicated by a tuning indicator on the modem such as a LED bar-graph, or best of all an oscilloscope display). The difference in tone standard *is* apparent when deciding what radio frequency the signal is occupying. By convention, the *mark* frequency is quoted. Modern transceivers such as the TS850 can be programmed so that in the FSK position the receiver's filters accommodate either low or high tones as required by the modem, and the dial then gives a direct read-out of the mark frequency. Where a transceiver is not equipped with an FSK option, then either USB or LSB is used, and there will be an offset between the true mark frequency and the dial reading. This offset needs to be understood and known if accurate netting to a mailbox is to be achieved. For European low tones with a 200Hz shift, USB is used and the dial reading will be approximately 1.46kHz lower than the true mark frequency (see Fig 2).

Fig 2. Relationship of transceiver dial readings to mark carrier frequency for USB and FSK operation

Transmission can be by means of FSK or AFSK. In the former, a DC signal from the modem is fed to an FSK input on the transceiver and directly switches the transmit carrier frequency. The transceiver is operated with the mode switch in a position marked 'FSK', which may well allow a narrower receiver filter to be selected, such as 500Hz.

For AFSK (audio frequency shift keying) transmission, the modem creates the high and low audio tones which are fed to the transceiver's MIC input. For a well-modulated transmitter, a listening station would not be able to tell if the signals were being produced by FSK or AFSK. It is essential that the microphone gain is adjusted to avoid over-modulation and, for continuous modes like RTTY, power should be restricted to half the transmitter rating to avoid overheating.

Handshaking modes

The basic problem with RTTY is the lack of any automatic feedback from the receiving station to the sender. Part way through a transmission, the sender would be quite oblivious to the occurence of severe fading or interference and consequent loss of text by the intended recipient. The next 'over' may well consist of a request for a repeat of all the vital information, and this request and the subsequent retransmission may be repeated several times in case of similar problems.

All the newer HF digital modes such as Amtor, Pactor and G-TOR tackle this problem by a hand-shaking (*ARQ* – automatic repeat request) arrangement between the two parties in the QSO. During any 'over' one party is referred to as the *information sending station* (ISS) and the other the *information receiving station* (IRS). The data to be sent is broken down into small individual packets, and transmission of one data packet by the ISS is followed by the automatic transmission of a short control packet by the IRS to inform the ISS the last packet was received OK, or to ask for a repeat transmission or a link turn-around.

Listening to any of these ARQ modes quickly demonstrates the chirpy nature of the transmissions. In Amtor, chirps occur at just over two per second. The Pactor cycle can be 1.25 or 1.4 seconds, and G-TOR uses 2.4 seconds.

In ARQ QSO operation, the first stage is to establish a link with your correspondent. This is done by invoking a special calling sequence that identifies just the one station you want to contact. Once his reply chirps are heard and synchronised to, the two stations stay locked in close co-operation, chirping and listening, throughout the QSO.

Although the mechanisms need to be understood, the whole process is automatically controlled by the software in the computer or TNC. The operator can just concentrate on the information being passed, confident of the accuracy of transfer. An indication such as 'REQ' on the computer screen or 'TNC' show when your partner is struggling to hear you, or when he is receiving you without difficulty. It is possible, and interesting, to reduce your power output to the minimum level that will sustain throughput. In practice, such an action does tend to mean the QSO will get stamped on by a third party who has not heard you, nevertheless this author has sustained solid contacts into Chile on 21MHz, using 10W of Amtor to a dipole antenna.

Of course, all these modes need a non-ARQ variation for broadcast purposes, such as sending a CQ call. In Pactor, packets with an identical structure to those used in the linked mode are simply sent as a continuous stream with no inter-packet gap. Each packet is repeated once or twice to improve the chance of valid reception. Amtor has a special *FEC* (forward error correction) broadcast mode which is very effective, and has also been borrowed by G-TOR. The stream of data is duplicated, with the repeat stream interleaved with the primary stream. Each character is self-checking, so the receiver assembles the desired text by picking valid characters out of either stream as available.

Amtor, Pactor and G-TOR do *not* take kindly to more than one pair of stations on a given HF channel. Do not assume that multiple occupancy will work – that belongs to VHF packet operation.

Amtor

Amtor has a data throughput rate similar to RTTY, at about six characters per second. So again it is ideal for live keyboard chats. Recent enhancements have extended the available character set to include lower-case text and more punctuation and symbols, and the effectiveness of the ARQ system has led to Amtor's use by many HF mailbox stations, many of which interchange data with local VHF packet radio networks.

Partly due to the mailboxes, which need to operate on well-defined frequencies, there is a tendency for ARQ modes to be used on 1kHz channels on the HF bands. Remember that by convention the mark frequency is quoted, and make any mental correction to the dial reading as appropriate to your equipment. On 40m, mailboxes operate on 7038kHz and above, and live QSOs occur below 7038kHz. Such an understanding would be of great benefit on other HF bands. In Amtor, full callsigns are *not* used during the QSO set-up phase. You need to call the *selcal* of the station you want to contact. This is a four-letter sequence, usually the first and last three characters of his callsign. In order to be able to accept incoming connects, you must ensure your software or TNC has been initialised with your own selcal. Once a link is established you need to identify yourself manually by sending your full callsign. This is *not* automatic in Amtor.

In Amtor, as in RTTY, choice of sideband is significant. You need to learn if your combination of equipment needs you to select a signal inversion option on either reception or transmission, and always remember to use the setting that works in each operating session. (Often this is simplified by control files on the computer which you can configure once and forget.)

Pactor

Pactor was designed specifically as an HF mode for faster throughput than Amtor, with a full 8-bit character set, and also with more reliable error detection. It features built-in data compression which activates automatically when advantageous, and dynamic speed changes between 100 and 200 baud depending on conditions.

With a maximum throughput of about 25cps, Pactor is more suited to mailbox operation, but can equally well be used for live keyboard chats. Some stations like to make use of the extended character set available to send ANSI encoded colour text and graphic block pictures, which can liven up a QSO.

Choice of sideband is not significant in Pactor – the listening equipment automatically detects which way up the signal is. As full callsigns of both stations are *automatically* exchanged during link set-up, there is no need to manually identify yourself once a link is underway.

Pactor is not well suited to homebrew software writing (except of course simple TNC driver software) as the protocol details have been kept largely secret by the originators, an unfortunate trend arising from increased commercialism and the competition between manufacturers.

An example of screen information during a Pactor contact using BMK-MULTY software is shown in Fig 3 on the next page.

G-TOR

G-TOR is a predominantly single-sourced mode, originating from Kantronics and available in the KAM controller. It features faster throughput than Pactor under good conditions. The letter 'G' refers to Golay forward error correction, which provides sufficient redundancy in the transmitted data to enable correction of simple errors without re-transmission. G-TOR can use speeds of 100, 200 and 300 baud.

Should other main players in the market decide to implement the mode, then there could be a big increase in G-TOR activity, as the mode can use the same sorts of modems currently used for Amtor and Pactor.

HF packet

As 300 baud packet radio *is* used on HF, we had better give it a mention. Many HF enthusiasts would prefer packet not to be used on HF, feeling it is inherently too inefficient. Certainly, there is much scope for improvement in the AX25 protocol, but most of the difficulties probably stem from the belief that packet on HF can operate as on VHF – ie with many stations active on one channel. With data and acknowledgments taking four times longer to communicate than on VHF, trying to interleave more than, say, two QSOs on one channel rapidly leads to the situation where only the short poll or ACK frames get through and data transfer is exceedingly slow. Where a powerful mailbox station can dominate an HF channel, then there is no doubt that useful amounts of data can be passed via packet on HF – but there are better ways of achieving that end.

Clover and Pactor II

These modes show the way forward for serious HF data enthusiasts, and should be seriously considered by the leading international mailboxes and BBS forwarding stations. Now the simple two-tone mark and space modulation is abandoned, and modern DSP techniques are used to provide a choice of more complex modulation schemes to make efficient use of narrow HF channels.

As the modulation is no longer just a choice of one tone or the other, FSK cannot be used. On many transceivers this means that wider USB or LSB speech filters have to be used, which might be a disadvantage. However, good DSP-based modems should more than compensate.

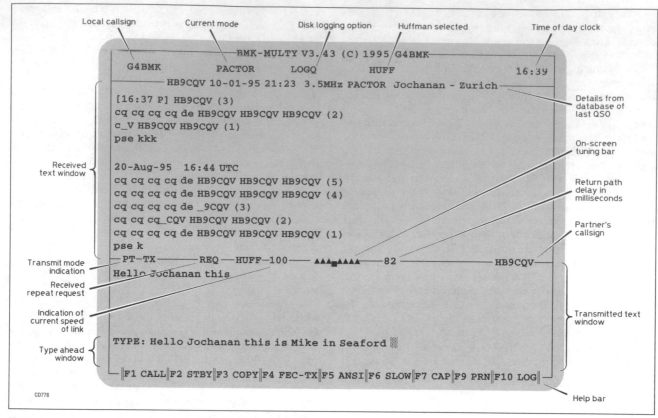

Fig 3. A sample computer screen from BMK-MULTY software showing the sort of on-screen indications which are helpful to a Pactor operator

In Clover, interestingly, the 'element rate' is actually reduced to 31.25 per second (compared to G-TOR's 100, 200 or 300). This is done to improve performance under all-to-common multi-path propagation conditions. 2 to 4ms of smearing by multi-path will destroy a 300 baud signal where the element length is 3.3ms. By adding different 'levels' of phase shift and amplitude modulation, much more information can be communicated in one signalling element. Clover claims an effective speed of two to 10 times that of simple two-tone modes. In addition, a link is bi-directional, so there is no need for an 'over' command.

Pactor II claims a maximum throughput of 1200 bits per second when the effect of the built-in Huffman data compression is included. Clover and Pactor II claim to have very narrow frequency spectra due to the use of DSP and clever modulation.

Currently, prices on these advanced modes are very significantly higher than for any of the two-tone ARQ modes, but we can expect prices to come down to more generally acceptable levels as DSP hardware continues to tumble in price, and basic algorithms become more widely understood and available, losing some of the current mystique.

Table 1. Summary of two-tone modes

Mode	Baud rate	Max CPS	Error	Character set
RTTY	45	6	None	Very limited
Amtor	100	6.5	Good	Limited
Pactor	100/200	25	Excellent	Full 8-bit
G-TOR	100–300	30*	Excellent	Full 8-bit
Packet	300	30	Excellent	Full 8-bit

* Ignoring possible run-length encoding

A summary of the basic parameters of all the two-tone modes is shown in Table 1.

Have a go
So why not give HF digital modes a try! There's always something interesting happening – be it a contest or a new prefix to work or a new mode to try. If you have a computer, it's a logical next step to just QSO logging. When you do decide to have a go, do spend adequate time at first just listening and monitoring QSOs to learn operating techniques and common practices. Digi-fans are a generally friendly bunch, and you won't go short of help and advice should you need it.

VHF PACKET RADIO
Most VHF data communications are carried out using packet radio. Like RTTY, packet radio is a means of sending messages from somewhere to elsewhere in the form of text data. However, it includes a number of important advantages, such as error correction and the ability of one frequency to handle more than one contact at one time. There are also advantages in the type of information which may be transmitted, which includes pictures, programs and text messages. Messages, like the e-mail seen on commercial systems, can be posted to or taken from a local packet bulletin board in the same manner as one can on a telephone BBS. The network of stations currently in use also provides other facilities such as conference and DX information nets.

In cases where the distance between stations is too high for normal point-to-point working, a network of stations, called *nodes*, exists for the purposes of relaying these messages to their destination. In this respect, they are akin to the FM repeaters used by mobile operators to extend the range of operation.

How it works

Packet radio has an affinity with RTTY, in that the messages are transmitted and received by the normal amateur radio station equipment and, as with other digital modes mentioned earlier, the signal comprises two tones, each representing mark or space. For most purposes, FM is used on VHF and UHF, while SSB may be used on HF. The data to be transmitted is assembled into *packets* which one can think of as being similar to a letter in the post. The message, or part of it, is transmitted together with address information. In this way it might be said to resemble the envelope of the letter.

The typical station

A typical installation for operating VHF/UHF packet radio comprises a number of parts:

1. A VHF/UHF FM radio.
2. A terminal node controller (TNC) which converts the computer data into a suitable form for transmission.
3. Either (a) a computer of some sort – maybe even the shack PC, together with some suitable software – or (b) a computer terminal unit (VDU).
4. A suitable power supply (usually 12V DC) for the TNC.

The radio

The choice of radio may require a little thought. Several makers of amateur equipment now incorporate a connector for data communications. Furthermore, various suppliers are able to supply ready-made cables for many of the amateur radios on the market.

However, most amateurs use a standard mobile radio or even a hand-held, but use of your favourite radio can tie up what amounts to a considerable investment. Many operators, particularly those who leave their packet stations on for long periods of time, have purchased surplus (ex-PMR) equipment. These radios represent a sound investment.

One thing *is* important: deviation. Most amateur FM radios are set to too wide a deviation. Many nodes and BBSs are run with ex-PMR equipment which often features narrow filters for the commercial standard 12.5kHz channel separation, and 5kHz and more deviation is simply too much. Reliable communication, particularly at 1200 baud, is satisfactory with a lower deviation than one might use on voice. So, when you set up the radio, set the packet deviation to about 3kHz on the high tone, and *no more*.

It is not usually necessary to have a couple of hundred watts into a whacking great beam antenna – useful though that is. This is because there are many stations out there and a lot of nodes which will act as a means of relaying your signals onwards to the final destination. These days, even satellites can be accessed on the power of a hand-held radio and a very modest antenna.

The TNC

The device which converts data from the computer (or terminal/VDU), is called a *terminal node controller* (TNC). This assembles the packets which are transmitted to the other station and converts the received packets for the computer.

The basic standard type of TNC is called the *TNC-2*, or *TNC-2 clone*, and sends signals at 1200 baud. Many TNC makers use this as the basis of their own design, including the built-in software. Some TNCs incorporate methods of generating the

An example of a basic TNC-2 clone: the Tiny 2

300 baud signals required for HF operation. Which TNC you choose will depend a lot upon what you want to do and whether there is one for sale on the club notice board or the selling skills of your local shop.

There are different types of TNC, some of which are dedicated to some facet of packet radio. For example, there are:

- TNCs which also handle other modes of transmission.
- TNCs which have twin radio ports, (HF/VHF operation, for example, or 1200/9600 baud speeds)
- TNC on a plug-in card fitted inside the PC. Some are dual powered, so the TNC is active even if the PC is switched off.

Actually, a TNC can be dispensed with altogether – a low-cost system called *BayCom* uses a PC to do the conversion work normally handled in the TNC and uses a small hardware unit connected to the serial port to generate and convert the transmitted tones. It is very similar in layout to Fig 1(c).

It might be unwise to use the same PSU that you use for your radio to power the TNC, at least in the long term. It is, however, important to ensure that the earths (frame, ground) are common. Remember that most of the chips used in the TNC and the computer are sensitive to static electricity. If the PSU is variable, set it to about 12.6V.

Terminal or computer?

Some stations use a terminal unit or VDU which has an RS-232, D-type serial communications connector to connect it to the TNC. It is fairly easy to pick up obsolete terminals at reasonable prices on the surplus market or your local rally. The disadvantage of a terminal is often its inability to keep a record or transfer files to or from your local bulletin board system (BBS). However, as a cheap way of getting on air and holding a QSO, it has much to commend it.

A more flexible solution is to use the computer already found in many shacks, although in some cases some form of serial interface card may be required. It really is vital that it is a true RS-232 serial port, although some TNCs can handle TTL-level signals. A PC-type computer is usually fitted with at least one, and usually two, serial ports in addition to a printer port.

Most computers have software available to enable them to emulate a terminal, and many have a complement of advanced facilities such as binary transfer. The more comprehensive the computer and its software, the better your chances of access to the files and software available on many BBSs. For many of us, this means a PC.

The ability to transfer files, whilst not being very important initially, may well be a useful consideration at a later stage. Many bulletin boards make available public domain software for a wide variety of computers, such as the PC, Archimedes/ BBC, Atari or Amiga.

The best advice that can be given is probably to choose a

simple software terminal emulation first; then, when you've a grasp of what's going on in the TNC, you can entertain thoughts of installing something better suited to your requirements.

The basic installation
See Fig 4, which shows a simple diagram of a packet radio installation.

The terminal (or computer) communicates with the TNC at a speed no slower than the TNC sends data for transmission by the radio. Many VHF operators set up the link at a baud rate of 4800 and some at 9600 for a transmitted baud rate of 1200. The manuals for your TNC will often detail both the ideal and minimum requirements for this serial link.

Many older TNCs are equipped with an industry standard 25-pin, D-type connector. Most of the 25 connections, you will be pleased to learn, can be ignored. Exactly what connector is fitted depends upon the type of TNC, as several of the modern ones

Fig 4. Packet radio station

now feature a nine-way D-type connector. Some of the miniature TNCs have non-standard connectors, such as (American) telephone jacks and so matching cables, unless supplied, could prove to be an expensive (if necessary) extra to your budget.

To send data back to other stations and communicate, the TNC needs control of your radio, usually via a three-core *screened* cable of suitable length. It needs to listen to the traffic on the channel (so the volume might need adjustment), send a suitable signal to the microphone input (so the microphone sensitivity may need adjustment) and be able to activate the PTT line. If it is unsuccessful, it will stop automatically – in other words, it will *time out*. Connections at the TNC end are usually a five-pin, 180° DIN plug, or a nine-pin D-type. These days, it is a lot easier to buy the necessary cables than to make them.

Layout
The beauty of packet radio is that many shacks already have a computer. The addition of a TNC is a minor matter, particularly the smaller types. As there is no adjustment of a TNC by any other methods than using the computer, there is no reason for it to be at the forefront of the shack in the manner of the radio or ATU.

Interference
Many computers, including their monitors, can develop a lot of radiated interference. Some computer makers screen their circuit boards and many PC-type computers are in metal cases which naturally cuts down the level of radiation. To minimise noise, screened leads should be used for all connections. Bonding the screen of the microphone connection to the case of the plug will also reduce interference in sensitive audio circuitry. This screen should not be connected to anything at the other end. Naturally, the common (earthy) lead should be connected. If the screen is connected at only at the radio end, made off to the actual case, you should find a marked improvement.

Attention should be given to the actual layout of both cables and main units in the installation. For instance, it would be folly to place the computer too near a sensitive preamplifier. Really difficult cases of radiation may be mitigated by placing the computer in some sort of earthed metal framework, which will act as a Faraday cage, but first check the mains earthing on a PC, most of which have metal cases. It may be possible to screen the interior of a computer, although this is not recommended without a good knowledge of the interior workings or the approval of the maker.

It might be worth buying or making a simple mains filter unit if your local mains is subject to interference. Filter units for mains (usually 3 or 6A rating), can often be purchased at your local rally for a modest sum. This has the advantage of separating the supplies to the radio and computer.

Typical signal levels
Much heartache can be caused by overloading either the TNC (volume turned up too high) or the radio (excessive deviation or distortion). The audio level *into* the TNC should lie in the range 100–600mV. For some reason it works best at the lower end of the range. Signals to the radio from the TNC should be sufficient to give a deviation of about 3kHz on the high tone. This is typically about 8–15mV RMS depending on the impedance presented at the microphone socket and the sensitivity of the microphone amplifier/s. A higher level of signal will be required for those radios having preamplifiers built into the microphone units.

Setting up
In the same way that an ATU should be carefully tuned to get the best from your radio, there are a number of adjustments which should be made to the TNC and the terminal software before going on air, because going on air is the easy part. Most parameters are set from the keyboard.

The TNC
Many TNCs have the settings for both serial and radio rates to be set by switches, although in some it is inside the case.

If you are starting out at VHF or UHF, set the radio rate to

1200 baud; on HF, to 300 baud. As mentioned before, the serial link speed should be at least 1200 baud, although 2400 or even 4800 is not unusual. 9600 is possible but, to a certain degree, it will depend on the speed of the TNC's internal clock.

Setting up the terminal software configuration

You may need to set up your terminal's parameters correctly before switching it all on. If you are using a computer program, check the configuration file. For the time being, set the computer software or terminal to give 1200 baud, 7-bit, even parity, 1 or 2 stop bits, which is what most TNCs default to. Check the manual for any particular default settings. For example, some TNCs default to 8-bit.

If you are able to set the TNC baud rate by the switches, set them up to 1200 baud for now; later you can set it to whatever speed you want the computer to communicate to the TNC. If your TNC has software settings for speed, set the computer up to communicate at that speed.

It is *vital* that both the computer and TNC are OFF when you plug in the serial cable. You might get away with it once, but the ICs inside are highly sensitive to voltage spikes and static, and you don't always know until some time later that you've 'crisped' something.

Plug the serial cable in. Make sure the PSU for the TNC is fully serviceable and switch on the computer. When it's all settled down, load the terminal program. If you are using a terminal or VDU, it should light up with little problem. Check that it is set up as mentioned above.

Switch on the TNC. If you have managed to get both the terminal and the TNC talking properly, you should see the 'sign on' screen followed by the prompt:

        cmd:

Pressing the Enter (Return) key should get you several more. It's a Very Good Sign.

Setting up the radio

At this point you should have your computer or terminal communicating with the TNC. We advise you *not* to try transmitting at this stage; there are several things within the TNC to set up first.

To receive 'normal' 1200 baud transmissions, all you have to do now is switch on and set up the radio to the appropriate frequency. On 2m, 144.650MHz is a good place to start or, on 70cm, 432.650MHz. You should hear the sound of packet radio traffic. Note: 144.625MHz is usually the place for TCP/IP transmissions, so you may hear traffic but not be able to decode it without the appropriate software. Local conditions may also enable you to find additional activity on the 4m, 6m and 23cm bands. Modulation is usually FM for 1200 baud signals.

Adjust the squelch so it is just on, as for normal FM operation. Turn the volume down to near-zero. Connect the TNC to the radio. Slowly adjust the volume control up from quiet and make sure that the DCD light on the TNC turns ON when a packet burst is detected. If your radio has a BUSY light, the DCD and BUSY lights should light up at roughly the same time. Stop when you have reliable flashes corresponding to received packet signal, as there is no point in deafening and de-sensitising the TNC. If it does not, check the cable connections between the TNC and the radio. Your screen should show packets, in the form of part-complete texts, whizzing up like something demented, unless you've found a quiet channel or your monitor command (MON) is set to OFF.

At this point, you might like to watch the traffic (don't send anything yet!), or get a friend to send something out. You can sometimes learn a lot by watching.

You should now be in a condition to make a few necessary adjustments. Don't try them unless you are confident that your serial settings are set correctly and that you have the cmd: prompt displayed. If, however, you are confident that all is well with your hardware and wiring, the next thing is to set up the TNC for your own particular installation by putting in the right commands.

Setting basic parameters

It is a very good idea to spend a while just looking at the traffic on a channel before trying a session yourself. Without a doubt, the one thing which will tell all and sundry that you are a newcomer to packet is to connect up the station and start sending packets willy-nilly.

It will be assumed, for the purposes of this present text, that you are using a PC and a TNC-2 clone. The principles should be the same for other combinations of computer and TNC.

With the exception of those commands using Alt or Ctrl, all commands entered to the TNC are implemented by pressing the Enter key. A TNC operates in what are known as *modes* of operation, each having a particular application to the job in hand. Fortunately, most terminal emulation software (ie packet programs) and the TNC will do the necessary changes automatically. The important one is called *command mode*, which has the prompt 'cmd:' at which you may type in a command to the TNC. The others are:

- Converse, which is the mode used when connected. Both text and commands (for example, to a BBS), entered in this mode will be transmitted.
- Transparent, which is used when moving certain files; and
- KISS, which is used only with particular program software.

To get to command mode enter Ctrl-C, which is often written as '^C'. The '^' indicates the control function of the PC. In case you are not familiar with this, it means:

1. Press and hold the Ctrl key;
2. press the C key;
3. release both.

By the same token, any Alt commands are done the same way, but using the Alt key in place of the Ctrl key. Other computer software may have alternative methods, so if you don't use a PC, look in your manual. Now you can turn to the TNC itself and set it up. The reply will be a sign-on display and a prompt, 'cmd:'.

The TNC possesses some 'intelligence' of its own and does not always require the whole word of command to be typed: You can use a bit of short-hand. For example, 'MYCALL' is the same as 'MY' or even 'my'. They aren't all as simple as this, but you should get the idea. To make life even easier the TNC will say what value the parameter was prior to any changes you may make. Note that *all* commands are executed after the Enter key has been pressed.

For example:

```
cmd:MY G8UYZ <Enter>      [enter my callsign & then
                           press the 'Enter' key]

MYCALL was NOCALL         [this is the old setting,]
cmd:                      [and returns the prompt]
```

Note that CAPITAL letters are not always needed and that many commands can be shortened to a few letters. This is an example of a *direct command* sent to the TNC for immediate execution.

If all you see on the screen is a load of gibberish, you can set up the terminal or the TNC (sometimes *both*), so that they talk in the same manner. Check out your TNC manual and the reference notes; then try a few simple commands. A command badly typed or not understood by the TNC will evoke a reply of "Eh?". You should try again.

It is possible to obtain the current state of a particular parameter by just typing in the command with no change, eg:

```
cmd:MY
MYCALL G8UYZ
cmd:
```

As might be expected, this is what tells the TNC your station's callsign. Typing "MY g9baa" will put the callsign G9BAA into the TNC's memory. Make sure that you put your own callsign in properly.

Parameters put in will stay in until changed or you issue a RESET command. The internal battery will maintain the parameters in the memory for as long as it lasts. Any changes that you do make, however, will affect the way that your TNC operates, so in these early stages you might like to make a note of what each parameter was before the change. That way, if you suddenly think "I wish I hadn't done that", you can change back to the factory settings without resorting to the big reset. Note: RESET is a software command and results in *all* settings being reset to the factory default, loss of whatever messages were stored in the PMS etc.

A few more commands need to be set prior to operating. These are 3rdparty, which you should make sure is OFF (the licensing requirements are different for a BBS) and the CW identification. The UK licence requires you to transmit a CW ident. Consult your TNC manual for full details, but make sure you *do* set it. If you have a TNC with an early-issue ROM which does not have a CWident, you will need to modify it. A new ROM will usually sort it out. Talk to your TNC dealer or local AX.25 user group; it is usually neither difficult nor expensive.

Moving on a bit

As you get more experience and wish to do more than pass simple text messages you will almost certainly find it necessary to make a change to 8-bit. Some of the features and benefits of packet radio are simply not possible without setting your whole installation to 8-bit use. These include file transfer and handling 7-PLUS files. To set your system to 8-bit, set the following TNC parameters:

```
AWLEN 8
PAR 0
RESTART
8bit ON
```

. . . and in that order! If you can manage to do it early on, it will probably save you a fair bit of confusion later. When doing it, it is important to set the TNC up *first*; then do the terminal or software on the computer.

A simple ASCII text file with these settings should be kept for just this problem. Provided that the RESTART command is included, the TNC will respond, and you should have no problem. Don't forget to set the terminal (or program) *after* you've set up the TNC.

If anything goes wrong, make sure that the program is set up and send the text file to the TNC (ASCII Send). Applications for setting it all up for 8-bit include binary transfer and use of 7PLUS files.

If, when turning on the TNC you don't get the 'cmd:' prompt, check your serial cable and settings at both ends. Don't go further forward until you do.

The connections to the radio can be made with fewer problems. The TNC needs an audio feed from the radio and access to the microphone and PTT inputs. A screened lead is of great benefit in helping to control interference. You can buy a suitable cable from your dealer. Consult the TNC and radio manuals if you wish to make your own.

Screen width and packet length

The default setting for *Screenln* is usually 0, which defines that you have a screen 256 characters wide. This can make for a cluttered appearance on the screen which is very difficult to read, bearing in mind that most screens are of 80 columns. Far better to set it to 80, which gives a screen width of 80 characters. Some circumstances may require this to be set to slightly less.

The other command sets up how much data in a packet is sent and it is called *PAClen*, which is set to 128 as a default. To some extent, how you set this is determined by how experienced you are in using a keyboard or the traffic density in your area but if you set it to 77 you will find that you send a packet at the end of every line you type.

Even if you have a machine with a display of 40 characters, you would be advised to use these settings, since those who have a wider screen will find it tricky to read. Note that if you pay no attention to your screen as you type, you may still get words cut in half, but this may be a function of your terminal software. Some have 'word wrap'; if so, set it to ON.

Timing parameters

Getting these wrong can cause havoc to a lot of local users. Experience has shown that these settings are the best values. Set up your TNC to the following:

DWait	0
PPersist	ON
FRack	7
RESPTIME	30
MAXframe	2
SLottime	30
PERSIST	38

Ideally PERSIST should be 25 but some TNC software has a bug which means that any setting of less than 37 will ensure it never transmits.

TXDelay

This timing will be different from station to station. It is the time the TNC waits (in tens of milliseconds) between keying the transmitter and actually starting to send the data. The short delay allows your transmitter to lock up prior to sending the packet data. The default setting is 30.

To find your ideal setting, slowly decrease the setting of TXD, one at a time until you stop connecting reliably. Then add two or three to this figure, and it will be about the best. Note: Don't set TXDelay too low, even if you can connect reliably with most stations. It's possible that other stations may need a comparatively long preamble to open the squelch on their receivers. If you have problems with a TXD setting of less than 25 on a fairly modern radio, your deviation could be too high or you could be off frequency a little.

Appearance on your screen

You can do a lot to make sure that what is printed on your screen is the way you like it. When monitoring packets (with

MON ON), it will be seen that the header, showing the stations involved, is in the same line:

```
G8ZWU > G8UYZ : Hi Dave, how are you today?
```

Setting the HEaderline command to ON will produce:

```
G8ZWU > G8UYZ :
Hi Dave, how are you today?
```

You may wish to include information on which station actually sent the signal. The command is MRpt (Monitor Repeater). With MR set to ON, the greeting message about might look like this:

```
G8ZWU > G8UYZ, G4RVK* :
Hi Dave, how are you today ?
```

The '*' indicates the callsign of the station actually being received.

You can 'date-stamp' your contacts with the date/time, using the MStamp command. Setting it to ON will produce:

```
G8ZWU > G8UYZ, G4RVK* [27-06-94 21:30] :
Hi Dave, how are you today?
```

The date and time may be displayed in two forms, USA or European. This uses the DAYUsa command, which defaults to ON so the date is shown in the American form, mmddyy, eg 06/27/94. Setting it to OFF gives you 27-06-94.

Of course if you'd rather see the month in letters, not numbers, use the AMonth command: AMonth On/Off.

If ON, the month in dates will be shown as Jan, Feb etc. If OFF, they will be 01, 02 etc.

It is possible to set the date and time held in the TNC by hand, although many terminal programs include a method of taking the data from the PC system's internal clock (it's also likely to be more accurate). The command is DA:

```
DA yymmddhhmm    [year, month, day, hour, minute]
                 [2 digits for each]
```

Connecting to another station

C (Connect) is the primary command telling the TNC to go out and find someone:

```
cmd:C G8ZWU
```

The TNC will then send a sequence of packets to the stated station, in this case, G8ZWU. If he is not otherwise engaged his screen will show:

```
** CONNECTED TO G8UYZ **
```

Suppose we are in a rural area, and that the nearest station is G3KQJ. If he leaves his 'digipeater' set to ON, G8UYZ can connect to G8NZU via this digipeater. In this case, the transmitting station will determine the route to be taken:

```
cmd:C G8NZU via G3KQJ
```

This will cause the TNC to transmit a packet to G3KQJ and request the digi to pass on the packet.

The contact can then continue as usual. You can use a digipeater to get into a BBS, but it can take a bit of patience. Although up to eight digipeating stations can be nominated, the network of nodes has made long-distance digipeating unnecessary and even undesirable. A node behaves like a digi, but does it better.

When using a node, the calling station must first connect to the node, then instruct it to connect to the next station:

```
cmd:C GB9PPP
```

Once you are connected, you will then get some form of

acknowledgement that you are connected and a prompt at which you can continue:

```
C G8NZU
```

When the node connects to the distant station, you get confirmation and you can continue the contact as normal. There are several variations to this theme and the complexity and development of the whole network is continually undergoing change, so we will restrict ourselves to the simple things for the moment.

Now might be a good time to arrange with a local packet station to attempt a connect to him/her by way of a little practice.

As the message you send is sent in small bits, sometimes only part of a line of text, it is advisable to use some symbol to indicate that your transmissions are complete and you await the reply. It is pointless to put your callsign in as you do on a local FM net; that information is already transmitted. So use the chevron symbol; it is as good as any: >>.

To conclude a contact, use ^C to gain the command prompt (cmd:) and type the letter "D", "DIS" or even "disconnect"; then press the Enter key. You should shortly see:

```
***DISCONNECTED
```

Note: Some nodes may be dedicated to some function, such as a DX cluster, or may simply include facilities such as 'Chat' or 'Conference' mode. An enquiry on the local BBS or to the system operator (sysop) should get you the information.

The personal mailbox system (PMS)

Several types of TNC are fitted with a system which makes it is possible to leave a message for the recipient in the manner of using a full-sized BBS. It's rather like an automatic telephone-answering machine, but looks a bit like a bulletin board.

The commands for the PMS in the TNC are very similar in operation, if not in name. Many users of these handy gadgets leave them on for long periods, thus ensuring that they can get any messages from, or even sending to, the local BBS.

Setting up your PMS

To set one up takes a little patience, the co-operation of your local sysop, and certain commands set in the TNC. Note that most PMSs have a limited memory in which to store the messages. You should clear them out quickly.

If someone tries to connect as if you were in and paying attention he would call you in the usual way. However, if he wanted to leave a message, there has to be some way of showing that there *is* a difference between your usual callsign and your letter box. This dictates the callsign to be used by callers wishing to leave a message. It is set by using the following command:

MYPcall n

where n is the callsign secondary ident (SSID) in the range of 1–15, and is the callsign used by the HOM BBS to connect to your PMS. In this author's case, it is set to G8UYZ-2. On 70cm, -7 might be more appropriate, but it is a matter of personal taste. *You should NOT set it to be the same as MYCall.* It can cause no end of confusion!

PMS on/off

Default is OFF. If it is OFF, callers will see:

```
*** G8UYZ-2 BUSY
*** DISCONNECTED
```

on their screens. Messages are stored numerically and this is set back to 1 on the issue of a RESET command). If it is set to ON, users will see the PMS sign-on screen.

3rdparty

This should be set OFF, since there are separate licences for operators of bulletin boards. Setting it to ON will allow your TNC to act in the same way as a BBS. As the owner of the MYPcall, you can send any message to anyone, but messages IN may only be left for *you*.

HOMebbs

Type in HOM followed by the callsign of your local BBS.

AUTO

Auto-forward. This marks any message with a callsign in the @ field to be marked for collection/forwarding.

KILONFWD

When ON, messages are deleted after forwarding. If OFF, they aren't. Note: A PMS has about 15kb of storage space, so if you are going to be away from your system for a while, and you expect to do several messages a day, leave it ON (default).

So much for the basic set-up. Given that your sysop has approved and done his bit, you may now have mail collected from your PMS. All you have to do first is put it in! The command to send mail (for collection) is the SEND command:

Send xxxx @ yyyy

where xxxx is the callsign and @ yyyy is the BBS address. Depending on the model or version, you may also be able to use SB or SP in place of Send. The 'Subject' has a maximum length of 20 characters. Text is terminated by either ^Z or /EX on a clear line. If successful, you will see "Message Saved as no. _" displayed.

You would be well advised to use an ASCII text editor to write any messages and then load them into the PMS.

So much for your acting as your own sysop. You'll also need to be able to manipulate the messages sent to you:

List

Lists your messages in order: Number, Month/Day, From, To & Subject. The short-form command entry is L.

Read n

This will display of message number n.

Kill n

This will delete the number n message from the memory. If successfully issued, you will see "Message Erased". Short-form command is KI or sometimes K.

Of course, it helps to know if someone has dared to use your PMS. When a message is on your box, the STA light will flash slowly, which indicates a message waiting. Reading the message/s will reset the flasher, but not necessarily wipe them from the memory.

Note: A change made in 1994 to the UK licensing regulations means that you need permission to run your station 'unattended'. Contact the RSGB or your local Radio Investigation Service (RIS) office for details. It is usually a question of a simple letter (or a form) stating who is available to switch the system off in your absence, and details of your particular set-up, such as frequency, power output etc. If approved, you will receive a confirming letter.

Packet radio and satellites

There are satellites transmitting the normal terrestrial 1200 baud signals which can be worked on very modest equipment. The NASA Shuttle missions also sometimes carry a packet transponder which can be worked with a bit of effort. To access these you will need satellite tracking software in addition to your basic installation. However, you do *not* require lots of power or special antennas; a simple pair of crossed dipoles and modest power is all that's needed, although good results have been obtained by many stations using a simple vertical or Yagi beam. Some satellites act as a 'flying BBS' and relay information about the globe. However, working these satellites is an art in itself and requires more comprehensive equipment. Contact AMSAT-UK for further details (see Chapter 7).

Bulletin boards

Your local bulletin board system is operated by a sysop. It usually comprises a computer and a number of TNCs and radios which enable a station to access on a number of frequencies. Typically these are 144.650 and 432.650MHz, although there are some in the 4m and 23cm bands. Most BBSs operate on 1200 baud, but many forward mail to other BBSs on special RF links running at 9600 baud.

Messages from one person to another in a more distant location are generally passed via a series of BBSs, which behave to the packet operator in the same way as those on the telephone system. There are different ways to send a message from a BBS:

SB – Send Bulletin   A message sent to everyone
SP – Send Private   A message to a person

There are a couple of variations. Suppose you've read a message you can send a reply without typing in the full address:

SR – Send Reply

If you want a friend to see a copy of a message, you can send him a copy:

SC <number> <callsign> [@ address]

This ends a copy of the message of <number> to the owner of the <callsign> at the address given.

Consult your sysop for full details of the facilities available on your local BBS. The 'help' file is usually obtained with a question mark '/?' or '/help'.

There is much that could be said on the contents of the message. It is better that you try and liken your packet messages to a letter written to a friend; polite and pertinent. If you are asking for help, it might be better if you gave as much information as possible. No facts, no help! See later for some tips on message content.

Addressing

In the same way you address an ordinary letter properly, with the postcode and so on, packet messages should be similarly addressed correctly. This is particularly true of mail to foreign parts. This is a typical UK address:

G8UYZ @ GB7MAX.#28.GBR.EU

This shows that G8UYZ has GB7MAX as his normal home BBS, but the rest is a bit more tricky. Reading from the back, the address is broken into parts. 'EU' is the particular part of the world. For example, America is broken into two: 'NA' and 'SA', while Australia is in OC (Oceania). Countries also have a code: 'GBR' is obviously Great Britain, whilst France is 'F'. Countries are broken down in turn to smaller areas, usually indicated by a # symbol. #28 shows that the station is located in region this and county that.

If you send mail to a person, you do not always need to put in anything other than, say, @ GB7MAX. However, if you are send mail outside the UK, you *must* put the whole thing in clearly and properly. For example:

QW1AAA @ WB7ZZZ.#SVA.VA.USA.NA

The CLIVE database

The 'other' interests and expertise of station operators span a great many subjects. The CLIVE database, which is distributed over several UK BBSs, contains a wealth of information which may easily be accessed by a simple request using the REQFIL server which is normally to be found on your local BBS. Contact your local sysop for details of this and other servers.

The DX cluster system

If you are a keen DX enthusiast, the DX cluster node system and the right software is just waiting for your attentions. When you have logged into the DX cluster node, the software keeps you from being disconnected (it's called *timing out*). The screen displays a list of one-line entries sent from those stations also logged on who have heard something of interest:

```
DX de G4BUO:    7005.2 W1KM     Greg. Very early indeed! 1558Z
DX de G3PSM-7: 10101.1 OY2H                              1601Z
DX de G3VMW:    7003.4 9N1KC                             1602Z
DX de G3MCS:   14260.0 VP29EI                            1602Z
DX de G0TOG:   21287.5 KQ4PL    JUST CLEARING ID G4JCZ   1603Z
DX de G0JHC:   50110.0 OM3ID    599 800Hz TX DRIFT!      1603Z
DX de G3VMW:    7003.4 9N1CC    C/S sorry - QRM heavy!   1607Z
DX de G0JHC:   50107.0 OK2PPP   59                       1605Z
DX de G0JHC:   50115.0 OM3ID    ssb                      1607Z
```

As you can see, in a few moments there was much of interest to the DX enthusiast. An enquiry via your local BBS should elicit the details of the local DX cluster node. You should join the local group (it shouldn't cost a lot but the software is commercial), and you'll get a full manual with details of all the commands.

Some operating guidelines for DX cluster operation are given in the panel on this page.

File transfer

Given a good path, text and text files are not the only thing that can be sent between stations using packet. It is possible to send binary files from one to another, given that the computer software and the TNC wiring are appropriate.

As the packet network is an essentially text-based message system, anything other than text distributed on the network needs to be converted into a form which can be sent as if it *is* text. Such utilities are called *ASCII code converters* and examples are 7-PLUS and UUCODE.

You are reminded not to send commercial software or material unrelated to amateur radio. See the panel on the next page for operating guidelines.

Local groups

If nobody in your local club knows anything, watching the screen for your local BBS should give you a good clue as to

DOS AND DON'TS FOR PACKETCLUSTER OPERATION

DON'T use ANNOUNCE/FULL unless the information is 'perishable' (ie time-sensitive and *really* needs to go to *all* users immediately.

DO ask yourself before you do an ANNOUNCE/FULL whether the info wouldn't be better in a message to ALL where a lot more people than those logged on at the time will see it.

DO try to keep ANNOUNCEments and mail to DX related matters. If you want to send out general mail, please use the BBS network.

DO send replies/comments to an ANNOUNCE back to the originator using TALK, *not* ANNOUNCE.

DO try the W6GO QSL database before putting out an ANNOUNCE/FULL to find a QSL manager.

DO update QSLNEW when you find a new QSL manager – then itwould be available to the rest of the folks using the cluster.

DON'T rise to the bait if someone is obviously abusing the cluster facilities.

DO hit Enter or Return after 68 characters or so when you are sending mail on the cluster.

DON'T fill your mail messages with lines of spaces – they all take air time to transmit; the object of the exercise is to convey information, not to make a message look pretty!

DO use your nearest PacketCluster. Don't DX through the node network, as this will probably slow the inter-cluster links down considerably.

DO use L4 connects to your cluster; if it appears in the node list on your local access node, use: C (Cluster callsign).

DON'T try to tailor a route through the network by connecting to intermediate nodes if it isn't necessary.

DO pick a cluster and stay with it – don't flit from one-to-another. Any mail for you will follow from cluster-to-cluster and this congests the network.

DO kill your mail when you've read it – *please!*

DO use the UPLOAD/USERCMD utility to tailor your own configuration, and especially the filters.

DON'T complain about VHF spots if you are an HF DXer, or HF spots if you are a VHF DXer. Use the SET/FILTER command inside a USERCMD file to tailor what you get to your own tastes.

DO if you have any problems, please send your sysop a mail message or ring him up. Please don't use the ANN/FULL facility to ask for advice which might well be in the user manual.

DO enjoy the facilities and if you have any suggestions for us that you think will improve the system, please let us know.

DO consider the effects of your actions on other users of the network; remember there is a rush hour and if possible, avoid heavy usage at that time.

DO SH/CLUS in preference to SH/CON whenever possible. Then, if you see a whole load of clusters connected, you can do a SH/CON GB7xxx for whichever cluster you want, rather than getting the whole lot.

DO send B or Q to disconnect rather than a hard disconnect which leaves the network cluttered with packets that have nowhere to go.

DON'T use ANNOUNCE to let folks know you have received QSL cards; use a message to ALL.

Issued by the UK Cluster Working Group in the interests of better Clustering for all.

RSGB GUIDELINES FOR SENDING 7PLUS FILES

During the RSGB Data Communications Committee meeting held on 6 November 1993, it was decided to issue a set of guidelines for the use of 7PLUS:

1. The files should be relevant to amateur radio.
2. Local tests should be carried out to prove successful sending and dealing with error requests.
3. The total file content should be no longer than 10 parts of 5k each, unless absolutely necessary.
4. All parts should *not* be sent out at the same time, but sent out over a period of a few days. Sysops should consider holding all locally generated mail.
5. An introductory message should be sent containing the details of the file contents.
6. Offer to make files available on disk.
7. It would be better to offer the distribution of files to other countries by post, for example EU and WWW.
8. Be careful not to breach copyright regulations when sending programs by 7PLUS.
9. Try to include '7+' in the subject line as this helps automatic servers; eg Subject: 7+ DCC.Zip P01/2

any local packet groups. Many are connected with a particular BBS, rather in the same way as repeater groups.

Writing packet messages

The tools

The art of writing clear messages is not as easy as you might first think. It is best to write the message as you would write a letter to a friend. If the quality of your writing is not quite up to standard then use a separate ASCII text editor with a spelling checker, if possible, and work it out on that.

The use of a simple ASCII text editor cannot be underlined enough and, although most of us possess one, we infrequently use it. Note that it is important that it *is* an ASCII text editor and not a real word processor, because these often use their own particular brand of storing the 'embedded format codes', which is *not* what we need. It *has* to be a simple ASCII output; even WordStar in 'non-doc' mode can include undesirable characters. Examples for the PC include EDIT (free with MS-DOS 5 and above), ZED, BREEZE and MicroStar. If you do normally use a word processor, make sure it will export the file in proper ASCII format.

Some text editors always make out a full page, filling up the unused lines with blanks, which can leave a whacking great hole in your log file. This has another disadvantage in that those operators with simple terminals may actually miss the message. Set it up so it only takes up the minimum needed to do the job right. Make sure that you use single line spacing. However, don't crush it all up into one big block of text. Use a line between paragraphs (yes, use them as well!).

The use of a text editor has the advantage that you can take your time to get it right, which is particularly important if the subject is controversial. There's nothing more embarrassing than having to issue an apology or correction because you failed to check what you were sending. Then you can upload the message with confidence, knowing that it says exactly what you want and that it can be understood by all.

If you really are going to write an opus, do it in several parts, if you please. With the increase in traffic, anything longer than 5k, particularly if sent to foreign parts, could mean truncation or even loss of a message.

Layout and contents

Let's face it, if you want a coherent reply, it's good practice to send an understandable message the first time out.

Do use capitals and lower case; it can make it easier to read. Excessive use of lower case can look really strange, to say nothing of taking away something of the message. Use upper case for abbreviations, (RSGB, DTI, IBM etc). You really do not need to be an expert typist; most of use one or two fingers of each hand and still manage to type at a respectable speed.

Off-line typing practice is a great teacher. If excessive use of lower case looks odd, the use of capitals and nothing else looks, at best, very impersonal. Such messages appear like a telegram or even a Telex message from head office. Such practice often stems from a familiarity with RTTY and you should practice using all the keys at your disposal. An all-capitals message can even look insulting; do you like being shouted at? Capitals are a good way of emphasising some point you are trying to make, so using only capitals denies you a useful tool to help make your point.

Don't use special characters, even the pound sign. There's been a growth of peculiar boxes (some quite pretty, even clever) which contain all manner of 'sign-off' text. Everything from shadows to blocked-out '73' and so on, to great logos of what the operator uses, his sports, affiliations and even an Internet address, all taking up half a page. Fine if you're proud of it, but not much good in a short text to say "thanks". Such extravagances really are not necessary and can spoil an otherwise good and simple layout. In fact, sometimes they can even look odd, particularly where the graphics characters used, for example, in the box, come out on the screen with a line like

MMMMMMMMMMMMMMMMMMMMMMMMMM

instead of a neat box line. Just leave the sign-off as a simple name, callsign and home BBS, please. You may think it looks a little lonely, even boring, but it's easier to read, especially for those using a simple VDU.

Spelling, grammar and punctuation are also matters which rise in the DEBATE @ GBR from time to time. A dictionary or a spelling checker, and careful use of the apostrophe, can avoid some spectacular howlers worthy of inclusion in the Hall of Fame. Remember the famous advert: "For Sale; cabinet, by lady with large legs". We all know what is meant, but there is often a clearer way of saying it.

A good, simple and clear message is preferable to one which may have a better standard of English, but don't take it to extremes. Take care and do try to spell simple words correctly. For instance, 'amatuer' is a common error, as is 'Epsom' for 'Epson'. A little care and thought can make your message clearer to all readers!

UK readers are reminded to note BR68 clause 1.4.a on the subject of what can and cannot be transmitted, and the RSGB/RA approved guidelines (see panel). And don't think that no one will see; you'd be surprised what *can* be examined.

Etiquette

Don't use the medium of packet radio (or any other mode) to attack a person. If you absolutely *must* air your view about what someone else has said, do it in a direct (SP) message to the station concerned. There are those who do but, to many operators' minds, vociferous SBs just clog up an already busy network with trivialities or inflammation. Don't do it as an SB to all, particularly if you are not quite sure about the details of the subject. Libel can have quite serious consequences, not least for what further restrictions might be imposed on the rest of us.

Don't use the packet network to air your grievances about some trader who cannot reply in the same manner. It's unfair and often rude. If you have a complaint with a supplier of any

RSGB GUIDELINES FOR THE USE OF THE PACKET RADIO NETWORK

The packet radio network in the UK and throughout the world is an immensely useful tool for the dissemination of information, the seeking of help and advice and the publication of amateur radio related news. It is not uncommon to find messages giving information on AMSAT, RAYNET or other similar amateur radio related activities. The GB2RS news is also available on the network, as is local club news in the area of a particular mailbox. This use of the network is what was in many operators' minds when they spent large amounts of time and money in developing it.

With the advent of high-speed modems and dedicated links, some in the microwave bands, the packet radio network is developing, and hopefully will continue to do so for many years to come.

The RSGB Data Communications Committee (DCC), in consultation with the Radiocommunications Agency, has devised the following guidelines with which all operators are urged to comply. These guidelines have been split into five sections in order to reflect:

1. The need for messages to be within the terms of the licence conditions and the implications if they are not.
2. Messages which could result in legal action being taken by other amateurs or outside bodies.
3. Actions to be taken when amateurs identify cases of abuse.
4. Unattended operation.
5. General advice.

Section 1. Types of message
(a) All messages should reflect the purposes of the amateur licence, in particular 'self training in the use of communications by wireless telegraphy'.
(b) Any messages which clearly infringe licence conditions could result in prosecution, or revocation, or variation of a licence. The Secretary of State has the power to vary or revoke licences if an amateur's actions call into question whether he is a fit and proper person to hold an amateur licence.
(c) The Radiocommunications Agency has advised that the Amateur Radio Licence prohibits any form of advertising, whether money is involved or not.
(d) Messages broadcast to ALL are considered acceptable but should only be used when of real value to other radio amateurs, in order to avoid overloading the network.
(e) Do not send anything which could be interpreted as being for the purpose of business or propaganda. This includes messages of, or on behalf of any social, political, religious or commercial organisation. However, our licence specifically allows news of activities of non-profit making organisations formed for the furtherance of amateur radio.
(f) Do not send messages that are deliberately designed to provoke an adverse response. Debate is healthy but can sometimes lead to personal attacks and animosity which have no place on the packet network.
(g) Unfortunately the very success of the network has resulted in messages appearing which are of doubtful legality under the terms of the UK licence. The use of 7+ and other like programs to pass text and binary-based material in compressed form via the network has become commonplace. Users must always be aware of the licence conditions in BR68 (also copyright, and illegal use of software, or software which when decoded and used may contravene the licence) when entering such messages into the network via their local BBS. If in doubt consult your local sysop or your local RSGB DCC representative.

Section 2. Legal consequences
(a) Do not send any message which is libellous, defamatory, racist or abusive.
(b) Do not infringe any copyright or contravene the Data Protection Act.
(c) Do not publish any information which infringes personal or corporate privacy, eg ex-directory telephone numbers or addresses withheld from the call book.

Section 3. Action in cases of abuse
(a) Any cases of abuse noted should be referred in the first instance to the RSGB DCC chairman, care of RSGB HQ.
(b) It is worth noting that any transmissions which are considered grossly offensive, indecent or obscene, or contain threatening language, may contravene the Wireless Telegraphy (Content of Transmission) Regulations 1988 and should be dealt with by the police. This action should also be coordinated by the RSGB DCC initially.
(c) Mailbox sysops have been reminded by the Radiocommunications Agency that they should review messages and that they should not hesitate to delete those that they believe to contravene the terms of the licence or these guidelines. It is worth remembering that their licence is also at risk as well as your own.

Section 4. Unattended operation
As of July 1994 unattended operation of digital communications cannot be carried out without giving seven days' notice in writing of operation to the manager of the local Radio Investigation Service (RIS) – see BR68 para 2 (5). The manager may, before the commencement of operation, prohibit the unattended operation or allow the operation on compliance with the conditions which he may specify.

The RSGB DCC recommends supplying the following information when applying to your local RIS office for permission to operate unattended digital operations:

(i) An external close down switch or other means of closing down the station, which is separate from the rest of the premises.
(ii) A list of four persons, including telephone numbers, who can close down the station. (Not all need to be amateurs.)
(iii) Travelling times and availability times (ie 24 hours) of close down operators of the station.
(iv) Frequencies of operation (within BR68 cluase 2 4(c)), antennas and power used.
(v) Use of station for digital operation (ie PMS, node etc).
(vi) Only the licensee can reactivate the station after permission from the RIS.

Section 5. General advice
(a) With the advance in software writing it is now possible for packet users to set up intelligent software nodes (G8BPQ and similar applications) via a PC and radio. The RSGB DCC strongly recommends that users contact their local packet group and local BBS sysop before starting operation of such nodes. Appearance of such nodes without co-ordination causes problems within the local and inter BBS/DX cluster/TCP/IP network routing tables. Network sysops work closely with each other to determine route qualities and node tables, to aid the fast movement of traffic via the national trunk system. The appearance of unco-ordinated ('rogue') nodes causes in some cases severe problems in traffic routing. Packet users can experiment with software nodes, without affecting the node tables of local network nodes, by setting the software parameters of the node to stop propagation of the node into the network. Advice can be sought on the setting of software parameters from local node sysops or BBS sysops.
(b) Do not send 'open bulletins' to individuals.
(c) Do not write in the heat of the moment. Word process your bulletin first, then re-read it. You may feel differently after a few minutes.
(d) Stop to think before sending GIF images and the like which are sometimes in large multi-part files. Do you really need them, are they amateur radio related, and would they be better sent on disc in the post?
(e) Please try to show some consideration for your local sysop. Remember that you are using in most cases his own equipment, which is in his home. Try to comply with any requests he makes of you.
(f) When accessing your local mailbox at busy times and having problems holding the link, try not to turn your power up just to maintain the link – try later when it is not as busy.
(g) Obey the Golden Rule: "If you would not say it on voice; do not send it on packet".

GLOSSARY OF DATA COMMUNICATIONS TERMS

Address A character or sequence of characters designating the origin or destination of the data being transmitted and, to some extent, routing information. It is also used to denote a particular location in memory in a computer.

Alias An alternative to the callsign of a station. Sometimes, notably with nodes, this may be a mnemonic of the location. With personal stations, this may be the same as the Secondary Station ID (SSID), as set in the MYAlias command in your TNC.

amprnet (AMateur Packet Radio NETwork). The designator for TCP/IP.

ampr.org The high-level 'domain' recognised on Internet for amateur packet radio TCP/IP.

ASCII American Standard Code for Information Interchange. The USA version of the ISO seven-bit data code with 128 letters and numbers. It is usually transmitted as eight-bit characters, with the addition of a 'parity' bit. The 'extended' ASCII set, usually found on most computers, is of 256 characters and is transmitted as eight bits.

AMTOR AMateur Teleprinter Over Radio. An error-correcting data transmission system sending seven-bit data, devised by Peter Martinez, G3PLX, based on the maritime SITOR system. It is usually used on the HF bands.

Analogue An analogue signal is one which can vary continuously between defined limits. The human voice is an analogue signal, varying in frequency, volume and timbre.

ARQ Automatic Repeat reQuest. A method of error correction whereby a transmitting station is requested to send again certain blocks of text found by the receiving station to be in error. This is the principal mode used by AMTOR stations.

Asynchronous transmission A method of transmission that allows data to be sent at irregular intervals by preceding each character with a 'start' bit and following it with a 'stop' bit. A simple example would be teleprinter signals. See also 'Synchronous transmission'.

BayCom A packet system of truly minimum configuration which relies on the PC to do all the functions of the PAD and terminal. The hardware is restricted to a few ICs in a small unit, forming the modem function of a TNC, connected directly to the serial port. Devices are available for both 1200 baud on the serial port and 9600 baud on the parallel port.

Baud A unit of measurement that indicates the number of discrete 'signal elements' (bits) transmitted per second. It is named after the French telegraph engineer J M E Baudot (1845–1903).

Binary file A number of sequential bytes, held in memory or stored on a disk, which may make up a complete program instruction sequence: They are the 'actual programs' which are in a form which may be executed or run. For the purposes of packet radio, this might also include image files. The transfer by packet of binary files requires an eight-bit transmission system.

Bit A bit is the smallest unit of storage within a computer. It is a contraction of 'Binary digIT, and can take a value of 1 or 0. In the International Telegraph Alphabet (ITA) No 5, seven bits are required to make up a character. ITA 5 is similar to the lower ASCII set. A bit is represented in packet radio by a mark or space tone. It compares equally with the 'signalling element', the smallest unit of transmitted data, like a dot in Morse or five in a group to make up a teleprinter character. See also 'Byte'.

bps or bit/s Bits per second. A measure of the transfer rate of information on a channel, usually used at higher rates of transmission.

Byte A group of consecutive bits, normally eight, forming a unit of storage within the computer, which represent one data character, such as a letter or number of the alphabet. It is also used to denote the storage capacity of floppy and hard disks, although generally seen in thousands (kilobytes) or millions (megabytes). Some hard disks can store several gigabytes.

Case Letters are described as being either upper or lower case. Upper case is CAPITALS (usually accessed by pressing the 'shift' key). Lower case is 'normal' like this text. The term has its roots in the printing industry. Sentences in messages should be made up of both cases. They are then easier to read.

Check sum See 'Parity checking' and 'CRC'.

Clock A commonly used name for any source of timing signals. Examples are those used in computer equipment to ensure that all processes are synchronised with respect to one another. This word is also used as a comparative reference to indicate the speed of a PC. Clock speeds in excess of 20MHz are common. Most TNCs are 2–10MHz. See also 'System clock'.

Clover An HF data mode where the simple two-tone mark and space modulation is abandoned, and modern DSP techniques are used to provide a choice of more complex modulation schemes to make efficient use of narrow HF channels.

Configuration/Config file A short file used by a program to determine initial settings prior to use. Most can be edited by use of a simple ASCII text editor and/or from within the program itself. Many have the extension '.CFG'. Some terminal emulation (comms) software will store changes automatically and adopt this setting when next switched on; one example is paKet.

Compression See 'File compression'.

CRC Cyclic redundancy check. A method of deriving a number, by the transmission of additional data, in order to ascertain whether an error has been received. It is also used on disk files in the computer.

CSMA Carrier sense multiple access. The system allowing many stations to use the same radio frequency simultaneously for packet communications.

DCE Data Circuit terminating Equipment. The equipment usually provides the functions required to establish maintain or terminate a connection, and signal conversions. Examples are a modem or TNC.

DSP Digital signal processing. The representation and manipulation of signals using numerical techniques and digital processors as opposed to analogue electronics.

DTE Data Terminal Equipment. Equipment comprising the data source, data sink or both. Examples include the computer serial port.

Digipeater DIGItal rePEATER. An ordinary packet radio station used for repeating packets, enabled by a command in the ROM. See also 'Node'.

Digi Short name for a digipeater.

Downlink The signals or data sent to you (downloaded); these are the signals you listen to or the file you take. Alternatively, the data you receive from the BBS. See also 'Uplink'.

Emulator A program running on one computer that mimics the action of a different computer or device. For example, the PC emulator for an Atari or Archimedes machines should enable the owner of one of these machines to run some PC software.

EOF End Of File. A marker or other indicator to show that it is the end of the file. It is usually transparent to an operator. Examples used in packet radio are ^Z (Ctrl-Z, ASCII 26) or /EX.

EOT End of Text. A marker to show that it is the end of the (transmitted) text. It is character 04 in the ASCII character set.

EPROM Erasable programmable read-only memory. A type of ROM which may be re-programmed. It is more usually seen as having a small quartz 'window' above the active elements through which UV light is passed to erase the contents prior to loading a new program. Data is not lost when power is removed; it is said to be 'non-volatile'. There are also 'electrically erasable' PROMs but they are not as common. Warning: these devices are sensitive to both static electricity and UV light, so keep the cover on and take the necessary precautions.

File A number of sequential bytes, held in memory or stored on a disk, which may make up some entity understood by the particular application program. It could be a program or part thereof, or a simple letter or even a picture.

File compression A process where a file is reduced in size for storage or transmission. It originated in a requirement to pack more information on a single disk, or to 'archive' sections of a hard disk. It may now be used as part of a security system by use of passwords. See also 'Self-expanding file'.

Firmware The name usually given to software supplied in a ROM, usually for a TNC. This is as opposed to other supply methods, such as files on a disk.

Frame An arbitrary unit making up a packet, consisting of different types, sent over the packet network.

G-TOR An HF data mode originating from Kantronics and available in the KAM controller. It features faster throughput than Pactor under good conditions. The letter 'G' refers to Golay forward error correction, which provides sufficient redundancy in the transmitted data to enable correction of simple errors without re-transmission. G-TOR can use speeds of 100, 200 and 300 baud.

Handshaking The process whereby the TNC and its computer exchange acknowledgement of each others' existence and functions. This may take the form of control codes sent with the data, called 'software' handshaking, or on control lines separate from those carrying the data, called 'hardware' handshaking. Hardware handshaking is used by some software in order that neither the binary file nor the transfer process are corrupted by control codes. Software handshaking may be used for most applications like normal messages and the transfer of text files which are ASCII.

Hex, Hexadecimal A base-16 numbering system used in a computer, where memory addresses are often quoted in hex numbers. The numbers run:

Hex	0	1	2	3	4	5	6	7	8	9	A	B	C	D	E	F
Decimal	0	1	2	3	4	5	6	7	8	9	10	11	12	13	14	15

The numbers are indicated as being hexadecimal in a number of ways. The simplest is hex or h (14h). However, for historical reasons you will often find the dollar sign, $, used ($14), particularly in American manuals. You may also occasionally see &H used to precede the hex number (&H14), a notation often used in programming.

KA-Node A simple node networking scheme where acknowledgements are passed between connected stations, not end-to-end. It was developed by TNC maker Kantronics and is similar in operation to a digipeater.

KA9Q NOS KA9Q Network Operating System. A TCP/IP program originally developed by Phil Karn, KA9Q. There are many different versions available for a variety of computers. The program (also called 'NET') is one of the most commonly used version of TCP/IP in packet radio. NOS was originally written for the PC compatible, but it has been ported to many different computers such as the Amiga, Macintosh and others systems like Unix.

Keps Satellite-tracking computer software use Keplerian elements (also known as 'orbital' or 'tracking' elements or 'Keps') to pinpoint the location of a satellite (or shuttle) at any given time. Keplerian elements, named after astronomer and mathematician Johannes Kepler, provide the software with a snapshot of a satellite's orbital track, which the computer uses to calculate the future whereabouts of the satellite. Using such a computer tracking program allows an observer to determine when a satellite is to appear above his or her horizon. Note: This information may also be on your local BBS as a simple message (TO KEPS @ GBR, for example). Some BBS software, such as the FBB, has the capability to display the predictions of a chosen satellite; yours may also include Shuttle data. Ask your sysop for details.

KISS "Keep it simple, stupid." Originally an admonition to servicemen, but now denotes (in the packet radio field) a simple interface developed for communications between the TNC and its host computer. Commonly used with TCP/IP, but increasingly with more conventional AX.25 packet programs (GP, SP etc), particularly in Germany.

Modem Short for 'MODulator/DEModulator'. In the packet radio application, it is usually part of the TNC. A device which converts digital data into audio tones for transmission (called 'base band' technique). A unit of similar nature at the 'other' end reverses the process. On its own it is used on the telephone network for access to the usual BBS facilities thereon. Modern high-speed devices do not use 'base band' techniques but employ complex modulation techniques, which are like those seen on some 9600 baud AX.25 transmissions. This has been described as 'modulated noise', but it sounds like a 'hiss'.

Multiplexing A technique whereby one circuit can carry several messages simultaneously. It was first developed by Emile Baudot in 1872.

Multi-tasking The process whereby several 'jobs' being executed by the CPU are apparently done simultaneously. Real multi-tasking would require multiple processors. It usually relies on a fast CPU executing instructions so quickly that there are periods of time where there is a pause (for example, something external is expected, like data from the serial port or a keystroke), and the CPU can get on with something else in that time. Software for the PC exists which purports to make it a multi-tasking system. Under these circumstances, a fast CPU and lots of RAM are vital.

NET/ROM A commercial software for packet radio networking nodes.

Node The digital equivalent of a voice repeater. It is a device that links two or more stations together, which enables messages to be passed over long distances between connecting stations. The packet network is made up of a multiplicity of nodes. Often a network node runs NET/ROM or similar software (TheNet etc but there are other types of node).

Pactor This data mode was designed specifically for use at HF with a faster throughput than Amtor, with a full 8-bit character set, and with more reliable error detection. It features built-in data compression which activates automatically when advantageous, and dynamic speed changes between 100 and 200 baud depending on conditions.

PAD Packet assembler/disassembler. A device in a TNC which converts the terminal's flow of data to and from packet frames and handles call set-up and addressing.

Parity A technique of error-checking in which one extra (parity) bit is added to the bits that make up the character, so the number of '1' bits per character is always even (or, in some cases, odd). See also 'CRC'.

Port The name given to a facility on a computer where signals may pass, such as 'serial' or 'parallel'. It is under the control of the I/O controller within the computer. The serial port passes bi-directional data bit-by-bit down one wire at one time although there may actually be several other wire connections involved at any one time (see also 'Hand-shaking'). The parallel port passes bi-directional data byte-by-byte on a 'bus' of eight wires simultaneously; for example, to the printer.

Protocol A set of rules governing information flow in a communication system. In practice, it includes electrical, electronic, software and hardware specifications.

Public domain Publication or software which is not subject to copyright and which may be freely copied, modified or re-written. Not the same as 'freeware' which may still be copyright even if the author allows it to be copied.

RAM Random access memory. Also known as 'read/write memory', because it can be written to and read from. The memory in a computer (or TNC) which stores or supplies the program or data in use. This data is lost when power is removed, ie it is 'volatile'.

RESET An immediate command sent to the TNC to put all the parameters back to their default values and re-initialise it. This can be made easier by uploading to the TNC a simple ASCII text file containing all your settings.

RESTART A command sent to the TNC to re-initialise it as if the power supply had been turned on. Previously entered or stored parameters are maintained.

ROM Read only memory. An array of memory cells organised in such a way as to present a program to the CPU. This memory cannot be written to, only read from. It is usually non-volatile (data is not lost on 'power off') and comes in different types and capacities. See also 'EPROM'. Not to be confused with CD-ROM, which is a compact disc holding up to 600Mb of read-only binary data.

RS-232 (RS-323C, EIA-232-D) The standard for interconnection of serial peripherals to all computer systems. In packet radio, RS-232 is the most common physical interface between TNCs and the computer or terminal.

Self-expanding file Many programs are now supplied as a single 'self-expanding' file. This usually involves placing all the files of a program (and there can be many) into a single, compressed-format file. When the file is run for the first time, it will 'un-compress' itself into its constituent parts, sometimes into the appropriate directory. Methods include LHArc and PKZip.

Shareware Commercial software not generally available via retailers. You usually get an early version which should be registered with the author. You may then get the most recent version together with full manuals etc, although this may depend on the source. Costs are markedly lower than retail software and some of it is very good.

Software The instructions or program routines which cause a desired action in the hardware. It is usually found in ROM or is loaded from some exterior source (eg disks or ports) and put into RAM, from where it is executed. Some is in the 'public domain', which see.

Start/stop A serial data transmission system which contains control information in the data stream. In packet practice, this may be described as 'software' handshaking. The term owes its origin to asynchronous transmission, where there is no additional timing information.

Synchronous transmission A method of transmission that allows data to be sent at regular, timed, intervals: one end makes a request and waits a finite period of time, then reads the reply. The system usually relies on an external clock for timing. See also 'Asynchronous transmission'.

Sysop SYStem OPerator. The person who runs your local BBS. Treated with normal respect and politeness, your local sysop can help you a lot, but remember he/she does it for the love of it.

System clock PCs and TNCs have a clock chip which keeps real time and date data which is maintained by a small rechargeable battery. This data is fed automatically to a TNC to update the time and date data by some software. See also 'Clock'.

TCP/IP Transmission Control Protocol/Internet Protocol. Two main network communication protocols, part of the commercially used Internet Protocol suite (used on, for example, the Internet). Another method of sending data used by amateurs which relies on a completely different system technique to AX.25. The TNC used *must* have KISS facilities, because all the hard work is done in the computer. The full TCP/IP suite contains different transmission facilities such as FTP (File Transfer Protocol), SMTP (Simple Mail Transport Protocol), Telnet (remote terminal protocol), and NNTP (Net News Transfer Protocol).

Terminal A device for sending and receiving data. Also sometimes known as a 'VDU' (visual display unit).

Terminal emulation A program within the computer to enable the computer to act as a terminal.

Time out Several processes in packet radio are controlled by internal timers which are reset by some expected event or other, such as the reception of a packet. When the expected event does not happen within the stated time, it is said to 'time out' and some other action is taken, such as automatic disconnection.

TSR Terminate and stay resident. A type of program running on the PC which remains active despite being 'switched off' from immediate use. Only a small 'hot key' section of the program is retained in memory which calls the main programme when activated.

Uplink The transmission of signals to the remote station, eg you 'upload' data to your BBS or even a satellite.

WA8DED firmware A program, usually in ROM, which enables a different method of achieving AX.25 data transmission. It has nothing to do with TCP/IP. It may be found in the standard ROM supplied with some PacComm TNCs (for instance, Tiny-2 Mk2) and it is accessed by use of a simple push switch as an alternative to the TAPR command set. It uses a different method of controlling the TNC. Used by such software as Graphic Packet.

YAPP Yet Another Packet Program. A protocol devised by Jeff Jacobsen, WA7MBL, to permit the transmission of binary and ASCII files between packet stations. It uses the TNC in 'Transparent' mode, and requires hardware handshaking to control the functions of the TNC. It is also the name of a program which acts as a terminal emulator. Many packet programs incorporate the YAPP protocol in some form (enhanced or not).

44 net The Class A network designator for TCP/IP amateur packet radio. All numerical TCP/IP addresses are in the format of: 44.131.xxx.yyy. The '44' represents the amateur network, and '131' the country (or state in the USA), 'xxx' is the region code and 'yyy' the user number.

7PLUS A program for encoding and decoding eight-bit (binary) files to seven-bit text so that they can be sent around the packet network. This widely-used program was devised and written by Axel Bauda, DG1BBQ.

sort, take it up with him *first*. You can always tell the tale later, when you have, hopefully, received some satisfaction. As the sign in a shop once put it: "If you're happy, tell your friends. If not, tell us". In the case of a rally, remember the legal maxim: "Caveat emptor" (Let the buyer beware).

On getting it out
General broadcast (SB) messages can be fraught with problems. Some mailboxes refuse to accept messages to 'ALL'. Known and used words like ICOM, YAESU, EPSON, DEBATE, and even HELP can make the purpose clearer.

There have been many examples of some stations which send out the same bulletin to different TO fields, which is a bit of overkill best left for dead. Examples include one to each of PC, IBM, HELP, and DISK, all with the same text content, seeking assistance with a disk problem on a PC. The network has enough traffic without cluttering it up unnecessarily. Pick the one you think best suits the problem and use that. If you don't get any satisfaction, try again later. Again, it is inadvisable to use 'special' characters not normally visible, such as the smiling face, which is Ctrl-C, since this is a command and some software may try to accept it.

You don't *have* to put an '@' in at all, in which case the message will stay on your local box for local users to read. Avoid @ EU unless important and you know that the answer is likely to come from Europe. As for @WWW (note that it is 'WWW' not 'WW'), it must be really vital for that to be put on. There are, however, good examples including QSL information and HUMOUR @ WWW, which, by the way, is not appreciated in France. Attempts to gain information on the correct destination for DOVE reports could not have been done any other way than @WWW. Even with the appearance of satellites which carry packet traffic, there's still a finite limit to the volume of traffic which can be borne by the global network. Think carefully before using it. Some mailboxes have a server facility for '@ REGION' addressing, which is of use if you want to locate something in a particular area. Ask your sysop for details.

The subject field (title) is another trap for the unwary. Ideally, both TO and SUBJECT should work together to illustrate the nature of the message. Obscure titles are more often ignored than read, so think carefully. You know what you want, but does your subject field make it clear? The maximum length is 29 characters, but don't go on typing as if you are in the message part already. Words may be shortened: Please = Pse, HELP = HLP etc. Another well-known horror is to see SB ALL @ GBR (or similar) in the subject field. A little thought can go

a long way to getting a useful reply. What can be more aggravating to see than:

```
HELP WANTED: TRANSISTOR TYPE
```
or
```
Hi, I am looking for help wi
```

It is also worth noting that some BBS software refuses a message without something in the SUBJECT field.

The actual layout of the message is important. It can be surprisingly difficult to read something upon which little or no visible care has been taken and it's frustrating when you're reading it in an effort to see if you can help him! Set your line width to something less than 76; anything longer may cause the reader to see a short extra line printed below each transmitted line, which can make it difficult to read.

THE BRITISH AMATEUR RADIO TELEDATA GROUP

This society, affiliated to the RSGB, is a specialist group for the data enthusiast. It offers a quarterly journal, *Datacom*, organises contests, an annual rally, an awards scheme, publishes a range of books and does lots more. For more details, contact the membership secretary at the address given in the current edition of the *RSGB Amateur Radio Call Book*.

FURTHER INFORMATION

[1] *The BARTG Guides to RTTY/Amtor/Pactor/AX25*, British Amateur Radio Teledata Group.
[2] 'Data Comms' column in *Radio Communication*.
[3] *Packet Radio Primer*, Dave Coomber, G8UYZ, and Martyn Croft, G8NZU, RSGB.
[4] *Practical Guide to Packet Operation in the UK*, Mike Mansfield, Compaid Graphics.
[5] *Your Gateway to Packet Radio*, Stan Horzepa, ARRL.
[6] *AX.25 Amateur Packet-Radio Link-Layer Protocol, Version 2, October 1984*, ARRL.

9 Image techniques

THE term *image techniques* as applied to amateur radio encompasses quite a wide selection of differing modes, which include in the main fast-scan television as in commercial broadcast television (FSTV), slow-scan television (SSTV), facsimile (fax) and remote imaging, which is essentially the reception of weather satellite images. However, this latter mode is more to do with the reception of extremely low-level signals, rather than with the technicalities of television or image techniques themselves.

SSTV and fax are narrow-band modes, which means that signals in these modes can be transmitted on normal voice channels. You can thus reach with SSTV and fax signals wherever you can reach by voice mode; in other words, on appropriate bands they are worldwide communication modes.

FSTV, on the other hand, is a wide-band mode, and as such is essentially a 'local' communication system although, when propagation conditions permit, relatively long-range contacts can be established over several hundreds of kilometres. However, it must be said that the quality of received pictures may not always be up to broadcast TV standards.

SLOW-SCAN TELEVISION

Slow-scan television has changed greatly since the idea was developed by Copthorne Macdonald and first used by radio amateurs many years ago. Nowadays, we have a plethora of systems within the mode and a variety of equipment that can be used to transmit and receive SSTV pictures. The original concept behind SSTV was to find a method by which a normal wide-band television picture could have its bandwidth reduced, so as to allow its transmission over a single-channel voice communication system. This means that a typical 6MHz or so wide colour television signal has to be reduced to around 3kHz – around a 2000 to 1 reduction in bandwidth! Because of this severe narrowing of the bandwidth, the system is only suitable for the transmission of still pictures – moving images are still the preserve of FSTV, but only until digital television becomes the norm.

To reduce the bandwidth of a television signal, both the horizontal (line) and the vertical (frame or field) scanning rates must be reduced to as low a frequency as possible. A convenient stable source from which to obtain these low scanning rates is the domestic mains supply, which is 50Hz in the UK and 60Hz in the USA and elsewhere.

The basic parameters of a slow-scan signal are shown in Table 1, from which it can be seen that the line rate of 16.6MHz is easily obtained by dividing the mains frequency by three and the frame rate by diving the mains by 360. This system resulted in a picture made up of 120 lines. However, with the wide use of computers in SSTV use it is more common to have pictures made up of 128 lines, which translates to a nicer binary number, ie 10000000.

Table 1. SSTV standards

Parameter	50Hz mains	60Hz mains
Line speed	120 or 128	120 or 128
Frame speed	7.2s or 7.68s	8s or 8.53s
Aspect ratio	1 to 1	1 to 1
Scanning direction:		
Horizontal	Left to right	Left to right
Vertical	Top to bottom	Top to bottom
Sync pulse duration:		
Horizontal	5ms	5ms
Vertical	30ms	30ms
Subcarrier frequency:		
Sync	1200Hz	1200Hz
Black	1500Hz	1500Hz
White	2300Hz	2300Hz
Required transmission bandwidth	1.0–2.5kHz	1.0–2.5kHz

The basics of a slow-scan picture

The composition of a single picture using the original specifications in Table 1 is shown in Fig 1. A complete picture line is 65ms long, with a 5ms line synchronisation (sync) pulse and 60ms of video information. The line sync pulse is the method by which the receiving system determines when to start 'writing' a new line. The frame pulses, which appear at the start of every 120 (or 128) lines of video information, are 30ms long, in order for the receiving system to recognise them apart from the line sync pulses. The frame pulses tell the receiving system when to start 'writing' a new picture from scratch. Unlike conventional TV the aspect ratio was set at 1:1, which results in a square picture. The reason for adopting this standard originally was the use then of round ex-radar display cathode ray tubes in the receiving system display monitor.

The base-band (audio) video signal is modulated onto a subcarrier, which helps to overcome phase shift and drift problems in SSTV demodulators. Obviously, this subcarrier had to be within the audio band, otherwise it could not be transmitted over the audio speech channel. With reference to Fig 1 it can be seen that the basic frequency representing the black level (no video information) is 1500Hz, which rises to 2300Hz representing peak white. The various tones, hues and grey levels being translated into frequencies within this spectrum.

Fig 1. Frequency composition of a single slow-scan line

The sync pulse frequency is 1200Hz, which is 'blacker-than-black', and thus the visible raster is blanked out when the spot moves to the beginning of the next video line or picture frame, which is normally termed the *retrace*.

Receiving slow-scan television

SSTV signals can be received using an ordinary communications receiver or transceiver covering the amateur bands. Table 2 shows the amateur bands where SSTV is to be found, the IARU recommended working frequencies and the popular operating spots. The mode of transmission may be either FM or SSB. No modifications are required to the receiver, although the internal IF filter should have a bandwidth not less than 2.5kHz and ideally 3kHz. The SSTV base-band signal is extracted either from the headphone or line-output jack of the receiver/transceiver.

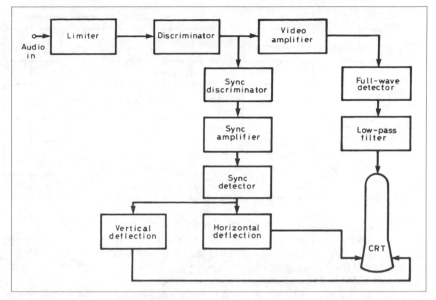

Fig 2. Block diagram of a slow-scan TV monitor

The SSTV base-band signal must now be further processed in a purpose-designed demodulator system. Essentially, over the years, there have been three systems for demodulating and viewing SSTV signals:

1. A monitor containing an integral long-persistence cathode-ray-tube (CRT), together with signal processing and deflection circuits.
2. A digital scan-converter in which the received signal is digitised and stored in a memory. This memory is then scanned at fast-scan (625 lines in the UK) rate for displaying on a conventional TV or monitor.
3. A computer which processes the picture either directly or via a hardware interface, depending on the software system in use.

This latter method is probably the most widely used now, particularly with the advent of full-featured, cost-effective software packages for the IBM PC, such as the JV-FAX package.

The SSTV monitor

The SSTV monitor, as outlined in the block diagram in Fig 2, is now only probably used by the SSTV purist, as it requires a great deal of home construction and the resulting pictures perhaps a little disappointing! In simple terms the incoming SSTV signal is FM detected, resulting in an AM signal, but still consisting of a subcarrier centred around 1500Hz. The two sync signals are recovered by using a tuned-circuit sync discriminator. The AM subcarrier signals are detected, often by using simple full-wave rectification.

The monitor deflection circuits are controlled by the sync pulses using similar methods to those employed in broadcast

Table 2. SSTV frequencies

Band (MHz)	IARU recommended frequency (MHz)	Popular frequency (MHz)
3.5	3.735	3.730
7	7.040	7.040
14	14.230	14.230
21	21.340	21.340
28	28.680	28.680
144	144.500	144.500

TV receivers. The nature of the long-persistence CRT used in an SSTV monitor requires that attention is paid that the scanning spot is not bright enough to burn the phosphor. In more sophisticated circuits spot suppression is included to blank out the raster, and thus the scanning spot, in the absence of received signals. The detected base-band video information is used to bright up the CRT as with a conventional TV, the principles of which are not being discussed here.

The results obtained from a slow-scan monitor are rarely comparable to those received by more modern systems. Because of the reliance on the long-persistence properties of the CRT often as not the top half of the picture fades out before the second half has been scanned in. Consequently, it is often necessary to view the received pictures in a darkened room. Also, there is no direct way to received colour pictures on a slow-scan monitor.

A digital scan converter

For many years now the most popular system for decoding SSTV pictures has been the digital scan converter. The popularity of this type of equipment has only been surpassed in latter years with the advent of versatile computer based systems. A simplified block diagram of a digital scan converter is shown in Fig 3. A distinct advantage of digital scan converters is the ability to use a standard domestic TV set or video monitor to view the received pictures.

The incoming audio signal from the receiver is firstly limited and then passed through a sync detection circuit. The remaining picture information signal is fed to an analogue-to-digital (A-D) converter, where each line of information is converted into 128 4-bit binary words. Two 512-bit shift registers act as odd and even line buffers, the necessary switching being carried out by a clock signal generated from the sync pulses. While a line is being read into a buffer the preceding line held in the other buffer is read out into memory. Without doing all the maths here, suffice it to say that a 16k memory is required to store a 128-line by 128-pixel picture.

The memory is continually scanned at fast scan rates by another clock, which is also controlled by the sync pulses. This fast scanned information is fed to a digital-to-analogue (D-A) converter, which results in a base-band fast-scan picture, which

Fig 3. Simplified block diagram of an SSTV digital scan converter

can either be fed direct to a composite video monitor or to a modulator for viewing on a conventional TV. For receiving colour pictures three 16k memory banks are required and also further circuits for detecting the extra control signals present in a colour SSTV signal that are used to inform the receiving system which of the three colours are being transmitted (a colour SSTV signal is transmitted as three separate signals, red, green and blue).

An immediate advantage of this type of system is that there is always a picture on the screen. As each new picture is received it is slowly scanned in over the preceding one. Consequently, a picture once received can be viewed on the screen for as long as you wish, without it slowly fading into the west!

As mentioned earlier, the aspect ration of SSTV pictures is 1:1, whereas with FSTV it is currently 4:3. If no correction was carried out on the received picture then it would appear distorted on the screen. To overcome this problem the converter is configured such that the first and last eighths of each line are blanked out during the fast-scan memory read cycle, resulting in a square picture of the TV/monitor screen.

Computerised SSTV

There have been computerised SSTV systems for just about all makes of computer, including the now-widespread PC. Most systems are full SSTV transceivers, although there have been one or two receive-only or transmit-only packages. Some of the earlier systems require quite complex signal processing circuitry that plugs into an expansion port on the computer, some of the PC-based ones utilise a purpose-built modem that plugs into an internal slot in the computer and some have very sophisticated software routines that require only a very simple A-D converter that plugs into a serial port for example. Further information on computers and SSTV will be examined in the following section dealing with transmitting SSTV.

Transmitting SSTV

Sending SSTV pictures over the air requires nothing special as far as the radio equipment is concerned – the video information on its 1500Hz subcarrier is simply fed into the microphone socket of the transmitter. The band on which you are operating largely dictates the mode of emission, although both FM and SSB are used on VHF.

No modifications to the transmitting equipment are required. However it must be borne in mind that if using an SSB mode of emission, unlike normal speech which has a low duty cycle, the SSTV signal has a 100% duty cycle. Therefore, the transmitter must be capable of producing full power continuously on SSB when transmitting SSTV.

Picture sources

Nowadays, the most common picture sources are computers, and it is not hard to see why with the graphics capabilities of modern machines. Also, with relatively inexpensive image digitisers now available, camera pictures can be digitised into the computer for use as SSTV pictures.

However, there have been and are still other picture sources available. Early SSTV stations built and employed SSTV keyboards, which were essentially electronic typewriters which allowed the operator to type messages which were output from the keyboard as a standard SSTV signal. The main drawback of using an SSTV keyboard however is that it is a text only mode, and television is of course a visual medium.

Digital scan converters have been the most widely used method of generating SSTV pictures for many years. The principle is the same as for the receive converter but in reverse. In actuality, of course, only one digital scan converter is used, it being in fact a transverter. The advantage here is that circuitry is incorporated which enables a video camera to be plugged in, allowing the user to 'snatch' a picture for transmission.

Other equipments have been used over the years for generating SSTV pictures including:

1. Slow-scan and sampling cameras, where the camera vidicon is scanned at slow-scan rates to produce the SSTV signal from the fast-scan picture the camera is looking at.
2. Flying-spot scanners – where a photographic slide of the required picture is held in front of a CRT being swept at slow-scan rates, causing a spot to move over the CRT screen exactly as if it was scanning the picture in. In front of the CRT and slide is located a photomultiplier tube, which reacts to the varying light intensity transmitted through the slide from the moving spot on the CRT. Further circuitry processes the output from the photomultiplier into the standard SSTV signal.

Commercial systems

Much of the equipment discussed here bears a great deal of home-brew construction. There are several commercially built slow-scan systems available, both new and second hand. The major makers, both current and past, are Wraase Electronik, Davtrend Ltd and Robot Research. Sadly, both the latter two are no longer in production, although examples of Robot digital scan converters are often seen advertised in *Radio Communication* and elsewhere. However, with the recent advent of extremely versatile computer based slow-scan systems, it is clear that the era of the hardware-based digital scan converter is coming to an end.

Slow-scan television, as it has developed over the years, has collected along the way a vast array of variations on the original theme, with many differing modes, speeds of transmission and internal protocols. This in itself has been good for slow-scan, because it has helped to maintain the interest in this specialist mode. However, it has also produced many problems, for example Robot Research with their large range of scan converters developed their equipment using strict protocols – the Robot Modes. Similarly, so did Wraase Electronik and all the other mainstays of SSTV over the years. This presents the

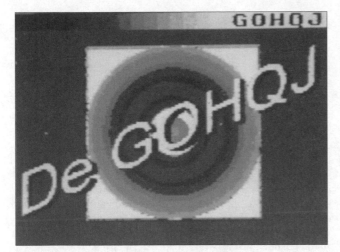

An attractive SSTV station identification picture

A SSTV picture received using the JV-FAX software

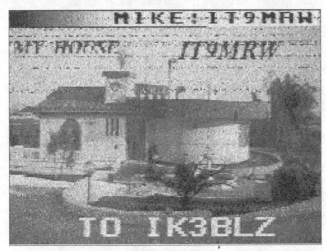

SSTV picture received off-air from IT9MRW

G0EDV and friend! It's good to get a talking point into your picture

SSTVer with a problem – generally speaking, for example, you can only receive Robot mode pictures using Robot equipment, or equipment specifically built and configured for Robot Modes. Thus there has developed over the years fractional elements within the SSTV side of the hobby that may have done a disservice to the mode.

Never fear though, all is not lost. With the advent of the PC in particular, SSTV systems have been developed for the computer, using its mode-independent versatility and immense processing power, which allow the user to receive just about any mode, speed and protocol of SSTV picture being transmitted, and what is more transmit pictures similarly in any format.

The age of the affordable high-specification computer has seen an upsurge in the interest in SSTV around the world. Whilst it is true to say that systems are available, and have been for many years, for other computers such as the Sinclair Spectrum, the Dragon, the Commodore series, the Amiga etc, it has only been the arrival of the PC in the amateur shack that has revolutionised SSTV as well as other amateur radio modes.

The two main systems that have been available world-wide are the software based JV-FAX package and the Pasokon TV system. The JV-FAX package is at present the most widely used system in SSTV. It is essentially a powerful software package that requires only a very simple interface between a serial port of the PC and the microphone and headphone sockets of

the transceiver. The software does not take long to master and allows a variety of slow-scan modes, speeds and protocols to be received and transmitted. The package is virtually shareware and as such is obtained at very low cost, complete with all information and a pre-built interface if required. A UK source for JV-FAX is given in reference [1].

Pasokon TV is also a very versatile PC-based SSTV system, but differs from the latter in that it has a dedicated modem which requires to be plugged into a spare 16-bit slot in the computer, connection to and from the transceiver being made to a nine-way plug at the rear of the card. The software package is extremely versatile and allows transmission and reception in all the current modes. The software has built-in selectable error correction and colour processing modes, and a graphic user interface for mouse operation. Whilst the package is excellent in operation and hard to fault, it is much more expensive than the JV-FAX system and perhaps a little less versatile in future expansion than a wholly software based system. Pasokon is only available direct from the developer in the USA, whose address is shown in reference [2].

Further details of the various SSTV modes, speeds, formats etc, plus full construction details on various units for operating SSTV can be found in the British Amateur Television Club (BATC) publication *Slow Scan Television Explained*. The BATC is an RSGB affiliated society which publishes its own quarterly journal *CQ-TV*; membership information etc is given in reference [3] at the end of this chapter.

How to start an SSTV contact

To start an SSTV contact simply call "CQ SSTV [your callsign] CQ SSTV" on one of the frequencies shown in Table 1 and then, once a contact has been established, change frequency to a mutually agreed one in the SSTV portion of the band. Decide who is to transmit first and establish the speed and mode to be used. Remember that it is not only good operating practice, but also plain good manners, to call "Is this frequency in use?" before calling CQ and moving there after a contact has been made. Often you will come across existing contacts or nets taking place. If this is the case, await a gap in the transmissions, announce your callsign on the frequency and await to be called in.

FACSIMILE

Facsimile (fax) is the process by which graphic information is converted into electrical signals which are transmitted by cable or radio and then reproduced exactly as the original. Until a few years ago the only method of operating fax available to the radio amateur was by converting ex-commercial equipment, which was essentially electromechanical in nature. Whilst it is still possible to obtain, modify and use this equipment today, most amateur fax operation is conducted using computer-based systems. Software packages are available for most of the popular makes of personal computer, including the JV-FAX package for the PC as described earlier.

Much of the amateur activity with fax is actually in the reception of the various weather and news fax services around the world, rather than by reception and transmission of this mode between amateur stations.

FAST-SCAN TELEVISION

Amateur fast-scan television (ATV) is perhaps one of the more fascinating and self-construction oriented modes in amateur radio today. Whilst there is an amount of commercially made equipment for ATV, this is mainly in the form of kits or units for the microwave bands. The starting place for all ATVers is 70cm, where relatively simple equipment can be built and contacts can be easily made. It must be mentioned here that it is not possible to use existing radio equipment for fast-scan television. Transmitters and receivers must be specially commissioned for this mode, whether it be for AM television on 70cm or FM television on 24cm or the microwave bands.

Fast-scan television is essentially a short DX mode, in that the average contact distance on 70cm is probably of the order of 30 to 50 miles or so for good-quality received pictures. It must be noted here that for a received picture to be of good, relatively noise-free quality, the received signal strength must be in excess of 20dB over S9 – much higher signal strength than for a noise-free phone contact!

Fast-scan ATV is, to all intents and purposes, identical to standard broadcast television, with a few relaxations of some of the more stringent specifications. In the UK, amateur television transmissions may be found on several of the UHF and microwave bands, the principal one traditionally being the amateur 70cm allocation (amplitude modulation around 436MHz – approx. channel 17). The 23cm band is where the ATV repeaters are to be found. Table 3 shows the various bands and frequencies where ATV activity may be found.

Table 3. Popular ATV frequency allocations

Band	Centre frequency (MHz)	Mode
70cm	435.4	AM
23cm	1249.0–1265.0	FM
	1316.5	
13cm	Not allocated	FM
3cm	10,000.150	FM

AM is used on the 70cm band, but on the higher bands FM is preferred because of the higher quality of pictures that can be sent and received and because of the better attributes of the signal-to-noise characteristics of FM transmissions. On 70cm only the video content is transmitted, with the audio channel being usually on 2m, nominally 144.750 which is the UK ATV calling channel. However, on 24cm and above, because of the much greater bandwidth available, ATV signals also carry the sound channel, just as with broadcast TV. So an ATV contact on 24cm can be, and usually is, conducted totally on the one band, without the use of the 2m talkback channel.

If portable operation appeals to you, then try 10GHz ATV, where by converting simple doppler microwave burglar alarm units a simple, but very effective, FM ATV station can be built.

An amateur TV station need be only as complex as the individual desires. Many stations employ no more equipment than a camera, transmitter and a receiver. This basic system is adequate for normal communication and has the advantage of being easy to use and maintain. The block diagram of such a basic amateur TV station is shown in Fig 4.

Amateurs who do not wish to put together a complete TV station often set up a simple receiving system in order to 'eavesdrop' on ATV pictures in their area. This can be very rewarding, especially if they live in a high-activity area, and particularly when lifts in propagation conditions occur. Looking-in on a local ATV repeater is a common pastime for many stations.

Transmitters and receivers

Full information on constructing simple ATV transmitters and receivers can be found in the RSGB *Radio Communication Handbook* (6th edition) and BATC publications *An Introduction to Amateur Television* and the *ATV Compendium* [3].

The simplest ATV station is a receive-only one. All that is required to receive 70cm fast-scan TV (FSTV) is a receive converter and a normal television set. The receive or up-converter converts the received signals around 436MHz to usually channel 36 on the TV set (approximately 700MHz). Assuming that you already own a TV set then all you need is the

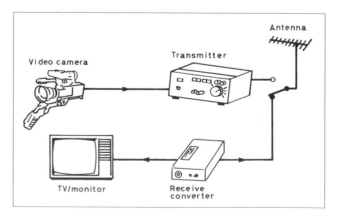

Fig 4. Block diagram of a basic fast-scan station

converter and a 70cm beam. It may be advantageous to use a preamplifier as well but it is not essential for starting out. With some of the Japanese TV sets in particular even the receive converter may not be required, as these sets often tune down to below 436MHz and still have enough RF gain to be useful, although if using this method considerable advantage can be obtained by using a preamplifier. The same is true for a variety of video cassette recorders, whose tuners often tune to the ATV operating area on 70cm.

To transmit FSTV then a purpose-built transmitter is required. Commercially built equipment is generally no longer available new in the UK, but several types can often be found at rallies or in the Members' Advertisements in *Radio Communication* or *CQ-TV*. The most popular commercial units made were probably the Microwave Modules series. This company produced a range of transmitters for 70cm and 24cm and a matching set of receive converters. They also produced a range of suitable linear amplifiers as well, which can often be found at rallies etc.

Another company that produced ATV equipment over the years was Wood & Douglas. Although they mainly marketed kits, much of their equipment can be found built and working offered for sale. A correctly built W&D unit will be as good as anything commercially built.

A specialist in 24cm component units has been, and at this time still is, Camtech Electronics. When new these modules are priced at the high end of the market, reflecting their quality, but again they can often be found for sale and are well worth investigating.

If you are into home construction then Mainline Electronics [4] offer a range of kits, many based on BATC designs, from 70cm converters through to 3cm transmitters. They use well-made quality printed-circuit boards and are easy to construct and align, using the minimum of equipment. You do not need to be an electronic genius or a master craftsman to build these kits. Another source of kits and pre-built 24cm ATV units is the Worthing & District Video Repeater Group [5].

Video sources

The most obvious video source is a camera. At one time the only cameras that were readily available to the amateur were ex-surveillance security black-and-white cameras, that more often than not had an imprint after the fashion of 'Fred Bloggs – Grocer to the Rich and Famous' permanently burnt into the vidicon. However, nowadays many households own camcorders, which have standard video and audio outputs and what is more are capable of colour.

Please note here that if a colour camera or colour source of any description is going to be used with a 70cm system, then a low-pass filter, cutting off at around 3MHz, should be incorporated between the source and the transmitter. If this is not done then the spectrum of the transmitted signal will cause severe interference with other users of 70cm and will probably also result in out-of-band transmissions.

Another video source easily obtained at rallies, or even from the lounge, is the video cassette recorder – useful for transmitting those wonderfully interesting videos of your holidays etc!

Computers can also be used as video sources, although certain models are difficult to modify so as to extract the necessary composite video and blanking signal (CVBS) – this unfortunately includes the PC. However, plug-in cards are available for the PC which will output the necessary signals from the computer, certain models also having a camera input allowing the camera pictures to be overlaid with the PC pictures and/or text to produce a combined output.

Computers such as the BBC 'B' and the Atari series are easily modified (some models already have a CVBS output) but it should be remembered that because computers generate their pictures digitally, large transient signals may appear at odd frequencies. Thus, if using these older computers, a low-pass filter cutting off at around 5MHz should be used and ideally also an amplitude limited/clipper as well. (PCs using plug-in cards should cause no problems, as the outputs from these purpose-built cards should meet the requirements of correctly filtered outputs etc.)

Test signals provide useful video sources, enabling the operator to correctly set up his camera, monitor, transmitter or receiver. The most commonly used test signal is a test card, of which there are two main types, those printed onto card and held in front of a camera and those which are digitally generated. Printed card types are the only type that can be used for setting up cameras and are available from the British Amateur Television Club. Digitally generated test cards are available in kit form from Maplin Electronics [6] and provide high-specification colour test cards for alignment or general transmission, the operator's callsign being encoded into the data.

Setting up a simple ATV studio

The term *television studio* tends to conjure up pictures of what we see and imagine is used by the broadcast TV programme makers. However, for ATV use we need nothing so complex, although if your interest in the hobby is the actual production of programmes then you may need something more sophisticated than the following.

A simple ATV station requires only one camera and perhaps a video casstte recorder. Alternatively the family camcorder can be pressed into service, which can double as both and will almost certainly also be colour. If a camcorder is being used then no particular attention needs to be paid to shack lighting. The author can see the purists cringing at that statement, but unless you wish to produce BBC-quality programmes then simple lighting will suffice. As long as the subject area is sufficiently lit to allow the camera to produce a well-contrasted and, if in colour, a nicely colour-balanced picture, then the use of fluorescent tubes is often more than adequate.

The content of the pictures is entirely your choice. However, try to avoid long transmissions with the camera staring back at you. Compose camera shots so that you are off-centre, with a nice shot of the rest of the shack taking centre stage. The rest is up to you.

ATV repeaters

The list in Appendix 11 shows the callsigns, locations and operating channels of the operational ATV repeaters in the UK, and as can be seen they now cover most of the major areas of the country. Apart from the Bath repeater GB3UT and the Hastings repeater GB3VI, which are AM or FM input and AM output, the mode is FM with vertical polarisation.

Essentially, ATV repeaters are much the same as their phone counterparts. However, there are three very important differences:

1. to access an ATV repeater all you need is a fast-scan FM TV signal with the video conforming to the CCIR specifications for 625-line television (ie exactly what you get from your camera, camcorder, VCR etc);
2. there are no time-outs operating on ATV repeaters; and
3. perhaps most importantly for the constructor, when a repeater is not repeating a received picture it broadcasts its

A typical test card – this is one received off-air from the GB3TG TV repeater on 10GHz

Off-air picture recived from G7SEC via the GB3LO TV repeater. Note the picture-in-picture feature

A picture received from G8XTW on 10GHz

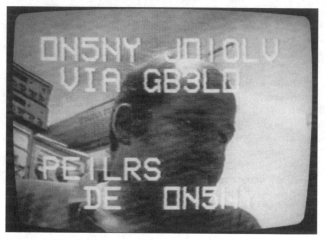

Here Belgian and Dutch amateurs are exchanging TV pictures via GB3LO

own pictures, from test cards, colour test screens, textual information screens, outside mast-head cameras shots etc, all scrolling round in an endless loop. When in repeat mode many ATV repeaters have large selections of options available, from relaying weather pictures to giving signal and picture reports, and in the case of GB3ZZ in Bristol to being able to select which of several receive antennas you are being picked up on.

In other words, ATV repeaters are operational 24 hours a day, either radiating on-board generated pictures or repeating incoming received pictures.

Table 4 gives the channel frequencies of UK ATV repeaters. Repeaters operating with their inputs on RT1-1 will accept either AM or FM signals, whilst inputs on RT1-2 and RT1-3

are FM only. Repeater output on RT1-1 is AM only and the outputs on RT1-2 and RT1-3 are FM only. A morse code identification giving callsign and location is present on the 6MHz audio carrier. FM transmissions can employ standard CCIR video pre-emphasis as an option.

Although the actual coverage of each repeater will depend on local geography, and in some cases antenna directivity, the average area covered is of the order of a 30km radius from the repeater. Apart from one or two exceptions, antenna are omni-directional. *All* ATV antennas operate horizontally, regardless of band. Details of ATV repeaters are given in Appendix 11.

The widest frequency difference between an input and an output signal is 67.5MHz. A check on the specification of commercial antennas will show that most of them lack the necessary bandwidth necessary for single-antenna ATV operation. Fortunately, there are one or two which are suitable for ATV applications: the helix, or helical beam, and the quad-loop Yagi are two of the more readily available designs. An excellent Yagi antenna for 24cm ATV work is available from the Severnside Television Group [7].

How to conduct an ATV contact

So, how do you start an ATV contact? The UK and international calling channel is 144.750MHz FM. If the frequency is clear,

Table 4. UK ATV repeater channel frequencies

Channel	Input (MHz)	Output (MHz)	Mode
RT1-1	1276	1311.5	AM
RT1-2	1249	1316.5	FM
RT1-2R	1249	1316	FM
RT1-3	1248	1308	FM
RT10-1	10,200	10,040	FM
RT10-2	10,255	10,150	FM
RT10-3	10,250	10,150	FM

5 EXCELLENT
No noise visible

4 GOOD
Slight noise visible

3 FAIRLY GOOD
Noticeable Noise

2 PASSABLE
High noise level

1 LIMITED USE
Objectionable noise

0 NOT USABLE
Picture lost in noise

Fig 5. The British Amateur Television Club ATV reporting chart for P0–P5 (Reproduced with acknowledgement to the BATC)

then simply put out a CQ call such as "CQ ATV, CQ ATV, [your callsign], CQ ATV, CQ 70cm ATV. [your callsign] listening". Alternatively, if you know an ATV station who may be listening then, as with any other mode, call the station direct. Once a contact has been established it is generally good practice, unless attempting to generate further activity, to QSY up or down 25kHz away fromn the calling channel.

Having established phone contact and lined the antennas up on each other, you then decide who is to transmit ATV first. The transmit station starts sending an ATV picture on 70cm (nominal centre frequency 432.4MHz) and the receive station starts tuning his/her ATV receiver until hopefully a picture is established.

It will often be necessary to fine tune the beam headings

until the best picture is received. The best method for achieving this is for the transmit station to start swinging his/her antenna first in one direction and then the other, announcing on the talkback channel, say, "Going north, going south", and dropping the carrier on 2m between changes. The receiving amateur watches the TV screen and announces over the talkback channel "Stop" when the received picture disappears for both antenna swings. The transmit station then splits the difference between the two extremes and points the antenna in that direction. The receive station then optimises the antenna direction by peaking for strongest picture.

Having thus established the best path headings, the two stations can enjoy a 70cm ATV QSO with talkback on 2m, swapping pictures, the content of which may be just about anything which complies with the licence conditions. During long periods of ATV transmission, the callsign of the transmitting station must be announced on the talkback channel with the information that he/she is transmitting fast-scan ATV on 70cm, and also the callsign must be sent either as a picture on its own or superimposed on to the transmitted TV picture.

For fast-scan TV on 24cm and above, the procedure is essentially the same, except that once a QSO has been established via 2m then the entire ATV contact may be conducted on the TV band, with the audio talkback being transmitted as part of the TV signal, just as with broadcast trasnmissions.

Signal reports on ATV are given using the P code – P0 representing no picture, to P5 representing a perfect, noise-free, broadcast-quality one. As with RST reports, the exact P report is very much in the eye of the beholder – what one person would call 'P4' another would call 'P5'. The chart reproduced in Fig 5 will, however, act as a guide.

FURTHER INFORMATION

[1] JV-FAX Software Package: Peter Lockwood, G8SLB, 36 Davington Road, Dagenham, RM8 2LR.
[2] Pasokon TV: Absolute Value Systems, 115 Stedman Street, Chelmsford, MA 01824-1823, USA.
[3] BATC Membership enquiries: BATC, Grenehurst, Pinewood Road, High Wycombe, HP12 4DD. BATC Publications: BATC, 14 Lilac Avenue, Leicester, LE5 1FN.
[4] Mainline Electronics, PO Box 235, Leicester, LE2 9SH.
[5] Worthing Video Repeater Group, 21 St James Avenue, Lancing, West Sussex, BN15 0NN.
[6] Maplin Electronics, PO Box 3, Rayleigh, Essex, SS6 8LR.
[7] Severnside Television Group, 15 Witney Close, Saltford, Bristol, BS18 3DX.

10 Special-event stations

FROM time to time groups of radio amateurs organise and operate special radio stations at exhibitions, conferences and other events. These fall mainly into two groups: (a) demonstration stations and (b) talk-in stations.

In the first case the object is to demonstrate amateur radio to members of the general public and the whole operation must be planned as a public-relations exercise. In the second case the purpose is to guide mobile amateur radio visitors to the event and efficient communication procedure and navigational expertise is more important.

GENERAL POINTS

Although quite different in their function, demonstration and talk-in stations do share some common ground in respect of planning matters, and these will be outlined briefly before discussing each type of station in more detail.

Personnel

One of the first steps is for a station manager to be appointed. In turn the manager can then appoint assistants to be in charge of various aspects such as equipment, power supplies, antennas etc. At the same time the identities of possible operators can be established.

Budget

Planning, establishing and operating a special-event station will almost invariably incur some expense, no matter how generous club members prove to be with support in terms of equipment and time. Therefore at the very earliest stage the club honorary treasurer should be asked to draw up a budget. This should include the cost of hire of any equipment (antennas, masts, tables, chairs and motor generators, and tents if the event is being held under canvas). Do not overlook coaxial cable and plugs, fuel for generators (very expensive if long periods of operation are undertaken) and the cost of refreshments.

If possible it is better for the operators to cater for themselves as they can then arrange meals to suit operating times. Sometimes exhibition organisers supply meals free of charge as an expression of gratitude to the amateurs concerned, but it is obvious that where a number of operators are involved for a period of more than a couple of days or so the cost becomes so restrictive that they have to ask for financial assistance.

Other items include postage and telephone charges incurred during the planning period, and gratuities to the venue staff in order to make sure that your antenna is placed at the very highest point possible. QSL cards may need to be printed and maps, felt-tipped pens, pencils and paper, logbooks and notice boards will all have to be purchased if they cannot be begged.

Having drawn up the budget make certain that you have sufficient funds to cover all items.

Security

Amateur equipment is expensive and much of it is readily portable. At the event make sure that all equipment is out of reach of light-fingered visitors. "Out of sight – out of mind" is a good motto to follow, and spare transceivers and accessories can be stored under tables or behind screens. Owners of equipment must make adequate insurance arrangements, and the station manager should discuss this subject with the event organiser.

While on the subject of insurance, cover should be obtained for personal injury to those participating in setting up and operating the station as well to members of the public. Antennas can blow down, electricity can be dangerous and claims could be substantial.

Licensing
GB or not GB?

From 1 June 1990, all club stations have been able to pass greetings messages sent by a non-licensed third party. This means that applying for a GB callsign no longer holds any operating advantages!

Provided the club uses the special club prefix letters, eg GX for England, the club station is allowed to pass greetings messages and to operate simultaneously on more than one band. The club prefixes are very distinctive and create interest through their rarity. If a club regularly operates a special-event station using the club callsign, this will help increase the club's identity. It will also benefit by being able to print its QSL cards in larger, more economic quantities.

Another advantage is that any suitably licensed and authorised club member may operate the club station. This gives greater flexibility over a GB callsign which is just a variation to an individual's licence. Best of all, there is no need to fill in any forms or wait 28 days!

Remember, when operating away from the Main Address, if you give prior written notice to the RIS office covering your area, you do not have to sign /P or give your location to within 5km.

Applying for a GB callsign

Since 1983 the RSGB has despatched on behalf of the Radio–communications Agency the Notices of Variation issued by the Secretary of State for Trade and Industry authorising special-event stations. Consequently, all enquiries and correspondence should be addressed to the Society and not to the RA.

The RA has stated that it ". . . requires the Society when distributing Notices of Variation allowing radio amateurs to set up special-event stations, to ensure that the request is for an event which is of special significance and therefore is generally accepted as one requiring celebration, and that the event is open to viewing by members of the public".

No charge is made by the RSGB for a special-event callsign,

but application forms must be returned at least 28 days prior to the start of the event!

Between two and four weeks before the start of the event, all successful applicants should receive their notice of variation from the Society. If nothing has been received once this time has elapsed, please contact the Amateur Radio Dept at RSGB HQ immediately. *Please note that no authority exists until this notice has been received.*

A special-event station will only be issued to an individual current licence holder. It will be valid for a maximum of 28 consecutive days. Please note that a notice of variation will only be issued for an individual's licence; variations will not be issued on a club licence.

The station may only be established and operated at one specified location. This must be the address stated on the application form which must be detailed enough for anyone to find easily. Operation of a special-event station from a licensee's home address is not normally permitted.

Only the person responsible for the station need sign the form, as the authorisation is by notice of variation to that individual's licence. This person is required to be present to supervise the correct operation of the station. Additional operators need only sign and write their callsigns in the logbook.

If you have not used the callsign before, you can avoid last-minute disappointment by first contacting RSGB. They can then check that it is available and reserve it for you. A GB callsign may be reserved for up to six months in advance. When a GB callsign has been used it will not normally be re-issued to another amateur for use at a different event for a period of 24 months.

If operation of the special-event station on the HF bands is desired, a Class A licence holder must apply for a Class A GB callsign.

Subject to availability special-event callsigns are available in the following formats:

Class A	Class B
GB0 + 2 or 3 letters	GB1 + 2 or 3 letters
GB2 + 2 or 3 letters	GB5 + 3 letters
GB4 + 2 or 3 letters	GB6 + 3 letters
GB5 + 2 letters	GB8 + 3 letters
GB6 + 2 letters, GB8 + 2 letters	

Other callsign formats

The RSGB is not authorised to issue callsigns in formats different from the above. Applications for special anniversaries which require the numbers such as 25, 40, 50, 60 or 75 must be specially supported by the RSGB to the RA. The latter will only consider applications via the RSGB from the headquarters of a nationally based organisation. Applications cannot be entertained from individuals, local clubs or branches of nationally based organisations.

Greetings messages

The guidelines agreed with the RA are:

1. Each greetings message should not exceed two minutes.
2. Each person may pass only one message to each station with which the originating station is in contact.
3. A non-licensed person may speak into the microphone, but the licensed radio amateur must identify the station and operate the transmitter controls at all times.
4. Greetings messages by third parties may only be sent from and received by stations within the UK, except that international greetings messages may be passed to and from stations

A few friendly faces, some posters and a couple of radios being operated in full view of passers-by was the welcoming scene at GB2STF

in the USA, Canada, Falkland Is and Pitcairn Is. The licensee may exchange greetings as in any QSO, with any station.

Charitable events

It is recognised that some special-event stations will be established at certain charitable events where a major concern will be the raising of funds.

The RA has agreed that the charity (if one is involved) or the reason for establishing the special-event station may be mentioned 'on-air' provided that under *no* circumstances may a donation be requested during the contact, and sending of QSL cards must *not* be conditional upon the pledge of a donation. It is in the interests of everyone who holds a special-event station licence that operators keep within the spirit of this by not asking for any money over the air.

The station may be sponsored per contact, ie the licensee may in advance of the event seek from his friends and relatives sponsorship assurances under the usual arrangements for sponsorship. You must *not* seek sponsors 'on-air' at any time.

QSL cards

If you are running a GB station, QSL cards should be printed in advance but obviously not until the RSGB advises that the callsign you wish to use has been accepted. Sometimes conflicting requests for the same callsign are received and alternatives have to be chosen.

As a rough guide, about 1000 cards are required for a week's operating. About 10% of these will be required to satisfy requests from listeners, and these might well be received up to at least two years after the event. Note that the cards should be completed while the station is in operation as this saves a lot of clerical labour afterwards. Information on the use of the QSL Bureau is supplied by the RSGB, and the special-event callsign sub-manager is also automatically informed of the dates of your event so as to avoid any possible confusion with a previous event which may have used that callsign.

Special-event stations generate a lot of QSL cards – do follow the guidelines given in Chapter 3 on how to use the QSL Bureau properly.

DEMONSTRATION STATIONS

The object of a demonstration station is to present amateur radio in an attractive and informative manner to the general public. Clearly, a poorly organised station with a confusing and unwelcoming display hardly serves this purpose – visitors will probably just pass straight on to the next stand!

Attention to the points outlined in the previous section well before the event is important and should provide the basis for a successful operation. At the same time the display should be planned. A few radio maps, some posters explaining the use of Q-signals etc and some colourful QSL cards will do much to brighten up the look of the station. It is also a good idea to have a few radio magazines handy and in addition it is possible to obtain posters and leaflets from the RSGB for display purposes. Contact the Amateur Radio Department for further details.

If you know a local amateur who is able to construct simple equipment, even if only for CW use, get him to display and operate it. The fact that an onlooker can see something working that he feels he could construct himself is a spur to his interest.

Publicity

If a GB licence is applied for, send details of the event to *Radio Communication* and all the other UK amateur radio magazines as soon as possible.

If you are involved with the Press at any stage make sure they do not print any misleading information. In fact it is advisable to provide them with an information handout to ensure the details are correct. The use of such terms as 'broadcasting' and 'message passing' should be avoided at all costs.

Power supplies

Unless the equipment will operate from batteries perhaps the most important single factor affecting the station is the electricity supply. If possible try to operate from a mains source as this is normally reliable and noiseless in comparison with generators. On the other hand, if the radio station is only one of many electrically operated displays and is near the end of the supply line it is quite possible for the voltage to drop well below 200V and render radio equipment inoperative. Also, the other displays may cause electrical interference and it is as well to check these points before operating commences.

If a generator is used, diesel fuel or petrol will be required and cost alone might easily restrict the number of operating hours. Generators must be tested before the event despite any verbal assurances that they are suitable. Check the voltage on full load (including lights) and your receiver on all frequencies for the amount of hash produced. The earth wire should be connected to a ground stake at both the generator and the equipment end of the supply line as this reduces hash.

Where more than one generator is in use it is an extremely important safety factor to ensure that the supplies are not only kept separate but are connected to entirely separate groups of equipment. Sharing can result in twice the supply voltage appearing across some distribution terminals – a very dangerous situation. See Chapter 5 for more safety information.

You will need lights for the evenings or for operation in dark locations and the use of spotlights will enhance the overall effect. Avoid fluorescent lights and keep as far away as possible from other displays using them as they can cause considerable interference. The fact that you are operating at an exhibition does not mean you can neglect the normal safety principles. Make sure the supply is correctly fused and that there is one main and clearly labelled switch to disconnect it in an emergency.

Accommodation and the station

When operating in the open try to obtain the use of the largest tent or marquee possible as this must not only house the station but a fair number of spectators too. The next most important decision will be where to actually locate the station on the site

and this will usually be a compromise. The station will obviously have to be located fairly near the mains source unless a generator is to be used. If late-evening operation is envisaged or a generator is to be used it is not advisable to be close to any sleeping areas.

Should a public address system be in operation, try to ensure that the station is sited as far away from the input end as possible, especially if they intend to use a wandering microphone with a long lead. If the station does cause interference carry out tests on all bands as you will normally find that only one or two are affected. Unless you can clear the interference it will be necessary to liaise with the PA operator to keep off the offending bands while his equipment is in use.

Unless the station has some definite objective (eg to make contacts in certain parts of the world involving directive antenna arrays) it is advisable to keep the antenna system as simple as possible. Complicated antennas and masses of equipment create their own problems and often need days of installation work in order to operate satisfactorily.

Once again remember that it is important to observe the normal safety principles and provide an efficient earthing system for the antenna arrays. Long cables carrying mains voltages should not be trailed over the ground and are better sited up in the air well out of reach.

If sleeping on site, it is as well to screen off a portion of the operating position as living accommodation. This has the added benefit that you will provide your own guard for the station equipment during the silent hours.

Try to make the display as attractive as possible – do not use so much material that it looks cluttered and 'bitty'. Battered old tables can be improved beyond recognition by covering them with cloths or crepe paper. If the stand is located against a wall this will probably be dull and uninspiring so cover it with sheets or curtains. Such action helps to highlight the equipment and posters etc, all of which are your 'selling' points to the public.

It is advisable to erect some form of barrier between the visitors and the operators to avoid crushing. Any really interested onlooker can always be invited 'in' to sit with the operators.

Running the station

When operating a demonstration station it should be remembered that one is dealing with varying degrees of interest. Some members of the public will be interested in becoming amateurs or short-wave listeners but the majority will be showing just a general interest. It is important to cater for this second group as it is an advantage for as many members of the public as possible to realise that radio amateurs are serious and responsible members of the community and that the hobby is controlled by examination, licensing and official inspection.

Unless the station is part of a technical exhibition the most friendly and able speakers should be in the front of your stand to explain what is going on. Remember the majority of the public will not be technically minded and what is required is a good 'salesman' and not a technical expert. It is important that the onlookers should receive a friendly welcome and are not faced with the backs of operators all far too busy to talk to them.

With the present state of telecommunications, where it is possible to pick up a hand-portable mobile phone and dial numbers on the other side of the world, speaking over great distances by radio no longer holds the mystery and excitement it did a few decades ago. It is therefore far more impressive to make clear audible local contacts than almost unreadable ones over thousands of kilometres.

Most of your audience will not have heard SSB signals previously so do remember that it takes some time for their ears to become accustomed to the sounds and for them to understand what is being said.

Also remember the many varied facets of amateur radio: short-wave listening, mobile working, packet radio, SSTV etc. All of these should be mentioned even if they are not demonstrated.

Fig 1. Talk-in organisation

Do not make your display too complicated as there is nothing to be gained by confusing the onlookers. The fixation in the minds of many amateurs that they must work as many stations as possible during these events is quite unfounded as the main aim is to arouse interest in the hobby.

TALK-IN STATIONS

"GB2VHF – This is G3AFT/mobile on the M1 near Watford – request talk-in – over."

This crisp message was sufficient to bring into action the talk-in station at a major RSGB event held in London some years ago. Half an hour later the relaxed visitor to London was personally thanking the talk-in operator for making the drive through the capital's northern suburbs so simple.

This section discusses the planning and operation of a talk-in service and the principal factors which must be taken into account. The object of a talk-in station is to guide mobile radio amateurs to a location through terrain with which they are not familiar. Information is provided in the form of advice rather than instruction and the car driver remains responsible in the final analysis for arriving safely at his destination.

Organisation

Any event, be it a major exhibition, a mobile rally or a local club junk sale, will invariably be organised by a committee. This committee will have to decide such matters as the dates, times and location of the event, how to attract trade support, and which guest speakers to invite if lectures are to be held. Further subjects to come before the organising committee will include catering, car parking, publicity, family attractions and of course talk-in facilities. It is therefore important that the person in charge of the talk-in service, the talk-in manager, is a member of this organising committee.

In turn the talk-in manager will gather round him a team of specialists to help set up and run the talk-in station. Formal reporting lines are indicated in Fig 1.

It is never too early to start planning, and as soon as the date and place of the event have been decided the talk-in manager must choose and bring together his team. If the event is not a major international meeting then one person can do more than one of the jobs identified in Fig 1. In the case of a very minor occasion such as a club social evening the whole operation could be undertaken single-handed. Even so, all the factors discussed in this section must be taken into account regardless of the number of people involved.

Frequencies

Frequency modulation in the 145–146MHz band is the mode of choice by the great majority of mobile operators. Furthermore, the constraints of band planning and the limitation in the number of fixed frequencies available in mobile equipment (see Chapter 6) has meant that in practice only a handful of frequencies need to be considered for a talk-in station.

All 144MHz transceivers are able to operate on 145.50MHz and 145.55MHz, but only the latter is suitable for a talk-in service. 145.50MHz (S20) is by convention a general mobile calling channel and should not be monopolised by one station. 145.55MHz (S22) is therefore usually selected as the primary frequency.

More ambitious talk-in stations will be equipped to operate on other modes and frequencies, for example SSB on, say, 144.280MHz or SSB on 3.715MHz. As SSB equipment is invariably VFO-controlled precise frequencies need not be specified.

70cm FM is also very popular and a talk-in station should be capable of operating on, for example, 433.55MHz.

Equipment

Whether a variety of frequencies is to be used or, as in the case of a more modest station, only 145.55MHz FM, it is vital that the talk-in operator can hear (and be heard loud and clear) over a wide area.

The merits or otherwise of individual commercial transceivers cannot be discussed here but in all cases reliability is of paramount importance. Transmitter power outputs in excess of 10W are usually unnecessary at VHF provided that the antenna is well sited. This often means that a 'black-box' transceiver running off a car battery is the only equipment needed. A standby battery together with a charger should be available as a sensible precaution, however. If two channels in the same band are to be used simultaneously it may be necessary to install cavity filters to provide sufficient separation – such a technical matter must be investigated well in advance of the event, as it can be a great disappointment having made plans for two transceivers only to find on the day that they cause mutual interference. This mode of operation can be very difficult if the frequencies are not far apart. There may also be adjacent-channel interference to mobiles in the close vicinity.

A desk microphone is more convenient than a handheld one, and a boom microphone attached to headphones is better still. If headphones are used it may be desirable from a public-relations point of view to connect extension loudspeakers.

The quality of transmission must always be of the highest order – decent punchy audio but without a high level of background noise (where did all those Second World War throat mikes go?) It is especially important to check performance and quality when the gear is running from (unknown) generators.

Antennas

At VHF the basic rule is to mount the antenna as high as possible. However, the choices open for the siting of antennas are often limited, and will be dictated by the type of building housing the event and by the position of the stand made available to the talk-in station.

The type of antenna can influence the efficiency of the station and advantage should be taken of the gain of a stacked array, collinear or 5λ/8 ground plane. An ideal arrangement would be a collinear mounted on a tall mast attached to the highest point of the building with the station in a room as close as possible. Use of low-loss coaxial cable together with attention to accurate matching will further help effective radiation and clear reception.

In a poor VHF location it may be worth considering locating the talk-in station at a site remote from the main event. For example central London is in a geographic saucer with poor VHF propagation characteristics, aggravated by the high density of metal-framed tall buildings. However, locating the talk-in station at the home of an amateur living on top of one of the several hills which surround London would almost certainly give better VHF coverage of the Greater London area. This solution also helps overcome the effects of adjacent-channel and 'desense' problems, and has been used most successfully at the Woburn Rally.

Another possibility, particularly if the event is being held in a single-storey building or under canvas, is to hire or borrow a telescopic mast.

A few words of warning to the person in charge of antennas (see also Chapter 5):

- take safety seriously;
- wear protective headgear;
- use correct clamps and other hardware. A good antenna system will almost certainly ensure a good talk-in station.

Operating procedures

Having installed the equipment and erected an efficient antenna system the next item to be considered is how best to provide talk-in advice. Talk-in information is divided into two parts; the approach phase and the final run-in.

Approach phase

With the aid of a map having a scale of about 500,000:1 (6km/cm or 10 miles to the inch) decide on the major routes from surrounding towns to the scene of the event. Observe if these roads converge on to a ring road, bridge over a river or some other unmistakable feature about 3km (two miles) from the destination. Try to choose features common to roads coming in from more than one outlying town. Two, or at most three, such features should be selected as 'reporting points'. The journey from a distant place to the reporting point can be considered as the approach phase and quite often only one instruction is needed for this part of the talk-in, eg "Continue towards London and turn left onto the North Circular Road" in the case where the North Circular Road is the reporting point.

Final phase

This stage of the talk-in begins at the reporting point and consists of detailed instructions to get the mobile station to the destination. If only two reporting points are chosen, then only

Fig 2. Wooden identification 'chuck'. These are placed on the operational map and show the position of all mobiles being worked; their position is updated as the talk-in proceeds. Use a fine felt-tipped pen for writing callsigns on cards, selecting contrasting colours if more than one talk-in station is to be used. Operators can then tell at a glance which mobiles are under their care

two sets of detailed instructions need be planned for the final phase. This will greatly simplify the job of the operators.

The object is therefore to identify and describe, say, six major approach roads leading to perhaps two reporting points. Even in the case of London the number of reporting points can be limited to the North Circular Road and Kew Bridge, Waterloo Bridge and the Blackwall Tunnel.

No doubt there will be endless debate as to the best routes to choose and in the event of a dispute the talk-in manager must make the final decision. To help in arriving at the right choice he will probably survey all likely roads and make careful notes of important road signs and other useful features. Familiarity with the locality is imperative and prior to the event all operators should tour the selected routes.

Having decided on routes it will next be necessary to describe each, briefly and through the eyes of a driver. The examples quoted in this chapter may give some guidance on this key part of the planning of the talk-in station.

Maps

Although Ordnance Survey and road maps will be needed at the planning stage it may be better to construct a special map for actual use by the talk-in operators. This would show only major roads and would highlight only those features of interest to a driver being talked-in. In this respect garages are very prominent, as are roundabouts, railway bridges and ring roads.

Another reason for constructing an operational map is to take advantage of the flexibility it can provide at a major event. At any moment perhaps a dozen or more mobile stations may be being talked-in. In order to keep track of this activity it will be helpful to use identification 'chucks'; see Fig 2. These are moved around the map as mobile stations report in, and will show the location of all approaching traffic.

Normal maps, being of fixed scale, will show too much detail in the outlying areas and not enough of the streets close in. A map with a variable scale will be much more useful, but it will take time and effort to draw.

Fig 3 shows an example of such a map of the south-east England which was drawn on 25 sheets of A2 paper (equivalent to 100 sheets of A4 paper). The main roads from Norwich, Dover and Southampton are shown in broad outline whereas the minor roads in the immediate vicinity of the exhibition, in this case at Alexandra Palace in North London, are shown in considerable detail.

The smaller scale at a greater distance is compatible with

Fig 3. Typical talk-in map

"Continue to Muswell Hill Roundabout (with bus depot in middle) – go in at 6 o'clock and out at 12 o'clock [see Fig 4], down steep hill and turn hard left left at bottom of hill into grounds of Alexandra Palace."

Lost procedure

Should a mobile station become lost, and this will usually occur in a large city, it is vital that the talk-in operator establishes an accurate 'fix' before trying to give further advice. First the lost mobile should be asked to check the name of the road on which he is driving together with the name of a side road. The operator then calmly looks up this reference on his town map and decides on a route back to a main road. If the whereabouts of the mobile cannot be readily established he should be asked to stop when safe to do so. (He will not mind this as he is relying on the talk-in operator for correct information to get him back on course.)

Courtesy at all times

The rationale for selecting frequencies for a talk-in service has already been explained and it is worth mentioning that no exclusive right can be claimed for them. However, a word or two on how to establish and maintain a clear channel may not be out of place.

Assuming a well-sited antenna and satisfactory equipment the talk-in station is likely to be heard over a wide area. Therefore if upon switching on another contact is in progress, wait until it is finished. Then call, say, "GB2ZZZ listening" once only. If you receive a reply from a mobile coming to the event, you are in business! If the reply comes from a fixed station, you should explain that you are listening out for mobiles who might request directions to the event.

the frequency with which a mobile station needs assistance. For example a mobile station calling in from Maidstone, 50km (30 miles) out, would be advised: "Continue on M20 and A20 towards Blackwall Tunnel – call again when approaching Blackwall Tunnel". This same mobile, when at Manor House and only 5km (3 miles) from his destination, would be told, "Turn right at Manor House – after 1½ miles turn left at Turnpike Lane and call again". The variable scale map will have been able to accommodate the mobile station both when 50km away near Maidstone and 5km away at Manor House. The talk-in operator will have known his whereabouts with an appropriate degree of accuracy in both circumstances. Incidentally the talk-in station will have transmitted only three messages from the Blackwall Tunnel to Alexandra Palace, on what many would describe as a nightmare journey across London.

Words

Having established contact with a mobile station needing advice the next question which arises is which words should be used? Brevity with clarity is the key and the following example may be helpful. In the case of the mobile who called in at the beginning of this section the assistance might go as follows (callsigns omitted):

"Your present location please."

The mobile gives his location which is pin-pointed on the map with a "chuck".

"Continue on M1 for eight miles – leave at junction 2 and call again at North Circular Road."

Later, when the mobile reports at the North Circular Road (and his 'chuck' having been moved accordingly) he is advised:

"Continue on North Circular Road for three miles – leave on B550 for Muswell Hill and call again."

The final instruction would be:

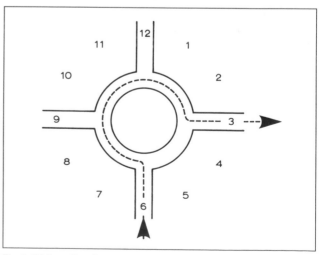

Fig 4. Giving directions at roundabouts

Should there be no reply, then the channel is almost yours; call again, "GB2ZZZ listening".

A procedure such as that suggested above will allow other amateurs to speak up if they feel that you are pushing your way in a little too hard. Radio amateurs will respond to a polite, brief explanation of what you are doing, but few will relish being steam-rollered off a frequency which they may have regarded as being 'theirs'.

Having gently eased your way onto a frequency the next problem becomes how best to hold on to it. 14MHz operators will know how easy it is to lose their place on a frequency by remaining silent for too long at the end of a contact. Somebody, somewhere is always waiting on the side, ready to take over the channel. Therefore you must make sure that other stations are aware that the frequency is in use. The simplest way, and the one which is least likely to aggravate other amateurs, is to announce "GB2ZZZ listening" every 20 to 30 seconds.

Do *not* put out a long call stating that you are the talk-in station to the such-and-such rally being held at so-and-so, and that you can provide a talk-in service for those needing navigation advice and that you are listening out for any mobiles etc etc etc! All that you need to do in order to hold on to the frequency is to say every 20 to 30 seconds "GB2ZZZ listening". To do otherwise will justifiably bring strong criticism that you are monopolising the air.

Personnel

How many people are needed to operate a talk-in service? The answer will depend mainly on the number of simultaneous frequencies in use and also upon the length of the event.

Each channel will need an operator who must have a thorough knowledge of the area as well as a good operating manner, and a logkeeper who should have a tidy hand. A third member of the team will be needed to take care of the maps, particularly during the period when a mobile reports being lost. He will also keep the operator up to date on the whereabouts of all stations being worked by moving the 'chucks' across the map.

A team of three can work well for two hours without a break, but if three-hour or four-hour shifts are decided upon, then tea, sandwiches and biscuits should be available. In the case of an elaborate talk-in station with perhaps a dozen or more people on each shift a catering manager should be appointed. Attention in the area of refreshments can make amateur radio that much more civilised. Note, however, that alcohol is absolutely prohibited prior to or during operating.

Next, having identified the jobs to be done, it is important to ensure that the workload does not fall upon too few shoulders. A personnel roster should be drawn up and when agreed to by all concerned it should be prominently displayed. If more than

12 or so people are involved it is as well to write formally to each enclosing a statement of their times on duty, together with a return slip on which they should signify their agreement to these times. Such a written commitment should ensure that personnel attend on time. The talk-in manager or his deputy must be present throughout the period of the event.

Public relations

An ambitious talk-in station can, if well presented and efficiently operated, be an excellent way of demonstrating amateur radio to the public. Nominate one person on each shift to answer questions about amateur radio in general and the talk-in station in particular. Do not overlook this opportunity to promote the usefulness of the hobby.

As the talk-in station is the centre of communication it is logical to have the public address system under the control of the talk-in manager. Once again it is essential to keep messages short and crisp: "ding-dong – G8DWL to the RSGB stand" is all that is necessary. Do not overuse the PA system; all messages must be checked with the talk-in manager before being broadcast.

Other points

The talk-in stations should be on the air early – ie if the rally opens at 11am the talk-in stations should be on the air by 9–9.30am.

If more than one station is running, care should be taken to ensure that they are not physically too close together so that each station turns up the receiver audio to drown the noise coming from the other!

Some mobiles like to have QSL cards – these should be available from the stand. Again, some mobiles appreciate *talk-out* after the event!

Conclusion

By now the reader may feel that so much planning is taking the matter rather too seriously, and that one could get by equally well without all this detail. Be warned! An ill-prepared and rambling talk-in is embarrassing to the casual listener, and frustrating to the mobile in need of clear navigation advice who finds he cannot get a word in edgeways. Tempers will fray and you would be doing a disservice to both your club and the event you are supposed to be supporting.

On the other hand a well-managed talk-in, carefully planned down to the last word of advice, is a pleasure to listen to, a real help to the distant visitor and can only bring goodwill to your club as well as a great deal of pleasure to all concerned.

"GB2VHF – this is G3AFT mobile – I've arrived in the car park – many thanks for your assistance – out."

Continental and regional maps

Map 1. IARU locator map of Europe

AFRICA, SOUTH ASIA and AUSTRALIA

Map 2

NORTH & SOUTH AMERICA

Map 3

Map 4

THE PACIFIC OCEAN

Map 5

Map 6

Map 7

Map 8

2 International callsign series holders

THIS appendix gives information of amateur radio interest for each organisation, country or group of countries which has been assigned one or more ITU international callsign series. This assignment has no significance with respect to the political independence or otherwise of the holder.

The callsign system information is supplemented by call area maps where possible; this information for larger countries may instead appear in Appendix 1. In some cases maps are not provided for countries with call area systems; here a city or town from each province is given in a table so that the reader can still locate the approximate area corresponding to a callsign in an atlas. A note to the effect that third-party traffic is permitted does not necessarily mean that such communication is possible with all other countries permitting it. Such traffic is by individual agreement between the countries concerned (see Chapter 1).

If foreign amateurs from certain countries are permitted to operate inside a particular country, some indication of these other countries is given where known but this may well be incomplete due to political change or fresh reciprocity agreements. It is therefore advisable to check the up-to-date position with the relevant national society or licensing administration. The amount of notice required for processing foreign amateur operation licences where given is in respect of completed applications on the correct forms with all necessary enclosures, including any necessary fee. Therefore allowance should be made for initial correspondence and answering of queries (see Chapter 6). The licensing administration addresses given are the correspondence addresses for foreign amateur licensing and may not be correct for other telecommunication matters. Such addresses are not given where application must be made via the national society which is the case in several countries.

All telephone numbers given are in the international form +x (y) z where x is the country code, y is the area code (if applicable) and z is the number. They will have to be prefaced by the appropriate international dialling prefix (00 in the UK). If dialling from within the country, the area code may need to be prefaced by a zero.

AFGHANISTAN (Democratic Republic of)

ITU allocation: YAA–YAZ.
Callsign system: Prefix: YA.
Licensing administration: Ministry of Communications, Kabul.

ALBANIA (Socialist People's Republic of)

ITU allocation: ZAA–ZAZ.
National society: Albanian Amateur Radio Association, PO Box N 66, Tirana.
Licensing administration: Direction générale des postes et télécommunications, 42 rue Myslym Shyri, Tirane.

ALGERIA (Algerian Democratic and Popular Republic)

ITU allocation: 7RA–7RZ, 7TA–7YZ.
Callsign system:

Prefix	City/town and area
7X2	Algiers (El Djezair)
7X3	Ghardaia
7X4	Oran
7X5	Constantine

Licence notes: Single licence class, 200W PEP.
Foreign amateur operation: 7X0 prefix. All countries except Israel.
National society: Amateurs Radio Algeriens, BP2, Alger-Gare. Tel: +213 (2) 644432.
Licensing administration: Ministère des postes et télécommunications, Secretariat générale, 4 boulevard Salah Bouakouir, Algiers.

ANDORRA (Principality of)

ITU allocation: C3A–C3Z.
Callsign system: Prefix: C3.
Licence notes: Single licence class: 1kW PEP.
National society: Unio de Radioaficionats Andorrans, PO Box 150, La Vella.

ANGOLA (People's Republic of)

ITU allocation: D2A–D3Z.
Callsign system: Prefix: D2.
Licensing administration: Service dos correios, telegrafos e telefones, Luanda.

ANTIGUA and BARBUDA

ITU allocation: V2A–V2Z.
Callsign system: Prefix: V2.
Licence notes: Single licence class: 1kW DC input.
Foreign amateur operation: Countries include: British Commonwealth, Canada and USA.
National society: Antigua and Barbuda Amateur Radio Society, PO Box 1111, St John's.
Licensing administration: Telecommunications Officer, Ministry of Public Works and Communications, St John St, St John's.

ARGENTINA (Argentine Republic)

ITU allocation: L2A–L9Z, AYA–AZZ, LOA–LWZ.
Callsign system: LU1–9 fixed stations, LU0 mobile stations. For call areas see map (letters shown are the first serial letter(s)).
Licence notes: Five licence classes: Special: all bands, 1kW DC input. Superior: all bands, 1kW DC input. General: all bands, 1kW DC input. Intermediate: VHF, restricted HF, CW only, 100W DC input. Novice: 3.5MHz and VHF, CW only, 50W.
Foreign amateur operation: Call is own call/LU. Countries include: USA, Venezuela, Costa Rica, Paraguay, Peru, Chile, Uruguay.
National society: Radio Club Argentino, Carlos Calvo 1420/24, 1102 Buenos Aires. Tel: +54 (1) 304-0555. Fax: +54 (1) 304-0555.
Licensing administration: Direccion National de Telecommunicaciones, Sección Radioaficionados, Sarmiento 141, 1000 Buenos Aires.

ARMENIA

ITU allocation: EKA–EKZ.
Callsign system: Prefix: EK.

ARUBA

ITU allocation: P4A–P4Z.
Callsign system: Prefix: P43.
National society: Aruba Amateur Radio Club, PO Box 2273, San Nicolas.

AUSTRALIA

ITU allocation: AXA–AXZ, VHA–VNZ, VZA–VZZ.
Callsign system: See Map 2 for prefixes. Licence class is denoted by serial letters as follows:

ARGENTINA – LU

VP8
Falkland Islands

AUSTRIA – OE

Suffix	Licence class
AA–ZZ	Unrestricted
AAA–GZZ	Unrestricted
IAA–IZZ	Full
JAA–KZZ	Limited plus novice (licensees holding both licences)
LAA–NZZ	Novice
PAA–PZZ	Novice
RAA–RZZ	Beacons and repeaters
SAA–SZZ	Unrestricted
TAA–UZZ	Limited
VAA–VZZ	Novice
WAA–WZZ	Unrestricted
XAA–ZZZ	Limited

Operation outside own call area uses CALL/VK followed by number denoting state.
Licence notes: Three classes of licence. Unrestricted call: 120W mean or 400W PEP SSB. Novice: crystal-controlled 3.525–3.565MHz, 21.125–21.200MHz, 28.100–28.600MHz, 146–148MHz phone/CW, 10W mean, 30W PEP. Limited: VHF phone only, 120W mean, 400W PEP. Third-party traffic permitted.
Foreign amateur operation: Three types of licensing. All require a fee and form. Three months' notice by post but can obtained over the counter at the local Spectrum Management Agency office in each state. *Category A*: Reciprocal. Countries include: Canada, Denmark, France (incl New Caledonia), Germany, India, Israel, Japan, Malaysia, New Zealand, Papua New Guinea, Poland, Solomon Is, Spain, Switzerland, UK, USA, Singapore. *Category B*: Unilateral. Countries include: Argentina, Falkland Is, Greece, Hong Kong, Indonesia, Irish Rep, Italy, Luxembourg, Malta, Nauru, Netherlands, Norway, Phillipines, Singapore, South Africa, Sri Lanka, Ceylon, Sweden, Vanuatu and West Indies. Category C: 10W 144MHz licence. All other countries.
National society: Wireless Institute of Australia, PO Box 2175, Caulfield Junction, VIC 3161. Tel: +61 (3) 528-5962. Fax: +61 (3) 523-8191.
Licensing administration: Offices in each state. The one in Victoria is: Spectrum Management Agency, PO Box 6444, St Kilda Road Central VIC 3004. Tel: +61 (3) 685-3555. Fax: +61 (3) 685-3500.

AUSTRIA

ITU allocation: OEA–OEZ.
Callsign system: See map for prefixes. Serial letters in the XAA–XZZ series denote special stations, beacons or repeaters.
Licence notes: Four licence classes: 25, 50, 100 and 250W anode dissipation. 250W class is VHF phone-only for clubs only.
Foreign amateur operation: *CEPT operation:* A + B using OE/own call. *Non-CEPT operation:* A + B. Fee. Six weeks' notice. Call is OE series. Countries include: Australia, Belgium, Costa Rica, Germany, Finland, France, UK, Israel, Italy, Yugoslavia, Canada, Liechtenstein, Luxembourg, Monaco, Netherlands, Norway, Poland, Romania, Sweden, Switzerland, Czechoslovakia, USA. Applications should be made to the local branch of the licensing administration. Further information can be obtained from the telecomm contact officer at ÖVSV.
National society: Österreichischer Versuchsenderverband, PO Box 999, A-1014 Vienna. Tel: +43 (1) 4085535 (Wednesdays, 4–8pm). Fax: +43 (1) 4031830.
Licensing administration: BMöWV – Sektion IV – Rechtsabteilung, Kelsenstr 7, A-1030 Vienna. Tel: +43 (1) 79731-4100. Fax: +43 (1) 79731-4109. Local offices are: *OE1, OE3, OE4* – Fernmeldebüro für Wien, NÖ und Bgld, Nordbergstrasse 15, A-1091 Vienna. *OE2, OE5* – Fernmeldebüro für OÖ und Salzburg, Domgasse 1, A-4010 Linz. *OE6, OE8* –Fernmeldebüro für Kärnten and Steiemark, Neutorgasse 46, A-8011 Graz. *OE7, OE9* – Fernmeldebüro für Tirol und Vorarlberg, Maximillianstrasse 7, A-6010 Innsbruck.

AZERBAIJAN

ITU allocation: 4JA–4KZ.
Callsign system: Prefix: 4K followed by area number (see below).

Area no	Area
2	Nakhichevan
3	Azerbaijan (except Nakhichevan and Baku)
4–9	Baku

BAHAMAS (Commonwealth of the)

ITU allocation: C6A–C6Z.
Callsign system: Prefix: C6.
Licence notes: Similar to USA General class. Maximum power: 100W PEP.
Foreign amateur operation: Unilateral. A only. Countries include UK, USA.
National society: Bahamas Amateur Radio Society, PO Box SS-6004, Nassau.
Licensing administration: Bahamas Telecomms Corp, PO Box N3048, Nassau. Tel: +1 (809) 323-4911.

BAHRAIN (State of)

ITU allocation: A9A–A9Z.
Callsign system: Prefix: A92.
Licence notes: Single licence class. Maximum power: 500W PEP.
Foreign amateur operation: Must have resident permit.
National society: Amateur Radio Association Bahrain, PO Box 22381, Muharraq.
Licensing administration: Secretary General, Permanent Telecommunications Committee, PO Box 831, Manama.

BANGLADESH (People's Republic of)

ITU allocation: S2A–S3Z.
Callsign system: Prefix: S2.
Foreign amateur operation: Call is own call/S2.
National society: Bangladesh Amateur Radio League, GPO Box 3512, Dacca 1000.
Licensing administration: Telegraph and Telephone Board of Bangladesh, Capital Exchange Building, Dacca 15.

BARBADOS

ITU allocation: 8PA–8PZ.
Calsign system: Prefixes: 8P6, 8P7 (advanced class).
Licence notes: Two licence classes: CW: all bands, CW only, 500W. General: all bands, all modes, 500W input. There is also an advanced class.
Foreign amateur operation: Unilateral. A only. Call is 8P9 series. Countries include: British Commonwealth countries, USA.
National society: Amateur Radio Society of Barbados, PO Box 814E, Bridgetown. Tel: +1 (809) 406-2502.
Licensing administration: Senior Telecomms Officer, Ministry of Public Works, Communications and Transportation, Herbert House, Fontabelle, St Michael. Tel: +1 (809) 426-2669.

BELARUS

ITU allocation: EUA–EWZ.
Callsign system: Prefixes: EU, EW followed by area number.

Area no	Area	Capital
1	Minsk city	
2	Minsk Obl	Minsk
3	Brest Obl	Brest
4	Grodno Obl	Grodno
6	Vitebsk Obl	Vitebsk
7	Mogilev Obl	Mogilev
8	Gomel Obl	Gomel

National society: Belarus Federation of Radio Amateurs and Radio-sportsmen, Ul Kazintca 48, 220099 Minsk. Tel: +7 (0172) 755325. Fax: +7 (0172) 786750.

BELGIUM

ITU allocation: ONA–OTZ.
Callsign system:

Prefix	Area	Licence class
ON0	Belgium	Repeaters
ON1	Belgium	Class BI, BII
ON4, 5, 6, 7	Belgium	Class A, BI, BII, C
ON9	Belgium	Foreign amateurs
OR4	Overseas incl Antarctica (Belg)	

Licence notes: Four classes of licence. Class A: 125W all bands, all modes. Class BI: 250W VHF bands only. Class BII: 125W VHF bands only. Class C: 500W all bands, all modes.
Foreign amateur operation: *CEPT*: A + B using ON/own call. *Non-CEPT*: Reciprocal. Two months' notice. Fee. Form. Countries include UK, USA.
National society: Union Belge des Amateurs Emetteurs, c/o Etienne David, ON5IA, A Vermeylenstraat 49, B-8400 Ostend.
Licensing administration: IBPT, Av de l'Astronomie 14, B-1030 Brussels. Tel: +3 (2) 207 77 77. Fax: +32 (2) 207 78 88.

BELIZE

ITU allocation: V3A–V3Z.
Callsign system: Prefixes: V31 (Class 1), V32 (Class 2). For call areas see below.

Serial letters	Area
AA–BZ	Corozel
CA–DZ	Orange Walk
FA–KZ	Belize
LA–MZ	Stann Creek
NZ–OZ	Cayo
PA–QZ	Toledo

National society: Belize Amateur Radio Club, PO Box 296, Belize.
Foreign amateur operation: Countries include USA.
Licensing administration: Belize Telecommunication Authority, PO Box 603, Belize City.

BENIN (People's Republic of)

ITU allocation: TYA–TYZ.
Licensing administration: M le Directeur général de l'Office des postes et télécommunications, Cotonou.

BHUTAN (Kingdom of)

ITU allocation: A5A–A5Z.
Callsign system: Prefix: A51.

BOLIVIA (Republic of)

ITU allocation: CPA–CPZ.
Callsign system: See map for prefixes. CP0 is a special station prefix.
Licence notes: Two licence classes: Second class: 3.5, 7MHz SSB/CW, 200W PEP. First class: all bands, SSB/CW, 1kW PEP. Third-party traffic permitted.

Foreign amateur operation: Call is own call/CP. Countries include: Colombia, Germany, Peru, Switzerland, Venezuela, USA.
National society: Radio Club Boliviano, PO Box 2800, Cochabamba. Tel: +591 (42) 31469. Fax: +591 (42) 29905.

BOSNIA-HERCEGOVINA

ITU allocation: T9A–T9Z.
Callsign system: Prefix: T9.
National society: Asocijacija Radioamatera Bosne i Hercegovine, PO Box 61, Dariela Ozme 7, 71000 Sarajevo.

BOTSWANA (Republic of)

ITU allocation: A2A–A2Z, 8OA–8OZ.
Callsign system: Prefixes: A22, A24 (novice).
Licence notes: Maximum power 150W DC input. Also novice class.
Foreign amateur operation: Reciprocal (A only). Countries include UK. Call is A25/own call.
National society: Botswana Amateur Radio Society, Box 1873, Gaborone.
Licensing administration: Botswana Telecoms Corporation, Radio Spectrum Management Division, PO Box 700, Gaberone. Tel: +267 358000.

BRAZIL (Federative Republic of)

ITU allocation: PPA–PYZ, ZVA–ZZZ.
Callsign system: See map for prefixes. Abrolhos Is also has PY0 prefix. WAA–WZZ serial letters: Class C or licensee aged 14–18 years. ZAA–ZZZ serial letters: foreign citizens. State prefix is added when operating outside own state, eg PY1ZZ/PT2.
Licence notes: Three licence classes. Class A: all bands, 1kW PEP. Class B: 1.8, 3.5MHz, 1kW PEP. Class C: 7MHz, 100W PEP. Third-party traffic permitted.
Foreign amateur operation: Reciprocal (A only). Temporary calls are own call/PY. Six months' notice. Countries include: Bolivia, Canada, Chile, Colombia, Guatemala, Denmark, Dominica, Germany, UK, Paraguay, Portugal, Sweden, USA, Venezuela, Uruguay.
National society: Liga Brasileira de Radioamadores, PO Box 07-0004, 70359 Brasilia DF. Tel: +55 (61) 223-1157. Fax: +55 (61) 223-1157.
Licensing administration: Departamento Nacional de Telecomunicações, Dentel 4° Andar, Ministerio das Comunicações, 70000 Brasilia, DF.

BRUNEI DARUSSALAM

ITU allocation: V8A–V8Z.
Callsign system: Prefix: V85.
Foreign amateur operation: Unilateral (A + B).
National society: Brunei Darussalam ARA, PO Box 73, Gadong, Bandar Seri Begawan 3100.

BRAZIL
NEW PREFIXES
SINCE 1975

Licensing administration: Controller of Telecommunications, Telecommunications Headquarters, Bandar Seri Begawan. Tel: +673 42324.

BULGARIA (People's Republic of)

ITU allocation: LZA–LZZ.
Callsign system: Prefix: LZ. KAA–KZZ serial letters denote club call.
Licence notes: Maximum power 1kW DC input.
Foreign amateur operation: *CEPT:* A + B. Call is LZ/own call. *Non-CEPT:* Unilateral (A only). Apply to BFRA.
National society: Bulgarian Federation of Radio Amateurs, PO Box 830, 1000 Sofia-C. Tel: +359 (2) 623022 ext 216. Fax: +359 (2) 467553.

BURKINA FASO (Republic of) (*previously Upper Volta*)

ITU allocation: XTA–XTZ.
Callsign system: Prefix: XT2.
National society: Association des Radioamateurs du Burkino Faso, c/o Youssouf Kaba, ONATEL, PO Box 01, Ouagadougou 10000.
Licensing administration: Office des postes et télécommunications, Ouagadougou.

BURUNDI (Republic of)

ITU allocation: 9UA–9UZ.
Callsign system: Prefix: 9U5.
Licensing administration: Ministère des Postes et Télécommunications, BP2000, Bujumbura.

CAMBODIA

ITU allocation: XUA–XUZ.
Callsign system: Prefix: XU.
Licensing administration: Ministère des postes et télécomunications, Phnom-Penh.

CAMEROON (United Republic of)

ITU allocation: TJA–TJZ.
Callsign system: Prefix: TJ.
Licensing administration: Ministère des postes et télécommunications, Yaounde.

CANADA

ITU allocation: CFA–CKZ, CYA–CZZ, VAA–VGZ, VOA–VOZ, VXA–VYZ, XJA–XOZ.
Callsign system:

Prefix	Province or island
CY0	Sable Is
CY9	St Paul Is
VE1	Nova Scotia
VE2	Quebec
VE3	Ontario
VE4	Manitoba
VE5	Saskatchewan
VE6	Alberta
VE7	British Columbia
VE8	NW Territories
VE9	New Brunswick
VO1	Newfoundland
VO2	Labrador
VY1	Yukon Territories
VY2	Prince Edward Is

Licence notes: Three licence classes. Amateur: all bands (CW on HF) 1kW. Advanced: all bands, all modes, 1kW. Digital: 220MHz and above, 1kW. Third-party traffic permitted.
Foreign amateur operation: Reciprocal (A + B). No notice required. Call is own call/Canadian prefix. All countries.
National society: Radio Amateurs of Canada, 614 Norris Court – Unit 6, Kingston, Ontario, K7P 2R9. Tel: +1 (613) 634-4184. Fax: +1 (613) 634-7118.
Licensing administration: Industry and Commerce, Amateur Radio Section, 300 Slater Street, Ottawa, Ontario K1A 0C8, and regional offices.

CAPE VERDE (Republic of)

ITU allocation: D4A–D4Z.
Callsign system: Prefix: D44.
Licensing administration: Servicios dos Correios, Telegrafos e Telefones, Praia.

CENTRAL AFRICAN REPUBLIC

ITU allocation: TLA–TLZ.
Callsign system: Prefix: TL8.
Licensing administration: Direction générale de l'office centrafricain des postes et télécommunications, Bangui.

CHAD (Republic of the)

ITU allocation: TTA–TTZ.
Callsign system: Prefix: TT8.
Licensing administration: Ministère des postes et télécomunications, N'Djamena.

CHILE

ITU allocation: CAA–CEZ, XQA–XRZ, 3GA–3GZ.
Callsign system: Prefixes: CE, XQ. See map for mainland prefixes CE1–8.

Prefix		Area
CE9	AA–AM	Antarctica
	AN–AZ	S Shetland Is
CE0		Easter Is
CE0		San Felix Is, San Ambrosio Is
CE0		Juan Fernandez Is

Licence notes: Four licence classes: 'Aspirante': 3.5, 7MHz (in presence of licensed operator only). Novice: 3.5, 7MHz, SSB/CW, 200W. General, Superior: all bands, 1kW.
Foreign amateur operation: Unilateral (A only). All countries. Apply to RCC.
National society: Radio Club de Chile, PO Box 13630, Santiago 21. Tel: +56 (2) 696-4707. Fax: +56 (2) 672-2623.

CHINA

ITU allocation: BAA–BZZ, XSA–XSZ, 3HA–3UZ.

PEOPLE'S REPUBLIC OF CHINA

Callsign system:

Prefix	Class
B	VHF and UHF stations and contest stations
BA–BC	Class 1
BD–BF	Class 2
BG–BI	Class 3
BR	Repeaters
BT	Special events
BY	Club stations
BZ	Club operators

Licence notes: Three licence classes for individual operators. Class 1: all bands, 500W HF, 50W VHF. Class 2: all bands (restricted), 100W HF, 25W VHF. Class 3: 3.5, 7, 21, 28 and VHF and above, 10W HF, 3W VHF. Three licence classes for club operators. Class 1: all bands, full power of club station. Class 2: all bands, 100W HF, 10W VHF. Class 3: all bands except 14MHz, 100W HF, 10W VHF.
Foreign amateur operation: Unilateral. Fee. Club operator licence only. Call is own call/club call or just club call. No individual operation permitted. Apply to CRSA.
National society: Liaison Department, Chinese Radio Sports Association, PO Box 6106, Beijing 100061. Tel: +86 (1) 702-5488. Fax: +86 (1) 702-5289.

National society: Liga Columbiana de Radioaficionados, PO Box 584, Bogota. Tel: +57 (1) 610-8499. Fax: +57 (1) 610-9877.
Licensing administration: Ministerio do communicaciones, Bogota, DE1.

COMOROS (Federal and Islamic Republic of the)

ITU allocation: D6A–D6Z.
Callsign system: Prefix: D68.
Licensing administration: Direction des télécommunications, BP 348, Moroni.

CONGO (People's Republic of the)

ITU allocation: TNA–TNZ.
Callsign system: Prefix: TN8.
Licensing administration: Office national des postes et télécommunications de la République Populaire du Congo, Brazzaville.

COSTA RICA

ITU allocation: TEA–TEZ, TIA–TIZ.
Callsign system:

Prefix	Area
TI2	San José
TI3	Cartago
TI4	Heredia
TI5	Alajuela
TI6	Limón
TI7	Peninsula de Nicoya
TI8	Puntarenas, Golfito
TI9	Cocos Is

Licence notes: Three licence classes: Class A: all bands, 1kW. Class B: 3.5, 7, 14MHz, 100W. Class C: 7, 14MHz, 100W. Third-party traffic permitted.
Foreign amateur operation: Unilateral (A only). Call is own call/TI. Most countries, including USA. Apply to RCCR.
National society: Radio Club de Costa Rica, Apartado 2412, San José 1000. Tel: +506 216903.

CROATIA

ITU allocation: 9AA–9AZ.
Callsign system: Prefix: 9A.
Foreign amateur operation: *CEPT*: A + B. Call is 9A/own call.

TAIWAN
Callsign system:

Prefix	Area
BO	Quemoy
BV	Taiwan
BV9P	Pratas Is
BV9S	Spratly Archipelago

National society: Chinese Taipei Amateur Radio League, PO Box 39, Chuanghua 500. Tel: +886 (4) 738-8746. Fax: +886 (4) 738-5441.

COLOMBIA (Republic of)

ITU allocation: HJA–HKZ, 5JA–5KZ.
Callsign system: See map for mainland prefixes HK1–9. HK0 prefix is used for Baja Nuevo, Malpelo Is, San Andres Is, Providencia Is and Serrana Bank.
Licence notes: Three licence classes: Class 1, 2, all bands, 2kW PEP. Class 3: 1.8, 3.5, 7MHz and 144MHz, 50W. Third-party traffic permitted.
Foreign amateur operation: Unilateral (A only). Call is HK7/own call. Countries include: Peru, Ecuador, Brazil, USA, Spain, Argentina, Bolivia, Dominican Rep, Canada. All others: 30 days only.

CUBA ~ CM,CO

National society: Hrvatski Radio-Amaterski Savez, PO Box 564, HR-41000 Zagreb. Tel: +385 (1) 433-025. Fax: +385 (1) 274-391.

CUBA

ITU allocation: CLA–CMZ, COA–COZ.
Callsign system: Prefixes: CO (Class A), CM (Class B). See map for call areas.
Licence notes: Two licence classes. Class A: all bands, 450W CW 1kW PEP SSB. Class B: 3.5, 7MHz, 200W CW, 500W PEP SSB.
National society: Federacion de Radioaficionados de Cuba, PO Box 1, Havana 10400.
Licensing administration: Ministerio de communicaciones, Plaza de la Revolucion "Jose Marti", Havana.

CYPRUS (Republic of)

ITU allocation: C4A–C4Z, H2A–H2Z, P3A–P3Z, 5BA–5BZ.
Callsign system: Prefix: 5B4. For UK bases, see UK Overseas Territories.
Licence notes: Single licence class, 150W DC input.
Foreign amateur operation: *CEPT*: A + B. Call is 5B4/own call. *Non-CEPT*: Reciprocal (A + B). One month's notice. No fee. All EU countries, USA, British Commonwealth.
National society: Cyprus Amateur Radio Society, PO Box 1267, Limassol.
Licensing administration: Director-General, Ministry of Communications and Works, Nicosia. Tel: +357 (2) 40 22 78.

CZECH REPUBLIC

ITU allocation: OKA–OLZ.
Callsign system: See map for call areas.

Prefix	Type of station
OK1, 2, 3	Ordinary stations (KAA–KZZ and RAA–RZZ serial letters denote club calls)
OK4, 5, 6, 7	Special stations
OK8	Foreign amateurs
OK0	Repeaters
OL	Novice

Licence notes: Four licence classes. Class A, B: all-band, 750W, 300W respectively. Class C: 1.8, 3.5, 10, 21, 28MHz plus VHF, 100W. Class D, 3.5MHz, 144MHz, 100W.
Foreign amateur operation: *CEPT*: A + B. Call is OK/own call. *Non-CEPT*: Unilateral.
National society: Czech Radio Club, PO Box 69, 11327 Prague 1. Tel: +42 (2) 87 22 240. Fax: +42 (2) 87 22 209.
Licensing administration: Czech Telecommunication Office, Att Mrs Bocková, Klimentská 27, 12502 Prague 1. Tel: +42 (2) 2491-1605. Fax: +42 (2) 2491-1658.

DENMARK

ITU allocation: OUA–OZZ, XPA–XPZ, 5PA–5QZ.
Callsign system: REA–REZ serial letters denote a repeater station.

Prefix	Area
OX3	Greenland (nationals)
OX5	Greenland (USA personnel)
OY	Faroe Is
OZ	Denmark
XP	Special

Licence notes: Four licence classes: Classes A, B: 500,100W DC input respectively, all bands. Class C: 10W DC input, HF bands CW only, plus 100W on VHF. Class D: 100W DC input, VHF phone-only.
Foreign amateur operation: *CEPT*: A + B. Call is OZ/own call (Denmark), OY/own call (Faroe Is), OX/own call (Greenland). *Non-CEPT*: Reciprocal (A + B). Call is OZ/own call (Denmark), OY/own call (Faroe Is), OX/own call (Greenland). One month's notice. Form. Fee. Countries include: Australia, Belgium, Brazil, Canada, Germany, Finland, France, Iceland, Luxembourg, Netherlands, Norway, Portugal, Spain, Sweden, Switzerland, UK, USA.

National societies: *Denmark* and *Greenland:* Eksperimenterende Danske Radioamatorer, PO Box 172, DK-5100 Odense C. Tel: +45 66 137700. *Faroe Is:* Foroyskir Radioamatorar, PO Box 343, FR-110 Torshavn. Tel: +298 10644.
Licensing administration: National Telecom Agency, Holsteingarde 63, DK-2100 Copenhagen Ø. Tel: +45 35 43 03 33.

DJIBOUTI (Republic of)

ITU allocation: J2A–J2Z.
Callsign system: Prefix: J28.
National society: Association des Radioamateurs de Djibouti, BP 1076, Djibouti.

DOMINICA (Commonwealth of)

ITU allocation: J7A–J7Z.
Callsign system: Prefix: J73.
Foreign amateur operation: Countries include USA.
National society: Dominica Amateur Radio Club, PO Box 389, Roseau. Tel: +1 (809) 448 8533. Fax: +1 (809) 448 7708.

DOMINICAN REPUBLIC

ITU allocation: HIA–HIZ.
Callsign system:

Prefix	Area	Town/city
HI1	Beata Is	
HI2	Saona Is	
HI3	North	Santiago
HI4	North-west	Montecristi
HI5	South-west	Barahona
HI6	West	San Juan
HI7	East	La Romana
HI8	South	Santo Domingo
HI9	North-east	Nagua

Licence notes: Four licence classes: Novice: 3.5, 7MHz, CW only 50W. Technician: all bands, 300W. General and Limited: all bands 1kW. Third-party traffic permitted.
Foreign amateur operation: Countries include: Canada, Brazil, El Salvador, UK, USA, Venezuela.
National society: Radio Club Dominicano Inc, Apartado Postal 1157, Santo Domingo. Tel: +1 (809) 533-2211.
Licensing administration: Direccion General de Telecomunicaciones, Santo Domingo.

ECUADOR

ITU allocation: HCA–HDZ.
Callsign system:

Prefix	City/town and region
HC1	Quito
HC2	Guayaquil
HC3	Loja
HC4	Esmeraldas, Portoviejo
HC5	Cuenca
HC6	Amabato
HC7	East Ecuador
HC8	Galapagos Is
HC9	Maritime mobile

Licence notes: 1kW DC input maximum. Third-party traffic permitted.
Foreign amateur operation: Call is own call/HC. Countries include: USA, Venezuela. Apply to GRC.
National society: Guayaquil Radio Club, PO Box 09-01-5757, Guayaquil. Tel: +593 (4) 294671. Fax: +593 (4) 392198.

EGYPT (Arab Republic of)

ITU allocation: SSA–SSM, SUA–SUZ, 6AA–6BZ.
Callsign system: Prefix: SU.
Licence notes: Four licence classes. Class A: all modes, 100W DC input. Class B: all modes 50W DC input. Class C: CW only, 25W DC input. Class D: CW only, 10W DC input. Separate VHF licence.
National society: Egypt Amateurs Wireless Club, PO Box 78, Heliopolis, Cairo 11341.
Licensing administration: Telecommunications Organisation, PO Box 2271, Cairo.

EL SALVADOR (Republic of)

ITU allocation: HUA–HUZ, YSA–YSZ.
Callsign system:

Prefix	City/town and area
YS1	San Salvador
YS2	Santa Ana
YS3	San Miguel
YS9	Foreign amateurs

Licence notes: Two licence classes: First class: all bands, 1kW. Second class: all bands, 250W. Third-party traffic permitted.
Foreign amateur operation: Callsign is own call/YS. Countries include: Canada, USA, UK, Dominican Rep, Guatemala, Nicaragua, Costa Rica.
National society: Club de Radioaficionados de El Salvador, PO Box 517, San Salvador. Tel: +503 224-6714. Fax: +503 224-6714.
Licensing administration: Administracion Nacional de Telecomunicaciones, Centro de Gobierno, San Salvador.

EQUATORIAL GUINEA (Republic of)

ITU allocation: 3CA–3CZ.
Callsign system: Prefixes: 3C (mainland), 3C0 (Pagalu Is).
Licensing administration: Direccion General de Telecomunicaciones, Malabo.

ERITREA

ITU allocation: E3A–E3Z.
Callsign system: Prefix: E3.

ESTONIA

ITU allocation: ESA–ESZ.
Callsign system: Prefix: ES.
Licence notes: Four licence classes: 200W, 50W, 20W and novice.
Foreign amateur operation: *CEPT*: Call is ESx/own call.
National society: Eesti Raadioamatooride Uhing, PO Box 125, EE-0090 Tallin. Tel: +372 (2) 449312.

ETHIOPIA

ITU allocation: ETA–ETZ, 9EA–9FZ.
Callsign system: Prefix: ET3.
Foreign amateur operation: Call is own call/ET3.
Licensing administration: Ethiopian Telecommunications Authority, PO Box 1047, Addis Ababa.

FIJI

ITU allocation: 3DN–3DZ.
Callsign system: Prefix: 3D2.
Licence notes: Two licence classes. General: all bands, 150W DC input. Technician: 144MHz only, 50W DC input.
Foreign amateur operation: Unilateral (A + B). Fee. Several weeks' notice. Local licence issued. All countries.
National society: Fiji Association of Radio Amateurs, PO Box 184, Suva.
Licensing administration: The Director, Regulatory Unit, Ministry of Information, Broadcasting, Television and Telecommunication, Government Buildings, Suva. Tel: +679 211257. Fax: +679 300766.

FINLAND

ITU allocation: OFA–OJZ.
Callsign system: See map for prefixes. Market Reef is also OH0M.
Licence notes: Three licence classes: General: all bands, 600W output. Technician: VHF, all modes, 150W output. Novice: 3.5, 7, 21MHz CW only, 28MHz SSB and 144MHz all modes, 15W output.
Foreign amateur operation: *CEPT*: A + B. Call is OH/own call. *Non-CEPT*: Reciprocal (A + B). Four weeks' notice. Fee. Form. All countries.
National society: Suomen Radioamatööriliitto RY, PO Box 44, SF-00441 Helsinki. Tel: +358 (0) 562-5973. Fax: +358 (0) 562-3987.
Licensing administration: Telehallintokeskus, PO Box 53, SF-00211 Helsinki. Tel: +358 (0) 69661. Fax: +358 (0) 6966410.

FRANCE

ITU allocation: FAA–FZZ, HWA–HYZ, THA–THZ.
Callsign system (France): New callsigns have prefix which indicates licence class A–E, ie FA–FE.

Prefix	Country
F, FA–FE	France
FF	Clubs (France)
FG	Guadeloupe
FH	Mayotte
FJ	St Barthelemy
FK	New Caledonia
FM	Martinique
FO	French Oceania: Clipperton Is, Gambier Is, Marquesas Is, Society Is (Tahiti), Tubuai Is
FP	St Pierre et Miquelon
FR	Reunion
FR/G	Glorieuses Is
FR/J	Juan de Nova Is

FINLAND **OH**

FR/T	Tromelin Is
FS	St Martin
FT-W	Crozet Is
FT-X	Kerguelen Is
FT-Y	Terre Adelie
FT-Z	Amsterdam and St Paul Is
FW	Wallis and Futuna Is
FX	beacons
FY	French Guiana and Inini
FZ	repeaters
TK	Corsica

Licence notes (France): Five licence classes. Class A: 144MHz only. Class B: 144MHz plus some CW segments in HF bands and 28MHz phone. Class C: above 30MHz. Class D: all bands. Class E: issued after three years in Class D.
Foreign amateur operation (France): *CEPT*: A + B. Call is F/own call. *Non-CEPT*: Reciprocal (A + B). Call is F series. Three months' notice. Form. Fee. Countries include: Andorra, Belgium, Canada, Germany, Luxembourg, Monaco, Netherlands, Spain, Switzerland, UK, USA.
National society: *France*: REF-Union, PO Box 2129, F-37021 Tours Cedex. Tel: +33 47-418873. Fax: +33 47-418888. *French Polynesia*: Club Oceanien de Radio et d'Astronomie, PO Box 2139, Papeete, Tahiti.
Licensing administration (France): Direction Génerale des Télécommunications, Direction des Affairs Industrielles et Internationales, Services des Affairs Internationales, 7 boulevard Romain Rolland, F-92128 Montrouge. Tel: +33 1-45-64-22-22.

GABON REPUBLIC

ITU allocation: TRA–TRZ.
Callsign system: Prefix: TR8.
National society: Association Gabonaise des Radio Amateurs, BP 1826, Libreville.

Licensing administration: M le Directeur général de l'Office des postes et télécommunications de la République Gabonais, Libreville.

GAMBIA (Republic of the)

ITU allocation: C5A–C5Z.
Callsign system: Prefix: C53.
Licence notes: Single class of licence. 3.5–28MHz bands only but endorsements available for 18 and 144MHz.
Foreign amateur operation: Unilateral (A + B). Call is C53/own call. Countries include UK.
National society: Radio Society of the Gambia, c/o Jean-Michel Voinot, C53GB, PMB 120, Banjul.
Licensing administration: The Managing Director, Gambia Telecommunications Co Ltd, PO Box 387, Banjul. Tel: +220 29999.

GEORGIA

ITU allocation: 4LA–4LZ.
Callsign system: Prefix: 4L.

First serial letters	Area	Capital
Q, S	Adzharia	Batumi
V, X	Abkhazia	Sukhumi
Other letters	Georgia	Tbilisi

GERMANY (Federal Republic of)

ITU allocation: DAA–DRZ, Y2A–Y9Z.
Callsign system:

Callsign series	Licence class	Notes
DA1AA–DA2ZZ	B	Military stations
DA4AA–DA4ZZ	C	Military stations
DB0AA–DB0ZZ	C	Clubs and repeaters
DB1AA–DB9ZZ	C	
DC0AA–DC0EZ	C	
DC0FA–DC0JZ	C	Reciprocal licence
DC0KA–DC0ZZ	C	
DC1AA–DC9ZZ	C	
DD0AA–DD4ZZ	C	
DD5AA–DD5ZZ	C	Reciprocal licence
DD6AAA–DD6ZZZ	C	
DD7AA–DD9ZZ	C	
DF0AAA–DF0ZZZ	B	Club station
DF1AA–DF9ZZ	B	
DG1AAA–DG9ZZZ	C	
DH0AAA–DH9ZZZ	A	
DJ0AAA–DJ0ZZZ	B/A	Reciprocal licence
DJ1AA–DJQZ	B	
DK0AA–DK9ZZ	B	
DL0AAA–DL9ZZZ	B	

Licence notes: Three licence classes. Class A: 3.5 and 21MHz (CW, rtty only), 28MHz plus VHF (all modes), 150W output. Class B: all bands, all modes, 750W output. Class C: VHF phone only, 75 output.
Foreign amateur operation: *CEPT*: A + B. Call is DL/own call (CEPT Class 1), DC/own call (CEPT Class 2). *Non-CEPT*: Reciprocal. Six weeks' notice. Fee. Call is DL/own call or DC/own call. Licence valid for three months only. Countries include UK, USA. Apply to DARC.
National society: Deutscher Amateur Radio Club, Postfach 1155, D-3507 Baunatal 1. Tel: +49 (561) 949880. Fax: +49 (561) 9498850.

GHANA

ITU allocation: 9GA–9GZ.
Callsign system: Prefix: 9G1.
Licence notes: Maximum power 400W PEP.
National society: Ghana Amateur Radio Society, Box 3936, Accra.
Licensing administration: Director-General, Posts and Telecommunications Corporation, Accra.

GREECE

ITU allocation: SVA–SZZ, J4A–J4Z.
Callsign system: See map for call areas.
Licence notes: Three licence classes. Classes A, B, C: all bands, 300, 150, 50W PEP respectively.
Foreign amateur operation: *CEPT*: A only. Call is SVx/own call. *Non-CEPT*: Two months' notice. Call is SVx/own call for temporary licence. All EU countries, otherwise reciprocal (including USA).
National society: Radio Amateur Association of Greece, PO Box 3564, GR-10210 Athens. Tel: +30 (1) 522-6516. Fax: +30 (1) 522-6505.

Licensing administration: Ministry of Transport and Telecommunications, Directorate of Communication Technique, Department of Electronic Applications, 49 avenue Sygrou, GR-11780 Athens. Tel: +30 (1) 923-2906. Fax: +30 (1) 923-7133.

GRENADA

ITU allocation: J3A–J3Z.
Callsign system: Prefix: J3
Licence notes: Maximum power 2kW PEP.
Foreign amateur operation: All countries.
National society: Grenada Amateur Radio Club, PO Box 737, St George's.
Licensing administration: Wireless Officer, Ministry of Communications and Works, St George's.

GUATEMALA (Republic of)

ITU allocation: TDA–TDZ, TGA–TGZ.
Callsign system:

Prefix	City/town area
TG4	Escuintia
TG5	Huehuetenango
TG6	Chiquimula
TG7	Izabal
TG8	Quezaltenango
TG9	Guatemala City
TG0	Special stations

Licence notes: Two licence classes. Novice: 7MHz CW/AM only. General: all bands, all modes, 2kW PEP. Third-party traffic permitted.
Foreign amateur operation: Call is own call/TG. Countries include USA.
National society: Club de Radioficionados de Guatemala, PO Box 115, Guatemala City 01901. Tel: +502 (2) 314683.
Licensing administration: Dirreccion General de Radio y Television Nacional, Guatemala City.

GUINEA (People's Revolutionary Republic of)

ITU allocation: 3XA–3XZ.
Callsign system: Prefix: 3X.
Licensing administration: Ministère des postes et télécommunications, Conakry.

GUINEA-BISSAU (Republic of)

ITU allocation: J5A–J5Z.
Callsign system: Prefix: J5.
Licensing administration: Commissariado de Estado dos Correios e Telecomunicações, Bissau.

Greece

HA–HG HUNGARY PREFIXES AND CALL-SERIES

GUYANA

ITU allocation: 8RA–8RZ.
Callsign system: Prefix: 8R.
Foreign amateur operation: Call is own call/8R. Countries include USA.
National society: Guyana Amateur Radio Association, c/o 221 Aubrey Barker Road, So Ruimveldt Gardens, Georgetown.
Licensing administration: The General Manager, Guyana Telecommunication Corporation, 55 Brickdam, Georgetown.

HAITI (Republic of)

ITU allocation: HHA–HHZ.
Callsign system: Prefix: HH.
Licence notes: Four licence classes: First, second and third class: all bands, 2kW DC input. Third class (B): all bands, 350W DC input. Third class (C): 1.8, 3.5, 7, 21MHz CW/phone, 100W DC input. Third-party traffic permitted.
Foreign amateur operation: Countries include: Canada, France, Switzerland, USA, Dominican Rep.
National society: Radio Club d'Haiti, PO Box 1484, Port-au-Prince.
Licensing administration: CONATEL, Ave Marie Jeanne, Port-au-Prince.

HONDURAS (Republic of)

ITU allocation: HOA–HRZ.
Callsign system:

Prefix	Area	City/town
HR1	—	Tegucigalpa, DC
HR2	Cortes	San Pedro Sula
HR3	Atlantida	La Ceiba
HR4	Valle	Amapala
HR5	Copan	Santa Rosa
HR6	Bay Is	
HR0	(mobile)	

Licence notes: 1kW DC input maximum. Third-party traffic permitted.
Foreign amateur operation: Call is own call/HR. Countries include USA.
National society: Radio Club de Honduras, Apartado 273, San Pedro Sula. Tel: +504 532035.
Licensing administration: Direccion de Radio Nacional, Hondutel, Tegucigalpa.

HUNGARY

ITU allocation: HAA–HAZ, HGA–HGZ.
Callsign system: See map. The letters shown in the map are the first letters after the call number. K is reserved for club stations and Y for youth club stations. HG is used on 28MHz band and above.
Licence notes: Five licence classes. Young class: 3.5MHz, 10W DC input. Class A: 3.5MHz, 7MHz, 25W DC input. Class B: all bands, 100W DC input. Class C: all bands, 250W DC input. Class C (contests): all bands, 500W DC input.
Foreign amateur operation: *CEPT:* A + B. Call is HA/own call (CEPT Class 1), HG/own call (CEPT Class 2). *Non-CEPT:* All countries. Apply to MRASZ.
National society: Magyar Radioamator Szovetseg, PO Box 11, H-1400 Budapest. Tel: +36 (1) 112-1616. Fax: +36 (1) 111-6204.
Licensing administration: Hungarian Telecommunications Corporation, Krisztina Krt 6-8, H-1541 Budapest. Tel: +36 (1) 175-6885. Fax: +36 (1) 175-3093.

ICELAND (Republic of)

ITU allocation: TFA–TFZ.
Callsign system: See map for call areas. Novice and Technician callsigns have N or T respectively as the last of three serial letters, eg TF1AN. Foreign amateurs who have passed the Icelandic amateur radio examination have X as the first of three serial letters, eg TF1XAA. Icelanders who have been licensed for 25 years or longer and have a Class C licence can obtain single-serial-letter callsigns, eg TF1A.
Licence notes: Five licence classes. Novice: 3.5, 7, 21MHz, crystal-controlled CW only, 5W DC input. Technician: VHF phone only, 50W DC input. Class A: all bands, CW only, 50W DC input. Classes B and C: all bands, all modes, 200 and 500W DC input respectively.
Foreign amateur operation: *CEPT:* A + B. Call is TF/own call. *Non-CEPT.* Reciprocal (A + B). Three months' notice. Form. Countries include: Canada, Denmark, Luxembourg, Norway, Sweden, Switzerland, UK, USA, Germany.
National society: Islenzkir Radioamatorar, PO Box 1058, IS-121 Reykjavik.
Licensing administration: Director General of Posts and Telecommunications, Landssimahusinu vid Austurvoll, IS-101 Reykjavik. Tel: +354 (1) 2 60 00.

INDIA (Republic of)

ITU allocation: ATA–AWZ, VTA–VWZ, 8TA–8YZ.
Callsign system: Prefix: VU2.
Licence notes: Three licence classes. Advanced, Grade 1, all bands, 150W DC input. Grade 2: 3.5, 7MHz CW only plus VHF, 25W DC input. Permitted powers on VHF are lower.
Foreign amateur operation: Reciprocal (A + B). Call is in VU series. Countries include: UK, USA, Canada, Brazil, Peru, Germany, Greece, Poland, Switzerland, Japan, Australia, New Zealand.
National society: Amateur Radio Society of India, PO Box 6538, Bombay 400026.
Licensing administration: Ministry of Communications, Sanchar Bhavan, 20 Ashoka Road, New Delhi 110001.

INDONESIA (Republic of)

ITU allocation: JZA–JZZ, PKA–POZ, YBA–YHZ, 7AA–7IZ, 8AA–8IZ.
Callsign system: See map on next page for call areas.

Prefix	Licence class
YB	General
YC	Middle
YD	Novice

Licence notes: Three licence classes: Novice: 3.5MHz, CW/AM, 10W. Middle: all bands except 14MHz, all modes, 75W. General: all bands, all modes, 500W.
Foreign amateur operation: Unilateral (A only). Countries include: USA, Canada, Germany, UK, France, Sweden, Argentina, Australia. Apply to ORARI.
National society: Organissai Amatir Radio Indonesia, PO Box 6797 JKSRB, Jakarta 12067. Tel: +62 (21) 582226.

IRAN (Islamic Republic of)

ITU allocation: EPA–EQZ, 9BA–9DZ.
Callsign system: Prefix: EP.
Licence notes: 100W maximum output.
Licensing administration: Directorate General of Telecommunications, PO Box 931, Teheran.

IRAQ (Republic of)

ITU allocation: HNA–HNZ, YIA–YIZ.
Callsign system: Prefix: YI.
National society: Iraqi Radio Amateur Club, PO Box 55072, Baghdad 12001. Tel: +964 (1) 8843521.
Licensing administration: The Director General of Posts, Telegraphs and Telephones, State Organisation, Baghdad.

IRELAND (Republic of)

ITU allocation: EIA–EJZ.
Callsign system: Prefixes: EI (mainland). EJ (offshore islands). Three serial letters denote VHF phone only except VAA–VZZ which denotes a visitor's licence.
Licence notes: Two licence classes. All bands, 150W DC input and VHF phone only.
Foreign amateur operation: *CEPT*: A + B. Call is EI/own call. *Non-CEPT*: Reciprocal (A + B). Call is in EI series. Countries include UK, USA.
National society: Irish Radio Transmitters Society, PO Box 462, Dublin 9.
Licensing administration: Dept of Transport, Energy and Comms, Telecomms and Radio (Regulatory) Div, Ely Court & Ely Place, Scotch House, Hawkins Street, Dublin 2. Tel: +353 (1) 671-5233.

ISRAEL (State of)

ITU allocation: 4XA–4XZ, 4ZA–4ZZ.
Callsign system: Prefixes 4X, 4Z. Serial letters NAA–NZZ denote Class C licence.
Licence notes: Three licence classes. Class A, B all bands, and 250W DC input respectively. Class C: 7 and 21MHz CW only, 10W DC input. Third-party traffic permitted.
Foreign amateur operation: Reciprocal (A + B). Call is 4X/own call (CEPT Class 1), 4Z7/own call (CEPT Class 2). Countries include UK, USA.
National society: Israel Amateur Radio Club, PO Box 17600, Tel-Aviv 61176.
Licensing administration: Ministry of Communications, PO Box 29107, Tel-Aviv 61290.

ITALY

ITU allocation: IAA–IZZ.
Callsign system: See map for prefixes. IW is Technician class prefix.
Licence notes: Four licence classes. Classes 1, 2, 3: 75,150, 300W DC input respectively. Technician: VHF only, 10W.
Foreign amateur operation: *CEPT*: A + B. Call is I/own call (CEPT Class 1), IW/own call (CEPT Class 2). *Non-CEPT*: Reciprocal (A + B). Fee. Form. Countries include: all EU, USA.
National society: Associazione Radioamatori Italiani, Via Scarlatti 31, I-20124 Milan. Tel: +39 (2) 6692192. Fax: +39 (2) 66714809.
Licensing administration: Ministero Poste e Telecomunicazioni,

DirezioneCentrale dei Servizi Radioelettrici, Divisione VI – Sezione IV, viale Europa 175, I-00144 Rome. Tel: +39 (6) 59584894. Fax: +39 (6) 59584859.

IVORY COAST (Republic of the)

ITU allocation: TUA–TUZ.
Callsign system: Prefix: TU2.
Licence notes: 1kW DC input maximum.
National society: Association des Radio Amateurs Ivoiriens, BP2946, Abidjan 01.
Licensing administration: Office des postes et télécommunication de la République de Côte d'Ivoire, Direction générale des télécommunications, Abidjan.

JAMAICA

ITU allocation: 6YA–6YZ.
Callsign system: Prefix: 6Y5.
Licence notes: 1kW DC input maximum. Third-party traffic permitted.
Foreign amateur operation: Unilateral (A only). Call is own call/6Y5. Countries include: British Commonwealth, USA, Netherlands.
National society: Jamaica Amateur Radio Association, 76 Arnold Road, Kingston 5. Tel: +1 (809) 926-7861.
Licensing administration: Headquarters, Posts and Telegraphs Dept, South Camp Road, Kingston.

JAPAN

ITU allocation: JAA–JSZ, 7JA–7NZ, 8JA–8NZ.
Callsign system: Prefixes: JA–JR except JD1 (Ogasawara Is, Minami Torishima), JR6 (Okinawa) and 7J–7N. See map for call areas.
Licence notes: Four licence classes. First class: 500W PEP. Second class: 100W PEP. Telegraphy class: 10W CW-only (except 14MHz) Telephony class: 10W PEP phone-only (except 1.9 and 14MHz).
Foreign amateur operation: Countries include: USA, Germany, Finland. Apply to JARL.
National society: Japanese Amateur Radio League, 1-14-5 Sugamo, Tokyo 170. Tel: +81 (3) 5395-3106. Fax: +81 (3) 3943-8282.

JORDAN (Hashemite Kingdom of)

ITU allocation: JYA–JYZ.
Callsign system: Prefixes: JY (individual stations), JY6 (club stations), JY9 (foreign amateurs).
Licence notes: 1kW DC input maximum. Third-party traffic permitted.
Foreign amateur operation: Unilateral. Call is in JY9 series. Countries include USA. Apply via RJARS.
National society: Royal Jordanian Radio Amateurs Society, PO Box 2353, Amman. Tel: +962 (6) 666235.

KAZAKHSTAN

ITU allocation: UNA–UQZ.
Callsign system: Prefix is UN.

ITALY

Telecommunications (Radio Licensing), PO Box 30301, Nairobi. Tel: +254 (2) 227401 ext 2385. Fax: +254 (2) 22848.

KIRIBATI (Republic of)
ITU allocation: T3A–T3Z.
Callsign system:

Prefix	Area
T30	West Kiribati (Gilbert Is)
T31	Central Kiribati (formerly British/American Phoenix Is), including Kanton and Enderbury Is
T32	East Kiribati (Line Is)
T33	Banaba Is (Ocean Is)

Foreign amateur operation: Most countries, including USA.
Licensing administration: Controller of Telecommunications, Ministry of Communications & Works, PO Box 487, Betio, Tarawa Atoll.

KOREA (Democratic People's Republic of)
ITU allocation: HMA–HMZ, P5A–P9Z.
Licensing administration: Ministry of Posts and Telecommunications, Pyongyang.

KOREA (Republic of)
ITU allocation: DSA–DSZ, HLA–HLZ, 6KA–6NZ.
Callsign system: Currently HM but subject to change to conform to above allocation.
Licence notes: Three licence classes: First class: all bands, all modes, 500W. Second class: all bands except 14MHz, 100W. Third class: 1.8, 3.5, 7MHz, 28MHz, VHF, 50W.
National society: Korean Amateur Radio League, Inc, CPO Box 162, Seoul 100-601. Tel: +82 (2) 817-7493. Fax: +82 (2) 817-7494.
Licensing administration: Ministry of Communications, Taepyong-ro Choong-Ku, Seoul.

1st serial letter	Area	Capital
A	Mangyshlak Obl	Shevchenko
B	Tselinograd Obl	Tselinograd
C	North Kazakh Obl	Petropavlovsk
D	Semipalatinsk Obl	Semipalatinsk
E	Kokchetav Obl	Kokchetav
F	Pavlodar Obl	Pavlodar
G	Alma-Ata city	—
I	Atyubinsk Obl	Atyubinsk
J	East Kazakh Obl	Ust-Kamenogorsk
K	Kzyl-Orda Obl	Kzyl-Orda
L	Kustanay Obl	Kustanay
M	Urals Obl	Uralsk
N	Chimkent Obl	Chimkent
O	Guryev Obl	Guryev
P	Karaganda Obl	Karaganda
Q	Alma-Ata Obl	Alma-Ata
R	Dzhezkazgan Obl	Dzhezkazgan
S	Kzyl-Ordinskaya	—
T	Dzhambul	Dzhambul
V	Taldy-Kurgan	Taldy-Kurgan
Y	Turgav Obl	Arkalyk

KENYA (Republic of)
ITU allocation: 5YA–5ZZ.
Callsign system: Prefix: 5Z4.
Licence notes: Single licence class: all bands, 150W DC input.
Foreign amateur operation: Unilateral (A only). Fee. Six months' notice or more. No short-term licences. Call is in 5Z4 series. Countries include UK.
National society: Radio Society of Kenya, PO Box 45681, Nairobi.
Licensing administration: Managing Director, Kenya Posts and

Liberia — EL

KUWAIT (State of)

ITU allocation: 9KA–9KZ.
Callsign system: Prefix: 9K2.
Foreign amateur operation: Countries include: USA.
National society: Kuwait Amateur Radio Society, PO Box 5240, Safat. Tel: +965 533-3762. Fax: +965 531-1188.

KYRGHYZSTAN

ITU allocation: EXA–EXZ.
Callsign system: Prefix: EX.

1st serial letter	Area	Capital
M	—	Frunze
N	Osh Obl	Osh
P	Naryn Obl	Naryn
Q	Issyk-Kul Obl	Przhevalsk
T	Talas Obl	Talas
V	Dzhalal-Abad Obl	

LAOS (Lao People's Democratic Republic)

ITU allocation: XWA–XWZ.
Callsign system: Prefix: XW8.
Licensing administration: Ministère des postes et télécommunications, Avenue Lane Xang, Vientane.

LATVIA

ITU allocation: YLA–YLZ.
Callsign system: Prefix: YL.
Licence notes: Four licence classes: 200W, 50W restricted, 20W restricted, novice.
Foreign amateur operation: CEPT: Call is YL/own call.
National society: PO Box 164, LV-1098, Riga.

LEBANON

ITU allocation: ODA–ODZ.
Callsign system: Prefix: OD5.
Licence notes: Single licence class, 1kW DC input.
Foreign amateur operation: All countries.
National society: Association des Radio Amateurs Libanais, PO Box 11-8888. Beirut.
Licensing administration: Ministère des PTT, Direction générale des télégraphes et téléphones, Bir Hassan, Beirut.

LESOTHO (Kingdom of)

ITU allocation: 7PA–7PZ.
Callsign system: Prefix: 7P8.
National society: Lesotho Amateur Radio Society, PO Box 949, Maseru 100.
Licensing administration: The Director of Posts and Telecommunications, PO Box 413, Maseru.

LIBERIA (Republic of)

ITU allocation: A8A–A8Z, D5A–D5Z, ELA–ELZ, 5LA–5MZ, 6ZA–6ZZ.
Callsign system: See map for prefixes. 5L is special-event prefix.
Licence notes: Two licence classes. Basic: 3.5, 7 and 21MHz CW, 75W DC input. General: all bands, 1kW DC input.
Foreign amateur operation: All countries.

National society: Liberian Radio Amateur Association, PO Box 10-1477, 1000 Monrovia 10.
Licensing administration: Ministry of Post & Telecommunications, Monrovia.

LIBYA (Socialist People's Libyan Arab Jamahiriya)

ITU allocation: 5AA–5AZ.
Callsign system: Prefix: 5A.
Licensing administration: Posts and Telecommunication Corporation, Tripoli.

LITHUANIA

ITU allocation: LYA–LYZ.
Callsign system: Prefix: LY.
Licence notes: Four licence classes: 160m only, 10W, 50W and 200W.
National society: Lietuvos Radijo Megeju Draugija, PO Box 1000, Vilnius 2001. Tel: +370 (2) 221-836 (Tuesday evenings and Sunday mornings). Fax: +370 (2) 662-470.

LUXEMBOURG (Duchy of)

ITU allocation: LXA–LXZ.
Callsign system:

Prefix	Licence category
LX1	Luxembourg nationals
LX9	Club stations
LX0	Beacons, repeaters, special

Licence notes: Two licence classes. Classes 1, 2: 35, 100W DC input respectively.
Foreign amateur operation: CEPT: A + B. Call is LX/own call. Non-CEPT: Unilateral (A only). Call is in LX series. Countries include: Austria, Belgium, Canada, Denmark, Faroes, France, Germany, Netherlands, Norway, Switzerland, UK, USA.
National society: Reseau Luxembourgeois des Amateurs d'Ondes Courtes, 23 route de Noertzange, L-3530 Dudelange.
Licensing administration: Direction des Postes et Télécommunications, L-2020 Luxembourg.

MACEDONIA

ITU allocation: Z3A–Z3Z.
Callsign system: Prefix: Z3.
National society: Radioamaterski Sojuz na Makedonija, PO Box 14, 91000 Skopje. Tel: +389 (1) 237371. Fax: +389 (1) 238257.

MADAGASCAR (Democratic Republic of)

ITU allocation: 5FA–5FZ, 6XA–6XZ.
Callsign system: Prefix: 5R8.
Licensing administration: Ministère des postes et télécommunications, Antaninarenina, Tananarive.

MALAWI (Republic of)

ITU allocation: 7QA–7QZ.
Callsign system: Prefix: 7Q7.
Licensing administration: The Postmaster General, PO Box 537, Blantyre.

MALAYSIA (Federation of)

ITU allocation: 9MA–9MZ, 9WA–9WZ.
Callsign system:

Prefix	State
9M0	Spratly Is
9M2	West Malaysia
9M6	Sabah
9M8	Sarawak

Licence notes: Single licence class: 150W DC input.
Foreign amateur operation: Reciprocal (A only). Countries include: UK, USA, Philippines, Japan, Australia plus certain European countries.
National society: MARTS, PO Box 10777, 50724 Kuala Lumpur.
Licensing administration: IBU Pejabat, Jabatan Telekom Malaysia, (Kementerian Tenega Telekom Dan Pos Malaysia), Wisma Damansra, Jalan Sematan, 50668 Kuala Lumpur. Tel: +60 32556687.

MALDIVES (Republic of)

ITU allocation: 8QA–8QZ.
Callsign system: Prefix: 8Q7.
Licensing administration: The Director, Telecommunication Department, Male.

MALI (Republic of)

ITU allocation: TZA–TZZ.

Callsign system: Prefix: TZ.
Licensing administration: Office des postes et télécommunications de la République du Mali, Bamako.

MALTA (Republic of)

ITU allocation: 9HA–9HZ.
Callsign system:

Prefix	Island
9H1	Malta
9H3	Malta (visitors and special)
9H4	Gozo

Licence notes: Two licence classes. Class A: all bands, 150W DC input. Class B: VHF phone only, 150W DC input.
Foreign amateur operation: Reciprocal (A + B). Call is in 9H3 series. Form. All countries.
National society: Malta Amateur Radio League, PO Box 575, Valletta.
Licensing administration: Wireless Telegraphy Dept, Evans Laboratory Buildings, Merchants Street, Valletta. Tel: +356 24-39-25. Fax: +356 24-44-94.

MARSHALL ISLANDS

ITU allocation: V7A–V7Z.
Callsign system: V73.
Foreign amateur operation: Countries include USA.

MAURITANIA (Islamic Republic of)

ITU allocation: 5TA–5TZ.
Callsign system: Prefix: 5T5.
Licensing administration: Office des postes et télécommunications de la République Islamique du Mauritanie, Nouakchott.

MAURITIUS AND DEPENDENCIES

ITU allocation: 3BA–3BZ.
Callsign system:

Prefix	Island
3B6	Agalega Is
3B7	St Brandon Is
3B8	Mauritius
3B9	Rodriguez Is

Licence notes: 150W DC input maximum.
Foreign amateur operation: UK licence is accepted as a qualification for the issue of a licence.
National society: Mauritius Amateur Radio Society, PO Box 104, Quatre Bornes.
Licensing administration: The Director, Telecommunications Dept, Edith Cavell Street, Port Louis.

MEXICO

ITU allocation: XAA–XZZ, 4AA–4CZ, 6DA–6JZ.
Callsign system:

Prefix	Area
XE1	Central Mexico
XE2	North Mexico
XE3	South Mexico
XF2	Islands W of 90°W
XF3	Islands E of 90°W
XF4	Revilla Gigedo Is

Licence notes: Four licence classes: First class: all bands, 1kW. Second class: all bands: 250W. Third class: all bands, 150W, no mobile operation. VHF: VHF only, 100W.
Foreign amateur operation: Must be resident in Mexico. Countries include USA.
National society: Federacion Mexicana de Radioexperimentadores, PO Box 907, 06000 Mexico, DF. Tel: +52 (5) 563-1405 (from 5pm–8pm). Fax: +52 (5) 563-2264.
Licensing administration: Direccion General de Telecomunicaciones, Av Lázaro Cardenas 567, Mexico 12, DF.

MICRONESIA (Federated States of)

ITU allocation: V6A–V6Z.
Callsign system: Prefix: V6.
Foreign amateur operation: Countries include USA.

MOLDOVA

ITU allocation: ERA–ERZ.
Callsign system: Prefix: ER.

MONACO (Principality of)

ITU allocation: 3AA–3AZ.

Callsign system:

Prefix	Licence class
3A1	VHF/UHF phone-only
3A2	All band

Licence notes: For licence classes see prefix table. All licences are for 100W anode dissipation.
Foreign amateur operation: *CEPT:* A + B. Call is 3A/own call. Note: Licensing administration must be informed of exact location of station prior to operation due to indistinct borders between Monaco and France. *Non-CEPT:* Reciprocal (A + B). Three months' notice. Call is 3A/own call. Countries include UK, USA.
National society: Association des Radio-Amateurs de Monaco, BP 2, MC-98001 Monaco Cedex. Tel: +33 92-50-29-71. Fax: +33 92-16-56-01.
Licensing administration: Direction générale de telecommunications, Service Radio-Amateurs, 25 boulevard de Suisse, MC98030 Monaco Cedex. Tel: +33 93-25-05-05. Fax: +33 93-25-15-15.

MONGOLIA (Mongolian People's Republic)

ITU allocation: JTA–JVZ.
Callsign system: Serial letters in the KAA–KZZ series denote club stations.

Prefix	Area/licence category
JT0	Foreign amateurs
JT1	Ulan Bator
JT2	Choibalsan

National society: Mongolian Radio Sports Federation, PO Box 639, Ulan Bator. Tel: +976 (1) 320058.
Licensing administration: Ministry of communications, Ulan Bator.

MOROCCO (Kingdom of)

ITU allocation: CNA–CNZ, 5CA–5GZ.
Callsign system: Prefix: CN.
Licence notes: 100W maximum.
Foreign amateur operation: Unilateral (A only). Call is own call/CN. Three months' notice. All countries except Israel but residents only.
National society: Association Royale des Radio-Amateurs du Maroc, BP 299, Rabat. Tel: +212 (7) 673703. Fax: +212 (7) 674757.
Licensing administration: Ministère des PTT, Division des télécommunications, Rabat.

MOZAMBIQUE (People's Republic of)

ITU allocation: C8A–C9Z.
Callsign system: Prefix: C9.
National society: Liga dos Radio Emissores de Mocambique, PO Box 25, Maputo.
Licensing administration: Ministerio dos Transportes e Communicações, Maputo.

MYANMAR (*previously Burma*)

ITU allocation: XYA–XZZ.
Callsign system: Prefix: XZ.
Licensing administration: Posts and Telecommunications Dept, Ministry of Transport and Communications, Ministers' Office, Rangoon.

NAMIBIA

ITU allocation: V5A–V5Z.
Callsign system: Prefix: V51.
National society: Namibian Amateur Radio League, PO Box 1100, Windhoek 9000. Tel: +264 (61) 44114. Fax: +264 (61) 2012519.

NAURU (Republic of)

ITU allocation: C2A–C2Z.
Callsign system: Prefix: C21.
Foreign amateur operation: Call is own call/C2.

NEPAL

ITU allocation: 9NA–9NZ.
Callsign system: Prefix: 9N1.
Licensing administration: Ministry of communications, Singha Durbar, Kathmandu.

NETHERLANDS (Kingdom of the)

ITU allocation: PAA–PIZ.
Callsign system:

Prefix	Licence category
PA0	Class A
PA2	Class A, B
PA3	Class A, B
PA6	Special
PD0	Class D

PE0	Class C
PE1	Class C
PE2	Class C
PI1	Class A (schools)
PI2	Class A (schools)
PI3	Class C (repeaters, beacons)
PI4	Club stations

Licence notes: Four licence classes. Class A: all bands, 100W output. Class B: 3.5, 21, 28MHz (CW only), 100W output, plus VHF and above, 30W output. Class C: VHF, phone-only, 30W output. Class D: 144MHz, phone-only, crystal-controlled (S10, S11, S13, S14, S15, S16 channels only), 15W output.

Foreign amateur operation: *CEPT*: A + B. Call is PA/own call. *Non-CEPT*: Reciprocal (A + B). Call is PA/own call (UK Class A), PE/own call (UK Class B). Fee. Form. Two months' notice. Call is own call/PA or /PE. Countries include: Belgium, Botswana, Canada, Denmark, France, Jamaica, Luxembourg, Netherlands Antilles, Mexico, Norway, Panama, Portugal, Sierra Leone, Sweden, Switzerland, UK, USA, Germany.

National society: VERON Centraal Bureau, Postbus 1166, NL-6801 BD Arnhem. Tel: +31 (85) 426760.

Licensing administration: HDTP-02, PO Box 450, NL-9700 AL Groningen. Tel: +31 (50) 222111. Fax: +31 (50) 135645.

NETHERLANDS ANTILLES

ITU allocation: PJA–PJZ.
Callsign system:

Prefix	Area
PJ2	Curaçao
PJ4	Bonaire
PJ5	St Eustatius
PJ6	Saba
PJ7, 8	St Maarten
PJ9	All other areas

Licence notes: Three licence classes. Class A: all bands, 1kW PEP. Class B: restricted bands, CW only, 150W. Class C: VHF phone-only, 150W PEP.

Foreign amateur operation: Six weeks' notice. Countries include: Netherlands, USA, Canada, UK, Australia, Indonesia, Jamaica.

National society: VERONA, PO Box 3383, Curaçao.

Licensing administration: Landsradio, PO Box 103, Willemstad, Curaçao.

NEW ZEALAND

ITU allocation: ZKA–ZMZ.
Callsign system: NAA–NZZ serial letters denote Novice licence, TAA–TZZ Grade 3.

Prefix	Area or licence category
ZK1	Cook Is, Manihiki Is
ZK2	Niue Is
ZK3	Tokelau Is
ZL1–ZL4	Mainland
ZL5	Antarctica
ZL6	Intruder watch and emergency
ZL7	Chatham Is
ZL8	Kermadec Is
ZL9	Auckland and Campbell Is

Licence notes: Four licence classes. Grade 1: full licence, 150W DC input. Grade 2: 1803–1813, 1875–1900, 3500–3900kHz and VHF, 150W DC input. Grade 3: VHF phone-only, 150W DC input. Novice: crystal-controlled 3525–3575kHz, 10W DC input.

Foreign amateur operation: *CEPT*: Call is own call/ZLx. *Non-CEPT*: Reciprocal (A + B). Call is own call/ZLx. Fee. Two weeks' notice. Countries include: British Commonwealth, USA, France, Switzerland.

National society: New Zealand Amateur Radio Transmitters, PO Box 40-525, Upper Hutt. Tel: +64 (4) 528-2170. Fax: +64 (4) 528-2170.

Licensing administration: Radio Operations, Communications Division, Ministry of Commerce, PO Box 1473, Wellington. Tel: +64 (4) 472-0030. Fax: +64 (4) 499-0797.

NICARAGUA

ITU allocation: HTA–HTZ, YNA–YNZ, H6A–H7Z.
Callsign system:

Prefix	City/town and area
YN1	Managua, DN
YN2	Granada
YN3	Leon
YN4	Bluefields
YN5	Jinotepe
YN6	Chinandega
YN7	Masaya, Rivas

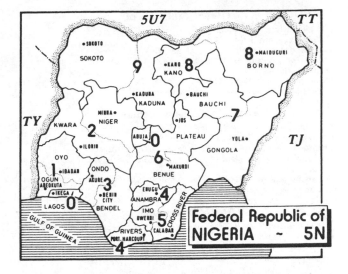

YN8	Esteli
YN9	Matagalpa

Licence notes: Two licence classes. Novice: 3.5, 7MHz, 100W DC input. General: all bands, 1kW DC input.

Foreign amateur operation: Countries include: USA, Canada, Guatemala, El Salvador, Honduras, Costa Rica, Panama; all others 90 days (in transit only).

National society: Club de Radio Experimentadores de Nicaragua, Apartado de Correos 925, Managua, DN. Tel: +505 (2) 71274. Fax: +505 (2) 665879.

Licensing administration: Jefatura de Comunicaciones, Managua, DN.

NIGER (Republic of the)

ITU allocation: 5UA–5UZ.
Callsign system: Prefix: 5U7.
Foreign amateur operation: Call is own call/5U7.
Licensing administration: Ministère des postes et télécommunications, Niamey.

NIGERIA (Federal Republic of)

ITU allocation: 5NA–5OZ.
Callsign system: Prefix: 5N. See map for call areas.
Licence notes: Single licence class, 150W DC input.
Foreign amateur operation: Fee. Two months' notice. All member countries of ITU and IARU. Apply to NARS.
National society: Nigerian Amateur Radio Society, PO Box 2873, Lagos. Tel: +234 (1) 884145. Fax: +234 (1) 863237.

NORWAY

ITU allocation: JWA–JXZ, LAA–LNZ, 3YA–3YZ.
Callsign system:

Prefix	Area/licence category
JW	Bear Is, Svalbard
JX	Jan Mayen Is
LA0	Norway (reciprocal)
LA1–9	Norway (Class A)
LB	Norway (Class B)
LC	NRRL Emergency Corps
LF	Norway (electronics companies)
LG	Morokuilen (LG5LG)
LH	Norway (scientific stations)
LJ	Norway (schools)
3Y	Antarctica (Norway), Bouvet Is

Licence notes: Two licence classes: Class A: all bands, 600W PEP input. Class B: all bands, CW only, 15W input. Electronic companies, scientific stations and schools permitted to operate within the amateur bands.

Foreign amateur operation: *CEPT*: A + B. Call is LA/own call. *Non-CEPT*: Reciprocal (A only). Fee. Form. One month's notice. For less than one year's operation, call is LA/own call. For longer periods, call is prefixed LA0, JW0 etc. Countries include: Austria, Canada, Denmark, Finland, France, Iceland, Spain, Sweden, Switzerland, UK, USA, Germany.

National society: Norsk Radio Relae Liga, Boks 21, Refstad, N-0513 Oslo 5. Tel: +47 (22) 213790. Fax: +47 (22) 213791.

Licensing administration: Statens Teleforvaltning, PO Box 2592, Solli, N-0203 Oslo. Tel: +47 (22) 926739. Fax: +47 (22) 562457.

OMAN (Sultanate of)

ITU allocation: A4A–A4Z.
Callsign system: Prefix: A4.
Licence notes: Single licence class: 150W DC input.
Foreign amateur operation: Call is A4XV–. All countries except Israel. Apply to ROARS.
National society: Royal Omani Amateur Radio Society, PO Box 981, Muscat. Tel: +968 600407. Fax: +968 698558.

PAKISTAN (Islamic Republic of)

ITU allocation: APA–ASZ, 6PA–6SZ.
Callsign system: Prefix: AP.
Licence notes: Single licence class: 100W DC input.
National society: Pakistan Amateur Radio Society, PO Box 65, Lahore.
Licensing administration: The Director-General, Telegraph & Telephone Dept, Zero Point, Islamabad.

PANAMA (Republic of)

ITU allocation: H3A–H3Z, H8A–H9Z, HOA–HPZ, 3EA–3FZ.
Callsign system:

Prefix	Area	City/town
HP1	—	Panamá
HP2	Canal Zone	Colon
HP3	Chiriqui	David
HP4	Bocas del Toro	Bocas del Toro
HP5	Herrera	Chitre
HP6	Veraguas	Santiago
HP7	Darién	La Palma

Licence notes: Three licence classes. Class A: all bands, 1kW DC input. Class B: all bands, 500W DC input. Class C: 3.5, 7, 144MHz, 200W. Third-party traffic permitted.
Foreign amateur operation: Unilateral. Call is own call/HP4X. Countries include: USA, Canada, Guatemala, Honduras, Costa Rica, Nicaragua, Ecuador, Peru, Chile, Argentina, Paraguay, Uruguay, Brazil, Bolivia, El Salvador. Applicant must be in Panama at time of application.
National society: Liga Panameña de Radio Aficionados, Apartado Postal 9A-175, Panamá. Tel: +507 263160. Fax: +507 263160.
Licensing administration: Ministerio de Gobierno y Justicia, Dirrecion Nacional de Medio de Comunicación Social, Apartada Postal 1628, Zona 1, Panamá.

PAPUA NEW GUINEA

ITU allocation: P2A–P2Z.
Callsign system: Prefix: P29. NAA–NZZ serial letters denote Novice, ZAA–ZZZ Limited (VHF).
Licence notes: Three licence classes. Amateur: all bands, 400W PEP. Novice: 3.5, 21 and 28MHz, 30W PEP. Limited (VHF): VHF only, 400W PEP.
Foreign amateur operation: Reciprocal (A + B). Call is in P29V series. Countries include: UK, USA, Canada, Australia, France, New Zealand, Germany, Japan, and others.
National society: Papua New Guinea Amateur Radio Society, PO Box 204, Port Moresby.
Licensing administration: The Manager, Radio Branch, Posts and Telecomms Corp, PO Box 1783, Port Moresby. Tel: +675 274236.

PARAGUAY (Republic of)

ITU allocation: ZPA–ZPZ.
Callsign system:

Prefix	Province	City/town
ZP1, 2	Chaco	Mariscal, Estagarribia
ZP3	Concepción	Concepción
ZP4	La Cordillera	San Bernadino
	San Pedro	San Pedro
ZP5	—	Asunción
ZP6	Central	Capiatá
	Paraguarí	Paraguarí
ZP7	Caaguazu	Yhú
	Caazapá	Caazapá
	Guaira	Villarica
ZP8	Misiones	San Ignacio
	Neembucu	Pilar
ZP9	Alto Parana	Puerto Adela
	Itapuá	Encarnación
ZP0	—	Asunción

Licence notes: Three licence classes. Class A: all bands, 2kW PEP. Class B: 1.8, 3.5, 7, 14MHz, 2kW PEP. Class C: 3.5, 7MHz, 2kW PEP.
Foreign amateur operation: All countries. Apply to RCP.
National society: Radio Club Paraguayo, Casilla Postal 512, Asunción. Tel: +595 (21) 446124. Fax: +595 (21) 446124.

PERU

ITU allocation: OAA–OCZ, 4TA–4TZ.
Callsign system: See map for prefixes.
Licence notes: 2kW PEP maximum. Third-party traffic permitted.
Foreign amateur operation: *CEPT*: A + B. Call is own call/OA. *Non-CEPT*: Unilateral (A only). Call is own call/OA. Countries include: Colombia, Bolivia, Canada, Chile, Germany, Uruguay, USA, Netherlands, Venezuela, Argentina, Switzerland, Poland, Spain, Ecuador; other countries 90 days (in transit) only.
National society: Radio Club Peruano, Box 538, Lima 100. Tel: +51 (1) 441-4837. Fax: +51 (1) 440-8944.
Licensing administration: Ministerio de Transportes, Comunicaciones, Vivienda y Construccion, Av Wilson y 28 de Julio, Cercado de Lima, Lima. Tel: +51 (1) 433-7800. Fax: +51 (1) 433-6622.

PHILIPPINES (Republic of the)

ITU allocation: DUA–DZZ, 4DA–4IZ.
Callsign system: Prefixes: DU (Advanced), DV (General), DW (Novice), DY (VHF only).

Area no	Island
1–4	Luzon
5	Leyte
6, 7	Panay, Negros, Cebu
8, 9	Mindanao

Licence notes: Four licence classes: Advanced, General, Novice and VHF only. 2kW PEP maximum.
Foreign amateur operation: Reciprocal. Call is own call/DU1. Countries include: USA, Canada.
National society: Phillipine Amateur Radio Association, PO Box 4083, Manila. Tel: +63 (2) 964069. Fax: +63 (2) 984705.
Licensing administration: Planning Division, Telecommunication Control Bureau, 5th Floor, Delos Santos Building, Quezon Avenue, Quezon City.

POLAND (People's Republic of)

ITU allocation: HFA–HFZ, SNA–SRZ, 3ZA–3ZZ.
Callsign system: See map for prefixes. Serial letters KAA–KZZ, PAA–PZZ, ZAA–ZZZ denote club stations.
Licence notes: Two main licence classes. Class 1: all bands, 20, 50, 250 or 750W. Class 2 VHF phone-only, 10W.

Foreign amateur operation: Reciprocal (A + B). Call is in SO series. Three months' notice. No mobile licences. Countries include UK.
National society: Polski Zwiazek Krotkofalocow, PO Box 61, 64-100 Leszno 1. Tel: +48 (65) 209529. Fax: +48 (65) 209529.
Licensing administration: Panstwowa Agencja Radiokomunikacyjna, Zarzad Krajowy, ul Kasprzata 18/20, 01-211 Warsaw.

PORTUGAL
ITU allocation: COA–CUZ, XXA–XXZ.
Callsign system:

Prefix	Area
CS1, 4, 5, 6, 7	Portugal (special)
CT1	Portugal
CT3	Madeira Is
CT4	Portugal
CT5, 6, 7	Portugal (special)
CT0	(Repeaters)
CU	Azores Is (see below)
XX9	Macao

Azores prefix	Area
CU1	Santa Maria
CU2	São Miguel
CU3	Terceira
CU4	Graciosa
CU5	São Jorge
CU6	Pico
CU7	Faial
CU8	Flores
CU9	Corvo

Licence notes (Portugal): Three licence classes. Class A: VHF phone only. Class B: all bands. Class C: HF/VHF only.
Foreign amateur operation: *Portugal*: *CEPT*: A + B. Call is own call/CT1. *Non-CEPT*: Reciprocal (A + B). Fee. Call is own call/area prefix. Licences can only be issued in Portugal. Countries include all EU countries, USA. *Madeira Is*: Reciprocal (A + B).
National society: (Portugal and Madeira): Rede dos Emissores Portugueses, Rua D Pedro V-7-4°, 1200 Lisbon. Tel: +351 (1) 361186.
Licensing administration: *Portugal*: Instituto das Comunicações Portugal, Rua de S Jose 20, 1193 Lisbon Cedex. *Madeira Is*: Instituto das Comunicações Portugal, Delegação do ICP Madeira, Centro Fiscalizacao, Pico da Cruz, 9000 Funchal. Tel: +35191 762868.

QATAR (State of)
ITU allocation: A7A–A7Z.
Callsign system: Prefix: A71.
National society: Qatar Amateur Radio Society, PO Box 22122, Doha. Tel: +974 439191. Fax: +974 439595.
Licensing administration: Director of Telecommunications, Ministry of Communications and Transport, PO Aox 2633, Doha.

ROMANIA (Socialist Republic of)
ITU allocation: YOA–YRZ.
Callsign system: See map for prefixes.

Licence notes: 400W maximum DC input.
Foreign amateur operation: *CEPT*: A + B. YO/own call. *Non-CEPT*: Unilateral. No fee. All countries. Three months' notice.
National society: Federatia Romana de Radioamatorism, PO Box 22-50, R-71100 Bucharest. Tel: +40 (1) 211-9787.
Licensing administration: General Inspectorate of Radiocommunications, 202A Splaiul Independentei sector 6, R-77208 Bucharest. Tel: +40 (1) 386981. Fax: +40 (1) 3124797.

RUSSIAN FEDERATION
ITU allocation: RAA–RZZ, UAA–UIZ.
Callsign system: Prefixes: U, RA, UA, RV, UV, RW, UW, RZ, UZ. Current 1st, 2nd and 3rd class callsigns are made up of a two-letter prefix, a number which denotes the geographical area, a letter corresponding to the administrative region and two serial letters, eg RA-3-M-AA. The two serial letters are AA–VZ for individual stations and WA–ZZ for club stations. Note: older two-letter calls do not follow these rules.

GEOGRAPHICAL AREA/ADMINISTRATIVE REGION
The number given in brackets after the geographical area denotes the callsign number for stations in that area. AO = autonomous oblast, AOk = autonomous okrug, Obl = oblast, Rep = republic.

North European Russia (1)

1st serial letter	Area	Capital
A, B	St Petersburg city	
C	Leningrad Obl	St Petersburg
D	St Petersburg city	
F–J	St Petersburg city	
L, M	St Petersburg city	
N	Karelian Rep	Petrozavodsk
O	Arkhangelsk Obl	Arkhangelsk
P	Nenets AO	Naryan-Mar
Q, R, S	Vologda Obl	Vologda
T, U	Novgorod Obl	Novgorod
W, X	Pskov Obl	Pskov
Y, Z	Murmansk Obl	Murmansk

The Baltic (2)

1st serial letter	Area	Capital
A–Z	Kaliningrad Obl	Kaliningrad

Central European Russia (3)

1st serial letter	Area	Capital
A, B, C	Moscow city	
D	Moscow Obl	Moscow
E	Orlov Obl	Orel
F	Moscow city	
G	Lipetsk Obl	Lipetsk
H	Moscow city	
I, J	Tvers Obl	Kalinin
L	Smolensk Obl	Smolensk
M	Yaroslavl Obl	Yaroslavl
N, O	Kostroma Obl	Kostroma
P	Tula Obl	Tula
Q	Voronezh Obl	Voronezh
R	Tambov Obl	Tambov
S	Ryazan Obl	Ryazan
T	Gorkiy Obl	Gorkiy

U	Ivanovo Obl	Ivanovo
V	Vladimir Obl	Vladimir
W	Kursk Obl	Kursk
X	Kaluga Obl	Kaluga
Y	Bryansk Obl	Bryansk
Z	Belgorod Obl	Belgorod

East European Russia (4)

1st serial letter	Area	Capital
A, B	Volgograd Obl	Volgograd
C, D	Saratov Obl	Saratov
F	Penza Obl	Penza
H, I	Samar Obl	
L, M	Ulyanovsk Obl	Ulyanovsk
N, O	Kirov Obl	Kirov
P, Q, R	Tatar Rep	Kazan
S, T	Mari Rep	Yoshkar-Ola
U	Mordov Rep	Saransk
W	Udmurt Rep	Izhevsk
Y, Z	Chuvash Rep	Cheboksary

South European Russia (6)

1st serial letter	Area	Capital
A–D	Krasnodar Kray	Krasnodar
E	Karacheyevo-Cherkessk Rep	Cherkessk
F, G, H	Stavropol Kray	Stavropol
I	Kalmyt Rep	Elista
J	North Osetia Rep	Ordzhonikdze
L–O	Rostov Obl	Rostov-na-Donu
P, Q, R	Chechen Rep, Ingush Rep	Grozny
U, V	Astrakhan Obl	Astrakhan
W	Dagestan Rep	Makhachkala
X	Kabardino-Balkar Rep	Nalchik
Y	Adigei Rep	Maykop

The Urals and West Siberia (9)

1st serial letter	Area	Capital
A, B	Chelyabinsk Obl	Chelyabinsk
C, D, E	Sverdlovsk Obl	Sverdlovsk
F	Perm Obl	Perm
G	Komi-Permiatsky AOk	Kudymkar
H, I	Tomsk Obl	Tomsk
J	Khanty-Mansiysky AOk	Khanty-Mansiysk
K	Jamalo-Nenets AOk	Salekhard
L	Tyumen Obl	Tyumen
M, N	Omsk Obl	Omsk
O, P	Novosibirsk Obl	Novosibirsk
Q, R	Kurgan Obl	Kurgan
S, T	Orenburg Obl	Orenburg
U, V	Kemerov Obl	Kemerov
W	Bashkir Rep	Ufa
X	Komi Rep	Syktyvkar
Y	Altay Kray	Barnaul
Z	Gorno-Altay AO (Altay Kray)	Gorno-Altaysk

East Siberia and the Far East (0, 8)

1st serial letter	Area	Capital
0A	Krasnoyarsk Kray	Krasnoyarsk
0B	Taymyr AOk	Dudinka
0C	Khabarovsk Kray	Khabarovsk
0D	Yevrev AO (Khabarovsk Kray)	Birobidzhan
0E–G	Sakhalin Obl	Yuzhno-Sakhalinsk
0H	Evenkiysk AOk	Tura
0I	Magadan Obl	Magadan
0J	Amur Obl	Blagoveshchensk
0K	Chukotsky AOk	Anadyr
0L, M, N	Primorsky Kray	Vladivostok
0O, P	Buryat Rep	Ulan-Ude
0Q, R	Yakutsk Rep	Yakutsk
0S, T	Irkutsk Obl	Irkutsk
0U, V	Chita Obl	Chita
0W	Khakass AO (Krasnoyarsk Kray)	Abakan
0X	Koriatsky AOk	Palana
0Y	Tuvinsk Rep	Kyzyl
0Z	Kamchatsky Obl	Petropavlovsk-Kamchatsky

8T	Ust-Ordinsky Buriatsky AO	Ust-Ordinsky
8V	Aginsky-Buriatsky AOk	Aginskoye

Polar regions

Prefix	Area
R1A	Antarctica
R1F	Franz Josef Land
R1M	Malyi Vysotsky

Licence notes: Four licence classes. 1st class: all bands, 200W. 2nd class: all bands, 40W. 3rd class: 1.8, 3.5, 7, 14, 28MHz and VHF, 10W. 4th class: 1.8MHz, 5W.
Foreign amateur operation: Unilateral (A only). Apply via URR.
National society: Union of Radioamateurs of Russia, PO Box 59, Moscow 105122. Tel: +7 (095) 166-4487. Fax: +7 (095) 166-5856.

RWANDA (Republic of)

ITU allocation: 9XA–9XZ.
Callsign system: Prefix: 9X5.
Licensing administration: Ministère des postes et télécommunications, BP 720, Kigali.

SAINT KITTS AND NEVIS

ITU allocation: V4A–V4Z.
Callsign system: Prefix: V44.

SAINT LUCIA

ITU allocation: J6A–J6Z.
Callsign system: Prefix: J6.
Foreign amateur operation: Application must be made in person. Countries include USA.
Licensing administration: Police HQ, Castries.

SAINT VINCENT (and Grenadines)

ITU allocation: J8A–J8Z.
Callsign system: Prefix: J88.
Foreign amateur operation: Call uses J87 prefix. Countries include USA.

SAN MARINO (Republic of)

ITU allocations: T7A–T7Z, 9AA–9AZ.
Callsign system:

Prefix	Licence class
T70	Club station
T71	Special events
T72	Second class
T77	First class

Licence notes: Two licence classes. Second-class is VHF only.
National society: Associazione Radioamatori della Repubblica di San Marino, PO Box 77, 47031 San Marino. Tel: +378 906790. Fax: +378 906790.
Licensing administration: Direzione Generale Poste e Telecommunicazioni, San Marino. Tel: +378 991349.

SAO TOME AND PRINCIPE (Democratic Republic of)

ITU allocation: S9A–S9Z.
Callsign system: Prefix: S92.
Licensing administration: Direcção dos Correios e Telecommunicações da Republica Democratica de São Tomé e Principe, São Tomé.

SAUDI ARABIA (Kingdom of)

ITU allocation: HZA–HZZ, 7ZA–7ZZ, 8ZA–8ZZ.
Callsign system: Prefix: HZ.
Licensing administration: The Deputy Minister of Posts, Telegraphs & Telephones, Riyadh.

SENEGAL (Republic of the)

ITU allocation: 6VA–6WZ.
Callsign system: Prefix: 6W.
National society: Association des Radio-Amateurs du Senegal, BP 971, Dakar.
Licensing administration: Ministère de l'Information et des Télécommunications, Dakar.

SEYCHELLES (Republic of)

ITU allocation: S7A–S7Z.
Callsign system: Prefix: S79.
Foreign amateur operation: Unilateral (A only). Call is in S79 series. Countries include UK, USA.
Licensing administration: Seychelles Licensing Authority, PO Box 3, Victoria Mahe.

SIERRA LEONE
ITU allocation: 9LA–9LZ.
Callsign system: Prefix: 9L1 (9L8 VHF/UHF only).
Licence notes: Two licence classes, General and Novice.
Foreign amateur operation: Reciprocal. Call is own call/9L1. Countries include the UK, USA and most others but residence required.
National society: Sierra Leone Amateur Radio Society, PO Box 10, Freetown. Tel: +232 223335.
Licensing administration: Licensing Office, P & T Dept, GPO, Freetown.

SINGAPORE (Republic of)
ITU allocation: S6A–S6Z, 9VA–9VZ.
Callsign system: Prefix: 9V1.
Licence notes: Single licence class: 150W DC input maximum.
Foreign amateur operation: Unilateral (A only). Call is in 9V1 series. All countries.
National society: SARTS, GPO Box 2728, Singapore 9047.
Licensing administration: Telecommunication Authority of Singapore, Radio Licensing Dept, 4–8 George Street #04-00, Singapore 0104. Tel: +65 538-0402.

SLOVAK REPUBLIC
ITU allocation: OMA–OMZ.
Callsign system: Prefix: OM. See map for call areas.

Callsign series	Type of station
OM1x–OM0x	Contest stations
OM1xx–OM8xx, OM0xx	Classes A and B
OM1xxx–OM8xxx, OM0AAA–JZZ	Classes C and D
OM3xx–OM3xxx	Existing callsigns from OK3 era. KAA–KZZ, RAA–RZZ serial letters used for club stations
OM9xx	Special event stations
OM9AAA–SZZ	Foreign visitors
OM0MAA–MZZ	Beacons
OM0NAA–NZZ	Packet
OM0PAA–PZZ	Packet BBS
OM0OAA–OZZ	Repeaters
OM0SAA–SZZ	Amtor, Pactor, Clover BBS

Licence notes: Four licence classes. Class A: all bands, 750W. Class B: all bands, 300W. Class C: 1.8, 3.5, 10, 21, 28MHz bands plus VHF and above, 100W. Class D: 3.5MHz band plus VHF and above, 100W.
Foreign amateur operation: *CEPT*: A + B. Call is OM/own call. *Non-CEPT*: Fee. Form. Call is in OM9AAA–SZZ series.
National society: Slovak Amateur Radio Association, PO Box 1, SK-85299 Bratislava. Tel: +42 (7) 847501. Fax: +42 (7) 845138.
Licensing administration: Telecomunikacný úrad SR, povol'ovanie rádiostanic, Jarosova 1, SK-83008 Bratislava. Tel: +42 (7) 2792704. Fax: +42 (7) 258971.

SLOVENIA
ITU allocation: S5A–S5Z.
Callsign system: Prefix: S5.
National society: Zveza Radioamaterjev Slovenije, Lepi Pot 6, 61000 Ljubljana. Tel: +386 (1) 222459.

SOLOMON ISLANDS
ITU allocation: H4A–H4Z.
Callsign system: Prefix: H44.
Foreign amateur operation: Unilateral (A + B). Call is in H44 series. All ITU member countries.
National society: Solomon Islands Radio Society, PO Box 418, Honiara.
Licensing administration: Director, Ministry of Posts and Communications, PO Box G25, Honiara.

SOMALI DEMOCRATIC REPUBLIC
ITU allocation: 6OA–6OZ, T5A–T5Z.
Callsign system: Prefix: T5.
Licensing administration: Ministry of Posts and Telecommunications, Mogadishu.

SOUTH AFRICA (Rep#ublic of)
ITU allocation: ZRA–ZUZ.
Callsign system: Prefixes: ZR (Class B licences), ZS (Class A licences). For call areas see map.
Licence notes: Two licence classes. Class A: all bands, 150W DC input or 400W PEP. Class B: VHF phone-only, 150W DC input or 400W PEP.
Foreign amateur operation: Reciprocal (A + B). Call is ZS/own call (UK Class A) or ZR/own call (UK Class B). Fee. Four weeks' notice. Countries include: UK, USA, Zimbabwe. Apply to SARL.
National society: South African Radio League, PO Box 807, Houghton, 2041, South Africa. Tel: +27 (11) 484-2830. Fax: +27 (11) 484-2831.

SPAIN
ITU allocation: AMA–AOZ, EAA–EHZ.
Callsign system: See map for call areas. EA8 is Canary Is.

Prefix	Licence class
EA	Class A
EB	Class B
EC	Class C

Licence notes: Three classes. Class A: all bands, 250W anode dissipation. Class B: VHF only, 50W anode dissipation. Class C: 3.550–3.575, 7.020–7.030, 21.000–21.150MHz CW only, 29.0–29.1MHz AM only, 20W anode dissipation.
Foreign amateur operation: *CEPT*: A + B. Call is EA/own call (UK Class A), EB/own call (UK Class B). *Non-CEPT*: Reciprocal (A + B). Call is EA/own call (UK Class A), EB/own call (UK Class B). Fee. Form. Countries include UK, USA.

National society: Union de Radioaficionados Espanoles, Apartado 220, E-28080 Madrid. Tel: +34 (1) 477-1413. Fax: +34 (1) 477-2071.
Licensing administration: Direccion General de Telecomunicacións, Subdireccion General de Ordenacion y Reglamentacion, Edificio Administrativo de Comunicaciones, CCP Chamartin, 28070 Madrid. Tel: +34 (1) 733-5500.

SRI LANKA (Democratic Socialist Republic of)
ITU allocation: 4PA–4SZ.
Callsign system: Prefix: 4S7.
Licence notes: 100W DC input maximum.
Foreign amateur operation: Reciprocal (A + B). No specified countries. UK licence is usually accepted as a qualification for the issue of a licence.
National society: Radio Society of Sri Lanka, PO Box 907, Colombo.
Licensing administration: The Director General of Telecomms, Regulatory Authority, EH Cooray Building, 4th floor, 411 Galle Road, Colombo 3.

SUDAN (Democratic Republic of the)
ITU allocation: SSN–STZ, 6TA–6UZ.
Callsign system: Prefixes: ST, 6U.
Licensing administration: The Director, Department of Telecommunications, Ministry of Communications, Khartoum.

SURINAME (Republic of)
ITU allocation: PZA–PZZ.
Callsign system:

Prefix	City/town and area
PZ1, PZ5	Paramaribo
PZ2	Niew Nickerie
PZ9	Moengo

Licence notes: 150W DC input maximum.
Foreign amateur operation: Countries include: USA, Netherlands, Netherlands Antilles (reciprocal). All other countries on production of licence. Apply to VRAS.
National society: Vereniging van Radio Amateurs in Suriname, PO Box 1153, Paramaribo.

SWAZILAND (Kingdom of)
ITU allocation: 3DA–3DM.
Callsign system: Prefix: 3DA.
Licence notes: 500W DC input maximum.
Foreign amateur operation: Reciprocal (A + B). Countries include UK.
National society: Radio Society of Swaziland, PO Box 3744, Manzini.
Licensing administration: Engineer Frequency Management, Managing Director of Posts and Telecomms, PO Box 125, Mbabane.

SWEDEN (Kingdom of)
ITU allocation: SAA–SMZ, 7SA–7SZ, 8SA–8SZ.
Callsign system: For call areas see map and table. Serial letters RAA–RZZ in the SK prefix series are allocated to repeaters.

Prefix	Area/licence category
SJ9	Morokulien
SK	Club stations, repeaters, beacons
SL	Military
SM	Individual
SM8	Maritime mobile

Licence notes: Four licence classes. Class A (advanced): all bands, 500W DC input. Class B (general): all bands CW, 28MHz and above phone, 75W DC input. Class C (basic): all bands CW, 28MHz and above phone, 10W DC input. Class T (technician): VHF phone-only, 75W DC input.
Foreign amateur operation: *CEPT*: A + B. Call is SM/own call. *Non-CEPT*: Unilateral (A + B). Call is SM/own call. Fee. Form. Two months' notice. All countries.
National society: Föreningen Sveriges Sändareamatörer, Ostmarksgatan 43, S-123 42 Farsta. Tel: +46 (8) 604-4006. Fax: +46 (8) 604-4007.
Licensing administration: Telestyrelsen, Frequency Division, Box 700, S-136 27 Haninge. Tel: +46 (8) 707-3500.

SWITZERLAND (Confederation of)
ITU allocation: HBA–HBZ, HEA–HEZ.
Callsign system: Prefixes: HB9 (Switzerland), HB0 (Liechtenstein). HB4 prefix is used for military amateur radio clubs. Serial letters MAA–MZZ and PAA–PZZ are allocated to D3 and D4 licences.
Licence notes: Four licence classes. Class D1: all bands, 200W. Class D2: all bands, 1kW. Class D3: VHF, 200W. Class D4: VHF, 1kW.
Foreign amateur operation: *CEPT*: A + B. Call is HB9/own call

Call areas and provinces (Län)

Sweden   SM · SK · SL

(Switzerland), HB0/own call (Liechtenstein). *Non-CEPT*. Reciprocal. Fee. Form. One month's notice. Countries include: Australia, Austria, Belgium, Brazil, Canada, Chile, Cyprus, Czech Rep, Denmark, Finland, France (incl overseas terr), Germany, Greece, Iceland, India, Irish Rep, Israel, Italy, Kuwait, Luxembourg, Malta, Monaco, New Zealand, Netherlands, Norway, Papua New Guinea, Peru, Portugal, Qatar, Slovakia, South Africa, Sweden, Thailand, UK, USA.
National society: *Switzerland*: Union Schweizerischer Kurzwellen-Amateure, PO Box 9, CH-4511 Rumisberg BE. *Liechtenstein*: Amateurfunk Verein Liechtenstein, Postfach 629, FL-9495 Triesen.
Licensing administration: *Switzerland*: General Directorate, Swiss Telecom, Radiocom and Broadcast Licensing, Speichergasse 6, CH-3030 Berne. Tel: +41 (31) 338 1111. Fax: +41 (31) 338 5191. *Liechtenstein*: Office pour Relations internationales, Regierung des Furstentums Liechtenstein, FL-9490 Vaduz. Tel: +4175 66111.

SYRIA (Syrian Arab Republic)
ITU allocation: YKA–YKZ, 6CA–6CZ.
Callsign system: Prefix: YK1.
Licence notes: 500W DC input maximum.
Foreign amateur operation: Call is own call/YK.
National society: Technical Institute of Radio, PO Box 245, Damascus.
Licensing administration: Direction générale de l'établissement des postes et des télécommunications, Damascus.

TADJIKISTAN
ITU allocation: EYA–EYZ.
Callsign system: Prefix: EY.

Prefix	Area	Capital
EY4	Gorno-Badakstan AO	Khorog
EY5	Kulyab Obl	Kulyab
EY6	Kurgan-Tyube Obl	Kurgan-Tyube
EY7	Leninabad Obl	Leninabad
EY8	—	Dushanbe

TANZANIA (United Republic of)
ITU allocation: 5HA–5IZ.
Callsign system: Prefixes: 5H1 Qanzibar), 5H3 (Tanzania).
Licensing administration: Director-General, East African P&T Corporation, PO Box 9070, Dar-es-Salaam.

THAILAND
ITU allocation: HSA–HSZ, E2A–E2Z.
Callsign system:

Prefix	City/town and area
HS0	(Club stations)
HS1	Bangkok
HS3	Korat
HS5	Chiang Mai

Licence notes: 1kW DC input maximum.
Foreign amateur operation: Countries include: USA, UK, Japan, Malaysia, Canada, Switzerland, Germany, Sweden, Denmark, Australia, New Zealand, Spain, and others. Apply to RAST.
National society: Radio Amateur Society of Thailand, GPO Box 2008, Bangkok 10501. Tel: +66 (2) 277-9453. Fax: +66 (2) 275-7288.

TOGO (Togolese Republic)
ITU allocation: 5VA–5VZ.
Callsign system: Prefix: 5V7.
Licensing administration: Ministère des travaux publics, de la construction des postes et télécommunications, Lomé.

TONGA (Kingdom of)
ITU allocation: A3A–A3Z.
Callsign system: Prefix: A35.
Licence notes: Single licence class, 500W PEP.
Foreign amateur operation: Unilateral (A + B). Call is in A35 series. Most countries.
National society: Amateur Radio Club of Tonga, c/o Manfred Shuster, PO Box 1078, Nuku'alofa.
Licensing administration: Tonga Telecom, PO Box 46, Nuku'alofa. Tel: +676 24255. Fax: +676 22200.

TRINIDAD & TOBAGO
ITU allocation: 9YA–9ZZ.
Callsign system: Prefix: 9Y4.
Licence notes: 1kW DC input maximum. Third-party traffic permitted.
Foreign amateur operation: Countries include: USA, Canada, UK, British Commonwealth. Apply in person to the Chief Wireless Officer.
National society: Trinidad and Tobago Amateur Radio Society, PO Box 1167, Port of Spain.
Licensing administration: Chief Wireless Officer, Ministry of Works, Transport and Communications, Wrightson Road, Port of Spain.

TUNISIA
ITU allocation: TSA–TSZ, 3VA–3VZ.
Callsign system: Prefix: 3V8.
Licensing administration: Ministère des transports et communications, 3 bis rue d'Angleterre, Tunis.

TURKEY
ITU allocation: TAA–TCZ, YMA–YMZ.
Callsign system: Prefix: TA. See map for call areas.
Foreign amateur operation: *CEPT*: A + B. Call is TA/own call. *Non-CEPT*: Unilateral.
National society: Telsiz Radyo Amatorieri Cemiyeti, PO Box 109, Istanbul. Tel: +90 (1) 571-1651.
Licensing administration: Directorate General of PTT, Ankara. Tel: +90 (4) 312-5252.

TURKMENISTAN
ITU allocation: EZA–EZZ.
Callsign system: Prefix: EZ.

Prefix	Area
EZ3	Akhalsky veloyat
EZ4	Balkansky veloyat
EZ5	Maryisky veloyat
EZ6	Dashkhovuzsky veloyat
EZ7	Lebapsky veloyat
EZ8	Ashgabat

National society: Liga Radiolyubitely Turkmenistana, PO Box 555, Ashgabat 744020.

TUVALU
ITU allocation: T2A–T2Z.
Callsign system: Prefix: T2.
Foreign amateur operation: Countries include USA.

UGANDA (Republic of)
ITU allocation: 5XA–5XZ.
Callsign system: Prefix: 5X5.
Licensing administration: The Director-General, East African P&T Corporation, PO Box 7106, Kampala.

UKRAINE
ITU allocation: EMA–EOZ, URA–UZZ.
Callsign system: Prefixes: UR–UU, UY, UX.

1st serial letter	Area	Capital
A	Sumy Obl	Sumy
B	Ternopol Obl	Ternopol
C	Cherkassy Obl	Cherkassy
D	Zakarpatsk Obl	Uzhgorod
E	Dnepropetrovsk Obl	Dnepropetrovsk
F	Odessa Obl	Odessa
G	Kherson Obl	Kherson
H	Poltava Obl	Poltava
I	Donetsk Obl	Donetsk
J (UU)	Krymsk Obl	Simferopol
J (UU9)	Sevastopol City	
K	Rovno Obl	Rovno
L	Kharkov Obl	Kharkov
M	Voroshilovgrad Obl	Voroshilovgrad
N	Vinnitsa Obl	Vinnitsa
P	Volynsk Obl	Lutsk
Q	Zaporozhe Obl	Zaporozhe
R	Chernigov Obl	Chernigov
S	Ivano-Frankovsk Obl	Ivano-Frankovsk
T	Khmelnitsky Obl	Khmelnitsky
U	Kiev Obl	Kiev
U	Kiev city	
V	Kirovgrad Obl	Kirovgrad
W	Lvov Obl	Lvov
X	Zhitomir Obl	Zhitomir
Y	Chernovtsy Obl	Chernovtsy
Z	Nikolayev Obl	Nikolayev

The appropriate prefix is given in brackets.

National society: Ukrainian Amateur Radio League, PO Box 57, Kiev 252001. Tel: +7 (044) 446-2239.

UNITED ARAB EMIRATES
ITU allocation: A6A–A6Z.
Callsign system: Prefix: A61.
Licensing administration: The Director-General, Posts and Telecommunications, PO Box 902, Abu Dhabi.

UNITED KINGDOM (of Great Britain and Northern Ireland)
ITU allocation: GAA–GZZ, MAA–MZZ, VPA–VSZ, ZBA–ZJZ, ZNA–ZOZ, ZQA–ZAZ, 2AA–2ZZ.
Callsign system (UK): See table for prefixes. Serial letters in the 1AAA–0ZZZ, 6AAA–6ZZZ, 7AAA–7ZZZ and 8AAA–8ZZZ series denote Class B licences. Prefix varied when operating outside own area.

BRITISH ISLES

Prefix	Club prefix	Novice prefix	Area/licence category
G	GX	2E	England
GD	GT	2D	Isle of Man
GI	GN	2I	Northern Ireland

GJ	GH	2J	Jersey
GM	GS	2M	Scotland
GU	GP	2U	Guernsey and dependencies
GW	GC	2W	Wales
GB0, GB2, GB4	—	—	Special (all areas), Class A
GB3	—	—	Beacons and repeaters (all areas). Beacons have GB3+3 callsigns, repeaters GB3+2 callsigns.
GB1, GB6, GB8	—	—	Special (all areas), Class B
GB7	—	—	Data repeaters and mailboxes (all areas). Repeaters have GB7+2 callsigns, mailboxes GB7+3 callsigns.

UK OVERSEAS TERRITORIES

Prefix	Area
VP2E	Anguilla
VP2M	Montserrat
VP2V	British Virgin Is
VP5	Turks and Caicos Is
VP8	Falkland Is, Graham Land, S Orkney Is, S Sandwich Is, S Shetland Is, Antarctica (UK)
VP9	Bermuda
VQ9	Chagos Is
VR2	Hong Kong
VR6	Pitcairn Is
VS6	Hong Kong
ZB2	Gibraltar
ZC4	Cyprus (UK bases only)
ZD7	St Helena Is
ZD8	Ascension Is
ZD9B	Tristan da Cunha
ZD9G	Gough Is
ZF1	Cayman Is

Licence notes: *UK:* Two standard licence classes. Class A: all bands, 20dBW carrier, 26dBW PEP SSB. Class B: VHF and above, 20dBW carrier, 26dBW PEP. There are also two corresponding Novice classes. Novice Class A: 1950–2000kHz, 3560–3585kHz, 10,130–10,140kHz, 21,100–21,149kHz, 28,060–28,190 and 28,225–28,500kHz, plus VHF and above, CW and phone, 5W DC input. Novice Class B: VHF and above only, CW and phone, 5W DC input. *Overseas territories:* Usually similar to UK but without Class B licences.

Foreign amateur operation: *Bermuda:* Unilateral (A only). Call is own call/VP9. *Cayman Is:* Unilateral. Call is in ZF1 series. *Falkland Is:* Unilateral (A + B). Call is in VP8 series. *Gibraltar:* Reciprocal (A + B). Call is ZB2/own call. *Hong Kong:* Reciprocal (A + B). Call is in VR2 series. *Montserrat:* Unilateral. Call is in VP2M series. *Pitcairn & Henderson Is:* Unilateral. *UK: CEPT:* A + B. Call is area prefix/own call. *Non-CEPT:* Reciprocal. Two types are available: Two month (no fixed address required) or 12 month (main station address required). Call is area prefix/own call. Fee. Form. 30 days' notice required. Countries include: Austria, Australia, Belgium, Bermuda, Botswana, Brazil, Canada, Cyprus, Denmark, Dominican Republic, Finland, France, Germany, Gibraltar, Hong Kong, Iceland, India, Irish Republic, Israel, Italy, Kenya, Malaysia, Malta, Monaco, Netherlands, New Zealand, Norway, Papua New Guinea, Pitcairn Is, Poland, Portugal, Sierra Leone, South Africa, Spain, Sri Lanka, Sweden, Switzerland, Trinidad & Tobago, USA, Vanuatu, Zimbabwe. *Virgin Is:* Unilateral (A + B). Call is VP2V/own call.

National society: *Bermuda:* Radio Society of Bermuda, PO Box HM 275, Hamilton HM AX. *British Virgin Is:* British Virgin Islands Radio League, PO Box 4, West End, Tortola. *Cayman Is:* Cayman Amateur Radio Society, PO Box 1029, Grand Cayman. *Gibraltar:* Gibraltar Amateur Radio Society, PO Box 292. *Hong Kong:* HARTS, PO Box 541. *Montserrat:* Montserrat Amateur Radio Society, PO Box 448, Plymouth. *Turks and Caicos Is:* Turks and Caicos Amateur Radio Society, PO Box 218, Providencales. *UK:* Radio Society of Great Britain, Lambda House, Cranborne Road, Potters Bar, Herts EN6 3JE. Tel: +44 (1707) 659015. Fax: +44 (1707) 645105. *Virgin Is:* British Virgin Is Radio League, PO Box 4, West End, Tortola.

Licensing administrations: *Bermuda:* Dept of Telecomms; PO Box 101, Hamilton 5. Tel: +1 (809) 295-5151 ext 1120. *Cayman Is:* The Postmaster, General Post Office, Grand Cayman. Tel: +1 (809) 949-2474. *Falkland Is:* Superintendent, Posts and Telecommunications, The Post Office, Port Stanley. Tel: +500 27135. *Gibraltar:* The Wireless Officer, General Post Office, 104 Main Street. Tel: +350 75624. *Hong Kong:* Officer-in-charge, Telecommunications Branch, 19th Floor, Sincere Building, 173 Des Voeux Road, Central Hong Kong. *Montserrat:* The Ministry of Communications and Works, General Turning Road, Plymouth. *Pitcairn & Henderson Is:* Office of the Governor of Pitcairn, Henderson, Ducie and Oeno Is, c/o British Consulate General, Auckland, New Zealand. *UK:* Amateur and Citizens' Band Radio Unit, Radiocommunications Agency, South Quay Three, 189 Marsh Wall,

London, E14 9SX. Tel: +44 (171) 211 0211. *Virgin Is:* Telecommunications (Radio) Officer, Ministry of Communications and Works, Government of the BVI, Road Town, Tortola.

UNITED NATIONS ORGANIZATION

ITU allocation: 4UA–4UZ.
Callsign system: Prefix: 4U1.
Licence notes: Only separate permanent stations located at ITU HQ, Geneva, and UN HQ, New York.
Foreign amateur operation (4U1ITU, Geneva): Four weeks' notice. Apply to station manager at IARC.
Society: International Amateur Radio Club, Box 6, Place des Nations. CH-1211 Geneva 20. Switzerland.

UNITED STATES OF AMERICA

ITU allocation: AAA–ALZ, KAA–KZZ, NAA–NZZ, WAA–WZZ.
Callsign system: The current callsign system came into effect on 24 March 1978. Amateurs were, however, permitted to continue to hold existing callsigns. The digit or prefix from the tables is determined by the location of the licensee's bona-fide postal address at the time of issuing the licence. If the postal address subsequently changes, the same callsign will be retained, even if this no longer corresponds to the correct digit or prefix for that location.

GEOGRAPHICAL LOCATION
Contiguous 48 states and District of Columbia

Digit	Location
1	Maine, New Hampshire, Vermont, Massachusetts, Rhode Island, Connecticut
2	New York, New Jersey
3	Pennsylvania, Delaware, Maryland, District of Columbia
4	Virginia, North Carolina, South Carolina, Georgia, Florida, Alabama, Tennessee, Kentucky
5	Mississippi, Louisiana, Arkansas, Oklahoma, Texas, New Mexico
6	California
7	Oregon, Washington, Idaho, Montana, Wyoming, Arizona, Nevada, Utah
8	Michigan, Ohio, West Virginia
9	Illinois, Indiana, Wisconsin
0	Colorado, Nebraska, North Dakota, South Dakota, Minnesota, Iowa, Missouri, Kansas

Other locations (current system)

Prefix	Location
AH0, KH0, NH0, WH0	Northern Mariana Is
AH1, KH1, NH1, WH1	Baker, Howland Is
AH2, KH2, NH2, WH2	Guam
AH3, KH3, NH3, WH3	Johnston Is
AH4, KH4, NH4, WH4	Midway Is
AH5K, KH5K, NH5K, WH5K	Kingman Reef
AH5, KH5, NH5, WH5	(except K suffix) Palmyra, Jarvis Is
AH6, KH6, NH6, WH6	Hawaii
AH7, KH7, NH7, WH7	Kure Is
AH8, KH8, NH8, WH8	American Samoa
AH9, KH9, NH9, WH9	Wake, Wilkes, Peale Is
AL7, KL7, NL7, WL7	Alaska
KP1, NP1 WP1	Navassa Is
KP2, NP2 WP2	Virgin Is
KP4, NP4, WP4	Puerto Rico
KP5, NP5, WP5	Desecheo Is

Other locations (old system)

Prefix	Location
KA	Japan (USA military personnel)
KB6	Baker, Howland Is
KC4	Navassa Is, Antarctica (USA bases)
KC6*	Belau
KG4*	Guantanamo Bay
KG6	Mariana, Marcus and Guam Is
KH6	Hawaiian, Kure Is
KJ6	Johnston Is
KL7	Alaska
KM6	Midway Is
KP4	Puerto Rico
KP5	Desecheo Is
KP6	Palmyra and Jarvis Is
KS4	Swan Is, Roncador Cay and Serrana Bank
KS6	American Samoa
KV4	Virgin Is
KW6	Wake Is
KX6	Marshall Is

* Still current as these are not FCC administered.

Licence classes: Five licence classes: Advanced, Extra, General, Novice, Technician. Maximum power is 1.5kW PEP output except in

USA LICENCE CLASSES (current system)

First letter / No of serial letters	—	A	B	C	D	E	F	G	H	I	J	K	L	M	N	O	P	Q	R	S	T	U	V	W	X	Y	Z
A + 1		E	E	E	E	E	E	E	E	E	E	E	E														
A + 2	E	E	E	E	E	E	E	E	E	A	E	E	A														
A + 3																											
K + 1		E	E	E	E	E	E	E	E	E	E	E	E	E	E	E	E	E	E	E	E	E	E	E	E	E	E
K + 2	E	A[x]	A	A[a]	A	A	A	A	A[b]	GT	A	A	GT	A	A	A	A	A	A[c]	A	A	A	A	A	A[d]	A	A[e]
K + 3	GT	N	N	N[f]	N	N	N	N	N	N	N	N	N	N	N	N	N	N	N	N	N	N	N	N	N	N	N
N + 1		E	E	E	E	E	E	E	E	E	E	E	E	E	E	E	E	E	E	E	E	E	E	E	E	E	E
N + 2	E	A	A	A	A	A	A	A	A	GT	A	A	GT	A	A	A	GT	A	A	A	A	A	A	A	A	A	A
N + 3	GT																										
W + 1		E	E	E	E	E	E	E	E	E	E	E	E	E	E	E	E	E	E	E	E	E	E	E	E	E	E
W + 2	E	A	A	A	A	A	A	A	A	GT	A	A	GT	A	A	A	GT	A	A	A	A	A	A	A	A	A	A
W + 3	GT	N	N	Ra	N	N	N	N	N	C	N	M	N	N	N	N	N	N	R	Ty	N	N	N	N	N	A	

Key: A Advanced; C Club; E Extra; G General; M Military recreation; N Novice; R Repeaters; Ra RACES; T Technician; Ty Temporary.
Notes: *a* Except KC6. *b* Except KG4, KG6R, KG6S. *c* Except KR6. *d* Except KX6. *e* Except KZ5. *f* Except KC4AAA–AAF, KC4USA–USZ. *x* KA1 only.

the Novice segments of the bands and on 10MHz. For permitted HF bands see below. Third-party traffic permitted.

CW/RTTY/DATA SEGMENTS

Extra	Advanced	General	Technician Plus and Novice
3500–3750	3525–3750	3525–3750	3675–3725*
7000–7150	7025–7150	7025–7150	7100–7150*
10,100–10,150	10,100–10,150	10,100–10,150	—
14,000–14,150	14,025–14,150	14,025–14,150	—
18,068–18,110	18,068–18,110	18,068–18,110	—
21,000–21,200	21,025–21,200	21,025–21,200	21,100–21,200*
24,890–24,930	24,890–24,930	24,890–24,930	—
28,000–28,300	28,000–28,300	28,000–28,300	28,100–28,300

* CW only

CW/PHONE/IMAGE SEGMENTS

Extra	Advanced	General	Technician Plus and Novice
3750–4000	3775–4000	3850–4000	—
7150–7300	7150–7300	7225–7300	—
14,150–14,350	14,175–14,350	14,225–14,350	—
18,110–18,168	18,110–18,168	18,110–18,168	—
21,200–21,450	21,225–21,450	21,300–21,450	—
24,930–24,990	24,930–24,990	24,930–24,990	—
28,300–29,700	28,300–29,700	28,300–29,700	28,300–28,500*

* SSB only

Foreign amateur operation: Reciprocal (A + B). Call is US prefix/own call. Fee. Form 610-A. 60 days' notice. Operating privileges do not exceed those of foreign amateurs' own licence. Countries include: Antigua, Argentina, Australia, Austria, Bahamas, Barbados, Belgium, Belize, Bolivia, Botswana, Brazil, Canada, Chile, Colombia, Costa Rica, Cyprus, Denmark, Dominica, Dominican Republic, Ecuador, El Salvador, Fiji, Finland, France, Germany, Greece, Grenada, Guatemala, Guyana, Haiti, Honduras, Hong Kong, Iceland, India, Indonesia, Irish Republic, Israel, Italy, Jamaica, Japan, Jordan, Kiribati, Kuwait, Liberia, Luxembourg, Marshall Is, Mexico, Micronesia, Monaco, Netherlands, Netherlands Antilles, New Zealand, Nicaragua, Norway, Panama, Paraguay, Peru, Philippines, Portugal, St Lucia, St Vincent, Seychelles, Solomon Is, South Africa, Spain, Sierra Leone, Suriname, Sweden, Switzerland, Thailand, Trinidad, Tuvalu, UK (including VP2M, VP2S, VP2V, VP5, VP8, VP9, ZB2, ZD7 and ZF), Uruguay, Venezuela and Yugoslavia.
National society: American Radio Relay League, 225 Main Street, Newington, Connecticut 06111. Tel: +1 (203) 666-1541. Fax: +1 (203) 665-7531.
Licensing administration: Federal Communications Commission, 1270 Fairfield Road, Gettysburg, PA 17325.

URUGUAY (Oriental Republic of)

ITU allocation: CVA–CXZ.
Callsign system: Prefix: CX. First serial letter denotes province (see map). Z indicates mobile/portable operation.
Licence notes: Four licence classes. 1st, 2nd and 3rd classes, all bands, 500, 100 and 30W respectively. Special: 1.8, 3.5, 7, 28MHz, 30W. Third-party traffic permitted.
Foreign amateur operation: Unilateral (A only). All countries. Apply to RCU.
National society: Radio Club Uruguayo, PO Box 37, Montevideo 11000. Tel: +598 (2) 787879. Fax: +598 (2) 787523.

UZBEKISTAN

ITU allocation: UJA–UMZ.
Callsign system: Prefix: UK.

1st serial letter	Area	Capital
A	Tashkent city	
B	Tashkent Obl	Tashkent
C	Kashkadar'in Obl	Karshi
D	Syrdar'in Obl	Gulistan
F	Andizhan Obl	Andizhan
G	Fergana Obl	Fergana
I	Samarkand Obl	Samarkand
L	Bukhara Obl	Bukhara
O	Namangan Obl	Namangan
Q	Navoiy Obl	
T	Surkandar'in Obl	Termez
U	Khorezm Obl	Urgench
V	Dzhizak Obl	Dzhizak
Z	Kara-Kalpakstan	Nukus

VANUATU

ITU allocation: YJA–YJZ.
Callsign system: Prefix: YJ.

Foreign amateur operation: Reciprocal (A only). Call is in YJ0A series. Countries include UK.
National society: Vanuatu Amateur Radio Society, PO Box 665, Port-Vila. Tel: +678 3092.
Licensing administration: Director of Posts and Telecomms, Dept of Posts and Telecomms, Port-Vila.

VATICAN CITY STATE

ITU allocation: HVA–HVZ.
Callsign system: Prefix: HV.
Licensing administration: Governatorato – Secretariat General, Administration des PTT, Vatican City. Tel: +39 66982.

VENEZUELA (Republic of)

ITU allocation: YVA–YVZ, 4MA–4MZ.
Callsign system: See map for prefixes.
Licence notes: 1kW DC input maximum. Third-party traffic permitted.
Foreign amateur operation: Call is own call/area prefix/digit. Countries include: USA, Canada, Dominican Rep, Costa Rica, Peru, Argentina, Brazil, Paraguay, Germany, Sweden, Portugal, Spain, Ecuador, Bolivia.
National society: Radio Club Venezolano, PO Box 2285, Caracas 1010-A. Tel: +58 (2) 793-5404. Fax: +58 (2) 793-6883.
Licensing administration: Ministerio de Transporte y Comunicaciones, Division de Tramitacion, Esquina de Carmelitas, Caracas 101.

VIETNAM (Socialist Republic of)

ITU allocation: XVA–XVZ, 3WA–3WZ.
Callsign system: Prefix: XV.
Licensing administration: Direction génerale des postes et télécommunications, 18 rue Nguyên Du, Hanoi.

WESTERN SAMOA

ITU allocation: 5WA–5WZ.
Callsign system: Prefix: 5W1.
Licence notes: Three licence classes, similar to New Zealand Grade, 1, 2 and 3. 1kW DC input maximum.
Foreign amateur operation: Unilateral. Fee. All countries.
National society: Western Samoa ARC, PO Box 2015, Apia.
Licensing administration: Director, Post Office and Radio, Chief Post Office, Apia.

YEMEN

ITU allocation: 7OA–7OZ.
Callsign system: Prefix: 7O.
Licensing administration: Director General of Posts and Telephones, General Post Office, PO Box 1000, Aden.

YUGOSLAVIA (Socialist Federal Republic of)

ITU allocation: YTA–YUZ, YZA–YZZ, 4NA–4OZ.
Callsign system: Prefixes: YU1/YT1 (Serbia). The 0 digit is used for special activities. Clubs are allocated serial letters AAA–MZZ.

Prefix	Category
YT	Class F
YU	Classes A–E
YZ	Special
4N	Special and repeaters

Licence notes: Six licence classes. Class A: all bands, 2kW input. Class B: all bands, 250W input. Class C: 3.5, 7MHz and VHF, 250W input. Class D: VHF only, 100W input. Class E: VHF phone only, 50W input. Class F: 3.565–3.575MHz, CW only, 10W input.
National society: Savez Radio-amatera Jugoslavije, PO Box 48, YU-11001 Belgrade. Tel: +381 (11) 634248. Fax: +381 (11) 404149.
Licensing administration: Community of Yugoslavia Posts, Telegraphs and Telephones, Palmoticeva 2, 11001 Belgrade. Tel: +381 (11) 338921.

ZAIRE (Republic of)

ITU allocation: 9OA–9TZ.
Callsign system: Prefix: 9Q5.
Licence notes: Single licence class: 100W DC input maximum.
National society: Union Zairoise des Radio-Amateurs, PO Box 1459, Kinshasa 1.
Licensing administration: Département des postes, télégraphes et téléphones, PO Box 800, Kinshasa 1.

ZAMBIA (Republic of)

ITU allocation: 9IA–9JZ.
Callsign system: Prefix: 9J2.
Licence notes: Single licence class: 150W DC input maximum.
National society: Radio Society of Zambia, PO Box 20332, Kitwe.
Licensing administration: Chief of Operations, Telecommunications Services, PTC HQ, Box 1660, Ndola.

ZIMBABWE

ITU allocation: Z2A–Z2Z.
Callsign system: Prefix: Z2.
Foreign amateur operation: Reciprocal (A + B). Call is own call/Z2. Countries include UK.
National society: Radio Society of Zimbabwe, Postbox 2377, Harare.
Licensing administration: Manager, National Telecommunications Services, PO Box 8061, Causeway, Harare. Tel: +263 (4) 731989.

3 Callsign list

THIS list is intended to help in determining the country, continent, zones and true bearing of a station from its callsign. The prefixes given are those for standard stations; special stations may use other prefixes although these should nevertheless conform with the ITU allocations given in the first column (see Chapter 1).

The country given on the same line as an ITU allocation is the holder of that allocation; further information on its callsign system may be found in Appendix 2.

Certain countries encompass more than one zone; separate entries corresponding to each zone are therefore given on successive lines. Reference to Maps 7 and 8 in Appendix 1 should enable the correct zone to be ascertained in cases of doubt. The bearing information is based on London, England.

ITU allocation	Prefix	Country	Continent	CQ	ITU	Deg
A2A–A2Z	A22	Botswana	AF	38	57	157
A3A–A3Z	A35	Tonga	OC	32	62	350
A4A–A4Z	A4	Oman	AS	21	39	104
A5A–A5Z	A51	Bhutan	AS	22	41	72
A6A–A6Z	A6	United Arab Emirates	AS	21	39	103
A7A–A7Z	A71	Qatar	AS	21	39	103
A8A–A8Z		Liberia				
A9A–A9Z	A92	Bahrain	AS	21	39	103
AAA–ALZ		USA				
	AA–AG	USA (see W)				
	AH0	Northern Mariana Is	OC	27	64	35
	AH1	Baker Is	OC	31	61	349
	AH1	Howland Is	OC	31	61	349
	AH2	Guam	OC	27	64	36
	AH3	Johnston Is	OC	31	61	11
	AH4	Midway Is	OC	31	61	358
	AH5	Jarvis Is	OC	31	62	339
	AH5	Palmyra Is	OC	31	61	339
	AH5K	Kingman Reef	OC	31	61	339
	AH6	Hawaii	OC	31	61	338
	AH7	Kure Is	OC	31	61	338
	AH8	American Samoa	OC	32	62	346
	AH9	Peale Is	OC	31	65	13
	AH9	Wake Is	OC	31	65	13
	AH9	Wilkes Is	OC	31	65	13
	AI–AK	USA (see W)	NA			
	AL7	Alaska	NA	1	1	348
	AL7	Alaska	NA	1	2	348
AMA–AOZ		Spain				
APA–ASZ	AP	Pakistan	AS	21	41	87
ATA–AWZ		India				
AXA–AXZ		Australia				
AYA–AZZ		Argentina				
BAA–BZZ	BY	China	AS	23/24	42–44	50
	BV	Taiwan	AS	24	44	50
C2A–C2Z	C21	Nauru	OC	31	65	17
C3A–C3Z	C3	Andorra	EU	14	27	172
C4A–C4Z		Cyprus				
C5A–C5Z	C53	Gambia	AF	35	46	207
C6A–C6Z	C6	Bahamas	NA	8	11	278
C7A–C7Z		WMO				
C8A–C9Z	C9	Mozambique	AF	37	53	148
CAA–CEZ		Chile				
	CE0A	Easter Is	SA	12	63	266
	CE0X	San Felix Is	SA	12	14	247
	CE0Z	Juan Fernandez Is	SA	12	14	241
	CE1–5	Chile	SA	12	14	235
	CE6–8	Chile	SA	12	16	232
	CE9	Antarctica (Chile)	AN	13	73	209
	CE9	S Shetland Is	SA	13	73	209
CFA–CKZ		Canada				
CLA–CMZ	CM	Cuba	NA	8	11	279
CNA–CNZ	CN	Morocco	AF	33	37	196
COA–COZ	CO	Cuba	NA	8	11	279
CPA–CPZ	CP1	Bolivia	SA	10	12	243
	CP2–7	Bolivia	SA	10	14	243
	CP8, 9	Bolivia	SA	10	12	243
CQA–CUZ		Portugal				
	CT1, 4	Portugal	EU	14	37	208
	CT3	Madeira Is	AF	33	36	220
	CU	Azores	EU	14	36	248
CVA–CXZ	CX	Uruguay	SA	13	14	224
CYA–CZZ		Canada				
	CY0	Sable Is	NA	5	9	285
	CY9	St Paul Is	NA	5	9	287
D2A–D3Z	D2	Angola	AF	36	52	160
D4A–D4Z	D44	Cape Verde	AF	35	46	216
D5A–D5Z		Liberia				
D6A–D6Z	D68	Comoros	AF	39	53	171
D7A–D9Z		Korea (RK)				
DAA–DRZ	DA–DL	Germany	EU	14	28	96
DSA–DTZ		Korea (RK)				
DUA–DZZ	DU	Philippines	OC	27	50	57
E2A–E2Z		Thailand				
E3A–E3Z	E3	Eritrea	AF	37	48	
EAA–EHZ	EA	Spain	EU	14	37	199
	EA6	Balearic Is	EU	14	37	167
	EA8	Canary Is	AF	33	36	213
	EA9	Ceuta	AF	33	37	193
	EA9	Melilla	AF	33	37	193
EIA–EJZ	EI, EJ	Eire	EU	14	27	303
EKA–EKZ	EK	Armenia	AS	21	29	91
ELA–ELZ	EL	Liberia	AF	35	46	195
EMA–EOZ		Ukraine				
EPA–EQZ	EP	Iran	AS	21	40	96
ERA–ESZ	ER	Moldova	EU	16	29	91
ETA–ETZ	ET	Ethiopia	AF	37	48	129
EUA–EWZ	EU	Belarus	EU	16	29	71
EXA–EXZ	EX	Kyrghyzstan	AS	17	31	69
EYA–EYZ	EY	Tadjikistan	AS	17	30	77
EZA–EZZ	EZ	Turkmenistan	AS	17	30	81
FAA–FZZ	F	France	EU	14	27	–
	FG	Guadeloupe Is	NA	8	11	258
	FH	Mayotte	AF	39	53	171
	FK	Chesterfield Is	OC	30	56	45
	FK	Loyalty Is	OC	32	56	25
	FK	New Caledonia	OC	32	56	25
	FM	Martinique	NA	8	11	256
	FO	Clipperton Is	NA	7	10	291
	FO	Gambier Is	OC	32	63	313
	FO	Marquesas Is	OC	32	63	313
	FO	Society Is	OC	32	63	313
	FO	Tubuai Is	OC	32	63	313
	FP	St Pierre et Miquelon	NA	5	9	286
	FR	Europa Is	AF	39	53	130
	FR	Glorieuses Is	AF	39	53	130
	FR	Reunion Is	AF	39	53	130

ITU allocation	Prefix	Country	Continent	CQ	ITU	Deg
	FR	Tromelin Is	AF	39	53	130
	FR	Juan de Nova	AF	39	53	137
	FT-W	Crozet Is	AF	8	11	261
	FT-X	Kerguelen Is	AF	39	68	137
	FT-Y	Antarctica (France)	AN	30	70	165
	FT-Z	Amsterdam Is	AF	39	68	124
	FT-Z	St Paul Is	AF	39	68	124
	FW	Wallis Is	OC	32	62	356
	FW	Futuna Is	OC	32	62	356
	FY	French Guiana	SA	9	12	242
	FY	Inini	SA	9	12	242
GAA–GZZ		UK				
	G	England	EU	14	27	–
	GD	Isle of Man	EU	14	27	321
	GI	Northern Ireland	EU	14	27	317
	GJ	Jersey	EU	14	27	215
	GM	Scotland	EU	14	27	345
	GU	Alderney	EU	14	27	224
	GU	Guernsey	EU	14	27	224
	GU	Sark	EU	14	27	224
	GW	Wales	EU	14	27	285
H2A–H2Z		Cyprus				
H3A–H3Z		Panama				
H4A–H4Z	H44	Solomon Is	OC	28	51	28
H6A–H7Z		Nicaragua				
H8A–H9Z		Panama				
HAA–HAZ	HA	Hungary	EU	15	28	100
HBA–HBZ		Switzerland				
	HB0	Liechtenstein	EU	14	28	118
	HB	Switzerland	EU	14	28	125
HCA–HDZ	HC	Ecuador	SA	10	12	261
	HC8	Galapagos Is	SA	10	12	270
HEA–HEZ		Switzerland				
HFA–HFZ		Poland				
HGA–HGZ	HG	Hungary	EU	15	28	100
HHA–HHZ	HH	Haiti	NA	8	11	268
HIA–HIZ	HI	Dominican Rep	NA	8	11	267
HJA–HKZ	HK	Colombia	SA	9	12	260
	HK0	Malpelo Is	NA	9	12	266
	HK0	Providencia Is	NA	7	11	272
	HK0	San Andres Is	NA	7	11	272
HLA–HLZ		Korea (RK)	AS	25	44	40
HMA–HMZ		Korea (DPRK)				
HNA–HNZ		Iraq				
HOA–HPZ	HP	Panama	NA	7	11	267
HOA–HRZ	HR	Honduras	NA	7	11	277
HSA–HSZ	HS	Thailand	AS	26	49	72
HTA–HTZ		Nicaragua	NA	7	11	274
HUA–HUZ		Salvador				
HVA–HVZ	HV	Vatican	EU	15	28	132
HWA–HYZ		France				
HZA–HZZ	HZ	Saudi Arabia	AS	21	39	137
IAA–IZZ	I	Italy	EU	15	28	128
	IS0	Sardinia	EU	15	28	147
J2A–J2Z	J28	Djibouti	AF	37	48	123
J3A–J3Z	J3	Grenada	NA	8	11	255
J4A–J4Z		Greece				
J5A–J5Z	J5	Guinea-Bissau	AF	35	46	207
J6A–J6Z	J6	St Lucia	NA	8	11	260
J7A–J7Z	J73	Dominica	NA	8	11	260
J8A–J8Z	J88	St Vincent	NA	8	11	260
JAA–JSZ	JA	Japan	AS	25	45	35
	JD	Minami Torishima	OC	25	45	34
	JE–JR	Japan	AS	25	45	35
JTA–JVZ	JT	Mongolia	AS	23	32	45
	JT	Mongolia	AS	23	33	45
JWA–JXZ		Norway				
	JW	Svalbard	EU	40	18	25
	JX	Jan Mayen Is	EU	40	18	9
JYA–JYZ	JY	Jordan	AS	20	39	113
JZA–JZ		Indonesia				
KAA–KZZ		USA				
	K	USA (see W)				
	KA	USA (see W)				
	KB	USA (see W)				
	KC	USA (see W)				
	KC6	Belau	OC	27	65	49
	KD–KG	USA (see W)				
	KG4	Guantanamo Bay	NA	8	11	272
	KG6	Guam	OC	27	64	36
	KH0	Northern Mariana Is	OC	27	64	35
	KH1	Baker Is	OC	31	61	349
	KH1	Howland Is	OC	31	61	349
	KH2	Guam	OC	27	64	36
	KH3	Johnston Is	OC	31	61	11
	KH4	Midway Is	OC	31	61	358
	KH5	Jarvis Is	OC	31	62	339
	KH5	Palmyra Is	OC	31	61	339
	KH5K	Kingman Reef	OC	31	61	339
	KH6	Kure Is	OC	31	61	338
	KH7	Kure Is	OC	31	61	338
	KH8	American Samoa	OC	32	62	346
	KH9	Peale Is	OC	31	65	13
	KH9	Wake Is	OC	31	65	13
	KH9	Wilkes Is	OC	31	65	13
	KI, KJ	USA (see W)				
	KK	USA (see W)				
	KL7	Alaska	NA	1	1	348
	KL7	Alaska	NA	1	2	348
	KP1	Navassa Is	NA	8	11	270
	KP2	US Virgin Is	NA	8	11	262
	KP4	Puerto Rico	NA	8	11	263
	KP5	Desecheo Is	NA	8	11	263
	KP6	Jarvis Is	OC	31	62	339
	KP6	Palmyra Is	OC	31	61	339
KQ–KS		USA (see W)				
KW		USA (see W)				
KX		USA (see W)				
KY, KZ		USA (see W)				
L2A–L9Z		Argentina				
LAA–LNZ	LA, LB	Norway	EU	14	18	23
LOA–LWZ	LU A–U	Argentina	SA	13	14	229
	LU V–X	Argentina	SA	13	16	229
	LU Y	Argentina	SA	13	14	229
	LU Z	Antarctica (Argentina)	AN	13	73	209
LXA–LXZ	LX	Luxembourg	EU	14	27	108
LYA–LYZ	LY	Lithuania	EU	15	29	58
LZA–LZZ	LZ	Bulgaria	EU	20	28	108
MAA–MZZ		UK				
NAA–NZZ		USA				
	N	USA (see W)				
NA–NG		USA (see W)	NA			
	NH0	Northern Mariana Is	OC	27	64	35
	NH1	Baker Is	OC	31	61	349
	NH1	Howland Is	OC	31	61	349
	NH2	Guam	OC	27	64	36
	NH3	Johnston Is	OC	31	61	11
	NH4	Midway Is	OC	31	61	358
	NH5	Jarvis Is	OC	31	62	339
	NH5	Palmyra Is	OC	31	61	339
	NH5K	Kingman Reef	OC	31	61	339
	NH6	Hawaii	OC	31	61	338
	NH7	Kure Is	OC	31	61	338
	NH8	American Samoa	OC	32	62	346
	NH9	Peale Is	OC	31	65	13
	NH9	Wake Is	OC	31	65	13
	NH9	Wilkes Is	OC	31	65	13
NI–NK		USA (see W)				
	NL7	Alaska	NA	1	1	348
	NL7	Alaska	NA	1	2	348
NM–NO		USA Isee W)				
	NP1	Navassa Is	NA	8	11	270
	NP2	US Virgin Is	NA	8	11	262
	NP4	Puerto Rico	NA	8	11	263
	NP5	Desecheo Is	NA	8	11	263
	NP6	Jarvis Is	NA	31	62	339
	NP6	Palmyra Is	NA	31	61	339
NU–NZ		USA (see W)				
OAA–OCZ	OA	Peru	SA	10	12	249
ODA–ODZ	OD5	Lebanon	AS	20	39	109
OEA–OEZ	OE	Austria	EU	15	28	106
OFA–OJZ	OH	Finland	EU	15	18	42
	OH0	Aaland Is	EU	15	18	42
	OJ0	Market Reef	EU	15	18	42
OKA–OLZ	OK, OL	Czech Rep	EU	15	28	94
OMA–OMZ	OM	Slovak Rep	EU	15	28	94
ONA–OTZ	ON	Belgium	EU	14	27	94
	OR4	Antarctica (Belgium)	AN	–	67	–

ITU allocation	Prefix	Country	Continent	CQ	ITU	Deg
OUA–OZZ		Denmark				
	OX	Greenland	NA	40	5	340
	OX	Greenland	NA	40	75	340
	OY	Faroe Is	EU	14	18	343
	OZ	Denmark	EU	14	18	48
P2A–P2Z	P29	Papua New Guinea	OC	28	51	47
P3A–P3Z		Cyprus				
P4A–P4Z	P4	Aruba	SA	9	12	262
P5A–P9Z		Korea (DPRK)				
PAA–PIZ	PA–PI	Netherlands	EU	14	27	73
PJA–PJZ		Netherlands Antilles				
	PJ2	Curacao	SA	9	12	262
	PJ2	Bonaire	SA	9	11	262
	PJ5	St Eustatius	NA	8	11	262
	PJ5	Saba	NA	8	11	262
	PJ5	St Maarten	NA	8	11	261
PKA–POZ		Indonesia				
PPA–PYZ	PP1, 2	Brazil	SA	11	15	221
	PP5	Brazil	SA	11	15	221
	PP6–8	Brazil	SA	11	13	230
	PR7, 8	Brazil	SA	11	13	230
	PS7	Brazil	SA	11	13	230
	PT2	Brazil	SA	11	15	229
	PT7	Brazil	SA	11	13	230
	PT9	Brazil	SA	11	15	230
	PU8	Brazil	SA	11	13	230
	PV8	Brazil	SA	11	13	230
	PW8	Brazil	SA	11	13	230
	PY0F	Fernando de Noronha	SA	11	13	218
	PY0S	St Paul Is	SA	11	13	215
	PY0S	St Peter Is	SA	11	13	215
	PY0T	Trinidade Is	SA	11	15	208
	PY0	Martim Vaz Is	SA	11	15	208
	PY1–5	Brazil	SA	11	15	221
	PY6–8	Brazil	SA	11	13	230
	PY9	Brazil	SA	11	15	230
PZA–PZ	PZ	Suriname	SA	9	12	245
RAA–RZZ		Russia (see UAA–UIZ)				
	R1F	Franz Josef Land	EU	40	20/75	10
	R1M	Malyj Vysotskij Is	EU	16	29	10
S2A–S3Z	S2	Bangladesh	AS	22	41	74
S5A–S5Z	S5	Slovenia	EU	15	28	113
S6A–S6Z		Singapore				
S7A–S7Z	S79	Seychelles	AF	39	53	121
S9A–S9Z	S92	São Tomé, Principe	AF	36	47	171
SAA–SMZ	SK, SM	Sweden	EU	14	18	42
SNA–SRZ	SP	Poland	EU	15	28	79
SSA–SSM		Egypt				
SSN–STZ	ST	Sudan	AF	34	47	132
	ST	Sudan	AF	34	48	132
SUA–SUZ	SU	Egypt	AF	34	38	128
SVA–SZZ	SV	Greece	EU	20	28	119
	SV5	Rhodes	EU	20	28	115
	SV9	Crete	EU	20	28	121
T2A–T2Z	T2	Tuvalu	OC	31	65	2
T3A–T3Z	T30	W Kiribati	OC	31	65	13
	T31	Central Kiribati	OC	31	61	332
	T31	Central Kiribati	OC	31	63	320
	T32	E Kiribati	OC	31	62	350
T4A–T4Z		Cuba				
T5A–T5Z	T5	Somalia	AF	37	48	126
T6A–T6Z		Afghanistan				
T7A–T7Z	T7	San Marino	EU	15	28	125
T9A–T9Z	T9	Bosnia-Hercegovina	EU	15	28	113
TAA–TCZ	TA	Turkey	EU/AS	20	39	103
TDA–TDZ		Guatemala				
TEA–TEZ		Costa Rica				
TFA–TFZ	TF	Iceland	EU	40	17	331
TGA–TGZ	TG	Guatemala	NA	7	11	280
THA–THZ		France				
TIA–TIZ	TI	Costa Rica	NA	7	11	272
	TI9	Cocos Is	NA	7	11	271
TJA–TJZ	TJ	Cameroun	AF	36	46	166
TKA–TKZ		France				
	TK	Corsica	EU	15	28	141
TLA–TLZ	TL8	Central African Rep	AF	36	47	152
TMA–TMZ		France				
TNA–TNZ	TN8	Congo	AF	36	52	161
TOA–TOZ		France				
TRA–TRZ	TR8	Gabon	AF	36	52	165
TSA–TSZ		Tunisia				
TTA–TTZ	TT8	Chad	AF	36	47	151
TUA–TUZ	TU	Ivory Coast	AF	35	46	187
TVA–TXZ		France				
TYA–TYZ	TY	Benin	AF	35	46	176
TZA–TZZ	TZ	Mali	AF	35	46	187
UAA–UIZ		Russia				
	UA0A	Krasnoyarsk	AS	18	22	24
	UA0B	Taymyr	AS	18	22	24
	UA0C	Khabarovsk	AS	19	34	24
	UA0D	Yevrev	AS	19	34	24
	UA0E–G	Sakhalin	AS	19	34	24
	UA0H	Evenkiysk	AS	18	22	24
	UA0I	Magadan	AS	19	25	24
	UA0I	Magadan	AS	19	26	24
	UA0J	Amur	AS	19	33	24
	UA0L–N	Primorsky	AS	19	34	24
	UA0O, P	Buryat Rep	AS	18	32	24
	UA0Q, R	Yakutsk	AS	19	23	24
	UA0S, T	Irkutsk	AS	18	32	24
	UA0U, V	Chita	AS	19	33	24
	UA0W	Khakass	AS	18	32	24
	UA0X	Koriatsky	AS	19	25	24
	UA0Y	Tuvinsk	AS	23	32	24
	UA0Z	Kamchatsky	AS	19	35	24
	UA1	Russia (N European)	EU	16	29	51
	UA1N	Karelian Rep	EU	16	19	51
	UA1O	Arhangelsk	EU	16	20	13
	UA1P	Nenets	EU	16	20	13
	UA1Y, Z	Murmansk	EU	16	19	51
	UA2	Kaliningrad	EU	15	29	66
	UA3	Russia (C European)	EU	16	29	63
	UA4	Russia (E European)	EU	16	29	67
	UA4N, O	Kirov	EU	16	30	67
	UA4P–R	Tatar Rep	EU	16	30	67
	UA4W	Udmurt Rep	EU	16	30	67
	UA6	Russia (S European)	EU	16	29	77
	UA8T	Ust-Ordinsky	AS	18	32	24
	UA8V	Aginsky-Buriatsky	AS	18	33	24
	UA9A, B	Chelyabinsk	AS	17	30	60
	UA9C–E	Sverdlovsk	AS	17	30	60
	UA9F	Perm	AS	17	30	60
	UA9G	Komi-Permiatsky	AS	17	30	60
	UA9H, I	Tomsk	AS	18	31	49
	UA9J	Khanty-Mansiysky	AS	17	20	30
	UA9K	Jamalo-Nenets	AS	17	20	30
	UA9L	Tyumen	AS	17	21	30
	UA9M, N	Omsk	AS	17	30	60
	UA9O, P	Novosibirsk	AS	18	31	49
	UA9Q, R	Kurgan	AS	17	30	60
	UA9S, T	Orenburg	AS	16	30	62
	UA9U, V	Kemerov	AS	18	31	49
	UA9W	Bashkir	AS	16	30	62
	UA9X	Komi	AS	17	20	30
	UA9Y	Altay	AS	18	31	49
	UA9Z	Gorno-Altay	AS	18	31	49
UJA–UMZ	UK	Uzbekistan	AS	17	30	77
UNA–UQZ	UN–UQ	Kazakhstan	AS	17	30	67
URA–UTZ	UR–UZ	Ukraine	EU	16	29	82
V2A–V2Z	V2	Antigua, Barbuda	NA	8	11	260
V3A–V3Z	V3	Belize	NA	7	11	280
V4A–V4Z	V4	St Kitts & Nevis	NA	8	11	260
V5A–V5Z	V5	Namibia	AF	38	57	164
V6A–V6Z	V6	Micronesia	OC	27	64	32
	V6	Micronesia	OC	27	65	32
V7A–V7Z	V7	Marshall Is	OC	31	65	14
V8A–V8Z	V8	Brunei Darussalam	OC	28	54	67
VAA–VGZ		Canada				
	VE1	Canada	NA	5	9	290
	VE2	Canada	NA	2	9	293
	VE2	Canada	NA	5	9	293
	VE3	Canada	NA	4	4	308
	VE4	Canada	NA	4	3	315
	VE5	Canada	NA	4	3	319

ITU allocation	Prefix	Country	Continent	CQ	ITU	Deg
	VE6	Canada	NA	4	2	323
	VE7	Canada	NA	3	2	329
	VE8	Canada	NA	1	2	328
	VE8	Canada	NA	1	3	328
	VE8	Canada	NA	2	3	328
	VE8	Canada	NA	2	4	328
	VE8	Canada	NA	2	5	328
	VE8	Canada	NA	2	75	328
VHA–VNZ		Australia				
	VK0	Heard Is	AF	39	68	138
	VK0	Macquarie Is	OC	30	60	113
	VK1	Australia	OC	30	59	63
	VK2	Australia	OC	30	59	65
	VK3	Australia	OC	30	59	76
	VK4	Australia	OC	30	55	75
	VK5	Australia	OC	30	59	75
	VK6	Australia	OC	29	58	79
	VK7	Australia	OC	30	59	83
	VK8	Australia	OC	29	55	65
	VK9C	Cocos Keeling Is	OC	29	54	92
	VK9L	Lord Howe Is	OC	30	60	63
	VK9M	Mellish Reef	OC	30	56	
	VK9N	Norfolk Is	OC	32	60	27
	VK9W	Willis Is	OC	30	55	45
	VK9X	Christmas Is	OC	29	54	84
VOA–VOZ	VO	Canada	NA	5	9	288
VPA–VSZ		UK				
	VP2E	Anguilla	NA	8	11	260
	VP2M	Montserrat	NA	8	11	260
	VP2V	British Virgin Is	NA	8	11	260
	VP5	Caicos Is	NA	8	11	270
	VP5	Turks Is	NA	8	11	270
	VP8	Falkland Is	SA	13	16	216
	VP8	S Georgia	SA	13	73	202
	VP8	S Orkney Is	SA	13	73	202
	VP8	S Sandwich Is	SA	13	73	195
	VP8	S Shetland Is	SA	13	73	208
	VP9	Bermuda	NA	5	11	274
	VQ9	Chagos Is	AF	39	41	108
	VR6	Pitcairn Is	OC	32	63	285
	VS6	Hong Kong	AS	24	44	58
VTA–VWZ		India				
	VU	Andaman Is	AS	26	49	81
	VU	India	AS	22	41	85
	VU	Laccadive Is	AS	22	41	97
	VU	Nicobar Is	AS	26	49	81
VXA–VYZ		Canada				
VZA–VZZ		Australia				
WAA–WZZ	W0	USA	NA	4	7	305
	W1	USA	NA	5	8	290
	W2	USA	NA	5	8	290
	W3	USA	NA	5	8	289
	W4	USA	NA	4	8	288
	W4	USA	NA	5	8	288
	W5	USA	NA	4	7	292
	W6	USA	NA	3	6	317
	W7	USA	NA	3	6	316
	W7	USA	NA	4	6	316
	W8	USA	NA	4	8	294
	W8	USA	NA	5	8	294
	W9	USA	NA	4	8	297
	WA–WG	USA (see W)				
	WH0	Northern Mariana Is	OC	27	64	35
	WH1	Baker Is	OC	31	61	349
	WH1	Howland Is	OC	31	61	349
	WH2	Guam	OC	27	64	36
	WH3	Johnston Is	OC	31	61	11
	WH4	Midway Is	OC	31	61	358
	WH5	Jarvis Is	OC	31	62	339
	WH5	Palmyra Is	OC	31	61	339
	WH5K	Kingman Reef	OC	31	61	339
	WH6	Hawaii	OC	31	61	338
	WH7	Kure Is	OC	31	61	338
	WH8	American Samoa	OC	32	62	346
	WH9	Peale Is	OC	31	65	13
	WH9	Wake Is	OC	31	65	13
	WH9	Wilkes Is	OC	31	65	13
	WI–WK	USA (see W)				
	WL7	Alaska	NA	1	1	348
	WL7	Alaska	NA	1	2	348

ITU allocation	Prefix	Country	Continent	CQ	ITU	Deg
WM–WO		USA (see W)				
	WP1	Navassa Is	NA	8	11	270
	WP2	US Virgin Is	NA	8	11	262
	WP4	Puerto Rico	NA	8	11	263
	WP5	Desecheo Is	NA	8	11	263
WO–WZ		USA (see W)				
XAA–XIZ	XE	Mexico	NA	6	10	294
	XF4	Revilla Gigedo Is	NA	6	10	299
XJA–XOZ		Canada				
XPA–XPZ		Denmark				
XQA–XRZ		Chile				
XSA–XSZ		China				
XTA–XTZ	XT	Burkina Faso	AF	35	46	182
XUA–XUZ	XU	Kampuchea	AS	26	49	71
XVA–XVZ		Vietnam				
XWA–XWZ	XW	Laos	AS	26	49	68
XXA–XXZ		Portugal				
	XX9	Macao	AS	24	44	58
XYA–XZZ	XZ	Myanmar (Burma)	AS	26	49	75
Y2A–Y9Z		Germany	EU	14	28	96
YAA–YAZ	YA	Afghanistan	AS	21	40	81
YBA–YHZ	YB–YD	Indonesia	OC	28	51	81
	YB–YD	Indonesia	OC	28	54	81
YIA–YIZ	YI	Iraq	AS	21	39	102
YJA–YJZ	YJ	Vanuatu	OC	30	56	20
	YJ	Vanuatu	OC	32	56	20
YKA–YKZ	YK	Syria	AS	20	39	106
YLA–YLZ	YL	Latvia	EU	15	29	58
YMA–YMZ		Turkey				
YNA–YNZ	YN	Nicaragua	NA	7	11	274
YOA–YRZ	YO	Romania	EU	20	28	101
YSA–YSZ	YS	El Salvador	NA	7	11	278
YTA–YUZ	YU	Yugoslavia	EU	15	28	113
YVA–YYZ		Venezuela				
	YV0	Aves Is	NA	8	11	259
	YV	Venezuela	SA	9	12	256
YZA–YZZ		Yugoslavia				
Z2A–Z2Z	Z2	Zimbabwe	AF	38	53	151
Z3A–Z3Z	Z3	Macedonia	EU	15	28	113
ZAA–ZAZ	ZA	Albania	EU	15	28	118
ZBA–ZJZ		UK				
	ZB2	Gibraltar	EU	14	37	196
	ZC4	Cyprus (UK bases)	AS	20	39	111
	ZD7	St Helena Is	AF	36	66	186
	ZD8	Ascension Is	AF	36	66	196
	ZD9	Gough Is	AF	38	66	188
	ZD9	Tristan da Cunha Is	AF	38	66	188
	ZF	Cayman Is	NA	8	11	276
ZKA–ZMZ		New Zealand				
	ZK1	Manihiki Is	OC	32	63	331
	ZK1	Cook Is	OC	32	62	324
	ZK2	Niue Is	OC	32	62	342
	ZK3	Tokelau Is	OC	31	62	345
	ZL	New Zealand	OC	32	60	5–68
	ZL7	Chatham Is	OC	32	60	40
	ZL8	Kermadec Is	OC	32	60	355
	ZL9	Auckland Is	OC	32	60	95
	ZL9	Campbell Is	OC	32	60	106
ZNA–ZOZ		UK				
ZPA–ZPZ	ZP	Paraguay	SA	11	14	230
ZQA–ZOZ		UK				
ZRA–ZUZ	ZR, ZS	South Africa	AF	38	57	160
	ZS8	Marion Is	AF	38	57	154
	ZS8	Prince Edward Is	AF	38	57	154
ZVA–ZZZ		Brazil				
2AA–2ZZ		UK				
	2E	England	EU	14	27	–
	2D	Isle of Man	EU	14	27	321
	2I	Northern Ireland	EU	14	27	317
	2J	Jersey	EU	14	27	215
	2M	Scotland	EU	14	27	345
	2U	Alderney	EU	14	27	224
	2U	Guernsey	EU	14	27	224
	2U	Sark	EU	14	27	224
	2W	Wales	EU	14	27	285
3AA–3AZ	3A	Monaco	EU	15	27	143
3BA–3BZ	3B	Mauritius	AF	38	53	125
3CA–3CZ	3C	Equatorial Guinea	AF	36	47	193
	3C0	Pagalu Is	AF	36	52	173

ITU allocation	Prefix	Country	Continent	CQ	ITU	Deg
3DA–3DM	3DA	Swaziland	AF	38	57	152
3DN–3DZ	3D2	Fiji	OC	32	56	3
3EA–3FZ		Panama				
3GA–3GZ		Chile				
3HA–3UZ		China				
3VA–3VZ	3V8	Tunisia	AF	33	37	150
3WA–3WZ		Vietnam				
3XA–3XZ	3X	Guinea	AF	35	46	195
3YA–3YZ		Norway				
	3Y	Bouvet Is	AF	38	67	178
3ZA–3ZZ		Poland				
4AA–4CZ		Mexico				
4DA–4IZ		Philippines				
4JA–4KZ	4J	Azerbaijan	AS	21	29	70
4LA–4NZ	4L	Georgia	AS	21	29	91
4MA–4MZ		Venezuela				
4NA–4OZ		Yugoslavia				
4PA–4SZ	4S7	Sri Lanka	AS	22	41	93
4TA–4TZ		Peru				
4UA–4UZ	4U1	United Nations				
4VA–4VZ		Haiti				
4XA–4XZ	4X	Israel	AS	20	39	113
4YA–4YZ		ICAO				
4ZA–4ZZ	4Z	Israel	AS	20	39	113
5AA–5AZ	5A	Libya	AF	34	38	143
5BA–5BZ	5B4	Cyprus	AS	20	39	111
5CA–5GZ		Morocco				
5HA–5IZ	5H	Tanzania	AF	37	53	137
5JA–5KZ		Colombia				
5LA–5MZ		Liberia				
5NA–5OZ	5N	Nigeria	AF	35	46	171
5PA–5QZ		Denmark				
5RA–5SZ	5R8	Madagascar	AF	39	53	137
5TA–5TZ	5T5	Mauritania	AF	35	46	200
5UA–5UZ	5U7	Niger	AF	35	46	163
5VA–5VZ	5V7	Togo	AF	35	46	178
5WA–5WZ	5W1	Western Samoa	OC	32	62	13
5XA–5XZ	5X5	Uganda	AF	37	48	140
5YA–5ZZ	5Z4	Kenya	AF	37	48	137
6AA–6BZ		Egypt				
6CA–6CZ		Syria				
6DA–6JZ		Mexico				
6KA–6NZ		Korea (RK)				
6OA–6OZ		Somalia				
6PA–6SZ		Pakistan				
6TA–6UZ		Sudan				
6VA–6WZ	6V	Senegal	AF	35	46	207
6XA–6XZ		Madagascar				
6YA–6YZ	6Y5	Jamaica	NA	8	11	272
6ZA–6ZZ		Liberia				
7AA–7IZ		Indonesia				
7JA–7NZ		Japan				
7OA–7OZ	7O	Yemen	AF	21	39	119
	7O	Socotra Is	AF	37	48	120
7PA–7PZ	7P8	Lesotho	AF	38	57	156
7QA–7QZ	7Q7	Malawi	AF	37	53	145
7RA–7RZ		Algeria				
7SA–7SZ		Sweden				
7TA–7YZ	7X	Algeria	AF	33	37	175
7ZA–7ZZ		Saudi Arabia				
8AA–8IZ		Indonesia				
8JA–8NZ		Japan				
	8J1	Antarctica (Japan)	AN	39	74	
8OA–8OZ		Botswana				
8PA–8PZ	8P6	Barbados	NA	8	11	254
8QA–8QZ	8Q	Maldives	AS	22	41	101
8RA–8RZ	8R	Guyana	SA	9	12	247
8SA–8SZ		Sweden				
8TA–8YZ		India				
8ZA–8ZZ		Saudi Arabia				
9AA–9AZ	9A	Croatia	EU	15	28	113
9BA–9DZ		Iran				
9EA–9FZ		Ethiopia				
9GA–9GZ	9G1	Ghana	AF	35	46	188
9HA–9HZ	9H	Malta	EU	15	28	140
91A–9JZ	9J	Zambia	AF	36	53	151
9KA–9KZ	9K2	Kuwait	AS	21	39	103
9LA–9LZ	9L	Sierra Leone	AF	35	46	197
9MA–9MZ		Malaysia				
	9M2	West Malaysia	AS	28	54	78
	9M6	Sabah	AS	28	54	72
	9M8	Sarawak	AS	28	54	73
9NA–9NZ	9N	Nepal	AS	22	42	75
9OA–9TZ	9Q5	Zaire	AF	36	52	160
9UA–9UZ	9U5	Burundi	AF	36	52	145
9VA–9VZ	9V	Singapore	AS	28	54	78
9WA–9WZ		Malaysia				
9XA–9XZ	9X5	Rwanda	AF	36	52	144
9YA–9ZZ	9Y4	Trinidad, Tobago	SA	9	11	254

4 DXCC countries list

THIS list gives the ARRL DXCC countries (current at the time of going to press) arranged in alphabetical order. Sample prefixes are given to enable quick cross reference to Appendix 3 for zones and bearings; full callsign information will be found under the appropriate ITU allocation holder in Appendix 2.

The list also acts as a gazetteer for Appendix 1. The first character of the map reference is the map number, the second and third defining the square on the map. In the case of Map 1, the remaining characters (if shown) are locator squares. An asterisk following the map reference indicates that the country also appears in a map in the section for the ITU allocation holder in Appendix 2.

As readers will often be working for several different awards, the bands/modes have been left blank on the checklist columns.

Note: See the current ARRL DXCC List application form and rules for effective dates if you are applying for the DXCC award. A copy may be obtained from the DXCC Desk at ARRL Headquarters (please include a business-size SASE). Some recent changes are detailed following the main table.

Country	Prefix	ITU alloc holder	Map	Worked/heard on							
Aaland Is	OH0	Finland	IKP00*								
Afghanistan	YA	Afghanistan	2Gb								
Agalega, St Brandon Is	3B6	Mauritius	2Be,f								
Alaska	KL7	USA	3Aa								
Albania	ZA	Albania	1								
Algeria	7X	Algeria	2Cc								
Amsterdam, St Paul Is	FT8Z	France	2Hg								
Andaman, Nicobar Is	VU	India	2Jd								
Andorra	C3	Andorra	1JN02								
Angola	D2	Angola	2De								
Anguilla	VP2E	UK	6Gc								
Annobon Is	3C0	Equatorial Guinea	2Ce								
Antarctica	CE9 etc	Various	5								
Antigua	V2A	Antigua	6Gc								
Argentina	LU	Argentina	3Hh*								
Armenia	EK	Armenia	—								
Aruba	P4	Aruba	6Fd								
Ascension Is	ZD8	UK	2Be								
Auckland, Campbell Is	ZL9	New Zealand	4Dg								
Australia	VK	Australia	2Mg*								
Austria	OE	Austria	1*								
Aves Is	YV0	Venezuela	6Gc								
Azerbaijan	4J	Azerbaijan	—								
Azores Is	CU	Portugal	2Ab								
Bahamas	C6	Bahamas	6Da								
Bahrain	A92	Bahrain	2Fc								
Baker, Howland Is	KH1	USA	4Ec,d								
Balearic Is	EA6	Spain	1*								
Banaba Is (Ocean Is)	T33	Kiribati	4Dd								
Bangladesh	S2	Bangladesh	2Jc								

Country	Prefix	ITU alloc holder	Map	Worked/heard on							
Barbados	8P6	Barbados	6Hd								
Belarus	EU	Belarus	1								
Belau	KC6	USA	4Bc								
Belgium	ON	Belgium	1								
Belize	V3	Belize	6Bc								
Benin	TY	Benin	2Cd								
Bermuda	VP9	UK	3Gc								
Bhutan	A51	Bhutan	2Jc								
Bolivia	CP	Bolivia	3Gg*								
Bonaire, Curacao	PJ	Netherlands Antilles	6								
Bosnia-Hercegovina	T9	Bosnia-Hercegovina	1								
Botswana	A22	Botswana	2Df								
Bouvet Is	3Y	Norway	2Ch								
Brazil	PY etc	Brazil	3Hg*								
Brunei	V8	Brunei	2Kd								
Bulgaria	LZ	Bulgaria	1								
Burkina Faso	XT2	Burkina Faso	2Bd								
Burundi	9U5	Burundi	2Ee								
Cambodia	XU	Cambodia	2Jd								
Cameroun	TJ	Cameroun	2Cd								
Canada	VE, VO	Canada	3Fb								
Canary Is	EA8	Spain	2Ac								
Cape Verde	D44	Cape Verde	2Ac								
Cayman Is	ZF	UK	6Cc								
Central African Rep	TL	Central African Rep	2Dd								
Ceuta, Melilla	EA9	Spain	1*								
Chad	TT	Chad	2Dc								
Chagos Is	VQ9	UK	2Ge								
Chatham Is	ZL7	New Zealand	4Ef								
Chile	CE	Chile	3Gh*								
China	BY	China	2								
Christmas Is	VK9X	Australia	2Ke*								
Clipperton Is	FO	France	3De								
Cocos Is	TI9	Costa Rica	3Fe								
Cocos-Keeling Is	VK9C	Australia	2Je								
Colombia	HK	Colombia	3Ge*								
Comoros	D68	Comoros	2Ee								
Congo	TN8	Congo	2Ce								
Conway Reef	3D2	Fiji	—								
Cook Is, North	ZK1	New Zealand	4Fe								
Cook Is, South	ZK1	New Zealand	4Fe								
Corsica	TK	France	1								
Costa Rica	TI	Costa Rica	6Ce								
Crete	SV9	Greece	1MV								
Croatia	9A	Croatia	1								
Crozet Is	FT8W	France	2Fh								
Cuba	CM, CO	Cuba	6Cb*								
Cyprus	5B4	Cyprus	1								

Country	Prefix	ITU alloc holder	Map	Worked/heard on									
Cyprus (UK sov bases)	ZC4	UK	1										
Czech Rep	OK	Czech Rep	1										
Denmark	OZ	Denmark	1										
Descheo Is	KP5	USA	6Fc										
Djibouti	J28	Djibouti	2Ed										
Dodecanese Is	SV5	Greece	1KM36*										
Dominica	J7	Dominica	6Gc										
Dominican Republic	HI	Dominican Republic	6Ec										
Easter Is	CE0	Chile	4Je										
Ecuador	HC1	Ecuador	3Ff										
Egypt	SU	Egypt	2Ec										
Eire	EI	Eire	1										
England	G, 2E	UK	1										
Equatorial Guinea	3C	Equatorial Guinea	2Cd										
Eritrea	E3	Eritrea	2										
Estonia	ES	Estonia	1										
Ethiopia	ET	Ethiopia	2Ed										
Faeroe Is	OY	Denmark	1										
Falkland Is	VP8	UK	3Hj										
Fernando de Noronha	PY0	Brazil	*										
Fiji	3D2	Fiji	4De										
Finland	OH	Finland	1*										
France	F	France	1										
Franz Josef Land	R1FJ	Russia	—										
French Guiana	FY	France	3He										
French Polynesia	FO	France	4Ge										
Gabon	TR8	Gabon	2Ce										
Galapagos Is	HC8	Ecuador	3Ef										
Gambia	C5	Gambia	2Ad										
Georgia	4L	Georgia	—										
Germany	DL etc	Germany	1										
Ghana	9G	Ghana	2Bd										
Gibraltar	ZB2	UK	1										
Glorieuses Is	FR/G	France	2Fe										
Gough, Tristan Da Cunha Is	ZD9	UK	2Bg										
Greece	SV	Greece	1*										
Greenland	OX	Denmark	2Ja										
Grenada	J3	Grenada	6Gd										
Guadeloupe	FG	France	6Gc										
Guam	KH2	USA	4Bc										
Guantanamo Bay	KG4	USA	6Db										
Guatemala	TG	Guatemala	3Ee										
Guernsey	GU, 2U	UK	1IN89										
Guinea	3X	Guinea	2Bd										
Guinea-Bissau	J5	Guinea-Bissau	2Bd										
Guyana	8R	Guyana	3He										
Haiti	HH	Haiti	6Ec										
Hawaiian Is	KH6	USA	4Fb										

Country	Prefix	ITU alloc holder	Map	Worked/heard on							
Heard Is	VK0	Australia	4Gh								
Honduras	HR	Honduras	6Bc								
Hong Kong	VS6	UK	2Kc								
Hungary	HA, HG	Hungary	1*								
Iceland	TF	Iceland	1*								
India	VU	India	2Hc								
Indonesia	YB–YD	Indonesia	2Ke*								
Iran	EP	Iran	2Fb								
Iraq	YI	Iraq	2Eb								
Isle of Man	GD, 2D	UK	1IO74								
Israel	4X, 4Z	Israel	2Eb								
Italy	I	Italy	1*								
ITU, Geneva	4U1	ITU	1JN36								
ITU, New York	4U1	ITU	2Gc								
Ivory Coast	TU2	Ivory Coast	2Bd								
Jamaica	6Y5	Jamaica	6Dc								
Jan Mayen Is	JX	Norway	—								
Japan	JA	Japan	2Mb*								
Jersey	GJ, 2J	UK	1IN89								
Johnston Is	KH3	USA	4Eb								
Jordan	JY	Jordan	2Eb								
Juan de Nova, Europa	FR/J	France	2Ef								
Juan Fernandez	CE0	Chile	3Fh*								
Kaliningrad	UA2	Russia	1KO05								
Kazakhstan	UN	Kazakhstan	—								
Kenya	5Z	Kenya	2Ed								
Kerguelen Is	FT8X	France	2Gh								
Kermadec Is	ZL8	New Zealand	4Ef								
Kingman Reef	KH5K	USA	4Fc								
Kiribati, Central	T31	Kiribati	4Ed								
Kiribati, East	T32	Kiribati	4Fd								
Kiribati, West	T30	Kiribati	4Dc, d								
Korea, South	HL	Korea (RK)	2Lb								
Kure Is	KH7	USA	4Eb								
Kuwait	9K2	Kuwait	2Fc								
Kyrgyzstan	EX	Kyrgyzstan	—								
Laccadive Is	VU	India	2Gd								
Laos	XW8	Laos	2Jc								
Latvia	YL	Latvia	1								
Lebanon	OD	Lebanon	2Eb								
Lesotho	7P8	Lesotho	2Dg								
Liberia	EL	Liberia	2Bd*								
Libya	5A	Libya	2Dc								
Liechtenstein	HB0	Switzerland	1JN47								
Lithuania	LY	Lithuania	1								
Lord Howe Is	VK9L	Australia	4Cf*								
Luxembourg	LX	Luxembourg	1								
Macao	XX9	Portugal	2Kc								

Country	Prefix	ITU alloc holder	Map	Worked/heard on								
Macquarie Is	VK0	Australia	4Cg									
Madagascar Republic	5R	Madagascar Rep	2Ff									
Madeira Is	CT3	Portugal	2Ab									
Malawi	7Q	Malawi	2Ee									
Malaysia, East	9M6, 8	Malaysia	2Kd									
Malaysia, West	9M2, 4	Malaysia	2Jd									
Maldives	8Q	Maldives	2Gd									
Mali	TZ	Mali	2Bc									
Malpelo Is	HK0	Colombia	3Fe									
Malta	9H	Malta	1									
Malyi Vysotskij Is	R1MV	Russia	—									
Mariana Is	KH0	USA	4Bb									
Market Reef	OJ0	Finland	1JP90*									
Marshall Is	V7	USA	4Dc									
Martinique	FM	France	6Gd									
Mauritania	5T	Mauritania	2Bc									
Mauritius	3B8	Mauritius	2Ff									
Mayotte	FH	France	2Ee									
Mellish Reef	VK9M	Australia	4Ce									
Mexico	XE	Mexico	3Ed									
Micronesia	V6	USA	4Cc									
Midway Is	KH4	USA	4Eb									
Minami Torishima	JD	Japan	4Cb									
Moldova	EU	Moldova	1									
Monaco	3A	Monaco	1									
Mongolia	JT	Mongolia	2Ja									
Montserrat	VP2M	UK	6Gc									
Morocco	CN	Morocco	2Bb									
Mount Athos	SV	Greece	1KN20									
Mozambique	C9	Mozambique	2Ef									
Myanmar (Burma)	XZ	Myanmar	2Jc									
Namibia	V5	Namibia	2Df									
Nauru	C2	Nauru	4Dd									
Navassa Is	KP1	USA	6Ec									
Nepal	9N	Nepal	2Hc									
Netherlands	PA	Netherlands	1									
New Caledonia	FK	France	4De									
New Zealand	ZL	New Zealand	4Df*									
Nicaragua	YN	Nicaragua	3Fe									
Niger	5U	Niger	2Cc									
Nigeria	5N	Nigeria	2Cd*									
Niue	ZK2	New Zealand	4Ee									
Norfolk Is	VK9N	Australia	4De*									
Northern Ireland	GI	UK	1									
Norway	LA	Norway	1									
Ogasawara Is	JD	Japan	4Bb*									
Oman	A4X	Oman	2Fc									
Pakistan	AP	Pakistan	2Gc									

Country	Prefix	ITU alloc holder	Map	Worked/heard on						
Palmyra, Jarvis Is	KH5	USA	4Fc,d							
Panama	HP	Panama	3Fe							
Papua New Guinea	P2	Papua New Guinea	2Me							
Paraguay	ZP	Paraguay	3Hg*							
Peru	OA	Peru	3Ff*							
Peter I Is	3Y	Norway	—							
Philippines	DU	Philippines	2Ld							
Pitcairn Is	VR6	UK	4He							
Poland	SP	Poland	1*							
Portugal	CT	Portugal	1							
Prince Edward, Marion Is	ZS2	South Africa	2Eh							
Puerto Rico	KP4	USA	6Fc							
Qatar	A71	Qatar	2Fc							
Reunion Is	FR	France	2Ff							
Revilla Gigedo	XF	Mexico	3Dd							
Rodriguez Is	3B9	Mauritius	2Ff							
Romania	YO	Romania	1*							
Rotuma Is	3D2	Fiji	—							
Russia (Asiatic)	UA9, 0	Russia	—							
Russia (European)	UA	Russia	—							
Rwanda	9X5	Rwanda	2Ee							
Sable Is	CY0	Canada	3Gc							
Sahara, Western	S0	—	—							
St Helena	ZD7	UK	2Bf							
St Kitts, Nevis	V4	St Kitts, Nevis	6Gc							
St Lucia	J6	St Lucia	6Gd							
St Maarten, St Eustatius, Saba	PJ	Netherlands Antilles	6Gc							
St Martin	FJ, FS	France	6Gc							
St Paul Is	CY9	Canada	3Gb							
St Peter and Paul Rocks	PY0	Brazil	*							
St Pierre et Miquelon	FP	France	3Hb							
St Vincent	J8	St Vincent	6Gd							
Salvador	YS	Salvador	6Bd							
Samoa	KH8	USA	4Ed							
Samoa, Western	5W	Western Samoa	4Ed							
San Andres, Providencia	HK0	Colombia	6Cd							
San Felix Is	CE0	Chile	3Fg							
San Marino	T7	San Marino	1							
São Tomé, Principe	S92	São Tomé, Principe	2Ce							
Sardinia	IS0	Italy	1*							
Saudi Arabia	HZ	Saudi Arabia	2Ec							
Scotland	GM, 2M	UK	1							
Senegal	6V	Senegal	2Bd							
Seychelles	S79	Seychelles	2Fe							
Sierra Leone	9L1	Sierra Leone	2Bd							
Singapore	9V1	Singapore	2Jd							
Slovak Rep	OM	Slovak Rep	1*							

Country	Prefix	ITU alloc holder	Map	Worked/heard on								
Slovenia	S5	Slovenia	1									
Solomon Is	H4	Solomon Is	4Cd									
Somalia	T5	Somalia	2Fd									
South Africa	ZS	South Africa	2Dg*									
South Georgia	VP8	UK	3Jj									
South Orkney Is	VP8	UK	5									
South Sandwich Is	VP8	UK	5									
South Shetland Is	VP8 etc	various	—									
Sovereign Military Order of Malta	1A	—										
Spain	EA	Spain	1*									
Spratly Is	1S	—	2Kd									
Sri Lanka	4S	Sri Lanka	2Hd									
Sudan	ST	Sudan	2Dc									
Sudan, South	ST0	Sudan	2Dd									
Suriname	PZ	Suriname	3He									
Svalbard	JW	Norway	—									
Swaziland	3DA	Swaziland	2Ef									
Sweden	SM	Sweden	1*									
Switzerland	HB	Switzerland	1									
Syria	YK	Syria	2Eb									
Taiwan	BV	China	2Lc									
Tajikistan	EY	Tajikistan	—									
Tanzania	5H	Tanzania	2Ee									
Thailand	HS	Thailand	2Jc*									
Togo	5V	Togo	2Cd									
Tokelau Is	ZK3	New Zealand	4Ed									
Tonga	A35	Tonga	4Ee									
Trinidad and Tobago	9Y4	Trinidad and Tobago	6Gd									
Trinidade, Martim Vaz Is	PY0	Brazil	*									
Tromelin Is	FR/T	France	2Ff									
Tunisia	3V	Tunisia	2Cb									
Turkey	TA	Turkey	2Eb*									
Turkmenistan	EZ	Turkmenistan	—									
Turks, Caicos Is	VP5	UK	6Eb									
Tuvalu	T2	Tuvalu	4Dd									
Uganda	5X	Uganda	2Ed									
Ukraine	UR	Ukraine	1									
United Arab Emirates	A6X	United Arab Emirates	2Fc									
Uruguay	CX	Uruguay	3Hh*									
USA	K, W etc	USA	3									
Uzbekistan	UK	Uzbekistan	—									
Vanuatu	YJ	Vanuatu	4De									
Vatican City	HV	Vatican City	1JN61									
Venezuela	YV	Venezuela	3Ge*									
Vietnam	3W, XV	Vietnam	2Kd									
Virgin Is, British	VP2V	UK	6Gc									
Virgin Is, US	KP2	USA	6Gc									

Country	Prefix	ITU alloc holder	Map	Worked/heard on							
Wake Is	KH9	USA	4Db								
Wales	GW, 2W	UK	1								
Wallis, Futuna Is	FW	France	4Dd								
Willis Is	VK9W	Australia	4Ce*								
Yemen	7O	Yemen	2Fc								
Yugoslavia	YU	Yugoslavia	1								
Zaïre	9O	Zaïre	2De								
Zambia	9J	Zambia	2De								
Zimbabwe	Z2	Zimbabwe	2Ef								

Recent changes

Prefix	Country	Effective from
Added		
4J1, R1MV	Malyj Vysotskij Is	First operation
3D2	Rotuma Is	15 Nov 1945
3D2	Conway Reef	15 Nov 1945
T33	Banaba Is (Ocean Is)	15 Nov 1945
ZS9	Walvis Bay	1 Sep 1990
7O	Yemen	22 May 1990
ZS0, 1	Penguin Is	15 May 1945
9A	Croatia	26 Jun 1991
S5	Slovenia	26 Jun 1991
T9	Bosnia-Hercegovina	15 Oct 1991
Z3	Macedonia	8 Sep 1991
OK, OL	Czech Rep	1 Jan 1993
OM	Slovak Rep	1 Jan 1993
Reactivated		
E3	Eritrea	24 May 1991
Deleted		
Y2-9	German Democratic Rep	2 Oct 1990
4W	Yemen Arab Rep	21 May 1990
7O	PDR of Yemen	21 May 1990
—	Abu Ail	31 Mar 1991
OK-OM	Czechslovakia	31 Dec 1992
ZS0, 1	Penguin Is	28 Feb 1994
ZS9	Walvis Bay	28 Feb 1994

5 Worldwide legal time

THE following list gives the legal times in each country in the world relative to GMT (UTC). Departures from the standard time, known as *daylight saving time* (DST) or *summer time* are also given. This lasts from March/April to September/October and vice versa in the Southern Hemisphere. This information has been provided by kind permission of the Reed Travel Group (tel: 01582 600111), publishers of the *ABC/OAG Airways Guides*.

Country	Standard time	DST
Afghanistan	+4½	—
Albania	+1	+2
Algeria	+1	—
Andaman Is	+5½	—
Andorra	+1	+2
Angola	+1	—
Anguilla	−4	—
Antarctica	−4	—
Antigua & Barbuda	−4	—
Argentina	−3	—
Armenia	+4	—
Aruba	−4	—
Ascension Is	0	—
Australia		
Lord Howe Is	+10½	+11
New South Wales	+10	+11
Northern Territory	+9½	—
Queensland	+10	—
South Australia	+9½	+10½
Western Australia	+8	—
Tasmania	+10	+11
Victoria	+10	+11
Australian Capital Territory	+10	+11
Austria	+1	+2
Azerbaijan	+4	—
Azores	−1	0
Bahamas	−5	−4
Bahrain	+3	—
Bangladesh	+6	—
Barbados	−4	—
Belarus	+2	+3
Belgium	+1	+2
Belize	−6	—
Benin	+1	—
Bermuda	−4	−3
Bhutan	+6	—
Bolivia	−4	—
Bosnia	+1	+2
Botswana	+2	—
Brazil		
NE Coast and E Para	−3	—
NW, W Para and Amazonas	−4	—
Acre	−5	—
Fernando de Noronha	−2	—
SE Coast inc Bahia, Goias and Brasilia	−3	−2
M Grosso, M Grosso do Sul	−4	−3
Brunei Darussalam	+8	—
Bulgaria	+2	+3
Burkina Faso	0	—
Burundi	+2	—
Cambodia	+7	—
Cameroon	+1	—
Canada		

Country	Standard time	DST
Newfoundland (Island)	−3½	−2½
Atlantic	−4	−3
Eastern	−5	−4
Central	−6	−5
Mountain	−7	−6
Pacific and Yukon Territory	−8	−7
E Quebec	−4	—
W Ontario	−5	—
Saskatchewan	−6	—
Some towns in NE BC	−7	—
Canary Is	0	+1
Cape Verde	−1	—
Caroline Is		
Truk, Ulithi, Yap	+10	—
Kosrae, Pohnpei	+11	—
Cayman Is	−5	—
Central African Rep	+1	—
Chad	+1	—
Chile		
Continental	−4	−3
Easter Is	−6	−5
China	+8	—
Christmas Is	+7	—
Cocos Is	+6½	—
Colombia	−5	—
Comoros	+3	—
Congo	+1	—
Cook Is	−10	—
Costa Rica	−6	—
Côte d'Ivoire	0	—
Croatia	+1	+2
Cuba	−5	−4
Cyprus	+2	+3
Czech Rep	+1	+2
Denmark	+1	+2
Djibouti	+3	—
Dominica	−4	—
Dominican Rep	−4	—
Ecuador		
Mainland	−5	—
Galapagos Is	−6	—
Egypt	+2	+3
El Salvador	−6	—
Equatorial Guinea	+1	—
Eritrea	+3	—
Estonia	+2	+3
Ethiopia	+3	—
Falkland Is	−4	−3
Faroe Is	0	+1
Fiji	+12	—
Finland	+2	+3
France	+1	+2
French Antilles	−4	—
French Guiana	−3	—

Country	Standard time	DST
French Polynesia		
Marquesas Is	−9½	—
Society Archipelago	−10	—
Tubuai Is	−10	
Tuamoto Archipelago except Gambier	−10	—
Tahiti	−10	—
Gambier Is	−9	
Gabon	+1	—
Gambia	0	—
Gambier Is	−9	—
Georgia	+4	+5
Germany	+1	+2
Ghana	0	—
Gibraltar	+1	+2
Greece	+2	+3
Greenland		
Greenland except Thule, Scoresbysund	−3	−2
Thule	−4	−3
Scoresbysund and Constaple Pynt	−1	0
Grenada	−4	—
Grenadine Is	−4	—
Guadeloupe	−4	
Guam	+10	—
Guatemala	−6	—
Guinea	0	—
Guinea-Bissau	0	—
Guyana	−4	—
Haiti	−5	−4
Honduras	−6	—
Hong Kong	+8	—
Hungary	+1	+2
Iceland	0	—
India	+5½	—
Indonesia		
West including Jakarta	+7	—
Central	+8	—
East	+9	—
Iran	+3½	+4½
Iraq	+3	+4
Irish Rep	0	+1
Israel including Gaza Strip and West Bank	+2	+3
Italy	+1	+2
Jamaica	−5	—
Japan	+9	—
Johnston Is	−10	—
Jordan	+2	+3
Kazakhstan	+6	+7
Kenya	+3	—
Kiribati		
All except as below	+12	—

Country	Standard time	DST
Kiritimati Is	−10	—
Phoenix Is	−11	—
Korea, North and South	+9	—
Kuwait	+3	—
Kyrgystan	+5	+6
Laos	+7	—
Latvia	+2	+3
Lebanon	+2	+3
Leeward Is	−4	—
Lesotho	+2	—
Liberia	0	—
Libya	+2	—
Liechtenstein	+1	+2
Lithuania	+2	+3
Loyalty Is	+11	—
Luxembourg	+1	+2
Macau	+8	—
Macedonia	+1	+2
Madagascar	+3	—
Madeira Is	0	+1
Malawi	+2	—
Malaysia	+8	—
Maldives	+5	—
Mali	0	—
Malta	+1	+2
Mariana Is	+10	—
Marquesas Is	−9½	—
Marshall Is	+12	—
Martinique	−4	—
Mauritania	0	—
Mauritius	+4	—
Mayotte	+3	—
Mexico		
All except as below	−6	—
Baja California Sur,		
Sinaloa, Sonora	−7	—
Baja California Norte	−8	−7
Micronesia		
Caroline Is	+10	—
Pohnpei and Kosrae	+11	—
Midway Is	−11	—
Moldova	+2	+3
Monaco	+1	+2
Mongolia	+8	+9
Montserrat	−4	—
Morocco	0	—
Mozambique	+2	—
Myanmar	+6½	—
Namibia	+1	+2
Nauru	+12	—
Nepal	+5¾	—
Netherlands	+1	+2
Netherlands Antilles	−4	—
New Caledonia	+11	—
New Zealand		
Mainland	+12	+13
Chatham Is	+12¾	+13¾
Nicaragua	−6	—
Niger	+1	—
Nigeria	+1	—
Niue	−11	—
Norfolk Is	+11½	—
Norway	+1	+2

Country	Standard time	DST
Oman	+4	—
Pakistan	+5	—
Palau	+9	—
Panama	−5	—
Papua New Guinea	+10	—
Paraguay	−4	−3
Peru	−5	—
Phillipines	+8	—
Pitcairn Is	−9	—
Poland	+1	+2
Portugal		
Mainland	+1	+2
Madeira	0	+1
Azores	−1	0
Principe Is	0	—
Puerto Rico	−4	—
Qatar	+3	—
Reunion Is	+4	—
Romania	+2	+3
Russia		
Kaliningrad	+2	+3
Moscow,		
St Petersburg,		
Astrakhan	+3	+4
Izhevsk and Samara	+4	+5
Perm, Nizhnevartovsk	+5	+6
Omsk and Novosibirsk	+6	+7
Norilsk, Kyzyl	+7	+8
Bratsk, Ulan Ude	+8	+9
Chita, Yakutsk	+9	+10
Khabarovsk,		
Vladivostock	+10	+11
Magadan, Yuzhno		
Sakhalinsk	+11	+12
Petropavlovsk		
Kamchatskiy	+12	+13
Rwanda	+2	—
St Helena	0	—
St Kitts and Nevis	−4	—
St Lucia	−4	—
St Pierre et Miquelon	−3	−2
St Vincent	−4	—
Samoa including		
American Samoa	−11	—
San Marino	+1	+2
São Tomé	0	—
Saudi Arabia	+3	—
Senegal	0	—
Seychelles	+4	—
Sierra Leone	0	—
Singapore	+8	—
Slovakia	+1	+2
Slovenia	+1	+2
Society Is	−10	—
Solomon Is	+11	—
Somalia	+3	—
South Africa	+2	—
Spain		
Mainland and		
Balearic Is	+1	+2
Canary Is	0	+1
Melilla	+1	+2

Country	Standard time	DST
Sri Lanka	+5½	—
Sudan	+2	—
Suriname	−3	—
Swaziland	+2	—
Sweden	+1	+2
Switzerland	+1	+2
Syria	+2	+3
Tahiti	−10	—
Taiwan	+8	—
Tajikistan	+5	—
Tanzania	+3	—
Thailand	+7	—
Togo	0	—
Tonga	+13	—
Trinidad and Tobago	−4	—
Tuamoto Is	−10	—
Tubuai Is	−10	—
Tunisia	+1	—
Turkey	+2	+3
Turkmenistan	+5	—
Turks and Caicos	−5	−4
Tuvalu	+12	—
Uganda	+3	—
Ukraine		
Ukraine except		
Simferopol	+2	+3
Simferopol	+3	+4
United Arab Emirates	+4	—
United Kingdom	0	+1
USA		
Eastern	−5	−4
Central	−6	−5
Mountain	−7	−6
Pacific	−8	−7
Aleutian Is E of 169.3°	−9	−8
Aleutian Is W of 169.3°	−10	−9
Hawaii	−10	—
Johnston Is	−10	—
Midway Is	−11	—
Wake Is	+12	—
Uruguay	−3	—
Uzbekistan	+5	—
Vanuatu	+11	—
Venezuela	−4	—
Vietnam	+7	—
Virgin Is, British and		
American	−4	—
Wake Is	+12	—
Wallis and Futuna Is	+12	—
Yemen	+3	—
Yugoslavia (ie Serbia)	+1	+2
Zaire		
Kinshasa, Mbandaka	+1	—
Kasai, Kivu, Haut		
Zaire, Shaba	+2	—
Zambia	+2	—
Zimbabwe	+2	—

Appendix

6 Amateur Service frequency allocations

THIS appendix shows all amateur allocations as determined by the World Administrative Radio Conference 1979 in the three ITU Regions.

Where in a box of the table a band is indicated as allocated to more than one service, such services are listed in the following order:
1. Primary services, which are printed in **bold**.
2. Secondary services, which are printed in ordinary type.

The footnotes appearing after this table apply only to bands, or parts of bands, allocated to the Amateur Service. They comprise only a small proportion of the total number of footnotes which appear in the Radio Regulations. The footnote references which appear in the table below the allocated services apply to the whole of the allocation concerned. The footnote references which appear after the name of the service are applicable only to that particular service.

Region 1	Region 2	Region 3
1800–1810kHz **Radiolocation** [487] [485, 486]	1800–1850 **Amateur**	1800–2000 **Amateur, Fixed, Mobile** except aeronautical mobile, **Radionavigation**, Radiolocation
1810–1850 **Amateur** [490, 491, 492, 493]	[489]	
1850–2000 **Fixed, Mobile** except aeronautical mobile [484, 488, 495]	1850–2000 **Amateur, Fixed, Mobile** except aeronautical mobile, **Radiolocation Radionavigation** [489, 494]	[489]
3500–3800 **Amateur** [510] **Fixed, Mobile** except aeronautical mobile [484]	3500–3750 **Amateur** [510] [509, 511]	3500–3900 **Amateur** [510]
3800–3900 **Fixed, Aeronautical Mobile** (OR), **Land Mobile**	3750–4000 **Amateur** [510] **Fixed, Mobile** except aeronautical mobile (R)	
3900–3950 **Aeronautical Mobile** (OR) [513]		3900–3950 **Aeronautical Mobile, Broadcasting**
3950–4000 **Fixed, Broadcasting**	[511, 512, 514, 515]	3950–4000 **Fixed, Broadcasting** [516]
7000–7100	**Amateur** [510], **Amateur-satellite** [526, 527]	
7100–7300 **Broadcasting**	7100–7300 **Amateur** [510] [528]	7100–7300 **Broadcasting**
10,100–10,150	**Fixed**, Amateur [510]	
14,000–14,250	**Amateur** [510], **Amateur-satellite**	
14,250–14,350	**Amateur** [510] [535]	

Region 1	Region 2	Region 3
18,068–18,168	**Amateur** [510], **Amateur-satellite** [537, 538]	
21,000–21,450	**Amateur** [510], **Amateur-satellite**	
24,890–24,990	**Amateur** [510], **Amateur-satellite** [542, 543]	
28–29.7MHz	**Amateur, Amateur-satellite**	
47–68 **Broadcasting** [553, 554, 555, 559, 561]	50–54 **Amateur** [556, 557, 558, 560]	
144–146	**Amateur** [510], **Amateur-satellite** [605, 606]	
146–149.9 **Fixed, Mobile** except aeronautical mobile (R) [608]	146–148 **Amateur** [607]	146–148 **Amateur, Fixed, Mobile** [607]
223–230 **Broadcasting**, Fixed Mobile [622, 628, 629, 631, 632, 633, 634, 635]	220–225 **Amateur, Fixed Mobile**, Radiolocation [607]	223–230 **Fixed, Mobile Broadcasting, Aeronautical Radionavigation**, Radiolocation [636, 637]
430–440 **Amateur, Radiolocation** [653, 654, 655, 656, 657 658, 659, 661, 662, 663, 664, 665]	430–440 **Radiolocation**, Amateur [653, 658, 659, 660, 663, 664]	
890–942 **Fixed, Mobile** except aeronautical mobile, **Broadcasting** [704], Radiolocation	902–928 **Fixed**, Amateur, **Mobile** except aeronautical mobile, Radiolocation [705, 707]	890–942 **Fixed, Mobile, Broadcasting** Radiolocation [706]

210

Region 1	Region 2	Region 3
1240–1260	**Radiolocation, Radionavigation-Satellite** [710] (space–to–Earth), Amateur [711, 712, 713, 714]	
1260–1300	**Radiolocation**, Amateur [664, 711, 712, 713, 714]	
2300–2450 **Fixed**, Amateur, Mobile, Radiolocation [664, 752]	2300–2450 **Fixed, Mobile, Radiolocation**, Amateur [664, 751, 752]	
3300–3400 **Radiolocation** [778, 779, 780]	3300–3400 **Radiolocation**, Amateur, Fixed, Mobile [778, 780]	3300–3400 **Radiolocation**, Amateur [778, 779]
3400–3600 **Fixed, Fixed-Satellite** (space-to-Earth), [781, 782, 785]	3400–3500 **Fixed, Fixed-Satellite** (space-to-Earth), Amateur, Mobile, Radiolocation [3736A] [664, 783]	
5650–5725	**Radiolocation**, Amateur, Space Research (deep space) [664, 801, 803, 804, 805]	
5725–5850 **Fixed–Satellite** (Earth-to-space), **Radiolocation**, Amateur [801, 803, 805, 800, 807, 808]	5725–5850 **Radiolocation**, Amateur [803, 805, 806, 808]	
5850–5925 **Fixed, Fixed-Satellite** (Earth-to-space), **Mobile**, Amateur, Radiolocation [806]	5850–5925 **Fixed, Fixed-Satellite** (Earth-to-space), **Mobile**, Amateur, Radiolocation [806]	5850–5925 **Fixed, Fixed-Satellite** (Earth-to-space), **Mobile**, Radiolocation [806]
10–10.45GHz **Fixed, Mobile, Radiolocation**, Amateur [828]	10–10.45 **Radiolocation**, Amateur [828, 829]	10–10.45 **Fixed, Mobile, Radiolocation**, Amateur [828]
10.45–10.5	**Radiolocation**, Amateur, Amateur-Satellite [830]	
24–24.05	**Amateur, Amateur–Satellite** [881]	
24.05–24.25	**Radiolocation**, Amateur, Earth Exploration–Satellite (active) [881]	
47–47.2	**Amateur, Amateur-Satellite**	
75.5–76	**Amateur, Amateur-Satellite**	
76–81	**Radiolocation**, Amateur, Amateur-Satellite [912]	
142–144	**Amateur, Amateur-Satellite**	
144–149	**Radiolocation**, Amateur, Amateur-Satellite [918]	
241–248	**Radiolocation**, Amateur, Amateur-Satellite [922]	
248–250	**Amateur, Amateur-Satellite**	

Footnotes

484 – Some countries of Region 1 use radiodetermination systems in the bands 1606.5–1625kHz, 1635–1800kHz, 1850–2160kHz, 2134–2300kHz, 2502–2850kHz and 3500–3800kHz. The establishment and operation of such systems are subject to agreement obtained under the procedure set forth in Article 14. The radiated mean power of these stations shall not exceed 50W.

488 – In the Federal Republic of Germany, Denmark, Finland, Hungary, Ireland, Israel, Jordan, Malta, Norway, Poland, the German Democratic Republic, the United Kingdom, Sweden, Czechoslovakia and the USSR, administrations may allocate up to 200kHz to their amateur service in the bands 1715–1800kHz and 1850–2000kHz. However, when allocating the bands within this range to their amateur service, administrations shall, after prior consultation with administrations of neighbouring countries, take such steps as may be necessary to prevent harmful interference from their amateur service to the fixed and mobile services of other countries. The mean power of any amateur station shall not exceed 10W.

489 – In Region 2, Loran stations operating in the band 1800–2000kHz shall cease operation by 31 December 1982. In Region 3, the Loran system operates either on 1850kHz or 1950kHz, the bands occupied being 1825–1875kHz and 1925–1975kHz respectively. Other services to which the band 1800–2000kHz is allocated may use any frequency therein on condition that no harmful interference is caused to the Loran system operating on 1850 or 1950kHz.

490 – Alternative allocation: in the Federal Republic of Germany, Angola, Austria, Belgium, Bulgaria, Cameroon, Congo, Denmark, Egypt, Spain, Ethiopia, France, Greece, Italy, Lebanon, Luxembourg, Malawi, the Netherlands, Portugal, Syria, the German Democratic Republic, Somalia, Tanzania, Tunisia, Turkey and the USSR, the band 1810–1830kHz is allocated to the fixed and mobile, except aeronautical mobile, services on a primary basis.

491 – Additional allocations: in Saudi Arabia, Iraq, Israel, Libya, Poland, Roumania, Chad, Czechoslovakia, Togo and Yugoslavia, the band 1810–1830kHz is also allocated to the fixed and mobile, except aeronautical mobile, services on a primary basis.

492 – In Region 1, the use of the band 1810–1850kHz by the amateur service is subject to the condition that satisfactory replacement assignments have been found and implemented in accordance with Resolution 38 for frequencies to all existing stations of the fixed and mobile, except aeronautical mobile, services operating in this band (except for the stations of the countries listed in Nos 490, 491 and 493). On completion of satisfactory transfer, the authorisation to use the band 1810–1830kHz by the amateur service in countries situated totally or partially north of 40°N shall be given only after consultation with the countries mentioned in Nos 490 and 491 to define the necessary steps to be taken to prevent harmful interference between amateur stations and stations of other services operating in accordance with Nos 490 and 491.

493 – Alternative allocations: in Burundi and Lesotho, the band 1810–1850kHz is also allocated to the fixed and mobile, except aeronautical mobile, services on a primary basis.

494 – Alternative allocation: in Argentina, Bolivia, Chile, Mexico, Paraguay, Peru, Uruguay and Venezuela, the band 1850–2000kHz is allocated to the fixed, mobile except aeronautical mobile, radiolocation and radionavigation services on a primary basis.

509 – Additional allocation: in Honduras, Mexico, Peru and Venezuela, the band 3500–3750kHz is also allocated to the fixed and mobile services on a primary basis.

510 – For the use of the bands allocated to the amateur service at 3.5MHz, 7.0MHz, 10.1MHz, 14.0MHz, 18.068MHz, 21.0MHz, 24.89MHz and 144MHz in the event of natural disasters, see Resolution 640.

511 – Additional allocation: in Brazil, the band 3700–4000kHz is also allocated to the radiolocation service on a primary basis.

512 – Alternative allocation: in Argentina, Bolivia, Chile, Ecuador, Paraguay, Peru and Uruguay, the band 3750–4000kHz is allocated to the fixed and mobile, except aeronautical mobile, services on a primary basis.

514 – Additional allocation: in Canada, the band 3950–4000kHz is also allocated to the broadcasting service on a primary basis. The power of broadcasting stations operating in this band shall not exceed that necessary for a national service within the frontier of this country and shall not cause harmful interference to other services operating in accordance with the Table.

515 – Additional allocation: in Greenland, the band 3950–4000kHz is also allocated to the broadcasting service on a primary basis. The power of the broadcasting stations operating in this band shall not exceed that necessary for a national service and shall in no case exceed 5kW.

526 – Additional allocation: in Angola, Iraq, Kenya, Rwanda, Somalia and Togo, the band 7000–7050kHz is also allocated to the fixed service on a primary basis.

527C – Alternative allocation: in Egypt, Ethiopia, Guinea, Libya, Madagascar, Malawi and Tanzania, the band 7000–7050kHz is allocated to the fixed service on a primary basis.

528 – The use of the band 7100–7300kHz in Region 2 by the amateur service shall not impose constraints on the broadcasting service intended for use within Region 1 and Region 3.

535 – Additional allocation: in Afghanistan, China, Ivory Coast, Iran and the USSR, the band 14,250–14,350kHz is also allocated to the fixed service on a primary basis. Stations of the fixed service shall not use a radiated power exceeding 24dBW.

537 – The band 18,068–18,168kHz is allocated to the fixed service on a primary basis subject to the procedure described in Resolution 8. The use of this band by the amateur and amateur-satellite services shall be subject to the completion of satisfactory transfer of all assignments to stations in the fixed service operating in this band and recorded in the Master Register, in accordance with the procedure described in Resolution 8.

538 – Additional allocation: in the USSR, the band 18,068–18,168kHz is also allocated to the fixed service on a primary basis for use within the boundary of the USSR, with a peak envelope power not exceeding 1kW.

542 – Additional allocation: in Kenya, the band 23,600–24,900kHz is also allocated to the meteorological aids service (radiosondes) on a primary basis.

543 – The band 24,890–24,990kHz is allocated to the fixed and land mobile services on a primary basis subject to the procedure described in Resolution 8. The use of this band by the amateur and amateur–satellite services shall be subject to the completion of the satisfactory transfer of all assignments to fixed and land mobile stations operating in this band and recorded in the Master Register, in accordance with the procedure described in Resolution 8.

556 – Alternative allocation: in New Zealand, the band 50–51MHz is allocated to the fixed, mobile and broadcasting services on a primary basis; the band 53–54MHz is allocated to the fixed and mobile services on a primary basis.

557 – Alternative allocation: in Afghanistan, Bangladesh, Brunei, India, Indonesia, Iran, Malaysia, Pakistan, Singapore and Thailand, the band 50–54MHz is allocated to the fixed, mobile and broadcasting services on a primary basis.

558 – Additional allocation: in Australia, China and the Democratic People's Republic of Korea, the band 50–54MHz is also allocated to the broadcasting service on a primary basis.

560 – Additional allocation: in New Zealand the band 51–53MHz is also allocated to the fixed and mobile services on a primary basis.

605 – Additional allocation: in Singapore, the band 144–145MHz is also allocated to the fixed and mobile services on a primary basis. Such use is limited to systems in operation on or before 1 January 1980, which in any case shall cease by 31 December 1995.

606 – Additional allocation: in China the band 144–146MHz is also allocated to the aeronautical mobile (OR) service on a secondary basis.

607 – Alternative allocation: in Afghanistan, Bangladesh, Cuba, Guyana and India, the band 146–148MHz is allocated to the fixed and mobile services on a primary basis.

629 – Additional allocation: in Oman, the United Kingdom and Turkey, the band 216–235MHz is also allocated to the radiolocation service on a secondary basis.

652 – Additional allocation: in Australia the United States, Jamaica and the Phillipines, the bands 420–430MHz and 220–450MHz are also allocated to the amateur service on a secondary basis.

653 – Additional allocation: in China, India, the German Democratic Republic, the United Kingdom and the USSR, the band 420–460MHz is also allocated to the aeronautical radionavigation service (radio altimeters) on a secondary basis.

654 – Different category of service: in France, the allocation of the band 430–434MHz to the amateur service is on a secondary basis (see No 424).

655 – Different category of service: in Denmark, Libya, Norway and Sweden, the allocation of the bands 430–432MHz and 438–440MHz to the radiolocation service is on a secondary basis (see No 424).

656 – Alternative allocation: in Denmark, Norway and Sweden, the bands 430–432MHz and 438–440MHz are allocated to the fixed and mobile, except aeronautical mobile, services on a primary basis.

657 – Additional allocation: in Finland, Libya and Yugoslavia, the bands 430–432MHz and 438–440MHz are also allocated to the fixed and mobile, except aeronautical mobile, services on a primary basis.

658 – Additional allocation: in Afghanistan, Algeria, Saudi Arabia, Bahrain, Bangladesh, Brunei, Burundi, Egypt, the United Arab Emirates, Ecuador, Spain, Ethiopia, Greece, Guinea, India, Indonesia, Iran, Iraq, Israel, Italy, Jordan, Kenya, Kuwait, Lebanon, Liechtenstein, Libya, Malaysia, Malta, Nigeria, Oman, Pakistan, the Philippines, Qatar, Syria, Singapore, Somalia, Switzerland, Tanzania, Thailand and Togo, the band 430–440MHz is also allocated to the fixed service on a primary basis and the bands 430–435MHz and 438–440MHz are also allocated to the mobile, except aeronautical mobile, service on a primary basis.

659 – Additional allocation: in Angola, Bulgaria, Cameroon, Congo, Gabon, Hungary, Mali, Mongolia, Niger, Poland, the German Democratic Republic, Roumania, Rwanda, Chad, Czechoslovakia and the USSR, the band 430–440MHz is also allocated to the fixed service on a primary basis.

660 – Different category of service: in Argentina, Colombia, Costa Rica, Cuba, Honduras, Panama and Venezuela, the allocation of the band 430–440MHz to the amateur service is on a primary basis (see No 425).

661 – In Region 1, except in the countries mentioned in No 662, the band 433.05–434.79MHz (centre frequency 433.92MHz) is designated for industrial, scientific and medical (ISM) applications. The use of this frequency band for ISM applications shall be subject to special authorisation by the administration concerned, in agreement with other administrations whose radiocommunication services might be affected. In applying this provision, administrations shall have due regard to the latest relevant CCIR Recommendations.

662 – In the Federal Republic of Germany, Austria, Liechtenstein, Portugal, Switzerland and Yugoslavia, the band 433.05–434.79MHz (centre frequency 433.92MHz) is designated for industrial, scientific and medical (ISM) applications. Radiocommunication services of these countries operating within this band must accept harmful interference which may be caused by these applications. ISM equipment operating in this band is subject to the provisions of No 1815.

663 – Additional allocation: in Brazil, France and the French Overseas Departments in Region 2, and India, the band 433.75–434.25MHz is also allocated to the space operation service (Earth-to-space) on a primary basis until 1 January 1990, subject to agreement obtained under the procedure set forth in Article 14. After 1 January 1990, the band 433.75–434.25MHz will be allocated in the same countries to the same service on a secondary basis.

644 – In the bands 435–438MHz, 1260–1270MHz, 2400–2450MHz, 3400–3410MHz in Regions 2 and 3 only, 5650–5670MHz the amateur-satellite service may operate subject to not causing harmful interference to other services operating in accordance with the Table (see No 435). Administrations authorizing such use shall ensure that any harmful interference caused by emissions from a station in the amateur-satellite service is immediately eliminated in accordance with the provisions of No 2741. The use of the bands 1260–1270MHz and 5650–5670MHz by the amateur-satellite service is limited to the Earth-to-space direction.

665 – Additional allocation: in Austria, the band 438–440MHz is also allocated to the fixed and mobile, except aeronautical mobile, services on a primary basis.

666 – Additional allocation: in Canada, New Zealand and Papua New Guinea, the band 440–450MHz is also allocated to the amateur service on a secondary basis.

667 – Different category of service: in Canada, the allocation of the band 440–450MHz to the radiolocation service is on a primary basis (see No 425).

705 – Different category of service: in the United States, the allocation of the band 890–942MHz to the radiolocation service is on a primary basis (see No 14) and subject to agreement obtained under the procedure set forth in Article 425.

707 – In Region 2 the band 902–928MHz (centre frequency 915MHz) is designated for industrial, scientific and medical (ISM) applications. Radiocommunication services operating within this band must accept harmful interference which may be caused by these applications. ISM equipment opereting in this band is subject to the provisions of No 1815.

710 – Use of the radionavigation-satellite service in the band 1215–1260MHz shall be subject to the condition that no harmful interference is caused to the radionavigation service authorized under No 712.

711 – Additional allocation: in Afghanistan, Angola, Saudi Arabia, Bahrain, Bangladesh, Cameroon, China, the United Arab Emirates, Ethiopia, Guinea, Guyana, India, Indonesia, Iran, Iraq, Israel, Japan, Jordan, Kuwait, Lebanon, Libya, Malawi, Morocco, Mozambique, Nepal Nigeria, Oman, Pakistan, the Philippines, Qatar, Syria, Somalia, Sudan, Sri Lanka, Chad, Thailand, Togo and Yemen (PDR of), the band 1215–1300MHz is also allocated to the fixed and mobile services on a primary basis.

712 – Additional allocation: in Algeria, the Federal Republic of Germany, Austria, Bahrain, Belgium, Benin, Burundi, Cameroon, China, Denmark, the United Arab Emirates, France,

Greece, India, Iran, Iraq, Kenya, Liechtenstein, Luxembourg, Mali, Mauritania, Norway, Oman, Pakistan, the Netherlands, Portugal, Qatar, Senegal, Somalia, Sudan, Sri Lanka, Sweden, Switzerland, Tanzania, Turkey and Yugoslavia, the band 1215–1300MHz is also allocated to the radionavigation service on a primary basis.

713 – In the bands 1215–1300MHz, 3100–3300MHz, 5250–5350MHz, 8550–8650MHz, 9500–9800MHz and 134–140GHz, radiolocation stations installed on spacecraft may also be employed for the earth exploration satellite and space research services on a secondary basis.

751 – In Australia, the United States and Papua New Guinea, the use of the band 2310–2390MHz by the aeronautical mobile service for telemetry has priority over other uses by the mobile services.

752 – The band 2400–2500MHz (centre frequency 2450MHz) is designated for industrial, scientific and medical (ISM) applications. Radio services operating within this band must accept harmful interference which may be caused by these applications. ISM equipment operating in this band is subject to the provisions of No 1815.

778 – In making assignments to stations of other services, administrations are urged to take all practicable steps to protect the spectral line observations of the radio astronomy service from harmful interference in the bands 3260–3267MHz, 3332–3339MHz, 3345.8–3352.5MHz and 4825–4835MHz. Emissions from space or airborne stations can be particularly serious sources of interference to the radio astronomy service (see Nos 343 and 344 and Article 36).

779 – Additional allocation: in Afghanistan, Saudi Arabia, Bahrain, Bangladesh, China, Congo, the United Arab Emirates, India, Indonesia, Iran, Iraq, Israel, Japan, Kuwait, Lebanon, Libya, Malaysia, Oman, Pakistan, Qatar, Syria, Singapore, Sri Lanka and Thailand, the band 3300–3400MHz is also allocated to the fixed and mobile services on a primary basis. The countries bordering the Mediterranean shall not claim protection for their fixed and mobile services from the radiolocation service.

780 – Additional allocation: in Bulgaria, Cuba, Hungary, Mongolia, Poland, the German Democratic Republic, Roumania, Czechoslovakia and the USSR the band 3300–3400MHz is also allocated to the radionavigation service on a primary basis.

781 – Additional allocation: in the Federal Republic of Germany, Israel, Nigeria and the United Kingdom, the band 3400–3475MHz is also allocated to the amateur service on a secondary basis.

783 – Different category of service: in Indonesia, Japan, Pakistan and Thailand the allocation of the band 3400–3500MHz to the mobile, except aeronautical mobile, service is on a primary basis (see No 425).

785 – In Denmark, Norway and the United Kingdom, the fixed, radiolocation and fixed–satellite services operate on a basis of equality of rights in the band 3400–3600MHz. However, these administrations operating radiolocation systems in this band are urged to cease operations by 1985. After this date these administrations shall take all practicable steps to protect the fixed-satellite service and co-ordination requirements shall not be imposed on the fixed-satellite service.

801 – Additional allocation: in the United Kingdom, the band 5470–5850MHz is also allocated to the land mobile service on a secondary basis. The power limits specified in Nos 2502, 2505, 2506 and 2507 shall apply in the band 5725–5850MHz.

803 – Additional allocation: in Afghanistan, Saudi Arabia, Bahrain, Bangladesh, Cameroon, Central African Republic, China, Congo, Korea (Republic of), Egypt, the United Arab Emirates, Gabon, Guinea, India, Indonesia, Iran, Iraq, Israel Japan, Jordan, Kuwait, Lebanon, Libya, Madagascar, Malaysia, Malawi, Malta, Niger, Nigeria, Pakistan, the Philippines, Qatar, Syria, Singapore, Sri Lanka, Tanzania, Chad, Thailand and Yemen (PDR of) the band 5650–5850MHz is also allocated to the fixed and mobile services on a primary basis.

804 – Different category of service: in Bulgaria, Cuba, Hungary, Mongolia, Poland, the German Democratic Republic, Czechoslovakia and the USSR, the allocation of the band 5670–5725MHz to the space research service is on a primary basis (see No 425).

805 – Additional allocation: in Bulgaria, Cuba, Hungary, Mongolia, Poland, the German Democratic Republic, Czechoslovakia and the USSR, the band 5670–5850MHz is also allocated to the fixed service on a primary basis.

806 – The band 5725–5875MHz (centre frequency 5800MHz) is designated for industrial scientific and medical (ISM) applications. Radiocommunication services operating within this band must accept harmful interference which may be caused by these applications. ISM equipment operating in this band is subject to the provisions of No 1815.

807 – Additional allocation: in the Federal Republic of Germany, the band 5755–5850MHz is also allocated to the fixed service on a primary basis.

808 – The band 5830–5850MHz is also allocated to the amateur-satellite service (space-to-Earth) on a secondary basis.

828 – The band 9975–10,025MHz is also allocated to the meteorological satellite service on a secondary basis for use by weather radars.

829 – Additional allocation: in Costa Rica, Ecuador, Guatemala. and Honduras, the band 10–10.45GHz is also allocated to the fixed and mobile services on a primary basis.

830 – Additional allocation: in the Federal Republic of Germany, Angola, China, Ecuador, Spain, Japan, Kenya, Morocco, Nigeria, Sweden, Tanzania and Thailand, the band 10.45–10.5GHz is also allocated to the fixed and mobile services on a primary basis.

881 – The band 24–24.25GHz (centre frequency 24.125GHz) is designated for industrial, scientific and medical (ISM) applications. Radiocommunication services operating within this band must accept harmful interference which may be caused by these applications. ISM equipment operating in this band is subject to the provisions of No 1815.

912 – In the band 78–79GHz radars located on space stations may be operated on a primary basis in the earth exploration–satellite service and in the space research service.

915 – The band 119.98–120.02GHz is also allocated to the amateur service on a secondary basis.

918 – The bands 140.69–140.98GHz, 144.68–144.98GHz, 145.45–145.75GHz and 146.82–147.12GHz are also allocated to the radio astronomy service on a primary basis for spectral line observations. In making assignments to stations of other services to which the bands are allocated, administrations are urged to take all practicable steps to protect the radio astronomy service from harmful interference. Emissions from space or airborne stations can be particularly serious sources of interference to the radio astronomy service (see Nos 343 and 334 and Article 36).

922 – The band 244–246GHz (centre frequency 245GHz) is designated for industrial, scientific and medical (ISM) applications. The use of this frequency band for ISM applications shall be subject to special authorisation by the administration concerned in agreement with other administrations whose radiocommunication services might be affected. In applying this provision administrations shall have due regard to the latest CCIR Recommendations.

7 Standard frequency stations

THIS appendix gives brief details of some stations transmitting standard frequencies and time signals. Transmission times are given in UTC.

The standard frequencies are maintained to an accuracy of typically one part in 10^{-11}. However, if the sky-wave is used there could be a larger error in reception due to Doppler shift and there will be fading of the signal. These problems can be avoided by using a low-frequency transmission such as those from MSF or WWVB.

Times are announced in GMT or UTC (coordinated universal time), the latter being the official standard time as maintained by atomic clocks. Any difference or error is likely to be of the order of 0.1ms. Since the Earth's rotation is somewhat irregular, astronomical time (UT1) can vary slightly from UTC and some stations broadcast the difference (DUT1).

For further information on the facilities provided by these stations see the *List of Radiodetermination and Special Service Stations* published by the ITU.

ARGENTINA

Callsign: LOL2.
Standard frequencies: 5000, 10,000, 15,000kHz simultaneous (1100–1200, 1400–1500, 1700–1800, 2000–2100, 2300–2400).
Time interval signals: 3min of 1kHz and 440Hz modulation (A2A) alternately, commencing all the minutes which are multiples of 5, except the 55th minute, this being reserved for a precision time signal which consists of a 5ms pulse every second for 3min (except the 59th second) at 1kHz.
Announcements: In between the 3min tone periods. For the first minute a DUT1 code is sent. For the second minute the station callsign in morse code is sent followed by the origin of the transmission, ie "Observatorio Naval Buenos Aires".
Location: Buenos Aires.

AUSTRALIA

Callsign: VNG.
Standard frequencies: 4500kHz (0945–2130), 7500kHz (2245–2230), 12,000kHz (2145–0930).
Time interval signals: Seconds pulses are normally 50 cycles of 1kHz modulation (A2A); shortened pulses precede the minute which is marked by 500 cycles of 1kHz.
Announcements: Voice identification (A3E) precedes the hour and quarter hours.
Location: Lyndhurst, Victoria.

CANADA

Callsign: CHU.
Standard frequencies: 3330, 7335, 14,670kHz simultaneous (24h).
Time interval signals: Seconds pulses are 300 cycles of 1kHz tone (H2A): the beginning of each pulse marks the exact second. Thc zero pulse of each minute is 0.5s long, and the zero pulse of each hour is 1s long. The sequence and form of the pulses are also modified as follows:
1. The 29th pulse of each minute is omitted.
2. The lst to 9th pulses are omitted from the first minute of each hour.
3. The 1st to 15th pulses of each minute may be split so as to indicate the difference DUT1 between UT1 and in magnitude to the nearest 0.1s and in sign.
4. The 31st to 39th pulses of each minute are shortened to 10 cycles of 1kHz and each is followed by a frequency shift code which can be employed to synchronise remote clocks to UTC (NRC).
Announcements: The 51st to 59th pulses of each minute are omitted. During this time station identification and time are announced in both French and English (H3E).
Location: Ottawa.

FRANCE

Callsign: FFH.
Standard frequencies: 2500kHz (0800–1625 except Sundays).
Time interval signals: Seconds pulses are five cycles of 1kHz

modulation (A2A), except at the zero second of each minute when the total duration is 0.5s.
Announcements: The callsign is transmitted in morse code (A2A) after the 30th second of 0, 10, 20, 30, 40 and 50 minutes of the hour.
Location: S Assise.

ITALY

Callsign: IBF.
Standard frequency: 5000kHz (from minute 45 to 60 of 0700, 0900, 1000, 1100, 1200, 1300, 1400, 1500, 1600, 1700, 1800). The schedule is advanced by 1h in summer.
Time interval signals: Seconds pulses are five cycles of 1kHz modulation (A2A). These pulses are repeated seven times on the minute.
Announcements: Voice announcement (A3E) at the beginning and end of each 15min transmission. Time announcement by morse code every 10min beginning at 0000.
Location: Turin.

JAPAN

Callsign: JJY.
Standard frequencies: 2500, 5000, 10,000, 15,000kHz simultaneous (24h).
Time interval signals: These are active for the 5min following each multiple of 10min and are followed by the standard frequency only radiated for 4min. (The transmitter does not radiate between the 35th and 39th minute). Seconds pulses are 5ms of 1.6kHz modulation. The beginning of each pulse marks the exact second. (There are 1kHz pulses in between the second markers). The minute is a 5ms pulse of 1.6kHz preceded by a 655ms pulse of 600Hz.
Announcements: At the minute preceding multiples of 10min, the callsign is sent twice by morse code at 1kHz modulation followed by Japanese Standard Time (four figures) once. This information is then transmitted by voice in Japanese. A warning of radio propagation is then sent by morse code at 1kHz modulation ("N" denotes normal, "U" unstable, "W" warning).
Location: Tokyo.

RUSSIA

Callsign: RWM.
Standard frequencies: 4996, 9996, 14,996kHz simultaneous (24h).
Time interval signals: Second pulses from 10min 00s to 19min 55s and 40min 00s to 49min 55s. Signals at the beginning of each minute are prolonged to 0.5s. From 20min 00s to 29min 55s and 50min 00s to 59min 55s there are signals with a 10Hz repetition rate. Signals at the beginning of each minute are prolonged.
Announcement: The callsign is sent at 9min and 39min past each hour.
Location: Moscow.

UNITED KINGDOM

Callsign: MSF.
Standard frequencies: 2500, 5000, 10,000kHz simultaneous (24h).

Time interval signals: Seconds pulses are five cycles of 1kHz modulation (A2A) which is lengthened to 100ms at each minute. These signals are radiated for the 5min following each multiple of 10min.

Announcements: The callsign is given twice in morse code (A2A) during the 5s immediately preceding each transmission period.

Location: Rugby.

Callsign: MSF.

Standard frequency: 60kHz (24h).

Time interval signals: Carrier interruptions (A1A) lasting 100ms at each second and lengthened to 500ms at each minute. The start of the interruption denotes the precise time.

Announcements: Each minute is also indicated by a BCD signal inserted in the 500ms carrier interruption. This consists of 13 bits at 100bit/s giving hour and minute information, together with a final parity bit. The signal can be decoded by suitable circuitry to give a continuous clock display. No transmissions are made for 5s preceding each hour when the callsign is given in morse code (A1A).

Location: Rugby.

USA

Callsigns: WWV and WWVH.

Standard frequencies: 2500, 5000, 10,000, 15,000, 20,000kHz (plus 25,000kHz from WVW only), simultaneous (24h). The higher frequencies (20 and 25MHz) tend only to be used at the peak of the sunspot cycle.

Time interval signals: Seconds pulses are five cycles of 1kHz on WWV (or six cycles of 1200Hz on WWVH) and occur each second except the 29th and 59th seconds. A long pulse (0.8s) marks the beginning of each minute. A modified IRIG-H time code is broadcast continuously on a 100Hz subcarrier. The format is 1 pulse per second with a 1min time frame. It gives day of the year, hours and minutes in BCD form.

Announcements: The time in GMT is announced once a minute with a male voice at WWV and a female voice at WWVH. The WWVH announcement occurs at 15s before the minute, while that of WWV occurs at 7.5s before the minute. Propagation data are sent by voice during the 18th minute of each hour from WWV. These include solar and geomagnetic indices, together with a summary of recent events and a forecast for the next 24h.

Locations: Fort Collins, Colorado (WWV) and Kekaha-Kauai Hawaii (WWVH).

Callsign: WWVB.

Standard frequency: 60kHz (24h).

Time interval signals: One pulse per second special binary code giving minutes, hours, days and DUT1.

Location: Fort Collins, Colorado.

8 Foreign-language phone contacts

THOUSANDS of operators across the world have contacts with only 100 or so words in a second language. It gives them great satisfaction, as well as many contacts which would otherwise have been impossible.

A basic contact consists of 10 parts: (1) calling CQ, (2) acknowledge reply, (3) name, (4) QTH, (5) signal report, (6) equipment used, (7) weather, (8) QSL via bureau, (9) 'Thanks for contact', (10) 73. Nearly every contact comes over in that order and all 10 parts usually come over in three of four transmissions, grouping two or three parts together in each one.

Every language can be found on the 14MHz band. For familiarisation and pronunciation of any of these four languages, search around the band for someone calling CQ who is speaking clearly and slowly with a strong signal. Do not waste time with weak signals or trying to understand a ragchew!

After some listening practice, make out the memory page with your name, QTH, rig etc. There are eight types of weather to choose from and the numbers down the side will cover station reports and temperatures up to 30°C. The memory page is just a prompt so that you do not forget your words in the middle of a transmission and so that you are able to give the other operator the information required correctly.

When ready to start transmitting, you will find it easier to contact an English-speaking station. After the preliminaries are established, tell your contact that you wish to practice his language and change straight over, reading from the prepared memory page. Do not be put off if your contact continues in English – he may wish to practice as well!

When you advance to calling CQ it is advisable to tell the other station that you "only speak the language for the QSO". This should prevent questions coming across which cannot be understood; if they do, repeat the same statement and continue to the end of the contact.

While four foreign languages are given here, you are strongly advised not to attempt more than one at a time – probably the second language which you learned at school – as it is very easy to get the words mixed up, particularly when you start to rely on memory.

FRENCH

0	zero
1	un, une
2	deux
3	trois
4	quatre
5	cinq
6	six
7	sept
8	huit
9	neuf
10	dix
11	onze
12	douze
13	treize
14	quatorze
15	quinze
16	seize
17	dix-sept
18	dix-huit
19	dix-neuf
20	vingt
21	vingt et un
22	vingt-deux
23	vingt-trois
24	vingt-quatre
25	vingt-cinque
26	vingt-six
27	vingt-sept
28	vingt-huit
29	vingt-neuf
30	trente
40	quarante
80	quatre-vingts

Calling CQ, CQ, CQ, this is

G . . . . calling CQ on

the . . . . . metre band

G . . . . standing by.

F . . . ., G . . . . returning,

The name here is . . . .

and the QTH . . . .

I spell . . . .

Your report here is . . . . and . . . . .

F . . . ., G . . . . over to you.

F . . . ., G . . . . returning,

the rig here is . . . .

with a . . . . antenna

and a . . . . microphone

the WX here is . . . .

1. sunny	5. fog
2. cloudy	6. warm
3. raining	7. cold
4. windy	8. snowing

and the temperature C

F . . . ., G . . . . back to you

---

F . . . ., G . . . . returning for
the final

I will send you my QSL card via the bureau,

Thank you for the very good QSO,
73, OM,

F . . . ., G . . . . closing,
cheerio.

CQ, CQ, CQ, (SAY KOO) appel général, appel

général, ici G . . . . qui lance appel

bande . . . . . mètres

G . . . . pass a l'écoute.

F . . . ., G . . . . qui revient

Le prénom ici est . . . .

et le QTH (KOO TAY ASSH) . . . .

je vous épele . . . .

Votre rapport ici est . . . . . et . . . . . .

F . . . ., G . . . . à vous.

F . . . ., G . . . . de retour

la condition de travail ici est . . . .

avec une antenne . . . .

et un micro . . . .

Le WX (DOUBLA VAY EKS) ici est . . . .

1. ensoleillé	5. du brouillard
2. nuageux	6. chaud
3. il pleut	7. froid
4. du vent	8. il neige

et la température . . . . . . dégrées Centigrad

F . . . ., G . . . . à vous

---

F . . . ., G . . . . qui revient
pour le final

Je vous enverrai ma carte QSL (KOO ES EL) via
le bureau,

Merci bien pour le très bon QSO (KOO ES AW)
Soixante-treize, cher OM

F . . . ., G . . . . qui termine
maintenant, au revoir.

ADDITIONAL PHRASES WHICH MAY BE REQUIRED

I only speak French for the QSO.	Je parle français seulement pour le QSO.
Please speak slowly.	Parlez lentement, s'il vous plâit.
Please give me my report again.	Donnez-moi mon rapport encore une fois, s'il vous plâit.
Please give me your name again.	Donnez-moi votre prénom encore une fois, s'il vous plâit.
Please give me your QTH again.	Donnez-moi votre QTH encore une fois, s'il vous plâit.

GERMAN

0	null, zero
1	ein, eins
2	zwei, zwo
3	drei
4	vier
5	fünf
6	sechs
7	sieben
8	acht
9	neun
10	zehn
11	elf
12	zwolf
13	dreizehn
14	vierzehn
15	fünfzehn
16	sechszehn
17	siebzehn
18	achtzehn
19	neunzehn
20	zwanzig
21	ein und zwanzig
22	zwei und zwanzig
23	drei und zwanzig
24	vier und zwanzig
25	fünf und zwanzig
26	sechs und zwanzig
27	sieben und zwanzig
28	acht und zwanzig
29	neun und zwanzig
30	dreissig
40	vierzig
80	achtzig

CQ, CQ, CQ . . . . . metres

This is the English station G . . . .
calling CQ

G . . . . going over to receive,
stand by

D . . . . , G . . . . returning

My name is . . . .

and my QTH is . . . .

I spell . . . .

Your report here is . . . . and . . . . .

D . . . . , G . . . . back to you

---

D . . . . , G . . . . coming back

My station is . . . .

with a . . . . antenna

and a . . . . microphone

The weather here is . . . .

1. sunny   5. foggy
2. cloudy   6. warm
3. raining 7. cold
4. windy   8. snowing

and the temperature . . . . degrees C

back to you D . . . . , G . . . .

D . . . . G . . . . Thank you for
the QSO

I will send you my QSL card via the bureau

Best wishes and good DX
73 until we meet again

D . . . . G . . . . cheerio

CQ, CQ, CQ (SEE KOO), ... meter Band

Hier ruft die englische Station G . . . .
mit einem allgemeinen Anruf

G . . . . geht auf empfang,
bitte kommen

D . . . . , G . . . . zurück

Mein Name ist . . . .

und mein QTH (KOO TAY HAA) ist . . . .

Ich buchstabiere . . . .

Ihr Rapport hier ist . . . . . und . . . . . .

D . . . . , G . . . . bitte
kommen

D . . . . , G . . . . zurück

Meine Station ist . . . .

mit eine . . . . Antenne

und ein . . . . Mikrophon

Das Wetter hier ist . . . .

1. sunnig   5. nebelig
2. bewoelkt 6. warm
3. es regnet 7. kalt
4. windig   8. es schneit

und das Temperatur . . . . Grad

zurück zu Ihnen D . . . . , G . . . .
bitte kommen

D . . . . G . . . . Danke
schön für das QSO (KOO ES OH)

Ich werde meine QSL-Karte via Bureau senden

Die besten Grüsse und gut DX
drei und siebzig, auf wiederhören

D . . . . G . . . . Tschuess

ADDITIONAL PHRASES WHICH MAY BE REQUIRED

I only speak German for the QSO.	Ich spreche Deutsch nur für das QSO.
Please give me your callsign again.	Bitte, geben Sie mir Ihr Rufzeichen noch einmal.
Please give me your name again.	Bitte, geben Sie mir Ihr Name noch einmal.
Please give me your QTH again.	Bitte, geben Sie mir Ihr QTH (KOO TAY HAA) noch einmal.
I give you back the microphone.	Ich gebe Ihnen das Mikrophon wieder zurück.

ITALIAN

0	zero
1	uno
2	due
3	tre
4	quattro
5	cinque
6	sei
7	sette
8	otto
9	nove
10	dieci
11	undici
12	dodici
13	tredici
14	quattordici
15	quindici
16	sedici
17	diciasette
18	diciotto
19	diciannove
20	venti
21	ventuno
22	ventidue
23	ventitré
24	ventiquattro
25	venticinque
26	ventsei
27	ventisette
28	ventotto
29	ventinove
30	trenta
40	quaranta
80	ottanta

CQ . . . . . metres, this is the English station G . . . . standing by

Chiamata generale . . . . . metri, questo è la stazione inglese G . . . . e vi ascolto, avanti

---

I . . . . , G . . . . returning, many thanks for the call.

The name here is . . . .

and the QTH is . . . .

Your report is . . . . . and . . . . .

Mike back to you, I . . . . , G . . . .

I . . . . G . . . . ritornando tante grazie per la risposta.

Il mio nome è . . . .

Il mio QTH (KOO TEE ACCA) è . . . .

Il vostro controllo è . . . . . e . . . . .

Vi ripasso il micro, I . . . . , G . . . . avanti, cambio

---

I . . . . , G . . . . returning

The rig here is . . . .

with . . . . linear

The microphone is . . . .

My antenna is . . . .

The WX here is . . . .

1. sunny   5. foggy
2. cloudy   6. warm
3. raining   7. cold
4. windy   8. snowing

The temperature is . . . . . degrees

I . . . . , G . . . . over to you

I . . . . , G . . . . ritornando

Il mio apparechio è . . . .

con amplificatore . . . .

Il micro è . . . .

La mia antenna è . . . .

Il tempo qui è . . . .

1. bellissimo   5. nebbioso
2. nuvoloso   6. caldo
3. piovoso   7. freddo
4. fa vento   8. nevica

La temperatura è . . . . . gradi

Vi ripasso il micro, I . . . . , G . . . . avanti, cambio

---

I . . . . , G . . . . returning for the final.

I will send my QSL card via the bureau.

Thank you for the excellent QSO, best wishes and good DX.

The mike to you for the final. Bye-bye.

I . . . . , G 73

I . . . . , G . . . . ritornando, per il finale.

Vi mandero la mia cartolina QSL (KOO ESS ELLE) via bureau (associatione).

Molti grazie per il QSO eccellente, tanti saluti e buon DX.

Il micro a voi caro amico per il finale. Ciao (CHOW).

I . . . . ,G . . . . Avanti, cambio, 73 (settanta tre)

ADDITIONAL PHRASES WHICH MAY BE REQUIRED

I only speak Italian for the QSO.
Please speak slowly.
I did not get your callsign.
What is my report?

Parlo Italiano soltanto per il QSO.
Prego, parlate lentamente.
Non ho capito il vostro nominativo.
Cos' è il mio controllo?

SPANISH

0	cero
1	uno
2	dos
3	tres
4	cuatro
5	cinco
6	seis
7	siete
8	ocho
9	nueve
10	diez
11	once
12	doce
13	trece
14	catorce
15	quince
16	diez y seis
17	diez y siete
18	diez y ocho
19	diez nueve
20	veinte
21	veintiuno
22	veintidos
23	veintitres
24	veinticuatro
25	veinticinco
26	veintiseis
27	veintisiete
28	veintiocho
29	veintinueve
30	treinta
31	treinta y uno
40	cuarenta
80	ochenta

Calling CQ CQ CQ, this is G . . . . calling CQ on . . . . . metres, G . . . . standing by.

Llamada general, G . . . . llamando, CQ . . . . . . metros, y G . . . . escuchando.

EA . . . . , from G . . . . returning,

EA . . . . , G . . . . retornando.

Thank you for returning my call.

Gracias por haber contestado a mi llamada.

My name is . . . . I spell . . . .

Mi nombre es . . . . como . . . .

My QTH is . . . . I spell . . . .

Mi QTH es . . . . como . . . .

Your report here is . . . . and . . . . .

Su control es . . . . . y . . . . . .

EA . . . . from G . . . . come in.

EA . . . . de G . . . . adelante

---

EA . . . . from G . . . . Thank you for your message.

EA . . . . de G . . . . Gracias por su mensaje.

My station is . . . .

Mis condiciones de trabajo . . . .

my antenna is dipole/multiband/beam.

mi antena es dipolo/multibanda/directional.

My microphone is crystal/dynamic.

Mi microfono es cristal/dinamico.

The weather here is

1. sunny
2. cloudy
8. raining
4. windy
5. fog
6. warm
7. cold
8. snowing

El tiempo aqui

1. hace sol
2. nublado
3. lloviendo
4. hace viento
5. nubuloso
6. hace calor
7. hace frio
8. nevando

The temperature is . . . . degrees.

La temperatura . . . . grados.

EA . . . . from G . . . . come in

EA . . . . de G . . . . adelante

---

EA . . . . from G . . . . for the final.

EA . . . . de G . . . . por el final.

I will send my QSL card via the bureau. Thank you for the QSO, 73, Cheerio.

Me enviaré la tarjeta de QSL via el bureau. Gracias por el QSO, 73 (setenta y tres).

EA . . . . de G . . . . adios!

ADDITIONAL PHRASES WHICH MAY BE REQUIRED

I only speak Spanish for the QSO.	Hablo el español solamente por el QSO.
Please speak slowly.	Por favor hablar despachio.
Please repeat my report/your name/your QTH.	Por favor repitir mi control/su nombre/su QTH.
Can you QSY . . . kHz higher/lower.	Puede Usted QSY . . . kHz alto/bajo.
I am sorry, I cannot copy, bad QRM.	Lo siento, no puedo copiar, mucho QRM.

9 Band plans

THE following pages give the IARU Region 1 band plans for all amateur bands from 1.8MHz to 47MHz, together with the UK interpretation. UK licence notes are also given so as to make this a comprehensive band-by-band reference.

Band plans are subject to slight changes from year to year – such changes are always described in *Radio Communication* as they happen and up-to-date plans are also published annually in the *RSGB Amateur Radio Call Book*.

HF band plan notes

1. The expression 'phone' includes all permitted forms of telephony.
2. If transmitting very close to a band edge, take care not to radiate outside of the band.
3. Before transmitting, all operators should check that the frequency is not already occupied. The normal advice is to use the phrase "Is this frequency in use?" on SSB or "QRL?" on CW.
4. Digimodes are defined as including: AMTOR, PACTOR, CLOVER, ASCII, RTTY (Baudot) and packet.
5. LSB is recommended on bands below 10MHz, and USB recommended on bands above 10MHz.
6. The IARU Region 1 HF band plans are designed to enable the best utilisation of the HF spectrum space available. They achieve this objective because the vast majority of licensed amateurs observe the voluntary recommendations. In some countries (eg the USA) licence regulations require that specific modes be confined to specific sections of each band.

VHF band plan notes

1. The beacon and satellite services must be kept free of normal communication transmissions to prevent interference with these services.
2. The use of the FM mode within the SSB/CW section and CW and SSL in the FM-only sector is not recommended.
3. Repeater stations are primarily intended as an aid for mobile working and they are not intended to be used for DX communication. FM stations wishing to work DX should use the all-modes section, taking care to avoid frequencies allocated for specific purposes.

UK Amateur Radio Band Plans

1.8 MHz (160 m)

LICENCE NOTES:

Amateur Service:	1.810 - 1.850 MHz, Primary. Remainder secondary. *Available on the basis of non-interference to other services (inside or outside the UK)*
Satellite Service:	No allocation
Power limit:	1.810 - 1.850 MHz: 26 dBW PEP. Remainder 15 dBW
Permitted modes:	Morse, telephony, RTTY, data, fax, SSTV

IARU	Novice	U/A Rem Ctrl	U/A Digital	U/A Beacon	UK Usage
1.810					
CW only					
1.838					
Digimodes *(and CW but excluding packet radio)*					*RTTY (baudot) is the preferred digital mode on this band* *Phone may be used above 1.840*
1.842					
Phone and (CW)	✓		✓		[1.950 - 2.000 Novice] 1.960 DF contest beacons (14 dBW) 12.5 kHz b/w max 1.970 Provisional Novice calling freq.
2.000					Note: packet radio should not be used on the 1.8 MHz band.

3.5 MHz (80 m)

LICENCE NOTES:

Amateur Service:	Primary, *Shared with other services*
Satellite Service:	No allocation
Power limit:	26 dBW PEP
Permitted modes:	Morse, telephony, RTTY, data, fax, SSTV
Unattended beacons:	Only for DF contests Sat & Sun only, 14 dBW ERP PEP max

IARU	Novice	U/A Rem Ctrl	U/A Digital	U/A Beacon	UK Usage
3.500					
CW only					3.500 - 3.510 *Priority for CW inter-continental working* 3.500 - 3.560 *CW contest preferred segment* [3.560 - 3.585 Novice]
3.580	✓				
Digimodes *(and CW)*			✓		3.590 - 3.600 *Preferred packet radio frequencies* *(Phone may be used and has priority above 3.600 MHz)*
3.620					3.600 - 3.650 *Phone contest preferred segment* 3.635 - 3.650 *Used by CIS stations for intercontinental working*
Phone *(and CW)*					3.700 - 3.800 *Phone contest preferred segment* 3.730 - 3.740 *SSTV/fax recommended* 3.775 - 3.800 *Reserved for intercontinental phone working*
3.800					

Novice Licence: powers and modes

The power levels shown in these band plans are for the full UK licences. Novice licencees are limited to 5 W DC input or 3 W RF output. Furthermore, the novice licence schedule makes some restrictions on the modes which are permitted *within* the bands shown in these pages as being available to novices. Please refer to the Amateur Radio Novice Licence and its schedule for full details.

7 MHz (40 m)

LICENCE NOTES:

Amateur Service:	Primary
Satellite Service:	Primary
Power limit:	26 dBW PEP
Permitted modes:	Morse, telephony, RTTY, data, fax, SSTV

IARU	Novice	U/A Rem Ctrl	U/A Digital	U/A Beacon	UK Usage
7.000					
CW only					
7.035					
Digimodes *(and CW, SSTV, Fax)*					*(Phone may be used above 7.040)*
7.045					
Phone *(and CW)*					
7.100					

10 MHz (30 m)

LICENCE NOTES:

Amateur Service:	Secondary
Satellite Service:	No allocation
Power limit:	26 dBW PEP
Permitted modes:	Morse, telephony, RTTY, data, fax, SSTV

IARU	Novice	U/A Rem Ctrl	U/A Digital	U/A Beacon	UK Usage
10.100					
CW only	✓				10.130
10.140					10.140
Digimodes					*(Unattended digimode stations should avoid the use of the 10 MHz band.)*
10.150					

10 MHz Band Plan notes:

Note: The 10 MHz band is allocated to the amateur service only on a secondary basis. Therefore IARU have agreed on a worldwide basis that only CW and digimodes being narrow bandwidth modes, are to be used on this band. Likewise this band is not to be used for contests or news bulletins.

14 MHz (20 m)

LICENCE NOTES:

Amateur Service :	Primary
Satellite Service :	14.000 - 14.250 MHz: Primary
Power limit:	26 dBW PEP
Permitted modes:	Morse, telephony, RTTY, data, fax, SSTV

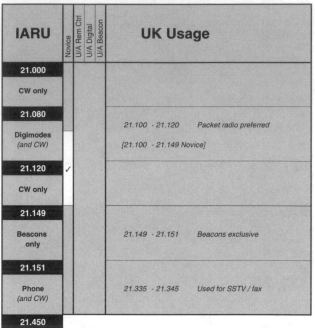

IARU	Novice	U/A Rem Ctrl	U/A Digital	U/A Beacon	UK Usage	
4.000						
CW only					14.000 - 14.060	CW only contest preferred segment
4.070						
Digimodes (and CW)					14.089 - 14.099	Packet radio preferred frequencies
4.099						
Beacons only					14.099 - 14.101	Reserved exclusively for beacons
4.101						
Digimodes (+ phone and CW)					14.101 - 14.112	Packet radio preferred frequencies
4.112						
Phone (and CW)					14.125 - 14.300	SSB only contest preferred segment
					14.225 - 14.235	Used for SSTV/fax
4.350						

21 MHz (15 m)

LICENCE NOTES:

Amateur Service:	Primary
Satellite Service :	Primary
Power limit:	26 dBW PEP
Permitted modes:	Morse, telephony, RTTY, data, fax, SSTV

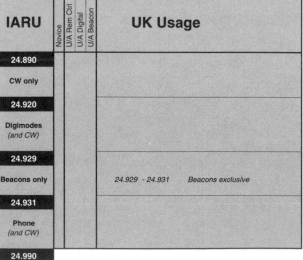

IARU	Novice	U/A Rem Ctrl	U/A Digital	U/A Beacon	UK Usage	
21.000						
CW only						
21.080						
Digimodes (and CW)					21.100 - 21.120	Packet radio preferred
					[21.100 - 21.149 Novice]	
21.120	✓					
CW only						
21.149						
Beacons only					21.149 - 21.151	Beacons exclusive
21.151						
Phone (and CW)					21.335 - 21.345	Used for SSTV / fax
21.450						

18 MHz (17 m)

LICENCE NOTES:

Amateur Service:	Primary
Satellite Service:	Primary
Power limit:	26 dBW PEP
Permitted modes:	Morse, telephony, RTTY, data, fax, SSTV

IARU	Novice	U/A Rem Ctrl	U/A Digital	U/A Beacon	UK Usage	
8.068						
CW only						
8.101						
Digimodes (and CW)						
8.109						
Beacons only					18.109 - 18.111	Exclusively beacons
8.111						
Phone (and CW)						
8.168						

24 MHz (12 m)

LICENCE NOTES:

Amateur Service:	Primary
Satellite Service:	Primary
Power limit:	26 dBW PEP
Permitted modes:	Morse, telephony, RTTY, data, fax, SSTV

IARU	Novice	U/A Rem Ctrl	U/A Digital	U/A Beacon	UK Usage	
24.890						
CW only						
24.920						
Digimodes (and CW)						
24.929						
Beacons only					24.929 - 24.931	Beacons exclusive
24.931						
Phone (and CW)						
24.990						

28 MHz (10 m)

LICENCE NOTES:

Amateur Service:	Primary
Satellite Service:	Primary
Power limit:	26 dBW PEP
Permitted modes:	Morse, telephony, RTTY, data, fax, SSTV
Unattended beacons:	Only for DF contests (14 dBW PEP max)

IARU	Novice	U/A Rem Ctrl	U/A Digital	U/A Beacon	UK Usage	
8.000						
CW only						
8.050						
Digimodes (and CW)	✓				[28.060 - 28.190 Novice]	
					28.120 - 28.150	Packet radio preferred
8.150						
CW only					[28.190]	
					28.190 - 28.199	Beacons operational
8.199						
Beacons only					28.199 - 28.201	Beacons exclusive
8.201						
Phone (and CW)	✓		✓		[28.225 - 28.500 Novice]	
					28.201 - 28.255	Beacons operational
					[28.500]	
					28.675 - 28.685	used for SSTV / fax
9.200						
Digimodes (+ phone and CW)					29.200 - 29.300	Preferred for packet radio (FM 2.5 kHz)
29.300						
Satellite downlinks					29.300 - 29.500	Reserved exclusively for satellite downlinks
9.550						
Phone (and CW)					Some experimental FM repeaters may be established in IARU Region 1	
9.700						

50 MHz (6 m)

LICENCE NOTES:

Amateur Service:	50.0 - 51.0 MHz, Primary; 51.0 - 52.0 MHz, Secondary. *Available on the basis of non-interference to other services (inside or outside the UK).*
Satellite Service :	No allocation
Power limit:	50.0 - 51.0 MHz, 26 dBW PEP; 51.0 - 52.0MHz, 20 dBW PEP
Permitted modes:	Morse, telephony, RTTY, data, fax, SSTV

IARU	Novice	U/A Rem Ctrl	U/A Digital	U/A Beacon	UK Usage	
50.000						
CW only					50.020 - 50.080	Beacons
					50.090	CW calling frequency
50.100						
SSB and CW only		✓			50.100 - 50.130	DX window - note 1
					50.110	Intercontinental calling - note 2
					50.185	Cross-band activity centre
					50.200	SSB calling frequency
					50.300	CW MS calling frequency
					50.350	SSB MS calling frequency
50.500						
All modes					50.510	SSTV
					50.550	Fax
					50.600	RTTY (afsk)
					50.630 - 50.750	Packet radio - note 3
51.000		✓				
All modes					51.210	Emergency comms. priority
51.410						
All modes					51.210 - 51.390	Repeater inputs
					51.410 - 51.590	FM telephony
					51.510	FM calling
					51.530	Note 5
51.830						
All modes					51.810 - 51.990	Repeater outputs
					51.940 - 52.000	Emergency comms priority
52.000						

50 MHz Band Plan notes:

1. Only to be used for QSOs between stations in different continents.
2. No QSOs on this frequency. Always QSY when working intercontinental DX.
3. 20 kHz channel spacing. Channel centre frequencies start at 50.630 MHz.
4. 20 kHz channel spacing. Channel centre frequencies start at 51.410 MHz.
5. Used by GB2RS news and for slow morse transmissions.

70 MHz (4 m)

LICENCE NOTES:

Amateur Service: Secondary. Available on the basis of non-interference to other services (inside or outside the UK).

Satellite Service: No allocation
Power limit: 22 dBW PEP
Permitted modes: Morse, telephony, RTTY, data, fax, SSTV

IARU	Novice	U/A Rem Ctrl	U/A Digital	U/A Beacon	UK Usage	
70.000						
Beacons					70.030	Personal beacons
70.030						
SSB and CW only					70.150	Meteor scatter calling
					70.185	Cross-band activity centre
					70.200	SSB / CW calling
70.250						
All modes					70.260	AM / FM calling
70.300						
					70.3000	RTTY / fax
					70.3125	Packet radio
		✓	✓	✓	70.3250	Packet radio
					70.3375	Packet radio
					70.3500	Emergency comms priority
Channelised operation using 12.5 kHz channels					70.3625	
					70.3750	Emergency comms priority
					70.3875	
					70.4000	Emergency comms priority
					70.4125	
					70.4250	
					70.4375	
					70.4500	FM calling
					70.4625	
					70.4750	
			✓		70.4875	Packet radio
70.500						

144 MHz (2 m)

LICENCE NOTES:

Amateur Service: Primary
Satellite Service: Primary
Power limit: 26 dBW PEP
Permitted modes: Morse, telephony, RTTY, data, fax, SSTV
Unattended beacons: Only for DF Contests

144 MHz Band Plan notes:

1. CW meteor scatter operation can take place up to 26 kHz higher than the reference frequency.

2. Used by emergency communications subject to 14 dBW PEP limitation. This note will eventually be deleted from the band plans.

3. Frequencies in the range 144.5125 MHz to 144.6875 MHz may be used for data communications subject to the requirement that sidebands do not spread outside this range of frequencies. The use of frequencies beneath 144.600 MHz for data communications is a temporary measure pending a complete review of the band plan for 144.0 - 145.0 MHz scheduled to be completed in time for the 1996 IARU Region 1 Conference. Before any use is made of frequencies beneath 144.600 MHz for data communications, operators must make every effort to consult with existing operators using that part of the band.

IARU	Novice	U/A Rem Ctrl	U/A Digital	U/A Beacon	UK Usage	
144.000						
					144.000 - 144.035	Moonbounce
CW only					144.050	CW calling frequency
					144.100	MS CW ref frequency - note 1
					144.140 - 144.150	CW FAI working
144.150						
					144.150 - 144.160	SSB FAI working
					144.175	Microwave talk-back calling frequency (UK)
SSB and CW only					144.195 - 144.205	SSB random MS
					144.250	GB2RS and slow morse transmissions
					144.260	Emerg. comms priority
					144.300	SSB calling frequency
					144.395 - 144.405	SSB random MS
144.500						
					144.500	SSTV calling frequency
					144.5125 - 144.6875	Note 3
					144.600	RTTY calling frequency
All modes non-channel-ised					144.600 ±	RTTY working (fsk)
					144.625	Packet radio (TCP/IP)
					144.650	Packet radio mailboxes
					144.675	Packet radio
					144.700	Fax calling frequency
					144.750	FSTV calling+talk-back
					144.775 - 144.825	Emergency comms priority
144.845						
Beacons					144.845 - 144.990	Beacons
					144.850	Note 2
145.000		✓	✓		145.000 R0	
					145.025 R1	
					145.050 R2	
FM Repeater Inputs					145.075 R3	
					145.100 R4	
					145.125 R5	
					145.150 R6	
					145.175 R7	
145.200						
					145.200 S8	Emergency comms priority
					145.225 S9	Emergency comms priority
					145.250 S10	Used for slow morse transmissions
					145.275 S11	
					145.300 S12	RTTY afsk
					145.325 S13	
					145.350 S14	
FM Simplex Channels					145.375 S15	
					145.400 S16	
					145.425 S17	
					145.450 S18	
					145.475 S19	
					145.500 S20	FM calling channel
					145.525 S21	Used for GB2RS
					145.550 S22	Recommended channel for rally & exhibition talk-in
					145.575 S23	
145.600						
					145.600 R0	
					145.625 R1	
FM Repeater Outputs					145.650 R2	
					145.675 R3	
					145.700 R4	
					145.725 R5	
					145.750 R6	
					145.775 R7	
145.800						
Satellites						
146.000						

430 MHz (70 cm)

LICENCE NOTES:

Amateur Service: Secondary

Satellite Service: 435-438 MHz, Secondary

Exclusion: 431 - 432 not available for use within 100 km radius of Charing Cross, London. (51° 30' 30"N, 00° 7' 24"W)

Power limit: 430 - 432 MHz: 16 dBW ERP PEP, 432 - 440 MHz: 26 dBW

Permitted modes: Morse, telephony, RTTY, data, fax, SSTV, FSTV

IARU	UK Usage
430.000 All modes Note 1	430.400 - 430.600 Packet radio 430.600 - 430.800 Note 5 430.625 - 430.775 Packet radio (25 kHz channels)
430.800 Low power repeater i/p Note 1	430.825 R61 430.850 R62 430.875 R63 430.900 R64 430.925 R65 430.950 R66 430.975 R67
431.000 All modes Note 1	Licence note exclusion
432.000 CW only	432.000 - 432.025 Moonbounce 432.050 CW centre of activity
432.150 SSB and CW only	432.200 SSB centre of activity 432.350 Microwave talk-back calling frequency (Europe)
432.500 All modes non-chanelised	432.500 - 432.600 IARU Region 1 linear transponder outputs 432.600 - 432.800 IARU Region 1 linear transponder inputs 432.500 SSTV activity centre 432.600 RTTY (fsk) activity centre 432.625 Packet radio 432.650 Packet radio 432.675 Packet radio 432.700 Fax activity centre
432.800 Beacons	432.800 - 432.990 Beacons
433.000 FM repeater outputs in UK only Note 1	433.000 RB0 433.025 RB1 433.050 RB2 433.075 RB3 433.100 RB4 433.125 RB5 433.150 RB6 433.175 RB7 433.200 RB8 433.225 RB9 433.250 RB10 433.275 RB11 433.300 RB12 433.325 RB13 433.350 RB14 433.375 RB15
433.400	*Continued on next column*

IARU	UK Usage
433.400 FM simplex channels	433.400 SU16 433.425 SU17 433.450 SU18 433.475 SU19 433.500 SU20 FM calling channel 433.525 SU21 433.550 SU22 Recommended channel for rally and exhibition talk-in 433.575 SU23 433.600 SU24 RTTY afsk 433.625 Packet radio 433.650 Packet radio 433.675 Packet radio 433.700 Notes 2, 3 and 5 433.725 Notes 2 and 5 433.750 Notes 2 and 5 433.775 Notes 2 and 5
434.600 FM repeater inputs (in UK only) - note 1; and fast scan television - note 4	434.600 RB0 434.625 RB1 434.650 RB2 434.675 RB3 434.700 RB4 434.725 RB5 434.750 RB6 434.775 RB7 434.800 RB8 434.825 RB9 434.850 RB10 434.875 RB11 434.900 RB12 434.925 RB13 434.950 RB14 434.975 RB15
435.000 Satellites and fast scan TV - note 4	
438.000 Fast scan TV	438.025 - 438.175 Note 5 438.200 - 439.425 Note 1
438.425 Low power repeater o/p + fast scan TV	438.425 R61 438.450 R62 438.475 R63 438.500 R64 438.525 R65 438.550 R66 438.575 R67
438.575 Fast Scan TV	438.200 - 439.425 Note 1
439.750 Packet radio	439.775 - 439.975 Packet radio (25 kHz channels)
440.000	

430 MHz Band Plan notes:

1. In Switzerland, Germany and Austria, repeater inputs are 430.600 - 431.825 MHz with 25 kHz spacing, and outputs are 438.200 - 439.425 MHz. In France and the Netherlands repeater inputs are 430.025 - 430.375 MHz with 25 kHz spacing and outputs at 431.625 - 431.975 MHz. In other European countries repeater inputs are 433.000 - 433.375 MHz with 25 kHz spacing and outputs at 434.600 - 434.975 MHz ie the reverse of the UK allocation.
2. Emergency communications priority.
3. IARU Region 1 fax / afsk.
4. Fast Scan Television carrier frequencies shall be chosen so as to avoid interference to other users, in particular the satellite service and repeater inputs. IARU Region 1 recommends that video carriers should be in the range 434.000 - 434.500 MHz or 438.500 - 440.000 MHz.
5. IARU Region 1 packet radio.

1.3 GHz (23 cm)

LICENCE NOTES:

Amateur Service:	Secondary
Satellite Service:	1260 - 1270, Secondary *Earth to space only*
	1296 - 1297, Secondary *Earth to space only*
Power limit:	26 dBW PEP
Permitted modes:	Morse, telephony, RTTY, data, fax, SSTV, FSTV
Unattended operation:	Not permitted in Northern Ireland

IARU	Novice	U/A Rem Ctrl	U/A Digital	U/A Beacon	UK Usage	
,240.000						
All modes					1240.150	Packet radio (150 kHz b/w)
					1240.300	Packet radio (150 kHz b/w)
					1240.450	Packet radio (150 kHz b/w)
					1240.600	Packet radio (150 kHz b/w)
					1240.750	Packet radio (150 kHz b/w)
,243.250						
ATV					1248.000	RT1-3 FM TV input
					1249.000	RT1-2 FM TV input
,260.000						
Satellites						
,270.000						
All modes						
,272.000						
ATV					1276.500	RT1-1 AM TV input
,291.000	✓					
Repeater inputs					1291.000	RM0
						(UK) 25 kHz spacing
					1291.375	RM15
,291.500						
All modes						
,296.000						
CW only					1296.000 - 1296.025	Moonbounce
,296.150						
SSB and CW					1296.200	Narrow band centre of activity
					1296.400 - 1296.600	Linear transponder input
					1296.500	SSTV
					1296.600	RTTY
					1296.700	Fax
					1296.600 - 1296.800	Linear transponder output
,296.800						
Beacons exclusive					1296.800 - 1296.990	Beacons
,297.000						
Repeater outputs - note 1					1297.000	RM0
						(UK) 25 kHz spacing
					1297.375	RM15
,297.500						
FM simplex - note 1					1297.500	SM20
					1297.750	SM30
,298.000						
All modes		✓	✓		*Digital communications*	
,298.500						

IARU	Novice	U/A Rem Ctrl	U/A Digital	U/A Beacon	UK Usage	
1,298.500	✓	✓		✓	1299.000	Remote control
					1299.000	Packet radio (25 kHz b/w)
					1299.425	Packet radio (150 kHz b/w)
			✓		1299.575	Packet radio (150 kHz b/w)
					1299.725	Packet radio (150 kHz b/w)
1,300.000						
TV repeater oututs					1308.000	RT1-3 FM TV output
					1311.500	RT1-1 AM TV output
					1316.000	RT1-2 FM TV output
1,325.000						

1.3 GHz Band Plan notes:

1. Local traffic using narrow-band modes should operate between 1296.500 - 1296.800 MHz during contests and band openings.
2. Stations in countries which do not have access to 1298 - 1300 MHz (eg Italy) may also use the FM simplex segment for digital communications.

2.3 GHz (13 cm)

LICENCE NOTES:

Amateur Service:	Secondary. *Users must accept interference from ISM users*
Satellite Service:	2400 - 2450, Secondary. *Users must accept interference from ISM users.*
Power limit:	26 dBW PEP
Permitted modes:	Morse, telephony, RTTY, data, fax, SSTV, FSTV

ISM = Industrial Scientific and Medical

IARU	Novice	U/A Rem Ctrl	U/A Digital	U/A Beacon	UK Usage	
2,310.000						
Sub-regional (national band plans)					2310.000 - 2310.500	Repeater links
					2310.100	Packet radio (200 kHz b/w)
					2310.300	Packet radio (200 kHz b/w)
2,320.000					2310.000 - 2310.500	Remote control
CW exclusive					2320.000 - 2320.025	Moonbounce
2,320.150						
CW and SSB					2320.200	SSB centre of activity
2,320.800		✓	✓	✓		
Beacons exclusive					2320.800 - 2320.990	Beacons
2,321.000						
Simplex & repeaters (FM) - note 1						
2,322.000					2322.000 - 2355.000	ATV
All modes					2355.100 - 2364.000	Repeater links
					2355.100	Packet radio (200 kHz b/w)
					2355.300	Packet radio (200 kHz b/w)
					2364.000	Packet radio (1 MHz b/w)
					2365.000 - 2370.000	Repeaters
					2370.000 - 2390.000	ATV
					2390.000 - 2392.000	Moonbounce
2,400.000						
Satellites						
2,450.000						

Notes continued on next column

2.3 GHz Band Plan notes:

1. Stations in countries which do not have access to the All Modes section (2,322 - 2,390 MHz), use the simplex and repeater segment 2,321 - 2,322 MHz for data transmission
2. Stations in countries which do not have access to the narrow band segment 2,320 - 2,322 MHz, use alternative narrow band segments: 2,304 - 2,306 MHz and 2,308 - 2,310 MHz.

3.4 GHz (9 cm)

LICENCE NOTES:

Amateur Service:	Secondary
Satellite Service:	No allocation
Power limit:	26 dBW PEP
Permitted modes:	Morse, telephony, RTTY, data, fax, SSTV, FSTV

5.7 GHz (6 cm)

LICENCE NOTES:

Amateur Service :	5,650 - 5,680, Secondary; 5,755 - 5,765 + 5820 - 5850: Secondary. Users must accept *interference from ISM users*
Satellite Service:	5,650 - 5,670 Secondary *Earth to Space only;* 5,830 - 5,850 Secondary *Users must accept interference from ISM users Space to Earth only*
Power limit:	26 dBW PEP
Permitted modes:	Morse, telephony, RTTY, data, fax, SSTV, FSTV

ISM = Industrial, Scientific & Medical

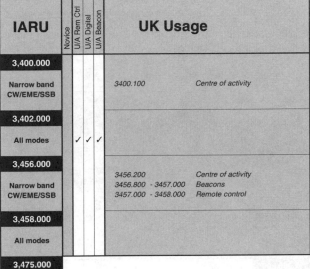

3.4 GHz band plan

IARU	Novice	U/A Rem Ctrl	U/A Digital	U/A Beacon	UK Usage	
3,400.000						
Narrow band CW/EME/SSB					3400.100	Centre of activity
3,402.000						
All modes	✓	✓	✓			
3,456.000						
Narrow band CW/EME/SSB					3456.200	Centre of activity
					3456.800 - 3457.000	Beacons
					3457.000 - 3458.000	Remote control
3,458.000						
All modes						
3,475.000						

5.7 GHz band plan

IARU	Novice	U/A Rem Ctrl	U/A Digital	U/A Beacon	UK Usage	
5,650.000						
Satellite uplinks						
5,668.000		✓	✓	✓	5668.200	Centre of activity
Narrow band and satellite					5668.800 - 5669.000	Beacons
5,670.000						
All modes						
5,680.000						
5,755.000						
All modes						
5,760.000						
UK Alternate narrow band CW/EME/SSB		✓	✓	✓	5760.200	Centre of activity (UK)
					5760.800 - 5761.000	Beacons
5,762.000						
All modes						
5,765.000						
5,820.000						
All modes						
5,830.000		✓	✓	✓		
Satellite downlinks						
5,850.000						

Unattended (U/A) Operation

Frequencies on which unattended (U/A) operation is permitted by full licensees are shown in these band plans. Novice licensees can also operate their stations unattended but the frequencies and powers are different – please see the Novice licence for the details. Remember that unattended operation requires the prior consent of the local Radio Investigation Service before operation can begin, to enable close down arrangements to be made.

Unattended beacons are limited to 14dBW ERP max. Do not confuse this type of unattended beacon operation with the normal beacon sections of the bands (these are fully site cleared, have special licences and are co-ordinated on an international basis.

Unattended low power remote control is limited to -20 dBW ERP and should not radiate outside the boundary of the premises from which you are operating.

Unattended digital operation is limited to 10 dBW on the 50 MHz band and 14 dBW on the other bands where it is permitted.

Changes in UK microwave band alloactions may take place during 1996 which could affect these band plans.

10 GHz (3 cm)

LICENCE NOTES:

Amateur Service:	Secondary
Satellite Service:	10,450 - 10,500: Secondary
Power limit:	26 dBW PEP
Permitted modes:	Morse, telephony, RTTY, data, fax, SSTV, FSTV

IARU	Novice	U/A Rem Ctrl	U/A Digital	U/A Beacon	UK Usage	
10,000.000						
All modes (ATV, data FM simplex, duplex and repeaters)		✓	✓	✓	10,006 - 10,026	Packet radio and repeater links / control
					10,040	RT10-1 FM TV output
					10,065	RT10-2 FM TV output
					10,090 - 10,110	Wideband beacons
					10,150	RT10-3 FM TV output
					10,200	RT10-1 FM TV input
					10,225	RT10-2 FM TV input
		✓	✓	✓	[10,270 - 10,300 unattended operation]	
					10,278	RT10-3 FM TV input
10,368.000						
Preferred narrow band CW/EME/SSB Beacons					10,368.1	Centre of activity (UK)
					10,368.2	SSB centre of activity
					10,368.8 - 10,369.0	Narrow band beacons
10,370.000	✓					
All modes					10,390 - 10,410	Wide band beacons
					[10,400 - 10,500 unattended operation]	
10,450.000		✓	✓	✓		
All modes + satellites					10,450 - 10,452	Alternative narrow band CW/EME/SSB - note 1
10,500.000						

10 GHz Band Plan notes:

1. Stations in countries who do not have access to the narrow-band segment 10.368 - 10.370 GHz, may use 10.450 - 10.452 GHz instead.

24 GHz (12 mm)

LICENCE NOTES:

Amateur Service:	24,000 - 24,050 Primary. *Users must accept interference from ISM users*; 24,050 - 24,150 Secondary, *May only be used with the written consent of the Secretary of State. Users must accept intereference from ISM users*; 24,150 - 24,250 Secondary. *Users must accept interference from ISM users.*
Satellite Service:	24,000 - 24,050 Primary. *Users must accept interference from ISM users*
Power limit:	26 dBW PEP
Permitted modes:	Morse, telephony, RTTY, data, fax, SSTV, FSTV

ISM = Industrial, Scientific & Medical

IARU	Novice	U/A Rem Ctrl	U/A Digital	U/A Beacon	UK Usage	
24,000.000						
Satellites		✓	✓	✓	24,025	Preferred operating frequency wide band equipment
					24,048 - 24,050	Preferred narrow band operating
24,050.000						
All modes					24,192 - 24,194	Narrow band op (UK)
24,250.000						

47 GHz (6 mm)

LICENCE NOTES:

Amateur Service:	Primary
Satellite Service:	Primary
Power limit:	26 dBW PEP
Permitted modes:	Morse, telephony, RTTY, data, fax, SSTV, FSTV

IARU	Novice	U/A Rem Ctrl	U/A Digital	U/A Beacon	UK Usage	
47,000.000						
		✓	✓	✓	47,088	Centre of narrow band activity
47,200.000						

Other amateur bands allocated in the UK are: 75.5 - 76.0, 142.0 - 144.0, 248.0 - 250.0 GHz.

10 Beacons

BEACONS are intended mainly as propagation indicators although, especially on the microwave bands, they may also serve as signal sources for alignment purposes. The table lists a selection, some of which may be heard regularly in the UK so that variation in strength gives an indication of conditions; others may be heard occasionally and the appearance of one can indicate exceptional propagation. For example, the 144MHz beacon GB3VHF can always be heard over much of the UK so, if its strength is above average, then there is a 'lift' on. If the 50MHz beacon in Namibia, not usually audible in the UK, appears then there is a path to Southern Africa. Conversely, the 28MHz beacon GB3RAL is of little interest to UK stations but can indicate to overseas operators the presence of propagation to the British Isles.

Some 20 years ago, in order to avoid interference between 144MHz beacons in Europe, the RSGB was asked by the International Amateur Radio Union (IARU) to co-ordinate their frequencies. The Society has done so since and has extended the service to other bands above 30MHz.

On HF, beacons are co-ordinated by IARU. The band 28.190–28.199MHz is used for regional networks and certain other beacons may operate between 28.201 and 28.225MHz. Note that not all transmitters have yet been modified and some beacons may still be heard up to 28.3MHz. At the time of going to press (1995) the RSGB beacon co-ordinators are: Martin Harrison, G3USF, for HF RSGB/IARU beacons, John Wilson, G3UUT, for 50, 70, 144, 432MHz RSGB/IARU and Graham Murchie, G4FSG, for RSGB microwave ones.

Freq (MHz)	Callsign	Nearest town	Locator	ASL (m)	Antenna	Beam direction	ERP (W)	Info from	Notes
1.817	ZS1J	Plettenberg Bay	KF15PF	1	λ/2 dipole	90°/270°		ZS1J	
1.840	OK0EM	Kromeriz	JN89		LW		5	OK1ADM	
3.558	DK0WCY [3]	Scheggerott	JO44VQ		Dipole		25	DL1FL	Solar info CW
3.600	OK0EN	Kam. Zehrovice	JO70		Dipole	90°/270°	0	OK1ADM	
3.699	VK2RCW	Turramurra	QF56					WIA	
3.821	GAM1/80	Chelmsford			Dipole		1000	G4FZH	Prop info CW
5.470	LN2A [2]	Sveio	JO29PO		Vertical	Omni	550	LA9AHA	
7.870	LN2A [2]	Sveio	JO29PO		Vertical	Omni	700	LA9AHA	
10.144	DK0WCY [3]	Scheggerott	JO44VQ		Horizontal loop	0°/180°	30	DL1FL	Solar info CW
10.407	LN2A	Sveio	JO29PO		Vertical monopole	Omni			
14.100	JA2IGY	Mt Asama	PM84JK		Vertical	Omni			T + 3min
14.100	KH6O	Honolulu	BL11BK		Vertical	Omni			
14.100	LU4AA	Buenos Aires	GF05		Vertical	Omni			
14.100	OH2B	Espoo	KP20KE		X Loops	Omni			
14.100	W6WX	Nr San Jose, CA	CM87		Turnstile	Omni			
14.100	4U1UN	UN, NY	FN20AS		Vertical	Omni		W6ISQ	T + 0min
14.100	4X6TU	Tel Aviv	KM72JC	20	Vertical	Omni		4X6KJ	T + 4min
14.100	CT3B	Funchal	JM82LS		Vertical	Omni		W6ISQ	T + 6min
14.100	JA2IGY	Mt Asama	PM84JK	540	Vertical	Omni		W6ISQ	T + 3min
14.100	KH6O/B	Honolulu, Hawaii	BL11BK	8	Vertical	Omni		W6ISQ	T + 2min
14.100	LU4AA	Buenos Aires	GF05		Vertical	Omni		W6ISQ	T + 8min
14.100	OH2B	Espoo	KP20KE		X loops	Omni		OH6DD	T + 5min
14.100	W6WX/B	San Jose, CA, USA	CM87	98	Turnstile	Omni		W6ISQ	T + 1min
14.405	LN2A [2]	Sveio	JO29PO		Vertical	Omni	750	LA9AHA	
18.068	IK6BAK	Montefelcino	JN63KR		2 × dipole	Omni	12	IK1PCB	
18.101	VE3RAT	Thornhill, ONT	FN03HO				1		
18.102	IK1PCB	Bordighera	JN33UT		5λ/8 Vertical	Omni	10	IK1PCB	
18.110	DL0AGS	Kassel	JO41NL		Ground plane	Omni	5	DL1VDL	
20.947	LN2A [2]	Sveio	JO29PO		Vertical	Omni	550	LA9AHA	
21.150	W6WX	San Jose, CA, USA	CM87	98	Turnstile	Omni		W6ISQ	2min cycle
21.151	I1M	Bordighera	JN33UT		2 × 5λ/8 vertical	Omni	10		
24.901	PY2AMI	Sao Paulo	GG67IG		Ground plane	Omni	15		Irregular
24.915	IK6BAK	Montefelcino	JN63KR		2 × dipole	Omni	12	IK1PCB	
24.930	DK0HHH	Hamburg	JO53AM		Dipole	Omni	10		
24.932	PY2AMI	Americana	GG67IF			Omni	15		Irregular
28.175	VE3TEN	Ottawa	FN25		Ground plane	Omni	10		
28.180	IK1PCB	Bordighera	JN33UT		5λ/8 vertical	Omni	20	IK1PCB	
28.183	SV3AQR	Amalias	KN06		Ground plane	Omni	4		Irregular
28.186	ZS6PW	Pretoria	KG44DE		3-el Yagi	337°	15	ZS6PW	
28.195	IY4M	Bologna	JN54QK		5λ/8 vertical	Omni	20	IK1PCB	
28.195	VE6YF	Edmonton	DO25		Ground plane	Omni	10	VE6YF	
28.200	5B4CY	Zyghi, Cyprus	KM64PR	20	Ground plane	Omni	26	5B4AZ	
28.200	W6WX	San Jose, CA, USA	CM87	98	Turnstile	Omni		W6ISQ	2min cycle
28.202	ZS1J	18k E Knysna	KF15PF	10	3-el	0°	4	ZS1J	0630-2000
28.205	DL0IGI	Mt Predigtstuhl	JN67KQ	1650	λ/2 Vertical	Omni	100	DL1VDL	
28.205	WA4SZE/4	Pembroke Pines							

Freq (MHz)	Callsign	Nearest town	Locator	ASL (m)	Antenna	Beam direction	ERP (W)	Info from	Notes
28.207	KE4NL	Ninety Six, SC					10	KC4DPC	Irregular
28.207	KJ4X	Pickens, SC	EM84		Vertical	Omni	2	KC4DPC	
28.208	W8FKL/4	Venice, FL	EL47EI		Vertical	Omni	10		Irregular
28.209	NX2O	Staten Is, NY	FN30		Ground plane	Omni	10		
28.210	KC4DPC	Winnabow, NC	FM14BF		Dipole		4		
28.213	PT7BCN	Fortaleza	HI06RF		Ground plane	Omni	5	PY2BBL	Irregular
28.215	GB3RAL	nr Didcot	IO91IN		λ/4 ground plane	Omni	25		
28.215	KA9SZX	Champagne, IL	EN50VD		CX-1000	Omni	0		
28.218	VE2TWO	Radisson	FO13					VE2TWO	
28.218	W8UR	Mackinaw C, MI	EN75		Vertical	Omni	1		
28.219	PT8AA	Rio Branco	FI60CA		Ground plane	Omni	5		Irregular
28.219	WB9VMY	Calumet OK	EM05						Irregular
28.220	KB9DJA	Mooresville, IN	EM69RO		Ground plane	Omni	35		
28.220	LU4XS	Tierra del Fuego	FD65PA						Irregular
28.222	W9UXO	Lake Bluff, IL	EN62BG		Ground plane	Omni	10		
28.223	HG5GEW	Tapolca	JN86NQ	110	Ground plane	Omni	10		
28.223	K5MW	Austin, TX	EM10DH				1		
28.225	KW7Y	Camano Is, WA	CN88SD		Vertical	Omni	4		
28.230	ZL1MHF	Mt Climie	RE78BU		Vertical dipole	Omni	1	ZL1BAD	
28.233	KD4EC	Jupiter, FL	EL		Vertical	Omni	7	KC4DPC	
28.233	W7JPI	Sonoita, AZ	DM41QP		3-el Yagi	45°	5		
28.235	KQ4TG	Leland, NC			Vee		1		
28.237	LA5TEN	Oslo	JO59JV	166	5λ/8 vertical	Omni	10	OH6DD	
28.237	NV6A	San Diego, CA	DM12		Yagi		1		
28.239	YO2X	Timisoara	KN05OS		Dipole		2	YO2IS	Irregular
28.241	AB8Z	Parma, OH	EN91DJ						
28.245	WA6APQ	Long Beach, CA	DM13		Vertical	Omni	30		
28.248	K8NHE	Mackinaw C. IN	EN75		Vertical	Omni	0		
28.250	EA3JA	Barcelona	JN1181						Irregular
28.250	K0HTF	Des Moines IA	EN31EN		Ground plane	Omni	10		
28.250	PI7BQC	Haarlem	JO22HK				2	PI7BQC	
28.250	WA4SLT	Hastings, FL			Vertical	Omni	20		
28.250	Z21ANB	Bulawayo	KG47		Vertical	Omni	25		
28.251	WJ9Z	Milwaukee, WI	EN63AD						
28.252	OH2TEN	Lohja	KP20AG	10	5/8λ ground plane	Omni	50	OH6DD	
28.252	WJ7X	Prior Lake, MN	EN34			Omni	5		
28.255	VK3SIX	Wannon Falls	QF02WH		Ground plane 5-el	Omni	10	WIA	
28.257	DK0TEN	Konstanz	JN57NP	440	Ground plane	Omni	40	DL1VDL	
28.257	KM4Y	Hollywood, FL	EL95						
28.259	KA1NSV	Hyannis, MA	FN41						
28.260	VK5WI	Adelaide	PF95UP		Ground plane	Omni	10	WIA	
28.262	VK2RSY	Dural nr Sydney	QF46LH	240	λ/2 vertical	Omni	25	WIA	
28.264	VK6RWA	Perth, WA	QF78WB	300				WIA	
28.265	LU1FHH	Sante Fe	FF98						
28.267	OH9TEN	Pirttikoski	KP36OI		λ/2 ground plane	Omni	20	OH6DD	
28.269	VK8VF	Darwin	PH57KP					WIA	
28.269	WB4JHS	Kissimmee, FL	EL96		Vertical	Omni	5		Irregular
28.270	KF4MS	St Petersburg, FL	EL87PS		Ground plane	Omni	5		
28.270	VK4RTL	Townsville	QH30JS					WIA	Irregular
28.275	DA2JH	Luedenscheid	JO31TF				20	DL1VDL	Irregular
28.275	ZS1LA	Still Bay	KF05QK	15	3-el Yagi	315°	20	Z86PW	
28.276	N0JAR	Newton, IA	EN31LP				5		
28.276	NS8V	Grand Rapids, MI	EN73EW		Vertical	Omni	5	WS8V	
28.278	DF0AAB	Kiel	JO54GH	163	Ground plane	Omni	10	DL1VDL	
28.279	KG5YB	Tyler, TX	EM22						
28.282	LU2HDX	Villa Carlos	FF78RO		Vertical	Omni	10		Irregular
28.282	OK0EG	Hradec Kralove	JO70		Dipole		10	OK1ADM	Irregular
28.282	VE2HOT	Montreal	FN35BJ		Vertical dipole	Omni	5		
28.285	KB7DQJ	Port Orchard, WA							
28.285	KB7EFZ	Portland, OR	CN85		5λ/8 ground plane	Omni	1	KB7EFZ	0, 15, 30, 45m
28.285	N2JNT	Troy, NY	FN32DR		Ground plane	Omni	1		
28.286	N5AQM	Chandler, AZ	DM43AH		Vertical	Omni	2		
28.290	SK5TEN	Straengnaes	JO89KK		Ground plane	Omni	75	OH6DD	
28.291	KB9NV	Collinsville, IL							
28.291	WB4WOR	Sophia, NC	FM06BB						
28.292	LU2FFV	San Jorge			Ground plane	Omni			Irregular
28.292	W3RGQ	Berwick, PA	FN11UB		Vertical	Omni	5		Irregular
28.293	WC8E	Deer Park, OK	EM79SD		Ringo	Omni	10		
28.294	KE0UL	Greeley, CO	DN70		Vertical	Omni	5		
28.295	W3VD	Laurel, MD	FM19NE	130	Vertical dipole	Omni	10		
28.302	PI7ETE	Amersfoort	JO22QD		Vertical	Omni	1	PA0VDV	Irregular
50.000	GB3BUX	Buxton, Derbys	IO93BF	457	Turnstile	Omni	20	G3RKL	
50.003	7Q7SIX	Malawi	KH74						
50.014	S55ZRS	Liubljana	JN76MC	1219	Ground plane	Omni	8	S57C	
50.015	SZ2DH	Athens	KM27		4-el Yagi		5		
50.018	V51VHF	Namibia	JG87		Ground plane	Omni	50		
50.020	GB3SIX	Anglesey	IO73TJ	58	3-el Yagi	275°	100	G3UUT	
50.021	OZ7IGY	Tollose	JO55VO	92	Turnstile	Omni	20	OZ7IS	
50.022	FR5SIX	Reunion Is	LG78	2970	Halo	Omni	2	FR5EL	
50.022	ZS6PW	Meyers Park	KG44DG		5-el Yagi	337°	30		0700-2100z
50.023	LX0SIX	Bourscheid	JN39AV	500	Horizontal dipole	0°/180°	5	LX1JX	

Freq (MHz)	Callsign	Nearest town	Locator	ASL (m)	Antenna	Beam direction	ERP (W)	Info from	Notes
50.023	SR5SIX	Wesola	KO02OF	130	Ground plane	Omni	3	SP5TAT	
50.025	9H1SIX	Malta	JM75FV	75	Ground plane	Omni	7	9H1ES	
50.025	OH1SIX	Ikaalinen	KP11QU	157	4 × turnstile	Omni	40		
50.025	YV4AB	Valensia	FK50		Ringo	Omni			
50.028	SR6SIX	Poland	JO81HH					SP6GZZ	
50.030	CT0WW	Portugal	IN61GE	400	Horiz dipole	45°/225°	40	CT1WW	
50.032	ZD8VHF	Ascension Is	II22TB	723	5λ/8 vertical	Omni	50		
50.035	ZB2VHF	Gibraltar	IM76HE		5-el Yagi	Varies	100	ZB2BL	
50.037	ES0SIX	Muhu Is	KO18PO	30	Horiz dipole	90°/275°	15	ES0CB	
50.039	FY7THF	Kourou	GJ35		Ground plane	Omni	100		
50.040	SV1SIX	Athens	KM17UX	130	Vertical dipole	Omni	30		
50.040	VO1ZA	St Johns	GN37		λ/4 vertical	Omni	10		
50.042	GB3MCB	St Austell	IO70OJ	320	Dipole	90°/275°	40	G3YJX	
50.045	OX3VHF	Julianhaab	GP60XR	15	Ground plane	Omni	20	OX3JUL	
50.047	JW7SIX	Svalbard	JQ88AD		4-el Yagi	190°/340°	40	LA0BY	
50.050	GB3NHQ	Potters Bar	IO91VQ	35	Turnstile	Omni	15	G3UUT	
50.050	ZS6DN/B	Pretoria	KG44DE		5-el Yagi	135°	100	ZS6DN	
50.051	LA7SIX	Tromso	JP99LO	30	4-el Yagi	190°	25	LA0BY	
50.052	Z21SIX	Zimbabwe	KH52NK				3		
50.054	OZ6SIX	Oestervraa	JO57EI		Turnstile	Omni	50	OZ1IPU	
50.055	V44K	St Kitts/Nevis	FK87QH		5λ/8 vertical	Omni	3.5		
50.057	TF3SIX	Iceland	HP94CC		5λ/8 vertical	Omni	50	TF3EJ	
50.060	GB3RMK	nr Inverness	IO77UO	270	Dipole	0°/180°	10	GM3WOJ	
50.062	GB3NGI	Garvagh	IO65PA	240	Dipole	140°/320°	15	GI6ATZ	
50.064	GB3LER	Lerwick	IP90JD	104	Dipole	0°/180°	30	GM4IPK	
50.065	GB3IOJ	St Helier	IN89WE	115	Vertical	Omni	10	GJ4ICD	
50.067	OH9SIX	Pirttikoski	KP36OI	192	2 × turnstile	Omni	35	OH6DD	
50.070	EA3VHF	Barcelona	JN01	235	3-el Yagi	315°	0.5	EA3DBQ	
50.070	SK3SIX	Bollnaes	JP71XF	500	X dipole	Omni	10	SM3JGG	
50.070	W2CAP/1	Cape Code, MA	FN41		Vertical dipole	Omni	15		
50.073	ES6SIX	Voeru	KO37MT	85	Ground plane	Omni	20	ES5MC	
50.075	EA8SIX		IL28GC			Omni	10	EA3DBQ	
50.079	JX7DFA	Jan Mayen Island	IQ60		3-el Yagi		40	LA7DFA	Irregular
50.080	SK6SIX	Hoenoe	JO57TQ	35	Vertical dipole	Omni	10/1		
50.087	YU1SIX		KN03KN		Dipole		15		
50.091	9L1US	Sierre Leone	IJ38		Vertical	Omni	14	WA8JOC	
50.315	FX4SIX	Neuville	JN06CQ	153	Turnstile	Omni	25	F5GTW	
50.321	ZS5SIX	South Africa	KG50		Halo	Omni	10		
50.500	5B4CY	Zyghi, Cyprus	KM64PR	30	Ground plane	Omni	20	5B4BBC	
50.904	ZS1STB	South Africa	KF05		5λ/8 vertical	Omni			
70.000	GB3BUX	Buxton, Derbys	IO93BF	456	2 × turnstile	Omni	20	G3RKL	
70.010	GB3REB	Chatham	JO01GK	65	2-el Yagi	270°	28	G3ZYV	
70.020	GB3ANG	Dundee	IO86MN	370	3-el Yagi	160°	100		
70.025	GB3MCB	St Austell	IO70OJ	320	2-el Yagi	45°	40	G3YJX	
70.030	G Personal Beacons								
70.114	5B4CY	Zyghi, Cyprus	KM64PR	30	4-el Yagi	315°	15	5B4BBC	
70.120	ZB2VHF	Gibraltar	IM76HE		4-el quad	0°	50		
70.130	EI4RF	Slane	IO63SN	120	2 × 5-el Yagi	45°/135°	25		
144.825	OY6VHF	Faroe Is	IP62OA	300	2 × 4-el	45°/135°	50	OY1A	
144.830	9H1A	Malta	JM75FV	160	Turnstile	Omni	1.5	9H1BT	
144.840	PI7PRO	Nieuwegein	JO22LN	10	Dipole	Omni	20		
144.846	DB0KI	Bayreuth	JO50WC	915	Vertical	Omni	5	DC9NL	
144.850	9A0BVH		JN85JO	489	Vertical dipole	Omni	1		
144.850	DL0UB	Trebbin	JO62QL	80	4 × dipole	Omni	5	DL7ACG	
144.850	HB9H	Locarno	JN46KE						
144.850	I5A	Lucca	JN53GW	1000	5-el Yagi	225°	6	IW5BSF	
144.852	OH2VHF	Nummi	KP10VJ	76	9-el Yagi	0°	150		
144.855	DB0FAI	Langerringen	JN58IC	590	16-el Yagi	305°	1000	DL4MEA	
144.855	LA5VHF	Bodo	JP77KI	260	2 × 6-el quad	15°/180°	100	LA1UG	
144.858	FX2VHF	Le Croquet	JO10EQ	98	Halo	Omni	7	F6BPB	
144.860	LA1VHF	Rjukan	JO49GT	1882	Turnstile	Omni	12	LA4PE	
144.865	HB9HB	Biel	JN37OE	1300	10-el Yagi	345°	120	HB9AMH	
144.865	LA6VHF	Kirkenes	KP59AL	70	14-el Yagi	210°	250	LA4OO	
144.865	SR5VHF	Wesola	KO02OF	130	Turnstile	Omni	0.75	SP5TAT	
144.868	EA1VHF	Curtis	IN53UG	100	5-el Yagi	45°	150	EA1RCA	
144.870	I2M	Cremona	JN55AD	46	Big wheel	Omni	10	IK2AWT	
144.870	LA2VHF	Melhus	JP53EG	710	10-el Yagi	15°	500	LA1K	
144.872	PI7ZWL	Zwolle	JO32BM	30		Omni	1.5	PA2SDL	
144.875	DB0GD	Rhoen	JO50AL	926	Dipole	Omni	1	DG6ZX	
144.875	IN3A	Trento	JN56NB		Ground plane	Omni		IN3IYD	
144.875	SK2VHF	Vindeln	JP94TF	300	2 × 10-el Yagi	0°/225°	100	SSA	
144.878	IV3A	Manzano UD	JN65QX		Ground plane	Omni	1		
144.880	LA3VHF	Mandal	JO38RA	30	16-el Yagi	180°	100	LA8AK	
144.885	OK0ED	Meririci	JN99BO	560	2 × dipole	Omni	0.06	OK2BJE	
144.890	I8A	Reggio C	JN78WD						
144.890	LA4VHF	Bergen	JP20LG	35	2 × 8-el Yagi	0°	380	LA6LU	
144.890	SK2VHG	Svappavara	KP07MV	380	16-el Yagi	180°	800	SK2CP	
144.892	LA7VHF	Tromso	JP99LO	30	10-el Yagi	190°	500	LA0BY	
144.895	IT9A	Alcamo TP	JM67LX	825	2 × big wheel	Omni	10	IT9QPF	
144.898	EA3VHF	Soria	JN11MV	155	Halo	Omni	1		Temp QRT
144.900	DB0ABG		JN59WI	522	Big wheel	Omni	4	DJ3TI	

Freq (MHz)	Callsign	Nearest town	Locator	ASL (m)	Antenna	Beam direction	ERP (W)	Info from	Notes
144.900	I6A	Ortona CH	JN72FH	150	2 × 5-el Yagi	340°/180°	24	IW6MME	
144.902	LX0VHF	Walferdange	JN39BP	420	Big wheel	Omni	10	LX1JX	
144.905	FX3THF	Lannion	IN88GS	145	9-el Yagi	90°	50	F6DBI	
144.908	EA8VHF	Canary Is	IL28GC			Omni	10		
144.910	DL0PR	Garding	JO44JH	100	4 × 6-el Yagi	0°/180°	1000	DK5LB	
144.910	IS0A	Olbia SS	JN40QW	350	Turnstile	Omni	3	IW0UGR	
144.915	DB0JW	Wurselen	JO30DU	225	10-el Yagi	22°	50	DL9KAS	
144.915	GB3MCB	St Austell	IO70OJ	320	3-el Yagi	45°	40	G3YJX	
144.918	EA6VHF	San Jose, Ibiza	JM08PV	150		Omni	20	EA6FB	
144.920	EI2WRB	Portlaw	IO62IG	248	5-el Yagi	95°	200		
144.920	SK7VHF	Falsterbo	JO65KJ	25	2 × cloverleaf	Omni	10		
144.925	GB3VHF	Wrotham, Kent	JO01DH	268	2 × 3-el Yagi	315°	40	G8JNZ	
144.925	I1AB	Bordighera IM	JN33UT	300	Big wheel	Omni	20	IK1PCB	
144.927	DB0JT	Oberndorf	JN67JT	785	8 × dipole	270°/337°	30	DJ8QP	
144.927	OK0EA	Nova Paka	JO70UP	1355	2 × dipole	Omni	0.002		
144.930	OZ7IGY	Tollose	JO55VO	96	Big wheel	Omni	25	OZ7IS	
144.932	Y41M	Leipzig	JO61FH	232	2 × dipole	Omni	0.2	Y21CM	
144.935	PI7CIS	Delft	JO22DC	40	Dipole	90°/275°	50	PA0CIS	
144.938	EA2VHF		IN91DJ			Omni	18		
144.939	TF8VHF	Iceland	HP84PA	100	6-el Yagi	100°	280		
144.940	DL0UH	Melsungen	JO41RD	385	Vertical dipole	Omni	1	DJ3KO	
144.940	SK3VHF	Ostersund	JP73HF	325	Horizontal Yagi	180°	1500	SM3MXR	MS beacon
144.945	OH9VHF	Prittikoski	KP36OI	310	10dBd gain	200°	200	OH6DD	
144.948	FX9VHB	Pic Neulos	JN12LL	1100	Halo	Omni	10	F6HTJ	
144.950	S55ZRS	Ljubljana	JN76MC	1219	Turnstile	Omni	1	S57C	
144.950	SK1VHF	Klintehamn	JO97CJ	55	2 × cloverleaf	Omni	20		
144.955	FX4VHF	Brive	JN05VE	600	Big wheel 6dB	Omni	25	F6IAL	
144.955	YO2X	Timisoara	KN05OS	80	Turnstile	Omni	1.5	YO2IS	
144.960	SK4MPI	Borlaenge	JP70NJ	520	4 × 6-el Yagi	315°/45°	1500	SM4GL	
144.963	OK0EB	Ujezd	JN78DU	1083	Big wheel	Omni	0.1		
144.965	DF0ANN	Altdorf	JN59PJ	630	Dipole	Omni	0.02	DL8ZX	
144.965	GB3LER	Lerwick	IP90JD	108	2 × 6-el Yagi	45°/135°	500	GM4IPK	
144.969	HG1BVA	Szentgotthord	JN86CW	370	Hybrid quad	80°	5	HA1YA	
144.975	GB3ANG	Dundee	IO86MN	370	4-el Yagi	160°	20		
144.975	Y41B	Schwerin	JO53QP	92	2 × big wheel	Omni	10	Y22GB	
144.978	OK0ET	Velkalda	KN08SU	990	HB9CV	275°	1	OK3AU	
144.980	OK0EC	Arzburg	JO60CF	790	3-el Yagi	90°	0.3	OK1AQF	
144.982	SK2VHH	Lycksele	JP94	300	Horizontal	22°	15kW		
144.984	ON4VHF	Louvain La Neuve	JO20FP	167	Big wheel	Omni	20	ON4ZN	
144.990	LZ2F	Tolbukhin	KN33WM	295		Omni	25		
432.805	DB0JZ	Detteln	JO31SN	125		Omni	1	DL4DBK	
432.815	DL0BQ	Pfungstadt	JN49GP		Discone	Omni	0.2	DF1ZY	
432.815	SK7UHI	Kristianstad	JO76	120	Horizontal	0°	30		
432.820	LA8UHF	Tonsberg	JO59DD	30	8-el Yagi	180°	50	LA6LCA	
432.825	OH2UHF	Nummi-Pusula	KP20VJ		2 × dipole	Omni	20	OH7TE	
432.830	FX1UHF	Preaux	JN18KF	166	4 × HB9CV	Omni	10	F6HZA	
432.830	LA7UHF	Bergen	JP20LG	35	13-el Yagi	0°	280	LA6LU	
432.835	ES0UHF	Hiiumaa Island	KO18CW	105	Horizontal	Omni	50	ES0NW	
432.840	OH6UHF	Uusikaarlepyy	KP13GM	55	3 × Big wheel	Omni	7	OH6UH	
432.841	DB0KI	Bayreuth	JO50WC	925	4 × 4-el Yagi	Omni	2		
432.845	LA9UHF	Geilo	JP40CM	1000	2 × 13-el Yagi	33°	250	LA3SP	
432.847	9A0BUH		JN85JO	489	Vertical dipole	Omni	1		
432.850	DL0UB	Pankow	JO62QL	80	4 × double quad	Omni	10	DL7ACG	
432.855	DB0AE	Bremerhaven	JO43GN	40	Big wheel	Omni	0.3	DC2BJ	
432.855	LA5UHF	Bodo	JP66WX	1110	10-el Yagi	15°	100	LA1UG	
432.855	SK3UHF	Raefsoen	JP92FW	200	4 × double quad	Omni	10	SM3AFT	
432.860	LA1UHF	Oslo	JO59IX	522	Mini wheel	Omni	10	LA4PE	
432.870	EI2WRB	Portlaw	IO62IJ	248	5-el Yagi	95°	250	EI9GO	
432.873	PI7HVN	Heerenveen	JO32	50	Horizontal	Omni	0.5		
432.875	OH7UHF	Kuopio	KP32TW	215	6dBd	225°	15		
432.875	SK2UHF	Vindeln	JP94WG	445	2 × 20-el coll	0°/225°	300	SK2AT	
432.880	HB9G	Geneva	JN36BK	1628	2 × turnstile	Omni	1		
432.880	LA3UHF	Mandal	JO38RA	12	15-el Yagi	180°	29	LA8AK	Temp QRT
432.885	OK0EP	Sumperk	JO80OB	1500	2 × 3-el Yagi	135°/275°	14	OK1VPZ	
432.885	OY6UHF	Faroe Is	IP62OA	300	7dB group	135°	50	OY1A	
432.886	FX4UHB	St Savin	JN06KN	144	Big wheel	Omni	50	F1EAN	
432.890	GB3SUT	Sutton Coldfield	IO92CO	270	2 × 8-el Yagi	0°/135°	10	G3VZZ	
432.890	LA4UHF	Haugesund	JO29PJ	75	10-el Yagi	200°	50	LA7GN	
432.895	OZ4UHF	Ronne	JO75KC	115	Clover leaf	Omni	30	OZ1HTB	
432.895	PI7YSS	Zutphen	JO32CD	45	Big wheel	Omni	4	PA0JAZ	
432.900	DB0YI	Hildesheim	JO42XC	480	Big wheel	Omni	4	DL4AS	
432.905	PI7QHN	Leiden	JO22KH	20	3dB gain	Omni	2	PA0QHN	
432.905	SK4UHF	Garphyttan	JO79LK	270	Horizontal	Omni	50		
432.908	EA8UHF	Canary Is	IL28GC			Omni	10		
432.910	GB3MLY	Emley Moor	IO93EO	600	8 over 8 Yagi	150°	50	G3PYB	
432.913	DB0AD	Kreuztal	JO30XS	290	2 × 11-el Yagi	22°/270°	20	DC9PX	
432.918	EA6UHF		JM08PV			Omni	10		
432.918	FX3UHB	Le Cronan	IN78VC	285	Big wheel	Omni	15	F1MZN	
432.920	SK7UHF	Taberg	JO77BQ	350	Big wheel	Omni	15	SM6DHW	
432.925	DB0JG	Bocholt	JO31GT	45	Clover leaf	Omni	1		
432.925	SK6UHF	Varberg	JO67EH	175	Clover leaf	Omni	10	SM6ESG	

Freq (MHz)	Callsign	Nearest town	Locator	ASL (m)	Antenna	Beam direction	ERP (W)	Info from	Notes
432.930	HG7BUA		JN97KR	690	Slot	Omni	0.1	HA1YA	
432.930	OZ7IGY	Tollose	JO55VO	93	9-el Yagi	Omni	300	OZ7IS	
432.934	GB3BSL	Bristol	IO81QJ	252	4 × 3-el Yagi	90°	250	GW8AWM	
432.938	OK0EA	Nova Paka	JO70UP	1350	2 × 15-el Yagi	135°/275°	80	OK1AIY	
432.940	DL0UH	Melsungen	JO41RD	385	Vertical dipole	Omni	0.3	DJ3KO	
432.940	SK7UHH	Faerjestaden	JO86GP	45	Horizontal	0°	300		
432.945	DB0LB	Ludwicksburg	JN48NV	367	Corner dipole	0°/180°	0.2	DK3PT	
432.945	DB0OS	Erndtebruck	JO40CW	745	2-el Yagi	275°	0.7	DG6YW	
432.945	OH9UHF	Prittikoski	KP36OI	307	9dBd gain	200°	70	OH6DD	
432.950	DB0IH	Oberthal	JN39ML	630	Big wheel	Omni	15	DC8DV	
432.950	S55ZRS	Ljubljana	JN76MC	1219	Slot dipole	Omni	1	S57C	
432.950	SK1UHF	Klintehamn	JO97CJ	55	2 × big wheel	Omni	20	SM1IUX	
432.955	OZ1UHF	Frederikshavn	JO57FJ	150	Big wheel	Omni	10	OZ9NT	
432.960	SK4UHJ	Saeter	JP70						
432.965	DF0ANN	Altdorf	JN59PJ	630	Clover leaf	Omni	1	DL8ZX	
432.965	OK0EO	Prerov	JN89QQ	610	Turnstile	Omni	0.05	OK2VLX	
432.965	GB3LER	Lerwick	IP90JD	104	12-el Yagi	165°	675	GM4IPK	
432.970	GB3MCB	St Austell	IO70OJ	320	4-el Yagi	45°	12	G3YJX	
432.970	OK0EB	Ujezd	JN78DU	1100	3 × dipole	Omni	0.05		
432.975	DB0JW	Aachen	JO30DU	225	2 × 11-el Yagi	45°	50	DL9KAS	
432.975	HG1BUA	Szombathely	JN87GG	370	Hybrid quad	90°	0.5	HA1YA	
432.975	SK5UHF	Bjoerklinge	JP80SA	90	Horizontal	0°/180°	80	SK0AY	
432.980	GB3ANG	Dundee	IO86MN	370	9-el Yagi	170°	100		
432.980	OK0EC	Cheb	JO60CF	790	10-el Yagi	90°	1		
432.980	S55ZCE	Celje	JN76OH	574	Ground plane	Omni	0.07	S57C	
432.982	OZ2ALS	Sonderborg	JO44WX	28	4 × dipole	Omni	40	OZ9DT	
432.982	SR5UHF	Wesola	KO02OF	130	Turnstile	Omni	0.25	SP5TAT	
432.984	HB9F	Interlaken	JN36XN	3573	Corner reflector	0°	15	HB9MHS	
432.990	DF0AAD	Eutin	JO54IF	250	4 × hybrid quad	Omni	10	DL8LAO	
432.990	ON4UHF	Brussels	JO20ET			Omni		ON4LC	
432.995	DB0VJ	Laufen	JN67LQ	1618	2 × double quad	315°	100	DL1XV	
1296.642	PI6ASD	Amsterdam	JO22KH	30		Omni	1	PA0AWP	Trnspnder
1296.739	FX6UHY	Strasbourg	JN38UO	144	Big wheel	Omni	4	F6BUF	
1296.800	DB0JS	Wassertrudingen	JN59GB	700	Slot	Omni	5	DL2QQ	
1296.800	SK6UHI	Hallandsaas	JO66LJ	230	Big wheel	Omni	10		
1296.805	DB0GP	Schwabischgmund	JN48WQ	760	4 × 5-el Yagi	Omni	4	DC1SO	
1296.810	GB3NWK	Orpington	JO01BI	180	15/15 slot Yagi	293°	50	G8BJG	
1296.812	FX6UHX	P. Ballon	JN37NX	1278	4-el Yagi	135°	1	F1AHO	
1296.815	DB0VI	Saarbrucken	JN39MF	400	13-el Yagi		1	DK1ME	
1296.815	SK7UHI	Kristianstad	JO76	120	Horizontal	0°	20		
1296.818	PI7DIJ	Drachten	JO33BC	15	5.5dB gain	Omni	4	PA3DIJ	
1296.820	DB0OT	Lathen	JO32QR	80	Big wheel	Omni	1	DL1BFZ	
1296.820	LA8UHG	Oslo	JO59JW	364	14-el Yagi	160°	10	LA4PE	
1296.825	DB0HF	Wandsbek	JO53BO	45	Big wheel	Omni		DK2NH	
1296.825	OE1XTB	Vienna	JN88EE	170		Omni	10	OE1MCU	
1296.830	GB3MHL	Martlesham	JO02PB	80	4 × 16 slot wg	90°/275°	700	G4DDK	
1296.835	DB0AJ	Dinslaken	JN57VX	620	12-el	0°	50	DK2RV	
1296.835	SK0UHG	Vaellingby	JO89WI	60	Horizontal	Omni	10		
1296.840	DB0KI	Bayreuth	JO50WC	925	4 × DQ 23	Omni	5	DC9NL	
1296.840	OH6SHF	Uusikaarlepyy	KP13GM	55	Dipole	Omni	8		
1296.847	FX1UHY	Faviers	JN18IR	160	Alford slot	Omni	30	F6ACA	
1296.850	DL0UB	Templehof	JO62QL	80	2 × helical	Omni	3	DL7ACG	
1296.850	GB3FRS	Farnborough	IO91PH	120	Disc	Omni	3	G8ATK	
1296.854	DB0JO	Witten	JO31SL	312	4 × 15-el Yagi	275°	350	DC6MR	
1296.855	OZ3UHF		JO56CE	150	5-el Yagi	180°	6	OZ1GMP	
1296.855	SK3UHG	Hudiksvall	JP81KQ	375	Horizontal	Omni	20		
1296.857	FX9UHY	Montpellier	JN13WO	50	Big wheel	Omni	1	F1QI	
1296.860	GB3MCB	St Austell	IO70OJ	300	15/15	45°	50	G3YJX	
1296.860	LA1UHG	Tonsburg	JO59DD	30	13dB horn	180°	60	LA6LCA	
1296.860	OE1XVB	Vienna	JN88EF	191	4 × 6-el	Omni	100		
1296.862	FX9UHZ	Istres	JN23MM	114	Slotted waveguide	Omni	150	F1AAM	
1296.865	HB9WW	Neuchatel	JN37LA	1145	15-el loop	125°	30	HB9HLM	
1296.875	FX3UHX	Landerneau	IN78UK	121	Quad	90°	1	F6CGJ	
1296.875	GB3USK	Bristol	IO81QJ	235	Slotted waveguide	90°	250	GW8AWM	
1296.875	PI7TGA	Nijmegen	JO21WU	70	Horizontal	Omni	15	PA0TGA	
1296.880	LA3UHG	Fleckkeroy	JO38XB	5	2 × 15-el Yagi	180°	10	LA8AK	
1296.880	ON5SHF	Ellignies St Anne	JO10UN	180		Omni	10		
1296.885	OE3XEA	Kaiserkogel	JN78SB	725			1		Temp QRT
1296.886	FX4UHY	Loudun	JN06BX	140	Alford slot	Omni	25	F1AFJ	
1296.890	GB3DUN	Dunstable, Beds	IO91RV	263	Alford slot	Omni	2	G3ZFP	
1296.900	DB0AN	St Mauritz	JO31SX	100	Big wheel	Omni	1	DF1QE	
1296.900	DB0JR	Peiss	JN67CR	1560	Corner reflector	337°		DJ1CR	
1296.900	GB3IOW	Newport, IOW	IO90IO	250	Alford slot	Omni	100	G3WXC	
1296.902	LX0SHF	Walferdange	JN39BP	420	2 × big wheel	Omni	3	LX1JX	
1296.902	OK0EA	Nova Paka	JO70VP	1350	4 × 15-el Yagi	Various	1	OK1AIY	
1296.905	OH4SHF	Haukivuori	KP31OX	200	7dBd Alford slot	15°			
1296.907	FX9UHX	Pic Neulos	JN12LL	1100	5-el Yagi	0°	90	F6HTJ	
1296.910	DB0JB	Karlsruhe	JN48FX	275	Big wheel	Omni	1	DK2DB	
1296.910	GB3CLE	Clee Hill, Salop	IO82RL	540	2 × 15/15 Yagi	0°/135°	20	G3UQH	Site change
1296.920	9A0BLB		JN83HG	778	Dipole		1		
1296.920	DB0VC	Lutjenberg	JO54IF	244	2 × big wheel	Omni	3	DL8LAO	

Freq (MHz)	Callsign	Nearest town	Locator	ASL (m)	Antenna	Beam direction	ERP (W)	Info from	Notes
1296.920	PI7QHN	Zandvoort	JO22FH	20	6dB gain	Omni	4	PA0QHN	
1296.920	SK7UHG	Taberg	JO77BQ	350	Big wheel	Omni	3	SM6DHW	
1296.925	SK6UHG	Hoenoe	JO57TQ	35	4 × big wheel	Omni	10	SM6EAN	
1296.930	GB3MLE	Emley Moor	IO93EO	600	Corner reflector	160°	50	G8AGN	
1296.930	OZ7IGY	Tollose	JO55VO	95	Big wheel	Omni	15	OZ7IS	
1296.935	DB0YI	Hucksheim	JO42XC	480	Big wheel	Omni	3	DL4AS	
1296.935	OH5SHF	Kuusankoski	KP30HV	145	Alford slot	Omni	25		
1296.940	DB0JK	Lovenich	JO30LX	260		Omni	30	DF7KB	
1296.940	DL0UH	Melsungen	JO41RD	385	Vertical dipole	Omni		DJ3KO	
1296.945	DB0OS	Hitchembach	JO40CW	745	6-el array	275°	1	DG6YW	
1296.945	HB9F	Bern	JN46SW	1015	Corner reflector	0°	15	HB9MHS	
1296.945	OH9SHF	Pirttikoski	KP36OI	236	10dBd	200°	30	OH6DD	
1296.945	PI71VA	Ede	JO22TA	15	Horizontal	Omni	4	PE1IVA	
1296.948	FX4UHX	St Aignan	IN94UW	88	2 × big wheel	Omni	50	F6CIS	
1296.950	DB0HG	Frankfurt am Main	JO40HG	300	Big wheel	Omni	1	DH2FAH	
1296.950	OZ5UHF	Kobenhavn	JO65GQ	35	Collinear	Omni	1	OZ3TZ	
1296.955	OZ1UHF		JO57FJ	150	Big wheel	Omni	10	OZ9NT	
1296.960	HG7BUB		JN97KR	690	Slot	Omni	0.5	HA1YA	
1296.960	SK4UHG	Hagfors	JP60VA	440	2 × helix	Omni	20		
1296.965	DF0ANN	Lauf	JN59PJ		4 × DQ 23	Omni	2	DL8ZX	
1296.975	HG1BSA	Szombathely	JN87GG	370	2 × Hybrid quad	90°	2.5	HA1YA	
1296.975	OH3RSE	Tampere	KP11UM	247	Big wheel	Omni	7		Part time
1296.980	DB0JU		JO31CV	150	Helical	Omni		DF5EO	
1296.980	SK2UHG	Kristineberg	JP95HB	500	Horizontal	Omni/180°S	500		
1296.985	OZ2ALS	Als	JO44WX	28	2 × slot	Omni	8	OZ9DT	
1296.990	DB0JN	Telgate	JO31WP	80	Mini wheel	Omni		DB8DN	
1296.990	GB3EDN	Edinburgh	IO85HW	117	2 × corner reflector	45°/315°	25	GM8BJF	
1296.995	DB0JQ	Frauenau	JN68TU	1150	4 × DQ 23	Omni	6	DB7RP	
1297.010	DB0JW	Ubach-Palenburg	JO30DU	200	4 × 11-el Yagi	45°	50	DL9KAS	
1297.040	DB0LB	Bietigheim	JN48NV	367	Dipole	Omni		DK3PT	
2304.080	S55ZNG	Nova Gorica	JN65UU	643	Vertical J slot	Omni	0.1	S57C	
2320.800	SK6UHJ	Goeteborg	JP57	120	Horizontal	Omni			
2320.805	SK0UHH	Taeby	JO99BM	90	Horizontal	Omni	25		
2320.815	DB0IH	Nohfelden	JN39ML	630	Big wheel	Omni	5	DC8DV	
2320.820	DB0OT	Esterwegen	JO32QR	80	Big wheel	Omni	1	DL1BFZ	
2320.825	DB0HF	Harksheide	JO53BO	45	Big wheel	Omni		DK2NH	
2320.830	DB0JX	Willich	JO31FF	115	Double Heliax	Omni		DK4TJ	
2320.840	DB0KI	Bayreuth	JO50WC	925	4 × 6-el	Omni	1	DC9NL	
2320.850	DB0GW		JO31JK	80	Do wendel	Omni	8	DL4JK	
2320.850	GB3NWK	Orpington	JO01BI	180	Alford slot	Omni	5	G8BJG	
2320.850	OE1XTB	Vienna	JN88EE	170		Omni	1	OE1MCU	
2320.857	PI7GHG	Capelle	JO21GW	49	20dB gain	135°	400	PE1GHG	
2320.860	LA1UHH	Tonsberg	JO59DD	30	13dB horn	180°	50	LA6LCA	
2320.865	OE1XVB	Vienna	JN88EF	191	4 × 6-el	Omni	100		
2320.879	PI7TGA	Nijmegan	JO21WU	75	10dB gain	275°/315°	10	PA0TGA	
2320.880	DB0GO		JO41ED	738	4 × DQ 13	Omni	1	DB1DI	
2320.880	DB0YI	Hildesheim	JO42XC	480	Slot	Omni		DL4AS	
2320.880	LA3UHH	Flekkeroy	JO38XB	5	2 × 6dB horn	90°/180°	1	LA8AK	
2320.890	GB3ANT	Norwich	JO02PP	75	Alford slot	Omni	5	G8VLL	
2320.899	DB0JO	Kamp-Lintfort	JO31SK	312	Horn	275°	0.2	DC6MR	
2320.900	DB0JB	Grotzingen	JN48FX	275	Big wheel	Omni	1	DK2DB	
2320.900	DB0JW		JO30DU	200	4 × 11-el Yagi	45°	50	DL9KAS	
2320.902	LX0THF	Walferdange	JN39BP	420	Double quad	Omni	0.5	LX1JX	
2320.920	DB0VC	Albersdorf	JO54IF	244	Big wheel	Omni	5	DL8LAO	
2320.920	PI7QHN	Zandvoort	JO22KH	45	6dB gain	Omni	4	PA0QHN	
2320.930	OZ7IGY	Tollose	JO55VO	91	Alford slot	Omni	20	OZ7IS	
2320.935	PI7PLA	Zuidaren	JO33IC	50	6dB gain	Omni	1	PA0PLA	
2320.940	DB0GB	Rosrath	JO30OQ	324	Slot	Omni	2	DL1KCO	
2320.945	DB0OS	Hitchinbach	JO40CW	745	8-el array	275°	1	DC1DB	
2320.950	OZ9UHF		JO65HP	30	Slot	Omni	5	OZ2TG	
2320.955	GB3LES	Leicester	IO92IQ	220	Slot	160°	30	G3TQF	
2320.955	OZ1UHF		JO57FJ	150	Slot	Omni	8	OZ9NT	
2320.965	DF0ANN	Lauf	JN59PJ	630	4 × Double quad	Omni		DL8ZX	
2320.967	DB0AS	Rosenheim	JN67CR	1560	28-el	337°		DL2AS	
2320.980	DB0JU	Doesburg	JO31CV	150	Helical	Omni	2	DF5EO	
3400.955	GB3LEF	Leicester	IO92IQ	222	Alford slot	135°	8	G3TQF	
3456.005	DB0EZ	Zevengar	JO31BS	110				DB9JC	
3456.840	DB0KI	Bayreuth	JO50WC	925	Slot	Omni		DC9NL	
3456.850	DB0GW	Duisburg	JO31JK	80	Do wendel	Omni	8	DL4JK	
3456.900	GB3OHM	S Birmingham	IO92AJ	171	16 Slot waveguide	Omni	8	G6KOA	
5760.040	PI7EHG	Schipol Airport	JO22JH	80	Horizontal	Omni	6	PA0EHG	
5760.050	DB0EZ	Didam	JO31BS	110	Slot	Omni	1	DB9JC	
5760.840	DB0KI	Bayreuth	JO50WC	925	Slot	Omni		DC9NL	
5760.860	LA1SHF	Tonsberg	JO59DD	30	13dB horn	180°	25	LA6LCA	
5760.865	OE1XVB	Vienna	JN88EF	191	Horn		4		
5760.930	OZ7IGY	Tollose	JO55VO	91	Slotted waveguide	90°/275°	15	OZ7IS	
5760.950	OZ9UHF		JO65HP	30	Slotted waveguide	Omni	2	OZ2TG	
5760.955	OZ8SHF		JO57FJ	150	Slotted waveguide	Omni	8	OZ9NT	
10120.000	GB3ALD	Alderney	IN89VR	90	Sectoral horn	30°	1		
10368.020	DB0EZ		JO31BS	110	Slot		1	DB9JC	
10368.030	PI7EHG	Schipol Airport	JO22JH	90	13dBi slot	Omni	30	PA0EHG	

Freq (MHz)	Callsign	Nearest town	Locator	ASL (m)	Antenna	Beam direction	ERP (W)	Info from	Notes
10368.040	PI7SHY	Eindhoven	JO21RK	80	21dBi	315°	1	PA0SHY	
10368.050	OZ9UHF		JO65HP	30	Slotted waveguide	Omni	3	OZ2TG	
10368.060	FX0SHF	Orleans	JN07WT	160	Slotted waveguide	Omni	0.2	F1GHB	
10368.070	PI7GOE	Kapelle	JO11XL	50	Slot	Omni		PA0TGA	
10368.100	PI7TGA	Nijmegan	JO21WU	75		Omni		ON5VK	
10368.140	ON4TNR	Namur	JO20JK	220			1	G4KUJ	
10368.240	GB3SWH	Watford	IO91TP	187	Slotted waveguide	45°/225°	1	DJ8VY	
10368.270	DL0WY	Rosenheim	JN67CR	1560	10dB slot horn	315°		PE1GHG	
10368.270	PI7GHG	Capelle Ijssel	JO21GW	50		Omni	10	DK4TJ	
10368.830	DB0JX	Wickrath	JO31FF	115	10dB	Omni		G4DDK	
10368.830	GB3MHX	Martlesham	JO02PB	80	12 slot waveguide	Omni	1	DC9NL	
10368.835	SK0SHG	Kista	JO89XJ	60	Horizontal	Omni	0.5	G0OLX	
10368.840	DB0KI	Bayreuth	JO50WC	925	Slot	Omni	3	LA6LCA	
10368.850	GB3SEE	Reigate	IO91VG	250	Slotted waveguide	Omni	10		
10368.860	LA6SHG	Tonsberg	JO59DD	30	13dB horn	180°	4		
10368.865	OE1XVB	Vienna	JN88EF	191	Horn		1	G4UVZ	
10368.870	GB3KBQ	Taunton	IO80LW	167	Slotted waveguide	Omni		DK6AB	
10368.880	DB0IS	Bodenwerder	JO51GR	1020	Slot		1	G3AYJ	
10368.880	GB3CEM	Birmingham	IO92BN	137	Slotted waveguide	Omni	1	G0API	
10368.900	GB3SCX	Purbeck Hills	IO90AP		Slotted waveguide	Omni	4	OZ2OE	
10368.900	OZ5SHF		JO45WX	170	Slotted waveguide	Omni	4	GW4ADL	
10368.910	GB3RPE	Swansea	IO81AO	60	Slotted waveguide	Omni	10	OZ1UM	
10368.915	OZ4SHF		JO65BV	22	Slotted waveguide	Omni	1	G8AGN	
10368.930	GB3MLE	Emley Moor	IO93EO	600	Sectoral horns	0°/180°	0.8	OZ9NT	
10368.955	OZ9SHF		JO57FJ	150	Slotted waveguide	Omni	1	G3TQF	
10368.955	GB3LEX	Leicester	IO92JP	220			3	G4ZPE	
10368.960	GB3CMS	Chelmsford	JO01GR	107	Slotted waveguide	Omni	0.1	HA1YA	
10368.970	HG5FMV		JN97KR	690	Slot	Omni	1	ON4ADD	
10368.970	ON4LVN	Leuven	JO20IV	125	Slotted waveguide	Omni	2	OZ1IN	
10368.975	OZ3SHF		JO45NL	58	Slotted waveguide	Omni	1	G3WXC	
10368.987	GB3IOW	Newport, IOW	IO90IO	250	Slotted waveguide	Omni	8	G8IDZ	
24025.000	GB3IOW	Newport, IOW	IO90IO	250	Sectoral horn		0.1	PA0EHG	
24048.300	PI7EHG	Schipol Airport	JO22JH	90	Slot	Omni		DF1EQ	
24192.120	DB0JL							DK2RV	
24192.200	DB0AJ		JN57	620	Slot	0°		DC9NL	
24192.800	DB0KI	Bayreuth	JO50WC	925	Slot	0°		DJ7FZ	
24192.900	DB0CU		JN48BI	970	Horn	180°	10	OZ1UM	
24192.915	OZ4SHF		JO65BV	22	Slotted waveguide	Omni	1	ON4ADD	
24192.970	ON4KUL	Leuven	JO20IV	125	Slotted waveguide	Omni			

Note: All frequencies are rounded. Many stations' frequencies vary from day to day.

² **LN2A hourly schedule is:**

1	14,409	00–04	20–24	40–44 mins
2	20,947	04–08	24–28	44–48
3	5470	08–12	28–32	48–52
4	10,407	16–20	36–40	56–00

These transmissions form part of an ITU field strength measurement programme.

³ **DK0WCY – Propagation beacon**

Normal transmission: DK0WCY beacon (x3) + 4 second dash

During auroras: DK0WCY beacon (9x3) aurora + short dashes or DK0WCY beacon (x3) strong aurora + 9 second dash

At every full 5 minutes solar/geophysical information and forecast on CW updated around 0630 UTC.

3558 may not operate on contest weekends. Summer schedule 1 hour earlier.

11 Repeaters

THIS appendix gives a list of all repeaters operational in the UK at the time of going to press (1995), including ATV and microwave repeaters.

For more information on the CTCSS system, please see Chapter 6. More details on any repeater may be obtained by contacting the keeper listed in the table. This list is of course subject to change; an up-to-date repeater list is available from RSGB (Sales).

Callsign	Channel	CTCSS	Location	Keeper
GB3AS	R0	C	Carlisle	G0JGS
GB3CF	R0	C	Leicester	G0ORY
GB3EL	R0	D	East London	G4RZZ
GB3FF	R0	F	Burntisland	GM0GNT
GB3LY	R0	H	Limavady	GI3GGY
GB3MB	R0	D	Bury	G8NSS
GB3SR	R0	E	Brighton Centre	G8VEH
GB3SS	R0	A	Elgin	GM7LSI
GB3WR	R0	F	Wells	G0MBX
GB3YC	R0	E	Scarborough	G0OII
GB3GD	R1	H	Douglas	GD3LSF
GB3HG	R1	J	Northallerton	G0RHI
GB3KS	R1	G	Dover	G4HHX
GB3MH	R1	J	Worcester	G3PWJ
GB3NB	R1	F	Norwich	G8VLL
GB3NG	R1	A	Fraserburgh	GM4OBD
GB3PA	R1	G	Paisley	GM0BFW
GB3SC	R1	B	Central Bournemouth	G0API
GB3SI	R1	C	St Ives	G3NPB
GB3WL	R1	D	West London	G8SUG
GB3AY	R2	G	Ayrshire	GM3YKE
GB3BF	R2	C	Bedford	G1BWW
GB3HS	R2	E	Hull	G7JZD
GB3MN	R2	D	Stockport	G8LZO
GB3OC	R2	C	Kirkwall	GM4TYU
GB3PO	R2	H	Ipswich	G8CPH
GB3SB	R2	J	Selkirk	GM0FTJ
GB3SL	R2	D	Crystal Palace,London	G3PAQ
GB3TR	R2	F	Torquay	G8XST
GB3WH	R2	J	Swindon	G8HBE
GB3BX	R3	A	Wolverhampton	G4JLI
GB3ES	R3	G	Hastings	G4BCO
GB3LD	R3	H	Barrow in Furness	G6LMW
GB3LG	R3	G	Lochgilphead	GM4WMM
GB3LU	R3	C	Lerwick	GM4SWU
GB3NA	R3	B	Barnsley	G7DWY
GB3PE	R3	F	Peterborough	G1ARV
GB3PR	R3	F	Perth	GM8KPH
GB3RD	R3	J	Reading	G8DOR
GB3SA	R3	F	Swansea	GW6KQC
GB3AR	R4	H	Caernarfon	GW4KAZ
GB3BB	R4	G	Brecon	GW0GHQ
GB3BT	R4	J	Berwick on Tweed	GM1JFF
GB3EV	R4	C	Cumbria	G0IYQ
GB3HH	R4	B	Buxton	G3RKL
GB3HI	R4	E	Oban	GM3RFA
GB3KN	R4	G	Maidstone	G3YCN
GB3VA	R4	J	Aylesbury	G6NB
GB3WD	R4	C	Plymouth	G6URM
GB3BI	R5	A	Inverness	GM0JFL
GB3DA	R5	H	Chelmsford	G1FOA
GB3LM	R5	B	Lincoln	G8VGF
GB3NC	R5	C	St Austell	G3IGV
GB3NI	R5	H	Belfast	GI3USS
GB3RA	R5	G	Llandrindod Wells	GW0KQX
GB3SN	R5	B	Alton	G4EPX
GB3TP	R5	D	Keighley	G3RXH
GB3TW	R5	J	Durham	G4GBF
GB3VT	R5	G	Stoke on Trent	G8DZJ
GB3BC	R6	F	Newport, Gwent	GW8ERA

Callsign	Channel	CTCSS	Location	Keeper
GB3CS	R6	G	Salsburgh	GM4COX
GB3MP	R6	H	Denbigh	GW4GTE
GB3MX	R6	B	Mansfield	G0UYQ
GB3PI	R6	C	Royston	G4NBS
GB3WS	R6	E	Crawley	G4EFO
GB3DG	R7	G	Gatehouse of Fleet	GM4VIR
GB3FR	R7	B	Spilsby	G8LXI
GB3GN	R7	A	Aberdeen	GM4NHI
GB3IG	R7	E	Stornoway	GM4PTQ
GB3NL	R7	D	Enfield	G3TZZ
GB3PC	R7	B	Portsmouth	G4NAO
GB3PW	R7	G	Newtown, Powys	GW4NQJ
GB3RF	R7	D	Burnley	G4FSD
GB3TE	R7	H	Clacton-on-Sea	G7HJK
GB3WK	R7	A	Leamington	G6FEO
GB3WT	R7	H	Omagh	GI3NVW
GB3WW	R7	F	Cross Hands, Dyfed	GW6ZUS
GB3SF	R7X	D	Buxton	G3RKL
GB3BN	RB0	D	Bracknell	G4DDN
GB3CK	RB0	G	Ashford	G0GCQ
GB3DT	RB0	B	Blandford Forum	G8BXQ
GB3EX	RB0	F	Exeter	G8UWE
GB3LL	RB0	H	Llandudno	GW8WFS
GB3MK	RB0	C	Milton Keynes	G4NJU
GB3MS	RB0	J	Worcester	G3PWJ
GB3NR	RB0	F	Norwich	G8VLL
GB3NT	RB0	J	Newcastle Upon Tyne	G4GBF
GB3NY	RB0	E	Scarborough	G4EEV
GB3PF	RB0	D	Blackburn	G4FSD
GB3PU	RB0	F	Perth	GM8KPH
GB3SO	RB0	B	Boston	G8LXI
GB3SV	RB0	H	Bishops Stortford	G6YMV
GB3US	RB0	G	Sheffield	G3RKL
GB3WN	RB0	A	Wolverhampton	G4OKE
GB3BA	RB1	A	Stonehaven	GM4NHI
GB3BV	RB1	D	Hemel Hempstead	G6NB
GB3DV	RB1	E	Doncaster	G4LUE
GB3HO	RB1	E	Horsham	G7JRV
GB3MA	RB1	D	Bury	G8NSS
GB3AV	RB2	D	Aylesbury	G6NB
GB3CH	RB2	C	Liskeard	G8CMG
GB3CI	RB2	B	Corby	G8MLA
GB3EK	RB2	G	Margate	G4TKR
GB3FC	RB2	A	Blackpool	G4EZM
GB3HK	RB2	J	Hawick	GM0FTJ
GB3LS	RB2	B	Lincoln	G8VGF
GB3LV	RB2	D	Enfield	G3KSW
GB3NN	RB2	F	Wells Next The Sea	G8KZP
GB3NX	RB2	E	Crawley	G0DSU
GB3OS	RB2	A	Stourbridge	G1PKZ
GB3PH	RB2	B	Portsmouth	G8PGF
GB3ST	RB2	G	Stoke on Trent	G8DZJ
GB3UL	RB2	H	Belfast	GI3USS
GB3YS	RB2	F	Yeovil	G0LHX
GB3CC	RB3	E	Chichester	G3UEQ
GB3ER	RB3	H	Chelmsford	G1FOA
GB3HL	RB3	D	West London	G8SUG
GB3HU	RB3	E	Hull	G3TEU
GB3KA	RB3	G	Galston, Ayrshire	GM0HSC
GB3KR	RB3	J	Kidderminster	G8NTU

Callsign	Channel	CTCSS	Location	Keeper
GB3MD	RB3	B	Mansfield	G8EHX
GB3NH	RB3	C	Northampton	G4IIO
GB3TD	RB3	J	Swindon	G4XUT
GB3VS	RB3	F	Taunton	G4UVZ
GB3GC	RB4	E	Goole	G0GLZ
GB3IH	RB4	H	Ipswich	G8CPH
GB3IW	RB4	B	Newport, IOW	G0ISB
GB3KL	RB4	F	Kings Lynn	G3ZCA
GB3LE	RB4	C	Leicester	G0ORY
GB3NK	RB4	G	Wrotham	G8JNZ
GB3OH	RB4	F	Bo'ness	GM6WQH
GB3SP	RB4	F	Pembroke	GW4VRO
GB3UB	RB4	J	Bath	G0LIB
GB3EB	RB5	H	Brentwood	G6IFH
GB3GH	RB5	J	Cheltenham	G6AWT
GB3HY	RB5	E	Haywards Heath	G3XTH
GB3IM	RB5	H	Douglas	GD3LSF
GB3OV	RB5	F	Huntingdon	G8LRS
GB3WB	RB5	F	Weston Super Mare	G7KUD
GB3WJ	RB5	B	Scunthorpe	G3TMD
GB3BD	RB6	C	Ampthill, Beds	G1BWW
GB3BR	RB6	E	Brighton	G8VEH
GB3CR	RB6	H	Clywd	GW4GTE
GB3CW	RB6	G	Powys	GW4NQJ
GB3DI	RB6	J	Didcot	G8CUL
GB3HA	RB6	E	Hornsea	G4YTV
GB3HC	RB6	J	Hereford	G4JSN
GB3LW	RB6	D	London	G8AUU
GB3ME	RB6	A	Rugby	G8DLX
GB3SK	RB6	G	Canterbury	G6DIK
GB3SY	RB6	B	Barnsley	G7DWY
GB3WG	RB6	F	Port Talbot	GW3VPL
GB3BL	RB7	C	Bedford	G1BWW
GB3HZ	RB7	D	High Wycombe	G4DDM
GB3MF	RB7	G	Macclesfield	G0AMU
GB3MG	RB7	F	Bridgend	GW3RVG
GB3NM	RB7	B	Nottingham	G2SP
GB3TS	RB7	J	Middlesbrough	G8MBK
GB3WY	RB7	D	Halifax	G8NWK
GB3AN	RB8	H	Amlwch	GW6DOK
GB3CM	RB8	F	Carmarthen	GW0IVG
GB3EH	RB8	A	Banbury	G4OHB
GB3LA	RB8	D	Leeds	G8ZXA
GB3PY	RB8	C	Cambridge	G4NBS
GB3TF	RB8	G	Telford	G3UKV
GB3BE	RB8	H	Bury St Edmunds	G8KMM
GB3CL	RB9	H	Clacton	G7HJK
GB3CV	RB9	A	Coventry	G3ZFR
GB3HD	RB9	D	Huddersfield	G1FYS
GB3PG	RB9	G	Greenock	GM4PLM
GB3SW	RB9	B	Salisbury	G4YRV
GB3AW	RB10	B	Newbury	G8DOR
GB3BS	RB10	J	Bristol	G4SDR
GB3DD	RB10	F	Dundee	GM4UGF
GB3DY	RB10	B	Derby	G3ZYC
GB3LI	RB10	D	Liverpool	G3WIC
GB3LT	RB10	C	Luton	G6OUA
GB3ML	RB10	G	Airdrie	GM3SAN
GB3MW	RB10	A	Leamington Spa	G6FEO
GB3NS	RB10	D	Reigate	G0OLX
GB3PB	RB10	C	Peterborough	G1ARV
GB3AH	RB11	F	Swaffham	G8PON
GB3BK	RB11	D	Reading	G8DOR
GB3DC	RB11	J	Sunderland	G6LMR
GB3GR	RB11	B	Grantham	G4WFK
GB3GY	RB11	E	Grimsby	G1BRB
GB3HN	RB11	D	Hitchin	G3ZQI
GB3HT	RB11	C	Hinckley	G8SHH
GB3LR	RB11	E	Newhaven	G0ENJ
GB3SH	RB11	F	Honiton	G6WWY
GB3ZI	RB11	G	Stafford	G1UDS
GB3EE	RB12	B	Chesterfield	G6SVZ
GB3GF	RB12	E	Guildford	G4EML

Callsign	Channel	CTCSS	Location	Keeper
GB3HM	RB12	J	Boroughbridge	G0RHI
GB3MT	RB12	D	Bolton	G8NSS
GB3OX	RB12	J	Oxford	G4WXC
GB3CA	RB13	C	Carlisle	G0JGS
GB3CY	RB13	E	York	G4FUO
GB3DS	RB13	B	Worksop	G3XXN
GB3GU	RB13	C	St Peter Port, CI	GU4EON
GB3HW	RB13	H	Romford	G4GBW
GB3LC	RB13	B	Louth, Lincs	G6GZS
GB3SM	RB13	G	Leek	G8DZJ
GB3VH	RB13	D	Welwyn Garden City	G4THF
GB3XX	RB13	C	Daventry	G1ZJK
GB3AB	RB14	A	Aberdeen	GM1LKD
GB3CB	RB14	A	Birmingham	G8AMD
GB3CE	RB14	H	Colchester	G3WRT
GB3ED	RB14	F	Edinburgh	GM3GBX
GB3GL	RB14	G	Glasgow	GM3SAN
GB3HE	RB14	G	Hastings	G4FET
GB3HR	RB14	D	Harrow	G4KUJ
GB3LF	RB14	H	Lancaster	G8UHO
GB3MR	RB14	D	Stockport	G8LZO
GB3ND	RB14	F	Bideford	G4JKN
GB3SD	RB14	B	Weymouth	G0EVW
GB3TL	RB14	B	Spalding	G7JBA
GB3WF	RB14	D	Leeds	G8ZXA
GB3YL	RB14	F	Lowestoft	G4TAD
GB3FN	RB15	J	Farnham	G4EPX
GB3HB	RB15	C	St Austell	G3IGV
GB3LH	RB15	G	Shrewsbury	G3UQH
GB3OM	RB15	H	Omagh	GI4SXV
GB3PP	RB15	D	Preston	G3SYA
GB3SG	RB15	F	Cardiff	GW8ERA
GB3SU	RB15	H	Sudbury	G8AAR
GB3SZ	RB15	B	Bournemouth	G0API
GB3TH	RB15	A	Tamworth	G0FEO
GB3WI	RB15	F	Wisbech	G4NPH
GB3WU	RB15	D	Wakefield	G0COA
GB3MC	RM0	D	Bolton	G8NSS
GB3NO	RM0	F	Norwich	G8VLL
GB3FM	RM2	J	Farnham	G4EPX
GB3CP	RM3	E	Crawley	G3GRO
GB3PS	RM3	C	Royston	G4NBS
GB3SE	RM3	G	Stoke on Trent	G8DZJ
GB3CN	RM5	C	Northampton	G6NYH
GB3BW	RM6	C	Bedford	G1BWW
GB3MM	RM6	A	Wolverhampton	G4OKE
GB3RU	RM9	J	Reading	G8DOR
GB3UY	RM13	B	York	G7AUP
GB3WC	RM15	D	Wakefield	G0COA
GB3UT	RT1-1		Bath	G0LIB
GB3AF	RT1-2		Durham	G1FBY
GB3ET	RT1-2R		Emley Moor	G8HUA
GB3GV	RT1-2		Leicestershire	G8OBP
GB3LO	RT1-2R		Lowestoft	G4TAD
GB3MV	RT1-2R		Northampton	G4WIM
GB3NV	RT1-2R		Nottingham	G6SKO
GB3PV	RT1-2R		Cambridge	G4NBS
GB3RT	RT1-2R		Coventry	G6IQM
GB3TM	RT1-2R		Amlwch	GW8PBX
GB3TN	RT1-2R		Fakenham	G4WVU
GB3TT	RT1-2R		Chesterfield	G1IOR
GB3TV	RT1-2		Dunstable	G4ENB
GB3UD	RT1-2		Stoke on Trent	G0KBI
GB3VR	RT1-2R		Brighton	G8KOE
GB3ZZ	RT1-2R		Bristol	G6TVJ
GB3TG	RT1-2R	C	Bletchley	G4NJU
GB3EY	RT1-3		Hull	G8EQZ
GB3HV	RT1-3		High Wycombe	G8LES
GB3TG	RT10-3		Bletchley	G4NJU
GB3UD	RT10-3		Stoke on Trent	G0KBI
GB3XG	RT10-3		Bristol	G6TVJ
GB3XT	RT10-3		Burton on Trent	G8OZP

144MHz REPEATERS

Channel	Input	Output
R0	145.000	145.600
R1	145.025	145.625
R2	145.050	145.650
R3	145.075	145.675
R4	145.100	145.700
R5	145.125	145.725
R6	145.150	145.750
R7	145.175	145.775
GB3SF	*145.185*	*145.785* (PSSB)

LU 3

OC 2

IG 7

SS 0

NG 1

BI 5

GN 7

HI 4

PR 3

LG 3

FF

PA 1

CS 6

0

BT 4

AY 2

SB 2

LY 0

AS 0

TW 5

WT 7

DG 7

EV 4

YC 0

NI 5

GD 1

LD 3

HG 1

TP 5

HS 2

RF 7

NA 3

MB 0

MN 2

SF 7

HH 4

LM 5

MP 6

VT 5

MX 6

FR 7

AR 4

BX 3

CF 0

PE 3

NB 1

PW 7

BM 2

BF 2

PI 6

PO 2

RA 5

WK 7

VA 4

DA 5

TE 7

BB 4

MH 1

NL 7

WW 7

SA 3

WH 2

RD 3

WL 1

SL 2

EL 0

KN 4

KS 1

BC 6

WR 0

SN 5

WS 6

ES 3

WD 4

SC 1

PC 7

SR 0

NC 5

TR 2

SI 1

Channel Islands

GJ 2

CD414/1

432MHz REPEATERS

Channel	Input	Output
RB 0	434.600	433.000
RB 1	434.625	433.025
RB 2	434.650	433.050
RB 3	434.675	433.075
RB 4	434.700	433.100
RB 5	434.725	433.125
RB 6	434.750	433.150
RB 7	434.775	433.175
RB 8	434.800	433.200
RB 9	434.825	433.225
RB 10	434.850	433.250
RB 11	434.875	433.275
RB 12	434.900	433.300
RB 13	434.925	433.325
RB 14	434.950	433.350
RB 15	434.975	433.375

Channel Islands

GU 13

CD449/2

MICROWAVE REPEATERS

While not being talked through, microwave repeaters revert to a beacon mode

23cm speech

Channel	Input (MHz)	Output (MHz)
RM0	1291.000	1297.000
RM2	1291.050	1297.050
RM3	1291.075	1297.075
RM5	1291.125	1297.125
RM6	1291.150	1297.150
RM9	1291.225	1297.225
RM12	1291.300	1297.300
RM15	1291.375	1297.375

Amateur television

Channel	Input (GHz)	Output (GHz)	Use
RT1-1	1.276	1.3115	AM
RT1-2	1.249	1.3185	FM
RT1-2R	1.249	1.3160	FM
RT1-3	1.248	1.3080	FM
RT10-1	10.200	10.040	FM
RT10-2	10.255	10.150	FM
RT10-3	10.250	10.150	FM

CD415/2

CTCSS REPEATER AREAS

Tone Area	CTCSS Tone (Hz)
A	67.1
B	71.9
C	77.0
D	82.5
E	88.5
F	94.8
G	103.5
H	110.9
J	118.8

12 Packet nodes and mailboxes

THIS appendix gives a list of packet radio nodes and mailboxes in the UK. These details are subject to frequent change, but are reprentative at the time of going to press (1995).

Further details of your local nodes and mailboxes, and their user groups, can be obtained from the contact or sysop shown in the table.

VHF PACKET NODES

Callsign	Alias	Freq	Contact	Location
GB7AR		50.650	GW4KAZ	Caernarfon
GB7CR	CATA61	50.650	G4APL	Caterham
GB7ES		50.650	G1NNB	Colchester
GB7EY	SC61	50.730	G4AJJ	Scarborough
GB7GH	GLOS52	50.650	G6CMG	Gloucester
GB7LI		50.650	G4PGO	Bootle
GB7MB		50.650	G8EIA	Middlesborough
GB7MC			G3WPF	Hyde
GB7OS		50.650	GW6HVA	Llandudno
GB7PE			G1ARV	Peterborough
GB7RM	ROCH60	50.650	G3WPF	Rochdale
GB7RS	ARMY	50.650	G6FPC	Blandford
GB7WP	WP	50.650	G0COA	Wakefield
GB7YK		50.650	G6TVA	Barnsley
GB7YS		50.650	G3VMW	Sheffield
GB7YW		50.730	G3VMW	Wetherby
GB7AN		70.4875	GW4KAZ	Anglesey
GB7AR		70.4875	GW4KAZ	Caernarfon
GB7AY	GALS41	70.4875	GM1VBE	Kilmarnock
GB7CD	CD42	70.4875	G6ANN	Bolsover
GB7CN		70.3125	G3HTA	Crediton
GB7EA		70.325	G1UGJ	Bury St Edmunds
GB7EP	EP40	70.3125	G1FOA	Chelmsford
GB7EY	SC41	70.325	G4AJJ	Scarborough
GB7EY	SC42	70.4875	G4AJJ	Scarborough
GB7FC	WRW	70.4875	G4WRW	Bristol
GB7GH	GLOS4I	70.4875	G6CMG	Gloucester
GB7HD		70.325	G3HVX	Hereford
GB7HZ	CDF4	70.4875	GW8HEZ	Penarth
GB7IP			G6GLP	Newton Abbot
GB7IW		70.3125	G0ISB	Isle of Wight
GB7JD	JED42	70.4875	GM4UPX	Jedburgh
GB7KC	KILN40	70.4875	GM1VBE	Lanark
GB7LI		70.325	G4PGO	Bootle
GB7LX	LX4	70.4875	G4GOU	Louth
GB7LY		70.3125	G3XVV	Haverhill
GB7MC			G3WPF	Hyde
GB7MH	MLVN41	70.4875	G4FPV	Malvern
GB7MX		70.4875	G8KBB	Ipswich
GB7OR		70.4875	G1VSJ	Oldham
GB7OX	IPS4	70.4875	G0JVU	Ipswich
GB7PE	PE40	70.4875	G1ARV	Peterborough
GB7PW		70.4875	GW4NQJ	Newtown, Powys
GB7RM	ROCH40	70.4875	G3WPF	Rochdale
GB7RP	RP40	70.4875	G0CXD	Wirksworth, Derbys
GB7RS	ARMY	70.4875	G6FPC	Blandford
GB7RV		70.4875	GW1DOI	Rhonda, Mid Glam
GB7SM		70.4875	GM1VBE	Chatton
GB7SO		70.4875	G4TUP	Southport
GB7ST	STRD41	70.4875	G3ILO	Stroud
GB7SW	SAL40	70.4875	G4WPT	Salisbury
GB7TM		70.4875	G3YJQ	Plymouth
GB7UX	BATH4	70.4875	G0TMB	Bath
GB7VG		70.4875	GW0JCB	Barry, Wales
GB7WG		70.4875	GW8TVX	Swansea
GB7WH	WILL42	70.4875	G3WPF	Horwich
GB7WP	WP	70.4875	G0COA	Wakefield
GB7YA			G4DYA	Stone, Staffs
GB7YK		70.3375	G6TVA	Barnsley
GB7YM	RHB41	70.325	G4AJJ	Whitby
GB7YN		70.4875	G3VMW	Richmond, N. Yorks
GB7YS		70.4875	G3VMW	Sheffield
GB7YW		70.325	G3VMW	Wetherby

Callsign	Alias	Freq	Contact	Location
GB3JP	JSY2	144.650	GJ4YAD	Jersey
GB3LP		144.650	GW4HDR	Llandudno
GB3PQ		144.650	G3TQA	Halifax
GB7AD	DUND21	144.650	GM1VBE	Dundee
GB7AN		144.650	GW4KAZ	Anglesey
GB7AP	AP21	144.650	G8KHV	Lichfield
GB7AR		144.650	GW4KAZ	Caernarfon
GB7AY	GALS21	144.650	GM1VBE	Kilmarnock
GB7BA	ABER21	144.650	GM1VBE	Stonehaven
GB7BC		144.675	GW8ERA	Mynydd Machen
GB7BG	BG22	144.675	G0OOY	Cockermouth
GB7CD	CD21	144.650	G6ANN	Bolsover
GB7CK	CK2	144.650	G3TIS	Ashford
GB7CN		144.650	G3HTA	Crediton
GB7CS	SALS21	144.650	GM1VBE	Salsburgh, Lanarks
GB7EA		144.650	G1UGJ	Bury St Edmunds
GB7EP		144.625	G1FOA	Chelmsford
GB7ES		144.650	G1NNB	Colchester
GB7EX	EXE2	144.650	G4WJZ	Exeter
GB7EY	SC21	144.650	G4AJJ	Scarborough
GB7FC	WRW	144.650	G4WRW	Bristol
GB7GH	GLOS21	144.650	G6CMG	Gloucester
GB7GI	GI2	144.650	GI4NRE	Enniskillen
GB7GP		144.650	GU4YMV	Guernsey
GB7HP	HP2	144.650	G4WPT	Portsmouth
GB7HZ	CDF2	144.650	GW8HEZ	Penarth
GB7IW			G0ISB	Isle of Wight
GB7JD	JED21	144.650	GM4UPX	Jedburgh
GB7JK	MAT	144.625	G0HMZ	Matlock
GB7KC	KILN21	144.675	GM1VBE	Lanark
GB7KL		144.650	G1LOK	Kings Lynn
GB7LI		144.675	G4PGO	Bootle
GB7LX	LX2	144.650	G4GOU	Louth
GB7LY		144.625	G3XVV	Haverhill
GB7MH	MLVN21	144.650	G4FPV	Malvern
GB7MN			G4OTJ	Bath
GB7MX		144.675	G8KBB	Ipswich
GB7NU	UIST21	144.650	GM1MLY	North Uist
GB7OR		144.675	G1VSJ	Oldham
GB7OX	IPS2	144.650	G0JVU	Ipswich
GB7PE	PE21	144.650	G1ARV	Peterborough
GB7PH	EDIN21	144.650	GM1VBE	Currie, Midlothian
GB7PX	PX2	144.650	G4BIK	Cambridge
GB7RS	ARMY	144.650	G6FPC	Blandford
GB7RV		144.650	GW1DOI	Rhonda, Mid Glam
GB7SB		144.675	GM4UPX	Peebles
GB7SD	WEY2	144.650	G3VPF	Weymouth
GB7SH	AXE2	144.650	G1DII	Honiton
GB7SM		144.650	GM1VBE	Chatton
GB7ST	STRD21	144.650	G3ILO	Stroud
GB7SW	SAL21	144.650	G4WPT	Salisbury
GB7TM		144.675	G3YJQ	Plymouth
GB7UX	AQUSUL	144.650	G0TMB	Bath
GB7VR		144.650	G8DHE	Brighton
GB7WG			GW8TVX	Swansea
GB7WP	WP	144.650	G0COA	Wakefield
GB7YA		144.675	G4DYA	Stone, Staffs
GB7YK		144.650	G6TVA	Barnsley
GB7YM	RHB22	144.675	G4AJJ	Whitby
GB7YP		144.650	G1SSO	Sheffield
GB7AY		430.650	GM1VBE	Kilmarnock
GB7BH		430.650	G4OTJ	Bath
GB7CN		430.625	G3HTA	Crediton

Callsign	Alias	Freq	Contact	Location
GB7EP		430.775	G1FOA	Chelmsford
GB7ES		430.675	G1NNB	Colchester
GB7EY		430.725	G4AJJ	Scarborough
GB7FC	WRW	430.650	G4WRW	Bristol
GB7JT			G6LOH	Towcester
GB7KC		430.625	GM1VBE	Lanark
GB7ME		430.650	G1EUC	Danbury, Essex
GB7ML	MEND	430.650	G4WRW	Wells
GB7PL		430.650	G7AUQ	Plymouth
GB7RS	ARMY	430.650	G6FPC	Blandford
GB7SA		430.650	G1EQT	Nottingham
GB7YA			G4DYA	Stone, Staffs
GB7ZX		430.675	G0LZX	Liverpool
GB7AD	DUND70	432.675	GM1VBE	Dundee
GB7AM	HAYTOR	432.675	G1ZBJ	Islington
GB7AP	AP72	432.675	G8KHV	Lichfield
GB7AY	GALS70	432.675	GM1VBE	Kilmarnock
GB7BA	ABER70	432.675	GM1VBE	Stonehaven
GB7BC		432.675	GW8ERA	Mynydd Machen
GB7BG	BG72	432.675	G0OOY	Cockermouth
GB7BH		432.650	G4OTJ	Bath
GB7BY		432.675	G4GSY	Bury, Lancs
GB7CD			G6ANN	Bolsover
GB7CN		433.675	G3HTA	Crediton
GB7CR	CATA70	432.625	G4APL	Caterham
GB7CR	CATA72	432.675	G4APL	Caterham
GB7CS	SALS70	432.675	GM1VBE	Salsburgh, Lanarks
GB7EC		432.675	G4YYW	Scarborough
GB7ES		432.650	G1NNB	Bristol
GB7EY	SC74	432.625	G4AJJ	Scarborough
GB7EY	SC70	432.625	G4AJJ	Scarborough
GB7FC	WRW	432.675	G4WRW	Bristol
GB7GH	GLOS73	432.675	G6CMG	Gloucester
GB7GP	GSY7	433.650	GU4YMV	Guernsey
GB7HZ	CDF7	432.675	GW8HEZ	Penarth
GB7IP	IPP70	432.675	G6GLP	Newton Abbot
GB7IW		432.675	G0ISB	Isle of Wight
GB7JK	MAT	432.675	G0HMZ	Matlock
GB7JK	MAT	432.675	G0HMZ	Matlock
GB7JT			G6LOH	Towcester
GB7KC	KILN70	432.675	GM1VBE	Lanark
GB7KK		433.675	GM1VBE	Kirkconnel
GB7LI		432.675	G4PGO	Bootle
GB7LX	LX7	432.675	G4GOU	Louth
GB7MC			G3WPF	Hyde
GB7MH	MLVN72	432.675	G4FPV	Malvern
GB7ML	MEND9	432.675	G4WRW	Wells
GB7ML	MEND7	433.675	G4WRW	Wells
GB7MX		433.625	G8KBB	Ipswich
GB7ND		433.625	G6YAL	Alfreton
GB7NE		432.625	G1YAA	Alnwick
GB7NN		432.675	G8AMG	Wellingborough
GB7OR		432.675	G1VSJ	Oldham
GB7OX		432.650	G0JVU	Ipswich
GB7PE	PE72	432.625	G1ARV	Peterborough
GB7PH	EDIN70	432.675	GM1VBE	Currie, Midlothian
GB7PL		432.650	G7AUQ	Plymouth
GB7PP	PP72	432.650	G1DKI	Wolverhampton
GB7RP	RP72	432.675	G0CXD	Wirksworth, Derbys
GB7RS	ARMY	432.675	G6FPC	Blandford
GB7RU			G4FIS	Uppingham
GB7RV		432.675	GW1DOI	Rhonda, Mid Glam
GB7SA		433.625	G1EQT	Nottingham
GB7SN		432.675	G7GXP	Sheffield
GB7SS		432.675	G0NJD	Sheffield
GB7ST	STRD72	432.675	G3ILO	Stroud
GB7SY	PMBNET	432.675	G3UQH	Minsterley, Salop
GB7UY		432.625	G0GHD	Derby
GB7VS		433.625	G0ORC	Belper
GB7WC			G6CRV	Kendal
GB7WG		432.675	GW8TVX	Swansea
GB7WH	WILL74	433.650	G3WPF	Horwich
GB7WP	WP	432.675	G0COA	Wakefield
GB7WV		432.675	G1DKI	Wolverhampton
GB7YA			G4DYA	Stone, Staffs
GB7YK		433.675	G6TVA	Barnsley
GB7YM	RHB75	433.675	G4AJJ	Whitby
GB7YN		432.675	G3VMW	Richmond, N. Yorks
GB7YP		433.675	G1SSO	Sheffield
GB7YS		432.675	G3VMW	Sheffield
GB7YW		432.650	G3VMW	Wetherby
GB7ZX		432.675	G0LZX	Liverpool
GB7JD	JED70	432.675	GM4UPX	Jedburgh
GB7BF		439.925	G4BLH	Nelson
GB7BH		439.850	G4OTJ	Bath
GB7CM			G0HHR	Stockport
GB7CN		439.850	G3HTA	Crediton

Callsign	Alias	Freq	Contact	Location
GB7CS		439.800	GM1VBE	Salsburgh, Lanarks
GB7EP		439.975	G1FOA	Chelmsford
GB7EY	SC83	439.875	G4AJJ	Scarborough
GB7FC	WRW	439.850	G4WRW	Bristol
GB7HN		439.825	G4OAA	Hoddesdon
GB7IP			G6GLP	Newton Abbot
GB7JD		439.875	GM4UPX	Jedburgh
GB7JT			G6LOH	Towcester
GB7KC		439.850	GM1VBE	Lanark
GB7KK		439.825	GM1VBE	Kirkconnel
GB7LI		439.825	G4PGO	Bootle
GB7MC			G3WPF	Hyde
GB7ME		439.875	G1EUC	Danbury, Essex
GB7MH		439.825	G4FPV	Malvern
GB7ML	MEND1	439.925	G4WRW	Wells
GB7MN			G4OTJ	Bath
GB7MX		439.850	G8KBB	Ipswich
GB7NE		439.825	G1YAA	Alnwick
GB7NN		439.825	G8AMG	Wellingborough
GB7OX		439.850	G0JVU	Nacton, Suffolk
GB7OX		439.850	G0JVU	Nacton, Suffolk
GB7PL		439.925	G7AUQ	Plymouth
GB7PX		439.825	G4BIK	Cambridge
GB7RM	ROCH80	439.975	G3WPF	Rochdale
GB7SA			G1EQT	Nottingham
GB7SB		439.875	GM4UPX	Peebles
GB7TH		439.825	G4OAA	Royston
GB7UX		439.875	G0TMB	Bath
GB7WC			G6CRV	Kendal
GB7WH	WILL85	439.975	G3WPF	Horwich
GB7YA			G4DYA	Stone, Staffs
GB7YK		439.850	G6TVA	Barnsley
GB7YP		439.850	G1SSO	Sheffield
GB7YS		439.825	G3VMW	Sheffield
GB7YW		439.825	G3VMW	Wetherby
GB7ZX		439.975	G0LZX	Liverpool
GB7AP			G8KHV	Lichfield
GB7BD			G4XGN	Bradford
GB7BH		1299.425	G4OTJ	Bath
GB7BM			G6ZRM	Brixham
GB7CD			G6ANN	Bolsover
GB7CS		1299.425	GM1VBE	Salsburgh, Lanarks
GB7CY		1299.000	G1FTA	York
GB7ES		1299.425	G1NNB	Colchester
GB7EX	EXE23	1299.425	G4WJZ	Exeter
GB7EY	SC92	1240.150	G4AJJ	Scarborough
GB7EY	SC91	1299.725	G4AJJ	Scarborough
GB7FC	WRW		G4WRW	Bristol
GB7GH	GLOS14	1299.000	G6CMG	Gloucester
GB7HG			G3VMW	Bilsdale, N. Yorks
GB7HX			G4NVS	Huntingdon
GB7IP			G6GLP	Newton Abbot
GB7IP	IPP23	1299.425	G6GLP	Newton Abbot
GB7IW		1299.000	G0ISB	Isle of Wight
GB7JD		1299.000	GM4UPX	Jedburgh
GB7LI		1299.000	G4PGO	Bootle
GB7MC			G3WPF	Hyde
GB7MH	MLVN90	1299.000	G4FPV	Malvern
GB7ML	MEND	1299.000	G4WRW	Wells
GB7MX		1299.425	G8KBB	Ipswich
GB7NP		1299.425	G3PDH	Norwich
GB7NY		1299.000	G4ATZ	Harrogate
GB7OX	IPS1	1299.000	G0JVU	Ipswich
GB7PE		1299.000	G1ARV	Peterborough
GB7PP		1299.000	G1DKI	Wolverhampton
GB7PW		1299.725	GW4NQJ	Newtown, Powys
GB7PX	PX1	1299.425	G4BIK	Cambridge
GB7RM	ROCH17	1299.000	G3WPF	Rochdale
GB7RP	RP15	1299.000	G0CXD	Wirksworth, Derbys
GB7RS	ARMY	1299.000	G6FPC	Blandford
GB7SB		1299.425	GM4UPX	Peebles
GB7SD	WEY23	1299.425	G3VPF	Weymouth
GB7SH	AXE23	1299.425	G1DII	Honiton
GB7SW		1299.000	G4WPT	Salisbury
GB7SY	SY92	1240.150	G3UQH	Minsterley, Salop
GB7VR		1299.000	G8DHE	Brighton
GB7WP	WP	1299.000	G0COA	Wakefield
GB7WV		1299.000	G1DKI	Wolverhampton
GB7WY			G3TQA	Halifax
GB7YK		1299.575	G6TVA	Barnsley
GB7YM	RHB18	1299.725	G4AJJ	Whitby
GB7YS		1240.300	G3VMW	Sheffield
GB7YS		1299.000	G3VMW	Sheffield
GB7YW		1299.575	G3VMW	Wetherby
GB7HG			G3VMW	Bilsdale, N. Yorks
GB7LX		2310.300	G4GOU	Louth
GB7WP	WP	2310.300	G0COA	Wakefield

HF MAILBOXES

Callsign	Band	Type	Contact	Location	Callsign	Band	Type	Contact	Location
GB7EMX	3.5	Amtor	GM4EMX	Aberdeen	GB7GMX	14	Packet	G3VOM	Manchester
GB7GMX	3.5	Packet	G3VOM	Manchester	GB7GUR	14	Packet	GU4YMV	Guernsey
GB7GUR	3.5	Packet	GU4YMV	Guernsey	GB7LDI	14	Packet	G3LDI	Norwich
GB7LDI	3.5	Packet	G3LDI	Norwich	GB7MSF	14	Packet	G4MSF	Gateshead
GB7SCA	3.5	Amtor	G4SCA	Plymouth	GB7SCA	14	Amtor	G4SCA	Plymouth
GB7SIG	3.5	Amtor	G6FPC	Blandford Forum	GB7SCA	18	Amtor	G4SCA	Plymouth
GB7EMX	7	Amtor	GM4EMX	Aberdeen	GB7EMX	21	Amtor	GM4EMX	Aberdeen
GB7GUR	7	Amtor	GU4YMV	Guernsey	GB7GMX	21	Packet	G3VOM	Manchester
GB7SCA	7	Amtor	G4SCA	Plymouth	GB7GUR	21	Packet	GU4YMV	Guernsey
GB7EMX	10	Amtor	GM4EMX	Aberdeen	GB7LDI	21	Packet	G3LDI	Norwich
GB7GMX	10	Packet	G3VOM	Manchester	GB7SCA	21	Amtor	G4SCA	Plymouth
GB7SIG	10	Amtor	G6FPC	Blandford Forum	GB7EMX	28	Amtor	GM4EMX	Aberdeen
GB7EMX	14	Amtor	GM4EMX	Aberdeen	GB7SCA	28	Amtor	G4SCA	Plymouth
GB7FLG	14	Packet	G0FLG	Whitwick, Leics.	GB7MAC	29	Packet	GM4AUP	Airdrie

VHF MAILBOXES

Callsign	Location	Sysop	Type	6m	4m	2m	70cm
GB7ABB	Caernarfon, Gwynedd	GW0ENT	AX25		70.4875	144.650	
GB7ABN	Aberdeen, Scotland	GM1THS	AX25	50.650	70.4875	144.650	430.650 432.675
GB7ADX	Anglesey, Gwynedd	GW4VEQ	DX Cluster	50.650	70.3255	144.675	432.675 439.850
GB7AEJ	Peterborough	G7AEJ	TCP/IP	50.710	70.4875	144.625	433.625 439.850
GB7AHE	Bridgwater, Somerset	G7AHE	AX25			144.650	432.650 439.925
GB7AKE	St Ives, Cornwall	G6AKE	AX25		70.4875	144.650	432.675
GB7AOB	Fort William, Inverness	GM8AOB		50.650	70.4875	144.650	
GB7AVM	Chinnor, Oxon	G0DFP			70.4875	144.650	433.650 439.850
GB7AYI	Leicester	G7SBS	IP/AX25			144.625	430.625 432.650 439.925
GB7AYR	Irvine, Ayrshire	GM0JQE	AX25		70.4875	144.650	432.675
GB7BAD	Nottingham, Notts.	G0INA	AX25	50.650	70.4875	144.550	430.675 432.625 439.825
GB7BAY	Criccieth, Gwynedd	GW8FVI	AX25		70.3375	144.650	433.650
GB7BBC	Acton, London	G8LWS	TCP/IP		70.4875	144.625	433.650 439.825
GB7BBS	Bridgnorth, Shropshire	G1DIL	AX25	50.650		144.550	432.625
GB7BDX	Kelso, Roxburghshire	GM6YRZ			70.3250	144.675	430.625 433.675 439.875
GB7BED	Bedford	G1HLF	AX25	50.670	70.4875	144.550	432.675
GB7BEN	Bletchley, Bucks	G8TTK	AX25	50.670	70.4875	144.650	432.675
GB7BHM	Wednesbury, W Mid	G7PEL	AX25			144.550	433.675 439.875
GB7BIR	Sutton Coldfield, W Mid	G7BGP	TCP/IP		70.4875	144.625	433.625 439.975
GB7BMR	Workington, Cumbria	G0EMM	AX25		70.4875	144.650	432.675
GB7BMX	Alnwick, Northumberland	G1YAA	AX25	50.650	70.4875	144.650	430.625 432.675 439.825
GB7BNM	Wimborne, Dorset	G4WPT	AX25	50.650	70.4875	144.550	432.625 439.850
GB7BPQ	Nottingham	G8BPQ	DX Cluster	50.650	70.3250		432.675
GB7BRK	nr Reading, Berks.	G1AWD		50.650		144.650	
GB7BST	Northwood, Middx	G0BST		50.650		144.650	432.675
GB7BSX	Sheffield	G0BSX	TCP/IP			144.625	433.625
GB7CAM	Saltburn, Cleveland	G7AOR	AX25		70.4875	144.650	432.675
GB7CAO	Caithness, Scotland	GM1AHC	AX25			144.650	432.675
GB7CFB	Huntingfield, Suffolk	G0CFB		50.650	70.4876	144.650	430.775
GB7CHS	Northwich, Cheshire	G3WCS	AX25	50.650		144.650	432.675 433.650 439.925
GB7CIP	Caterham on the Hill, Surrey	G4APL	TCP/IP	50.650	70.3125		432.625 433.625
GB7CLI	Leeds, Yorks	G4CLI	TCP/IP			144.625	
GB7COS	Clacton-on-Sea, Essex	G0MBA	AX25			144.650	433.675 439.850
GB7COV	Coventry, W Mids	G3ZFR	AX25		70.4875	144.550	430.625 432.650 439.875
GB7CWS	Sheffield	G1SSO	AX25		70.3375	144.650	430.675 433.675 439.850
GB7CYM	York	G0PWO	AX25		70.3375	144.550	432.675
GB7DID	Didcot, Oxon	G1SSL	AX25		70.4875	144.550	432.675 439.850
GB7DIY	St Peter Port, Guernsey	GU0FYR	TCP/IP			144.625	433.650 439.875
GB7DON	Doncaster, Yorkshire	G0UQQ	IP/AX25	50.710		144.625	432.625 433.650

Callsign	Location	Sysop	Type	6m	4m	2m	70cm
GB7DOR	Tadworth, Surrey	G6XVW		50.650	70.4875	144.650	432.675
GB7DTX	Lincoln	G7DTX	AX25		70.4875	144.650	432.675
GB7DUG	Basildon, Essex	G6FCL	AX25			144.550	439.875 432.650 433.675
GB7DXC	Cheltenham, Glos	G4PDQ	DX Cluster		70.3250	144.675	439.825 432.675
GB7DXD	Wimborne, Dorset	G0OFE	DX Cluster		70.3250	144.675	433.650 439.850
GB7DXH	Bovingdon, Herts	G3OUF	DX Cluster	50.710	70.3250	144.675	433.675 439.825
GB7DXI	Wokingham, Berkshire	G4LJF			70.3250		432.675
GB7DXK	Canterbury, Kent	G3MLO	DX Cluster	50.670	70.4875	144.675	430.650 433.675 439.875
GB7DXM	Ipswich, Suffolk	G4BAH	DX Cluster		70.3250		432.675 439.850
GB7DXS	Ansty, Sussex	G3VKW	DX Cluster		70.3250	144.675	432.650
GB7EBN	Eastborne, Sussex	G4MVN	AX25		70.4875	144.650	432.675 439.875
GB7EDN	Edinburgh	GM4GZW	AX25		70.4875	144.650	432.625
GB7EIP	Rivenhall, Essex	G3XVV	TCP/IP		70.3125		430.775 432.625 433.625 439.975
GB7EIY	Holytown, Lanarkshire	GM8FYJ	TCP/IP		70.4875	144.625	432.675
GB7EMX	Aberdeen	GM4EMX	AX25			144.650	432.625
GB7ESX	Witham, Essex	G1NNB	AX25	50.650	70.4875	144.550	432.675 433.650 439.825
GB7EYM	Scarborough, N Yorks	G4HRM	AX25	50.650		144.550	432.675 439.875
GB7FBH	Eastbourne, Sussex	G1FBH	TCP/IP	50.650	70.4875	144.625	430.650 432.625 433.625 439.875
GB7FCI	Blackpool, Lancs	G6FCI	AX25	50.650		144.650	430.725 432.675 439.925
GB7FDT	Portadown, Co Armagh	GI7FDT	TCP/IP		70.4875	144.625	430.825 432.625 439.825
GB7FLG	Leicester	G0FLG	AX25	50.670	70.4875	144.650	430.675 432.675 439.850
GB7GBR	Central London	G4NQO	IP/AX25	50.690	70.3125		430.675 439.875
GB7GBY	Grimsby, Lincolnshire	G0MUY	AX25		70.4875	144.550	
GB7GCW	Huddersfield, Yorks	G0GCW	AX25	50.650	70.4875	144.650	430.675 432.675
GB7GFD	Guildford, Surrey	G4NBC	AX25	50.650	70.4875	144.650	432.675 430.625
GB7GLO	Malvern, Worcs	G4FPV	AX25	50.650	70.3375	144.650	432.675 439.825
GB7GLP	Ipplepen, Devon	G6GLP		50.650	70.4875	144.650	
GB7GSY	St Peter Port, Guernsey	GU4WRP	AX25			144.550	430.650 432.650 439.875
GB7GUR	Valensey, Guernsey	GU4YMV	AX25	50.650	70.4875	144.650	430.650 432.675 439.875
GB7HAI	Skegness, Lincs	G4HAI	AX25			144.650	432.675
GB7HAS	St Leonards, E Sussex	G6DKB	AX25			144.650	430.675 432.675
GB7HHH	Bovingdon, Herts	G3OUF		50.650		144.650	432.675
GB7HIP	Waterlooville, Hants	G7PEW	TCP/IP	70.3125		144.625	430.725 432.625 439.850
GB7HJP	Waterlooville, Hampshire	G6HJP	AX25	50.650	70.3125	144.550	433.675
GB7HMI	Kircubbin, Co Down	GI3TLT	AX25	50.650		144.650	432.675
GB7HMZ	Matlock, Derbyshire	G0HMZ		50.650		144.650	432.675
GB7HSN	Mottingham, London	GIHSN	AX25	50.670	70.4875	144.650	433.650
GB7HUL	Hull	G8UVQ	AX25	50.650	70.4875	144.650	
GB7HVU	Blackburn, Lancashire	G0DTI	TCP/IP	50.630	70.4875	144.625	432.625
GB7HXA	Huntingdon, Cambs	G4UXV		50.650		144.650	432.675
GB7ICE	Rochester, Kent	G6CKK	AX25		70.4875	144.650	433.650
GB7IDE	Boston, Lincs	G4IDE	AX25		70.4875	144.650	432.650
GB7ILO	Nailsworth, Glos.	G3ILO		50.650		144.650	
GB7IMB	Bristol, Avon	G8IMB	AX25	50.650		144.650	
GB7INC	Potters Bar, Herts	G4POI	TCP/IP				432.675 430.650 432.625 433.625 439.925
GB7IND	Hoddesdon, Herts	G7FCE	TCP/IP		70.3375	144.625	430.650 432.625 439.925
GB7INE	Loughton, Essex	G8DZH	TCP/IP			144.625	430.625 439.925
GB7INF	St Albans, Herts	G6PFP	TCP/IP			144.625	430.725

Callsign	Location	Sysop	Type	6m	4m	2m	70cm
GBINF (continued)							432.625
							439.925
GB7ING	Edmonton, London	G4XRT	TCP/IP			144.625	432.625
							439.925
GB7INH	New Barnet, Herts	G4YSJ	TCP/IP			144.625	433.625
							439.925
GB7INV	Inverness	GM4JNB	AX25			144.650	430.650
							432.675
							439.850
GB7IOE	Ely, Cambs	G8JHE	TCP/IP		70.3125	144.5625	433.625
							439.975
GB7IOM	Douglas, Isle of Man	GD3YEO	AX25		70.3375	144.650	430.625
							432.675
							439.825
GB7IOW	Ventnor, Isle of Wight	G0HFO	AX25		70.3125	144.550	430.625
							432.675
GB7IPB	Ashford, Middx	G4HJG	TCP/IP		70.4875	144.625	430.725
							432.625
							439.925
GB7IPC	High Wycombe, Bucks	G4BIO	TCP/IP				430.675
							432.625
GB7IPD	High Wycombe, Bucks	G8ECJ	TCP/IP			144.625	430.675
							433.625
GB7IPE	Maidenhead, Berks	G1LIG	TCP/IP		70.3375	144.5625	430.675
							433.625
GB7IPF	Little Chalfont, Bucks	G4TNU	TCP/IP			144.625	430.675
							433.625
GB7IPH	Headcorn, Kent	G4ZXI	TCP/IP			144.5625	430.725
							432.625
							439.900
GB7IQB	Stevenage, Herts	G4ETG	TCP/IP		70.4875	144.625	433.625
							439.925
GB7JCB	Barry, Sth Glamorgan	GW0JCB	AX25		70.4875	144.550	432.675
							439.925
GB7JED	Jedburgh, Roxburghshire	GM4UPX	AX25	50.650	70.4875	144.650	430.625
							432.625
							439.875
GB7JSC	Bothwell, Lanarkshire	GM1VBE	AX25	50.6500	70.4875	144.650	432.650
							433.650
							439.925
GB7KEV	Scarborough, N Yorks	G3KEV	AX25	50.650	70.4875	144.650	432.675
GB7KHW	nr Biggleswade, Beds	G6KHW	TCP/IP	50.670	70.4875	144.5625	
GB7KLY	Keighley, W Yorks	G6WHL		50.650	70.4875	144.650	432.675
GB7LAN	Lancaster	G8TZJ	SATGATE			145.900	432.675
						145.975	
GB7LDI	Norwich	G3LDI		50.650	70.4875	145.900	432.675
						145.970	439.825
GB7LDX	Wallasey, Merseyside	G8ZCW	DX Cluster				
GB7LEN	Liverpool	G4LBJ	AX25		70.4875	144.650	430.675
							433.650
							439.975
GB7LIV	Wallasey, Merseyside	G4PGO	AX25			144.550	
GB7LNX	Lincoln	G4GOU		50.650	70.4875	144.650	
GB7LOB	Stoke-on-Trent, Staffs	G7LOB	TCP/IP			144.625	432.675
GB7LWB	Northampton	G4JLB	AX25	50.650	70.4875	144.650	432.675
GB7MAC	Airdrie, Strathclyde	GM4AUP	AX25		70.4875	144.550	433.650
GB7MAD	Madley, Hereford	G7BTI	AX25		70.3250	144.650	
GB7MAM	Alfreton, Derbys	G1EQT	AX25	50.650	70.4875	144.650	430.650
							432.650
							439.875
GB7MAX	Wolverhampton, W Mids	G1DKI	AX25			144.650	432.650
							439.875
GB7MDX	Whixhall, Shropshire	G4UJS	DX Cluster		70.3250	144.675	430.725
							432.650
							439.825
GB7MHD	nr St Ives, Cambs	G0MHD	TCP/IP		70.4875	144.625	430.625
							432.625
							439.975
GB7MIP	Solihull, West Midlands	G7IUB	TCP/IP			144.625	430.725
							432.625
							439.975
GB7MRU	Sheffield, Yorkshire	G4MRU	AX25	50.710		144.650	432.675
GB7MSF	Gateshead, Tyne & Wear	G4MSF	AX25		70.3125	144.550	430.625
							432.650
							439.825
GB7NOS	Golspie, Sutherland	GM0HBI		50.650		144.650	430.650
							432.675
							439.850
GB7NOT	Nottingham	G1MNB	TCP/IP				432.675
GB7NRC	Melton Mowbray, Leics	G4NRC		50.650		144.650	432.675
GB7NRY	Halifax, W Yorks,	G8NRY	IP/AX25	50.650	70.4875	144.625	432.675
							433.625
							439.825
GB7NWI	Southport, Merseyside	G4TUP	TCP/IP	50.650		144.625	430.675

Callsign	Location	Sysop	Type	6m	4m	2m	70cm
GB7NXL	London	G0NXL	AX25		70.4875		433.675
GB7OAR	Birkenhead, Wirral	G4OAR	AX25		70.4875	144.650	430.775
							432.650
							433.625
							439.925
GB7ODM	Oldham, Lancs	G1VSJ	AX25	50.650	70.4875	144.550	430.625
							432.650
							439.825
GB7OGY	Barwell, Leics	G7OGY	AX25			144.650	430.625
							433.675
							439.875
GB7OMM	Maidstone, Kent	G0OMM	AX25		70.4875	144.550	432.675
							439.850
GB7OPC	Wisbech, Cambs	G0OPC	AX25		70.4875	144.550	430.675
							432.675
							433.675
							439.975
GB7OQJ	Chelmsford, Essex	G6OQJ	TCP/IP			144.625	430.775
							433.625
							439.975
GB7OSP	Llandudno, Gwynedd	GW6HVA	TCP/IP	50.650	70.3125	144.625	432.675
GB7PAB	Plymouth, Devon	G7AUQ	AX25			144.550	430.650
							432.650
							439.925
GB7PAE	Basildon, Essex	G0PAE	TCP/IP			144.625	430.775
							433.625
							439.975
GB7PDX	Plymouth, Devon	G3YJQ	DX Cluster	50.650	70.3250		432.675
GB7PEJ	Hockley, Essex	G0PEJ	TCP/IP			144.625	430.775
							433.625
							439.975
GB7PEN	Penrith, Cumbria	G6BSK	AX25	50.650		144.550	430.725
							432.675
							439.875
GB7PET	Peterborough, Cambs	G1ARV	AX25		70.4875	144.650	432.675
							433.675
							439.850
GB7PIP	Portsmouth, Hants	G3RCE	TCP/IP		70.3125		430.675
							432.625
							439.850
GB7PIT	Ashby de la Zouch, Leics	G7PIT	TCP/IP		70.4875	144.625	433.625
GB7PLY	Plymouth, Devon	G3KFN		50.650	70.4875	144.650	432.675
GB7PMB	Minsterley, Shropshire	G3UQH	AX25	50.650	70.3375	144.550	433.650
							439.900
GB7PVO	Hyde, Cheshire	G6PVO	TCP/IP		70.4875	144.625	432.625
GB7PWY	Blackburn, Lancs	G6PWY	TCP/IP	50.630	70.4875	144.625	430.625
							432.625
							439.975
GB7PZT	Kidderminster, Worcs	G8PZT			70.4875	144.650	432.675
GB7RDG	Reading, Berks	G1NZO	AX25	50.650	70.4875	144.650	432.675
							439.850
GB7RMS	Romney Marsh, Kent	G1UTF	AX25		70.4875	144.650	433.650
							439.825
GB7RTW	Tunbridge Wells, Kent	G6AHK	TCP/IP	50.730		144.625	430.725
							432.625
							433.625
							439.900
GB7RUG	Rugeley, Staffs	G1KQH	AX25		70.4875	144.550	430.675
							432.650
GB7SAM	Newcastle-u-Lyme, Staffs	G7SDF	AX25			144.650	432.675
							439.825
GB7SAN	Glasgow	GM3SAN	AX25	50.650	70.4875	144.650	432.625
							439.850
GB7SCA	Plymouth, Devon	G4SCA		50.650		144.650	
GB7SDN	Swindon, Wilts	G8VRI	AX25	50.650		144.650	432.675
							439.825
GB7SDX	Glasgow	GM0OPS	DX Cluster		70.3375	144.675	430.775
							432.675
							439.975
GB7SEA	Seasalter, Kent	G0GCQ	TCP/IP	50.650		144.625	430.725
							432.625
GB7SFK	Haverhill, Suffolk	G7LDI	AX25		70.4875	144.650	432.675
GB7SIG	Blandford, Dorset	G3VXX		50.650	70.4875	144.650	432.675
GB7SMC	Eastleigh, Hants	G4SMC	DX Cluster		70.3250	144.675	432.675
							439.850
GB7SYP	Barnsley, S Yorks	G6TVA	AX25	50.650	70.4875	144.650	430.675
							433.675
							439.850
GB7TCM	Upton-upon-Severn, Worcs	G8ADH		50.650		144.650	
GB7TDG	Thetford, Norfolk	G0DVI	AX25		70.4875	144.650	430.675
							432.650
							439.825
GB7TDX	Newcastle upon Tyne	G1RUY	DX Cluster		70.3250	144.675	430.625

Callsign	Location	Sysop	Type	6m	4m	2m	70cm
GB7TDX (continued)							433.675 439.875
GB7TED	Hillsborough, Co Down	GI4AHP	AX25	50.650	70.3250	144.550	430.625 432.675 439.825
GB7TJF	Taunton, Somerset	G8TJF	AX25			144.650	430.525 432.650 439.925
GB7TJZ	Bristol	G6TJZ	AX25			144.650	433.650 439.850
GB7TLH	East Dereham, Norfolk	G1TLH	DX Cluster	50.650	70.3250	144.675	430.625 432.675
GB7TUT	Enfield, Middx	G4TUT	AX25		70.4875	144.550	432.650 439.850
GB7TXM	Ipswich, Suffolk	G7ANH	TCP/IP			144.625	
GB7TYR	Cookstown, Co Tyrone	GI3KEV	AX25	50.650	70.4875	144.650	
GB7UDX	Lisburn, Co Antrim	GI1ONL	DX Cluster		70.3125	144.675	430.650 432.675 439.850
GB7UHB	Glengormley, Co Antrim	GI0UHB	TCP/IP		70.4875	144.625	430.625 432.625 432.625 439.825
GB7UIM	Paignton, Devon	G6UIM	TCP/IP			144.625	432.625 432.625 439.925
GB7ULV	Ulverston, Cumbria	G4BDE	AX25	50.650	70.4875	144.650	432.675 439.925
GB7UWS	Eltham, London	G1UWS	AX25			144.650	432.675 439.950
GB7VES	Camberley, Surrey	G0VES	AX25	50.650	70.4875	144.550	430.650 432.650
GB7VLS	Norwich, Norfolk	G4VLS		50.650	70.4875	144.650	432.675
GB7VMR	Maidenhead, Berks	G3VMR		50.670		144.650	432.675
GB7VRB	Worthing, W Sussex	G8DHE	AX25	50.650	70.4875	144.650	430.675 432.675
GB7WAR	Warwick	G1FIP	AX25		70.4875	144.650	430.675 432.675 439.975
GB7WDX	Weston-Super-Mare, Avon	G7OPJ	DX Cluster	50.750	70.3250	144.675	433.675
GB7WIG	Gillingham, Kent	G4EGH	AX25	50.610	70.3125	144.650	430.625 433.650 439.825
GB7WIR	Slough, Berks.	G1LMI		50.670		144.650	432.675
GB7WMD	Farnborough, Hants	G1WMD	TCP/IP			145.625	432.675
GB7WPJ	Halstead, Essex	G6WPJ	TCP/IP			144.625	433.625
GB7WRG	Wakefield, W Yorks	G0COA	AX25	50.650	70.4875	144.550	432.650
GB7WRI	Randalstown, Co Antrim	GI4WRI	AX25	50.650	70.4875	144.650	430.625 432.675 439.825
GB7WRR	Leeds	G3XEP	AX25	50.610	70.3125		433.675 439.825
GB7WXM	Wrexham, Clwyd	GW8HBP	AX25		70.4875	144.650	432.675 439.900
GB7XDU	Maidenhead, Berks	G4XDU	AX25	50.670	70.3250 70.4875	144.525	432.675
GB7XJZ	Southampton, Hants	G0SBV	AX25		70.3125	144.650	430.625 432.650 439.850
GB7YAX	Bradford, Yorks	G0RLG	AX25		70.4875	144.650	
GB7YDX	Goole, Yorkshire	G4DBN	DX Cluster	50.690	70.3250	144.675	430.650 433.650
GB7YEW	Abernethy, Perth	GM3YEW	AX25		70.3250	144.650	430.625 432.675
GB7YUH	Margate, Kent	G3YUH	AX25		70.4875	144.650	430.625 433.650 439.875
GB7ZET	Dunrossness, Shetland	GM4IPK	AX25			144.650	433.650
GB7ZHR	Crayford, Kent	G8ZHR	TCP/IP	50.730		144.625	430.725 432.625 439.900
GB7ZPU	Sandy, Beds	G1ZPU	AX25	50.670	70.4875	144.650	433.650 439.825
GB7ZZZ	Ringmer, E Sussex	G0JDR	AX25			144.550	430.650 433.675 439.825

Index

Get more out of amateur radio . . . as an RSGB member!

Radio Communication

A magazine which covers a wide range of interests and which features the best and latest amateur radio news. The Society's journal has acquired a worldwide reputation for its content. With 100 pages, many in colour, 'RadCom' strives to maintain its reputation as the best available and is circulated free of charge to members throughout the world.

The regular columns in the magazine include those for HF, VHF/UHF, microwave, SWL, clubs, satellite, data and contests. In addition to the many technical articles, the highly regarded 'Technical Topics' feature caters for those wishing to keep themselves briefed on recent developments in technical matters.

The 'Last Word' is a lively feature in which members can put forward their views and opinions and be sure of receiving a wide audience. To keep members in touch with what's going on in the hobby, events diaries are published each month.

Advertisements for the equipment you wish to sell can be placed in the magazine, with the advantages of short deadlines and large circulation.

QSL Bureau

Members enjoy the use of the QSL Bureau free of charge for both outgoing and incoming cards. This can save you a good deal of postage.

Special Event Callsigns

Special event callsigns in the GB series are handled by RSGB. They give amateurs special facilities for displaying amateur radio to the general public.

Specialised News Sheets

The RSGB publishes the weekly DX News-sheet for HF enthusiasts and the Microwave Newsletter for those operating above 1GHz.

Specialised Equipment Insurance

Insurance for your valuable equipment which has been arranged specially for members. The rates are very advantageous.

Audio Visual Library

Films, audio and video tapes are available through one of the Society's Honorary Officers for all affiliated groups and clubs.

Reciprocal Licensing Information

Details are available for most countries on the RSGB computer database.

Government Liaison

One of the most vital features of the work of the RSGB is the ongoing liaison with the UK Licensing Authority – presently the Radiocommunications Agency (RA) of the Department of Trade and Industry. Setting and maintaining the proper framework in which amateur radio can thrive and develop is essential to the well-being of amateur radio. For example, the Novice Licence was introduced by the RA after long discussions with the RSGB. The Society also spares no effort in defence of amateur radio's most precious assets – the amateur bands.

Beacons and Repeaters

The RSGB supports financially all repeaters and beacons which are looked after by the appropriate committee of the Society, ie 1.8–30MHz by the HF Committee, 30–1000MHz (1GHz) by the VHF Committee and frequencies above 1GHz by the Microwave Committee. For repeaters, the Society's Repeater Management Group has played a major role. Society books such as the RSGB Amateur Radio Call Book give further details, and computer-based lists giving operational status can be obtained by post from HQ.

Operating Awards

A wide range of operating awards are available via the responsible officers: their names can be found in the front pages of Radio Communication and in the RSGB Amateur Radio Call Book. Details of these awards can be found in the latter and also this book.

Contests (HF/VHF/Microwave)

The Society has two contest committees which carry out all work associated with the running of contests. The HF Contests Committee deals with contests below 30MHz, whilst events on frequencies above 30MHz are dealt with by the VHF Contests Committee.

Morse Testing

The Society has responsibility for morse testing of radio amateurs in the UK. If you wish to take a morse test, write direct to RSGB HQ (Morse tests) for an application form.

Slow Morse

Many volunteers all over the country give up their time to send slow morse over the air to those who are preparing for the 5 and 12 words per minute morse tests. The Society also produces morse practice tapes.

RSGB Books

The Society publishes a range of books for the radio amateur and imports many others. Members are entitled to a discount on all books purchased from the Society – this discount can offset the cost of membership.

Propagation

The Society's Propagation Studies Committee is highly respected – both within the amateur community and professionally – for its work. Predictions are given in the weekly GB2RS news bulletins and the Society's monthly magazine *Radio Communication*.

Technical and EMC Advice

Although the role of the Society's Technical and Publications Advisory Committee is largely to vet material intended for publication, its members and HQ staff are always willing to help with any technical matters.

Breakthrough in domestic entertainment equipment can be a difficult problem to solve as well as having licensing implications. The Society's EMC Committee is able to offer practical assistance in many cases. The Society also publishes a special book to assist you. Additional advice can be obtained from the EMC Committee Chairman via RSGB HQ.

Planning Permission

There is a special booklet and expert help available to members seeking assistance with planning matters.

GB2RS

A special radio news bulletin transmitted each week and aimed especially at the UK radio amateur and short wave listener. The script is prepared each week by the Society's HQ staff. The transmission schedule appears in the *RSGB Amateur Radio Call Book*. The GB2RS bulletin is also sent out over the packet radio network.

RSGB Exhibitions and Mobile Rallies

The Society's Exhibition and Rally Committee organizes an annual exhibition and an annual mobile rally. Full details and a rally calendar can be found in *Radio Communication*.

RSGB Conventions

The Society's diary in *Radio Communication* contains details of all special conventions which are open to all radio amateurs. The Society holds several major conventions each year.

Observation Service

A number of leading national radio societies have volunteers who monitor the amateur bands as a service to the amateur community. Their task is to spot licence infringements and defective transmissions, and report them in a friendly way to the originating station.

Intruder Watch

This helps to protect the exclusive amateur bands by monitoring for stations not authorised to use them.

Send for our Membership Information Pack today and discover how you too can benefit from these services. Write to:

RADIO SOCIETY OF GREAT BRITAIN,
Lambda House, Cranborne Road,
Potters Bar, Herts EN6 3JE

Some other RSGB publications...

- ## Amateur Radio Logbook
The standard fixed-station logbook. The wire binding gives easy fold-back to save space, and the large A4 size ensures plenty of space for remarks.

- ## Great Circle DX Map
A wall map which shows the bearing in degrees from London of any DX station, and which is thus invaluable for the HF operator using a beam antenna.

- ## Instant Morse
A fully interactive multimedia course for learning morse on CD-ROM (Windows 3.1). An easy way to learn letters, numbers and miscellaneous characters, and test yourself as you progress. Includes timed samples of text, examples of typical morse tests, how to operate a morse key, and much more.

- ## Locator Map of Europe
This map shows locator squares for Europe at a glance with an inset world-wide locator map showing main squares for the rest of the world.

- ## The Radio Amateur's Guide to EMC
This excellent guide will help you to avoid EMC problems by practising good housekeeping, and assist you in the diagnosis and cure of any which do occur. The underlying causes, as well as the remedies, are given so that you should be well-prepared to tackle any problems which turn up now or in the future.

- ## RSGB Amateur Radio Call Book
Published annually, this is a comprehensive directory of the addresses of amateur radio stations in the UK and the Republic of Ireland. It also contains an information section giving the addresses of clubs, RAE centres and morse centres, plus details of GB2RS broadcasts, RSGB committees and much more.

- ## RSGB Prefix Guide
The definitive guide to country identification and information (formerly the *Geoff Watts Prefix-Country-Zone List*). It also contains much valuable information on DXCC matters, CIS callsigns, and much more. It is regularly revised to ensure that it contains the very latest information.

- ## Skycall Call Book
Skycall is a call book program running under Windows 3.1 which gives instant access to the addresses of over 55,000 UK amateurs plus data on hundreds of repeaters and packet radio bulletin boards.

- ## World Prefix Map
A superb wall map (Mercator projection) in full colour, giving amateur radio callsign prefixes worldwide.

RADIO SOCIETY OF GREAT BRITAIN
**Lambda House, Cranborne Road,
Potters Bar, Herts EN6 3JE, England**